1 MONTH OF
FREE
READING

at

www.ForgottenBooks.com

By purchasing this book you are eligible for one month membership to ForgottenBooks.com, giving you unlimited access to our entire collection of over 1,000,000 titles via our web site and mobile apps.

To claim your free month visit:
www.forgottenbooks.com/free764083

ISBN 978-0-428-37105-0
PIBN 10764083

LEPIDOPTERA HETEROCERA

(PYRALES)

FAM. ORNEODIDÆ

by E. MEYRICK

WITH 1 COLOURED PLATE

General characters. — Ocelli distinct. Tongue developed. Maxillary palpi sometimes developed, porrected. Forewings six-cleft; 5 absent. Hindwings six-cleft or seven-cleft; 5 absent.

This singular family is distinguished at once from all other insects by having all the wings divided for more or less of their length into six or seven plumes. Probably, in conjunction with the *Oxychirotidae* and *Pterophoridae*, it represents the remains of a peculiar branch of the *Pyralidina,* which exhibited this exceptional tendency to fission as its characteristic. Of these three families the *Oxychirotidae* have preserved the most primitive structure, the other two being more or less highly specialised and divergent; of these two latter types the *Orneodidae* are the less successful.

The forewings of the imago are more triangular than in the *Pterophoridae;* the six segments have veins 1*b*, 2, 3, 4, 6, 7 running to their tips. In the hindwings the same six veins occupy the six normal segments; if there is a seventh segment, it is occupied by 8; 1*c* is absent, and the lower margin of cell has no pecten of hairs towards base. The type of labial palpi is rather peculiar, but can be parallelled in certain Pyrales, as *Acropentias*. Maxillary palpi are usually absent, but in *Triscaedecia* are well-developed, and of a common Pyralid type. The legs are of normal type, not elongate, with the outer spurs one-half to three-fourths of inner.

Larva moderately elongate, with few hairs. Pupa in a cocoon above ground. Not much is known of the larval habits except in the case of the few European species; these feed in flowers, shoots, or stems of highly developed Dicotyledonous plants.

The geographical distribution indicates India as the centre of origin, and the family may have come into existence a little earlier than the *Pterophoridae*.

Triscaedecia is obviously the most primitive form, retaining an almost complete neuration, whilst in all the other genera three costal veins are lost; and also possessing well-developed maxillary palpi, not generally found in the rest, and the least deeply-cleft wings. *Paelia* and *Microschismus* have the wings less deeply-cleft than *Orneodes*, and show some other traces of an earlier type of structure, but these three latter genera are closely related.

The following is a tabulation of the genera :

KEY OF THE GENERA

1. *Hindwings seven-cleft*	4. Genus Triscædecia, Hampson.	
— *Hindwings six-cleft*		2.
2. *Forewings cleft to about middle*		3.
— *Forewings cleft to one-sixth*	1. Genus Orneodes, Latreille.	
3. *Palpi extremely long*	3. Genus Microschismus, Flet cher.	
— *Palpi rather short*	2. Genus Pælia, Walker.	

GROUP A. — Hindwings six-cleft; maxillary palpi usually absent

1. Genus ORNEODES, Latreille

Orneodes. Latreille, Précis Caract. Ins. p. 148 (1796). — Type : *O. hexadactyla*, Linnæus.
Euchiradia. Hübner, Verz. bek. Schmett. p. 431 (1826). — Type : *O. hexadactyla*, Linnæus.

Characters. — Labial palpi moderate or long, more or less ascending, second joint loosely scaled or with projecting scales or shortly tufted beneath, terminal long or short, more or less pointed. Forewings with discal cleft extending to one-sixth, cell very short, 8-10 absent, 11 from very near or usually out of 7, sometimes very short. Hindwings six-cleft, discal cleft extending to near base.

Geographical distribution of species. — Most characteristic of India and Ceylon, but has made its way to all the principal regions.

1. *O. ischalea*, Meyrick, Journ. Bombay Nat. Hist. Soc. Vol. 16, p. 583 (1905).	Ceylon.
2. *O. thapsina*, Meyrick, ibidem, p. 583 (1905).	Ceylon.
3. *O. xanthodes*, Meyrick, Proc. Linn. Soc. N. S. Wales. p. 1112 (1889).	E. Australia.
4. *O. ferruginea*, Walsingham, Trans. Ent. Soc. Lond. p. 285 (1881).	S. Africa.
5. *O. chloracta*, Meyrick, ibidem, p. 507 (1907).	W. Africa.
6. *O. nephelotoxa*, Meyrick, ibidem, p. 505 (1907).	India.
7. *O. toxophila*, Meyrick, Journ. Bombay Nat. Hist. Soc. Vol. 17, p. 133 (1906).	Ceylon.
8. *O. pluvialis*, Meyrick, Trans. Ent. Soc. Lond. p. 505 (1907).	India.
9. *O. tricausta*, Meyrick, ibidem, p. 506 (1907).	India.
10. *O. nasuta*, Zeller, Hor. Soc. Ent. Ross. p. 486, pl, 6, f. 172 (1877).	S. America.
11. *O. pinalea*, Meyrick, Trans. Ent. Soc. Lond. p. 506 (1907).	Ceylon.
12. *O. Hofmanni*, Pagenstecher, Zoologica, Vol. 29, p. 242 (1900).	Bismarck Islands.
13. *O. sycophanta*, Meyrick, Journ. Bombay Nat. Hist. Soc. Vol. 17. p. 133 (1906).	Ceylon.
14. *O. niphostrota*, Meyrick, Trans. Ent. Soc. Lond. p. 507 (1907).	Ceylon.
15. *O. ochrozona*, Meyrick, Journ. Bombay Nat. Hist. Soc. Vol. 17, p. 730 (1906).	India.
16. *O. sikhima*, Moore, Descr. Ind. Lep. p. 282 (1887).	India.

17. *O. trachyptera*, Meyrick, Journ Bombay Nat Hist. Soc. Vol. 17, p. 134 (1906). S. India, Ceylon.
18. *O. pygmaea*. Meyrick, Proc. Linn. Soc. N. S. Wales. p. 1112 (1889). E. Australia.
19. *O. angustestriata*, Walsingham. Fauna Hawaii. Vol. 1, p. 477, pl. 10, f. 10 (1907). Hawaii.
20.   *objurgatella*, Walsingham, ibidem, p. 477, pl. 10, f. 11 (1907). Hawaii.
21.   . *nannodactyla*, Rebel, Lep. Sokotra, p. 87 (1907). Sokotra.
22.   . *mesolychna*, Meyrick, Trans. Ent. Soc. Lond. p. 508 (1907). India, Ceylon.
23.   . *punctiferella*, Walker, List Lep. Het. Brit. Mus. Vol. 35, p. 1846 (1866). C. America.
24.   . *zonodactyla*, Zeller, Isis, p. 908 (1847). S. Europe, S. W. Asia.
25.   . *desmodactyla*, Zeller, ibidem, p. 908 (1847). C. and S. Europe.
26. *O. eudactyla*, Felder, Reise Novara, Lep. Het. pl. 140, f. 62 (1877). S. America, W. Indies.
27. *O. Huebneri*, Wallengren, Skand. Fjädermott. p. 24 (1859). Europe, Kashmir, S. Africa.
        hexadactyla, Hübner, Verz. bek. Schmett. Vol. 30, p. 31 (1826).
28.   . *capensis*, Felder, Reise Novara, Lep. Het. pl. 140. f. 63 (1877). S. Africa.
29.   . *Butleri*, Wallengren, Oefv. Vet.-Akad. Förh. p. 130 (1875). S. Africa.
30. *O. cymatodactyla*, Zeller, Linn. Ent. Vol. 6, p. 413 (1851). S. E. Europe.
31. *O. grammodactyla*, Zeller, Isis, p. 869 (1841). C. and S. Europe, S. W. Asia.
        palodactyla, Zeller, ibidem, p. 908 (1847).
        perittodactyla, Staudinger, Stett. Ent. Zeit. p. 259 (1859).
32. *O. magadis*, Meyrick, Trans. Ent. Soc. Lond. p. 510 (1907). India.
33. *O. synnephodactyla*, Alphéraky, Trudy. Soc. Ent. Russe, Vol. 10, p. 3 (1876). W. C. Asia.
34. *O. dodecadactyla*. Hübner, Verz. bek. Schmett. p. 29 (1826). C. Europe.
35. *O. hexadactyla*, Linnæus, Syst. Nat. (ed. 10), p. 542 (1758). Europe, Asia Minor, North America.
        polydactyla, Hübner, Verz. bek. Schmett. p. 28 (1826).
36. *O. cancellata*, Meyrick, Trans. Ent. Soc. Lond. p 510 (1907). S. W. Asia.
37. *O. spilodesma*, Meyrick, ibidem, p. 508 (1907). India.
38. *O. phricodes*, Meyrick, ibidem. p. 20 (1886). E. Australia.

2. GENUS PÆLIA, WALKER

Pælia. Walker, List Lep. Het. Brit. Mus. Vol. 35, p. 1846 (1866). — Type : *P. lunuligera*, Walker.

Characters. — Labial palpi moderate. ascending, second joint clothed with loose scales, terminal short. Forewings with discal cleft extending to about middle, cell moderate; 8-10 absent, 11 out of 7, short. Hindwings six-cleft, discal cleft extending to one-fifth.

Geographical distribution of species. — A collateral form of *Orneodes*, from South America.
1. *P. lunuligera*, Walker, List Lep. Het. Brit. Mus. Vol. 35, p. 1846 (1866). S. America.

3. GENUS MICROSCHISMUS, FLETCHER

Microschismus. Fletcher, The Entomologist (1909). — Type : *M. fortis*, Walsingham.

Characters. — Antennæ four-fifths, in ♂ ciliated or shortly bipectinated to near apex. Labial palpi very long, porrected, second joint very long, rough-scaled, terminal joint rather short, filiform. Forewings with discal cleft extending to about middle, cell moderate; 8-10 absent, 11 separate. Hindwings six-cleft, discal cleft extending to one-fifth.

Geographical distribution of species. — Distinguished by the peculiar palpi. Only two African species are described.
1. *M. fortis*, Walsingham, Trans. Ent. Soc. Lond. p. 284, pl. 13, f. 49 (1881). S. Africa.
2. *M. antennatus*, Fletcher, The Entomologist (1909). S. Africa.

GROUP B. — Hindwings seven-cleft; maxillary palpi developed

4. GENUS TRISCÆDECIA, HAMPSON

Triscædecia. Hampson, Trans. Ent. Soc. Lond. p. 247 (1905). — Type : *T. dactyloptera*, Hampson.
Hofmannia. Pagenstecher, Zoologica, Vol. 29, p. 241 (1900, præocc. *Hofmannia*, Wocke, 1877). —
Type : *T. septemdactyla*, Pagenstecher.

Characters. — Labial palpi long, second joint porrected, with projecting scales beneath, terminal joint shorter, ascending. Maxillary palpi moderate, loosely scaled, porrected. Forewings evenly six-cleft from about two-thirds, cell moderate; 2 from two-thirds of cell, 7 and 8 stalked, 7 to apex, 9-11 separate. Hindwings evenly seven-cleft from beyond middle, segments occupied by 1*b*, 2, 3, 4, 6, 7, 8 respectively, 6 and 7 approximated at base.

Geographical distribution of species. — A singular primitive form of much interest, probably Indo-Malayan in origin. I have inspected the type; the neuration of hindwings is wrongly given by Hampson, and is certainly as above; that of forewings appears to be correct, but I cannot discern it quite clearly.

1. *T. dactyloptera*, Hampson, Trans. Ent. Soc. Lond. p. 247 (1905).   Ceylon.
2. *T. septemdactyla*, Pagenstecher, Zoologica, Vol. 29, p. 241 (1900).   Solomon Isl.

EXPLANATION OF PLATE

Fig. 1. *Orneodes trachyptera*, Meyrick.
— 2. — *ochrozona*, Meyrick.
— 3. — *sycophanta*, Meyrick.
— 4. — *magadis*, Meyrick.
— 5. — *pinalea*, Meyrick.
— 6. — *niphostrota*, Meyrick.
— 7. — *ischalea*, Meyrick.
— 8. — *phricodes*, Meyrick.
— 9. — *pygmaea*, Meyrick.
— 10. — *chloracta*, Meyrick.
— 11. — *thapsina*, Meyrick.
— 12. — *toxophila*, Meyrick.
— 13. — *mesolychna*, Meyrick.
— 14. — *eudactyla*, Felder.
— 15. *Microschismus fortis*, Walsingham.
— 16. *Orneodes spilodesma*, Meyrick.
— 17. — *xanthodes*, Meyrick.
— 18. *Paelia lunuligera*, Walker.

Marlborough, 15th May, 1910.

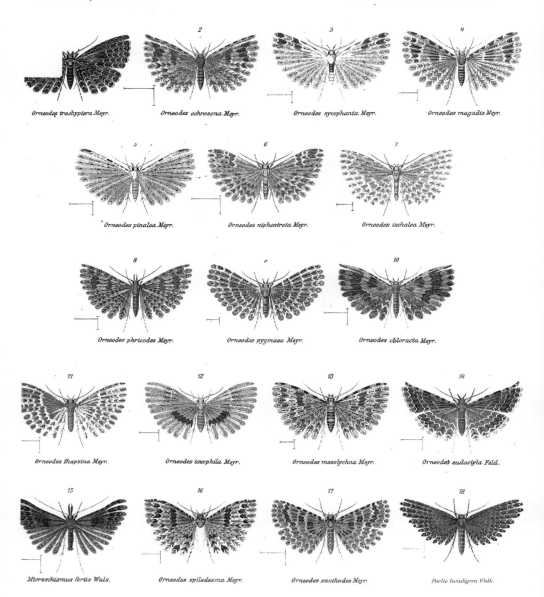

1. *Orneodes trachyptera* Meyr.   2. *Orneodes ochrozona* Meyr.   3. *Orneodes sycophanta* Meyr.   4. *Orneodes magadis* Meyr.

5. *Orneodes pinalea* Meyr.   6. *Orneodes niphostrota* Meyr.   7. *Orneodes ischalea* Meyr.

8. *Orneodes phricodes* Meyr.   9. *Orneodes pygmaea* Meyr.   10. *Orneodes chloracta* Meyr.

11. *Orneodes thapsina* Meyr.   12. *Orneodes toxophila* Meyr.   13. *Orneodes mesolychna* Meyr.   14. *Orneodes eudactyla* Feld.

15. *Microschismus fortis* Wals.   16. *Orneodes spilodesma* Meyr.   17. *Orneodes xanthodes* Meyr.   18. *Parlio lunuligera* Walk.

FAM. ORNEODIDÆ

109

ORTHOPTERA

FAM. BLATTIDÆ

SUBFAM. BLATTINÆ (= PERIPLANETINÆ)

ORTHOPTERA

FAM. BLATTIDÆ

SUBFAM. BLATTINÆ (= PERIPLANETINÆ)

by R. SHELFORD

WITH 2 COLOURED PLATES

THE Blattinæ (Periplanetinæ) form the fourth subfamily of the Blattidæ.

Characters. — Antennæ setaceous and usually much longer than the body, very rarely plumose or incrassated. Head with the vertex usually exposed. Eyes reniform. Ocelliform spots rarely absent. Tegmina and wings completely developed, reduced, rudimentary or absent; when present usually semicoriaceous; the costal veins of the wings irregular and much branched, ulnar vein of the wings multiramose, the branches irregular and bifurcated. Sub-genital lamina of male typically quadrate and symmetrical with a pair of slender genital styles. Sub-genital lamina of female modified to form a pair of apposed valves. Cerci variable, but generally flattened and acuminate. Femora generally strongly spined beneath. Tarsi variable. Ootheca chitinous, carried with the suture uppermost. None of the species viviparous.

This is a very well-defined subfamily on account of the valvular structure of the female sub-genital lamina, whilst the males can also be readily distinguished by the symmetry of the sub-genital lamina and by the slender but well-marked styles. I have met with no forms that can be regarded as intermediate between this and other subfamilies of Blattidæ. I cannot follow Bolivar in maintaining the subfamily *Nocticolinae* for the cavernicolous genera *Nocticola* and *Spelaeoblatta;* to my mind the undoubted Blattine features of the female sub-genital lamina in these genera over-ride in importance characters that have been called into existence by the cave-haunting habit. Sexual dimorphism is a very marked feature of the Blattinæ and some confusion has resulted from its non-recognition by some authors; there is no doubt that the number of known species of *Deropeltis* and *Pseudoderopeltis* will be reduced when we gain more exact knowledge of the two sexes of both genera; several species of *Pseudoderopeltis*, described from females alone, have been placed in *Stylopyga* by older authors, so that the synonymy is somewhat tangled. I have separated *Stylopyga* from the genus *Blatta* for what I consider a valid reason, viz. the similarity of the two sexes in the former genus, their dissimilarity in the latter. But I am far from satisfied that the species now included in *Blatta* form a natural group and I am only restrained from further depleting the genus by lack of knowledge concerning the structure of the two sexes in certain species; when this knowledge comes to hand — as eventually will surely be the case — the genus can be re-arranged satisfactorily.

KEY TO THE GENERA

1. *Eyes well-developed. Tarsal arolia present.*
2. *Posterior margin of fifth abdominal tergite not sinuate.*
3. *Tibiae with spines on outer aspect triseriately arranged.*
4. *Posterior metatarsus shorter or not longer than the remaining joints, which are unarmed beneath.*
5. *Distance apart of eyes on vertex of head less than or equal to the distance apart of the antennal sockets. Old-World forms.*
6. *Ocelli usually absent. Tegminal rudiments absent. Abdominal tergites with well-marked stigmatic dots. Supra-anal lamina (♀) more or less bilobate. Cerci blunt and flattened, generally not extending beyond the supra-anal lamina . . .*   2. Genus EUZOSTERIA, Shelford.
6'. *Ocelli present. Tegmina present, rudimentary or absent. Abdominal tergites rarely with stigmatic dots. Supra-anal lamina (♀) not bilobate. Cerci longer, apex usually acuminate.*
7. *Wings absent or rudimentary. Tegmina rudimentary or absent.*
8. *Tegmina absent or represented by squamiform lobes.*
9. *Posterior angles of the fifth and sixth abdominal tergites backwardly produced.*
10. *Posterior metatarsus short, not spined beneath or with only a few spines; its pulvillus usually large, and occupying at least half of the joint.*
11. *Lateral margins of pronotum not incrassated. Thoracic tergites more or less smooth and nitid.*
12. *Supra-anal lamina (♂) not produced to form an acute spine . . . .*   3. Genus PLATYZOSTERIA, Brunner von [Wattenwyl.
12'. *Supra-anal lamina (♂) produced to form an acute spine . . . .*   4. Genus LEPTOZOSTERIA, Tepper.
11. *Lateral margins of pronotum incrassated. Thoracic tergites punctate or tuberculate . . . . . .*   6. Genus ZONIOPLOCA, Stål.
10'. *Posterior metatarsus longer, spined beneath, its pulvillus not occupying one-half of the joint . . . .*   5. Genus CUTILIA, Stål.
9'. *Posterior angles of the fifth and sixth abdominal tergites not backwardly produced, or if produced the abdominal tergites are scabrous. Tegmina entirely absent.*

10. *Posterior angles of seventh abdominal tergite backwardly produced; abdomen above scabrous* . . . . .   7. Genus COSMOZOSTERIA, Stål.

10'. *Posterior angles of seventh abdominal tergite not backwardly produced; abdomen above smooth, nitid.*

11. *Lateral margins of pronotum not incrassated* . . .   8. Genus ANAMESIA, Tepper.

11'. *Lateral margins of pronotum incrassated* . . . .   9. Genus DESMOZOSTERIA, Shelford.

8'. *Tegmina quadrate, as long as the pronotum.*

9. *Wings absent* . . . .   10. Genus TEMNELYTRA, Tepper.

9'. *Wings rudimentary* . . . .   11. Genus SCABINA, Shelford.

7'. *Tegmina and wings well-developed.*

8. *Antennae not plumose nor incrassated.*

9. *Pronotum anteriorly-parabolic, sides deflexed* . . . .   12. Genus METHANA, Stål.

9'. *Pronotum discoidal, sides not deflexed* . . . . . .   13. Genus PARAMETHANA, Shelford.

8'. *Antennae plumose and incrassated* . . . . . .   14. Genus THYRSOCERA, Burmeister.

5'. *Distance apart of eyes on vertex of head greater than distance apart of antennal sockets. American forms.*

6. *Tegmina squamiform or much reduced, quadrate and not extending beyond the metanotum. Wings absent or squamiform* . . . .   15. Genus EURYCOTIS, Stål.

6'. *Tegmina and wings completely developed or ovate and extending to the middle of the abdomen* . . . .   16. Genus PELMATOSILPHA, Dohrn.

4'. *Posterior metatarsus longer than the remaining joints, the second and generally the third of which are armed beneath.*

5. *Pronotum trapezoidal or discoidal.*

6. *Both sexes apterous or with squamiform tegmina* . . . .   18. Genus STYLOPYGA, Fischer von [Waldheim.

6'. *Male sex only or both sexes with well-developed tegmina.*

7. *Second joint of posterior tarsi long, together with the third and fourth joints biseriately spined beneath. Pulvilli minute.*

8. *Tegmina of ♂ variable, but always shorter than the abdomen, of ♀ squamiform or truncate or lanceolate* . .   19. Genus BLATTA, Linnæus.

8'. *Tegmina of ♂ well-developed, exceeding apex of abdomen.*

9. *Tegmina of ♀ sub-truncate or squamiform.*

10. *Tegmina of ♀ sub-truncate. Meso- and metanotum of ♂ without membranous processes* . . . . .   20. Genus CARTOBLATTA, Shelford.

10'. *Tegmina of ♀ squamiform. Meso- and metanotum of ♂ with membranous processes* . . . . . .   21. Genus PSEUDODEROPELTIS, Krauss.

9'. *Tegmina of ♀ fully developed, exceeding the apex of the abdomen.*

10. *Pronotum broadest behind middle, its sides deflexed* .   22. Genus PERIPLANETA, Burmeister.

10'. *Pronotum broadest before middle, discoidal* . . .   23. Genus HOMALOSILPHA, Stål.

7'. *Second joint of posterior tarsi short. fourth joint unarmed beneath. Pulvilli moderately large* . . . . . .   17. Genus DORYLÆA, Stål.

5'. *Pronotum oblong* . . . .   24. Genus EROBLATTA, Shelford.

3'. *Tibiae with spines on outer aspect biseriately arranged.*

4. *Tibial spines well- or moderately well-developed.*
    5. *Tarsi very short. Entirely apterous* . . . .   1. Genus POLYZOSTERIA, Burmeister.
    5'. *Tarsi long. Winged* . . . .   26. Genus MIROBLATTA, Shelford.
4'. *Tibial spines weak and sparse.*
    5. *Pronotum very rugose, discoidal* (♂) *or trapezoidal* (♀) . .   27. Genus CATARA, Walker.
    5'. *Pronotum not very rugose, oblong.*
        6. *Posterior metatarsus longer than the remaining joints.* . .   28. Genus PROTAGONISTA, Shelford.
        6'. *Posterior metatarsus shorter than the remaining joints* . .   29. Genus ARCHIBLATTA, Vollenhoven.
2'. *Posterior margin of fifth abdominal tergite sinuate* . . . . .   25. Genus DEROPELTIS, Burmeister.
1'. *Eyes rudimentary or absent. Tarsal arolia absent.*
    2. *Eyes rudimentary. Head cordiform* . . . .   30. Genus NOCTICOLA, Bolivar.
    2'. *Eyes absent. Head oblong* . . . .   31. Genus SPELÆOBLATTA, Bolivar.

I. Genus POLYZOSTERIA, Burmeister

Polyzosteria. Burmeister, Handb. Ent., Vol. 2, p. 482 (1838).
Chalcolampra. Saussure, Mém. Soc. Sc. Phys. Nat. Genève, Vol. 17, p. 132 (1863).

    Characters. — Ocelli absent. Antennæ shorter than the body. Pronotum anteriorly somewhat cucullate, margins not reflected, posteriorly truncate. Tegmina and wings entirely absent. Posterior angles of the seventh abdominal tergite strongly produced backwards, angles of the preceding tergites not or scarcely produced, angles of the ninth tergite sometimes lobiform. Stigmatic dots on abdominal tergites well-marked. Supra-anal lamina : (♂) quadrate, angles acute, (♀) sub-bilobate cucullate. Sub-genital-lamina (♂) sub-quadrate, styles short, obtuse. Cerci short, flattened, blunt at apex. Tibiæ robust, almost quadrangular in section, spines on outer aspect in two rows. Posterior metatarsus very short, unarmed beneath, its pulvillus occupying the greater part of the joint.

    Geographical distribution of species. — Australia and Tasmania.

1. *P. limbata*, Burmeister, Handb. Ent., Vol. 2, p. 483 (1838).   Australia, Tasmania.
    P. aenea, Burmeister, ibidem, p. 483 (1838).
    P. purpurascens, Fischer, Orth. Eur. p. 93 (1853).
    P. pulchella, Saussure, Rev. Zool. (2) Vol. 16, p. 308 (1864).
    P. nitens, Walker, Cat. Blatt. Brit Mus. p. 155 (1868).
    ? *P. frenchii*, Tepper, Trans. Roy. Soc. S. Austral. Vol. 18, p. 178 (1894).
2. *P. iridicolor*, Tepper, ibidem, Vol. 17, p. 73 (1893).   South Australia.
3. *P. bagoti*, Tepper, ibidem, p. 79 (1893).   South Australia.
4. *P. cuprea*, Saussure, Mém. Soc. Sc. Phys. Nat. Genève, Vol. 17,   South and West Australia.
    p. 133, pl. 1, f. 2. — **Pl. I, Fig. I.**
    P. maculata, Brunner von Wattenwyl, Nouv. Syst. des Blatt. p. 206 (1865).
5. *P. impressa*, Tepper, *in* Horn. Exped. Centr. Austral., Vol. 2, p. 361   Central Australia.
    (1896).
6. *P. obscuroviridis*, Tepper, Trans. Roy. Soc. S. Austral., Vol. 17. p. 73   South Australia.
    (1893).
7. *P. pubescens*, Tepper. ibidem, p. 75 (1893). — **Pl. I, Fig. Ia.**   West Australia.
8. *P. oculata*, Tepper, ibidem, p. 75 (1893).   South Australia, Victoria.
9. *P. invisa*, Walker, Cat Blatt. Brit. Mus. p. 162 (1868).   Australia.
10. *P. viridissima*, Shelford, Trans. Ent. Soc. Lond. p. 262 (1909).   New South Wales.

2. Genus EUZOSTERIA, Shelford

Euzosteria. Shelford, Trans. Ent. Soc. Lond. p. 262 (1909).

Characters. — Similar to *Polyzosteria*, but the spines on outer aspect of tibiæ triseriately arranged. Margins of pronotum more or less reflected. Ocelli occasionally present. Supra-anal lamina : (♂) with less acute angles, (♀) more rounded, less bilobate.

Geographical distribution of species. — Australia.

1. *E. subverrucosa*, White, *in* Grey, Journ. Exped. Austral., Vol. 2, p. 467   Australia.
   (1841).
   > *Polyzosteria reflexa*, Brunner von Wattenwyl, Nouv. Syst. des Blatt. p. 208
   > (1865).
   > *Polyzosteria femoralis*, Walker, Cat. Blatt. Brit. Mus. p. 156 (1868).
   > *Polyzosteria figurata*, Walker, ibidem, p. 157 (1868).
2. *E. subreflexa*, Tepper, Trans. Roy. Soc. S. Austral., Vol. 19. p. 158 (1895).   South Australia.
3. *E. nobilis*. Brunner von Wattenwyl, Nouv. Syst. des Blatt. p. 209 (1865).   South and West Australia.
   > *Polyzosteria subnobilis*, Tepper, Trans. Roy. Soc. S. Austral.,Vol. 17, p. 81
   > (1893).
4. *E. patula*, Walker, Cat. Blatt. Brit. Mus. p. 157 (1868). — **Pl. I,**   South and West Australia.
   Fig. 2a.
5. *E. mitchellii*, Angas, S. Austral. Illustr., pl. 48, f. 1 (1847). — **Pl. I,**   Victoria, South and West
   Fig. 2.   Australia.
   > *E. mitchellii*, Saussure, Mém. Soc. Sc. Phys. Nat. Genève. Vol. 23, p. 106
   > (1873).

3. Genus PLATYZOSTERIA, Brunner von Wattenwyl

Platyzosteria. Brunner von Wattenwyl, Nouv. Syst. des Blatt. p. 204 (1868).
Melanozosteria. Stål, Bih. Svensk. Akad., Vol. 2, n° 13, p. 13 (1874).
Syntomaptera. Tepper, Trans. Roy. Soc. S. Austral., Vol. 17, p. 106 (1893).
Drymaplaneta. Tepper, ibidem. p. 109 (1893).

Characters. — Ocelli absent. Antennæ shorter than the body. Body depressed. Vertex of head not covered by pronotum. Pronotum not cucullate, its margins not reflected. Rudiments of tegmina present as squamiform lobes or absent. Wings absent. Posterior angles of all the abdominal tergites produced, those of the distal tergites strongly produced and spiniform. Supra-anal lamina variable in shape, but never sub-bilobate in ♀. Genital styles long, slender, acuminate. Cerci frequently exceeding the supra-anal lamina, apex acuminate. Tibiæ moderately spined, spines on outer aspect triseriately arranged. Posterior metatarsus very short, not spined beneath or with only a few spines, its pulvillus covering the greater part of the joint beneath.

Geographical distribution of species. — Formosa, Màlay Archipelago to Australia, Tasmania, New Zealand, Bombay.

1. *P. grandis*, Saussure. Mém. Soc. Sc. Phys. Nat. Genève. Vol. 23,   Victoria. South Australia.
   p. 110 (1873).
2. *P. melanaria*, Erichson, Arch. f. Naturg., Vol. 8, p. 247 (1842). —   Tasmania.
   Pl. I, Fig. 3c.
3. *P. analis*, Saussure, Rev. Zool. (2), Vol. 16, p. 306 (1864).   New South Wales, West
   > *Polyzosteria melanaria*, Brunner von Wattenwyl, Nouv. Syst. des Blatt.   Australia, Bombay.
   > p. 210 (1865).

Periplaneta invisa, Walker, Cat. Blatt. Brit. Mus. p. 137 (1868) (♂ only).
Periplaneta ruficornis, Walker, Cat. Derm. Salt. Brit. Mus. Vol. 5, Suppl.
  Blatt. p. 38 (1871).

4. *P. pseudatrata*, Tepper, Trans. Roy. Soc. S. Austral., Vol. 17, p. 86 (1893).   Central Australia.
5. *P. aterrima*, Erichson, Arch. f. Naturg., Vol. 8, p. 248 (1842).   Tasmania, Australia.
  Periplaneta glabra, Tepper, Trans. Roy. Soc. S. Austral. Vol. 17, p. 107 (1893).
  Syntomaptera tepperi, Kirby, Ann. Mag. Nat. Hist. (7), Vol. 12, p. 374 (1903).
6. *P. ferox*, Shelford, Trans. Ent. Soc. Lond. p. 273, pl. 7, f 7 (1909).   Central Australia.
  — Pl. I, Fig. 3a.
7. *P. armata*, Tepper, Trans. Roy. Soc. S. Austral., Vol. 17, p. 84 (1893).   West Australia.
8. *P. rufofusca*, Tepper, ibidem, p. 84 (1893).   South Australia.
9. *P. bifida*, Saussure. Mém. Soc. Sc. Phys. Nat. Genève, Vol. 23. p. 110.   Queensland.
  pl. 10, f. 37 (1873).
10. *P. atrata*, Erichson, Arch. f. Naturg , Vol. 8, p. 248 (1842).   Tasmania, New S. Wales,
  Victoria, West Australia.
11. *P. invisa*, Walker, Cat. Blatt. Brit. Mus. p. 137 (1868).   New S. Wales, West Aus-
12. *P. consobrina*, Saussure. Rev. Zool. (2), Vol. 16, p. 306 (1864).   Australia.   [tralia.
13. *P. ruficeps*, Shelford, Blattidæ, in Fauna Südwest Austral. Vol. 2,   West Austrialia.
  Lief. 9, p. 134, pl. 13, f. 3 (1909).
14. *P. punctata*, Brunner von Wattenwyl, Nouv. Syst. des Blatt. p. 211 (1865).   New S. Wales.
15.' *P. variolosa*, Bolivar, Ann. Soc. Ent. Fr. (6), Vol. 2, p. 460 (1882).   New Caledonia.
16. *P. scabra*, Brunner von Wattenwyl, Nouv. Syst. des Blatt. p. 213 (1865).   New S. Wales.
  Polyzosteria scabra, Walker, Cat. Blatt. Brit. Mus. p. 162 (1868).
17. *P. coxalis*, Walker, Cat. Derm. Salt. Brit. Mus. Vol. 5, Suppl. Blatt.   Bombay.
  p. 35 (1871).   [Wales.
18. *P. scabrella*, Tepper, Trans. Roy. Soc. S. Austral., Vol. 17, p. 88 (1893).   South Australia, New S.
19. *P. biglumis*, Saussure, Rev. Zool. (2), Vol. 16, p. 305 (1864).   New S. Wales, Victoria,
  P. subaptera, Brunner von Wattenwyl, Nouv. Syst. des Blatt. p. 212 (1865).   S. Australia.
20. *P. perplexa*, Shelford, Trans. Ent. Soc. Lond. p. 277 (1909).   Tasmania.
21. *P. rufipes*, Shelford, ibidem, p. 278 (1909). .   West Australia.
22. *P. biloba*, Saussure. Mém. Soc. Sc. Phys. Nat. Genève, Vol. 20, p. 258   Amboina.
  pl. 3, f. 20 (1869).
23. *P. curiosa*. Shelford, Blattidæ, in Fauna Südwest Austral. Vol. 2, Lief. 9,   West Australia.
  p. 135, pl. 13, ff 11, 12 (1909).
24. *P. bicolor*, Kirby, Ann. Mag. Nat. Hist. (7), Vol. 12, p. 373 (1903). —   Torres Straits.
  Pl. I, Fig. 3.
25. *P. novae-seelandiae*, Brunner von Wattenwyl, Nouv. Syst. des Blatt.   New Zealand.
  p. 218 (1865).
  Periplaneta fortipes, Walker, Cat. Blatt. Brit. Mus. p. 137 (1868).
26. *P. castanea*, Brunner von Wattenwyl, Nouv. Syst. des Blatt. p. 214 (1865).   New S. Wales, Victoria.
  P. avocaensis, Tepper, Trans. Roy. Soc. S. Austral., Vol. 17, p. 88 (1893).
  P. exaspera, Tepper, ibidem, p. 182 (1894).
.27. *P. obscura*, Tepper, ibidem. Vol. 17, p. 107 (1893).   South and West Australia.
28. *P. scabriuscula*, Tepper, ibidem, p. 108 (1893).   South and West Australia.
29. *P. rufoterminata*, Brunner von Wattenwyl, Nouv. Syst. des Blatt. p. 219   Australia.
  (1865).
30. *P. pseudocastanea*, Tepper, Trans. Roy. Soc. S. Austral , Vol. 17, p. 89   South Australia.
  (1893).
31. *P. ceratodi*, Krauss, Denkschr. Med.-nat. Ges. Jena, Vol. 8, p. 751 (1903)   Queensland.
32. *P. glabra*, Walker, Cat. Blatt. Brit. Mus. p. 139 (1868).   Australia.
33. *P. conjuncta*, Shelford, Blattidæ, in Fauna Südwest Austral. Vol. 2,   West Australia.
  Lief. 9. p. 136 (1909).
34. *P. morosa*, Shelford, ibidem, p. 136 (1909).   South and West Australia.
35. *P. provisionalis*, Tepper. Trans. Roy. Soc. S. Austral., Vol 17, p. 108 (1893).   South Australia.
36. *P. inclusa*, Walker, Cat. Blatt. Brit. Mus. p. 140 (1868).   West Australia.

37. *P. albomarginata*, Brunner von Wattenwyl, Nouv. Syst. des Blatt.	New S. Wales, West Aus-
p. 212 (1865).	tralia.	[Australia.
38. *P. brunnea*, Tepper, Trans. Roy. Soc. S. Austral., Vol. 17, p. 86 (1893).	South Australia, Central
39. *P. obscuripes*, Tepper, ibidem, p. 112 (1893).	South and West Australia.
40. *P. variegata*, Shelford, Blattidæ, in Fauna Südwest Austral., Vol. 2,	West Australia.
Lief. 9, p. 137, pl. 13. f. 14 (1909).
41. *P. spenceri*, Shelford, Trans. Ent. Soc. Lond. p. 284 (1909).	Central Australia.
42. *P. soror*, Brunner von Wattenwyl, Nouv. Syst. des Blatt. p. 219 (1865).	Formosa, Borneo, Austro-
    P. semicincta, Walker, Cat. Blatt. Brit. Mus. p. 140 (1868).	Malayan, Melanesian and
	Polynesian Islands.
43. *P. communis*, Tepper, Trans. Roy. Soc. S. Austral., Vol. 17, p. 110(1893).	Australia.
    Methana antipodum, Brancsik, Jahresh. Ver. Trencsin. Comit. Vol. 19-20,
    p. 58, pl. 1, f. 4 (1897).
44. *P. semivitta*, Walker, Cat. Blatt. Brit. Mus. p. 143 (1868). — **Pl. 1,**	South and West Australia.
Fig. 3d.
    P. semivitta, Shelford, Trans. Ent. Soc. Lond. p. 285. pl. 8, f. 26a-26f (1909).
45. *P. subbifasciata*, Tepper, Trans. Roy. Soc. S. Austral., Vol. 17, p. 112 (1893).	South Australia.
46. *P. liturata*, Saussure, Mém. Soc. Sc. Phys. Nat. Genève, Vol. 23, p. 108,	New Georgia.
pl. 10, f. 36 (1873).
47. *P. circumducta*, Walker, Cat. Blatt. Brit. Mus. p. 143 (1868).	South Australia.
    Drymaplaneta submarginata, Tepper, Trans. Roy. Soc. S. Austral., Vol. 17,
    p. 111 (1893).
48. *P. sex-guttata*, Walker, Cat. Blatt. Brit. Mus. p. 141 (1868).	Australia.
49. *P. balteata*, Tepper, Trans. Roy. Soc. S. Austral., Vol. 17, p. 91 (1893).	South Australia.
50. *P. latizona*, Tepper, ibidem, p. 92 (1893).	South Australia.
51. *P. coolgardiensis*, Tepper, ibidem, Vol. 19, p. 159 (1895). — **Pl. 1,**	West Australia.
Fig. 3b.
52. *P. aposematica*, Shelford, Trans. Ent. Soc. Lond. p.288. pl. 9, f. 29 (1909).	Central Australia.
53. *P. hartmeyeri*, Shelford, Blattidæ, in Fauna Südwest Austral., Vol. 2,	West Australia.
Lief. 9. p 138 (1909).

Doubtful species :

54. *P. zebra*, Tepper, in Horn, Exped Centr. Austral., Vol. 2, p. 362 (1896).	Central Australia.
55. *P. jungii*, Tepper, Trans. Roy. Soc. S. Austral., Vol. 19, p. 162 (1895).	Yorketown.
56. *P. parva*, Tepper, ibidem, p. 162 (1895).	New S. Wales.

4. GENUS LEPTOZOSTERIA, TEPPER

Leptozosteria. Tepper, Trans. Roy. Soc. S. Austral., Vol. 17, p. 96 (1893).

Characters. — Body very flat and thin, elongate. Integument soft. Supra-anal lamina of male triangular, terminating in an acute apical spine. Colour pale with dark bands.

Geographical distribution of species. — Central Australia.

1. *L. prima*, Tepper, Trans. Roy. Soc. S. Austral., Vol. 17, p. 96 (1893).

5. GENUS CUTILIA, STÅL

Cutilia. Ståyl, Oefv. Vet.-Akad. Förh., Vol. 34, n° 10, p. 36 (1877).

Characters. — Closely allied to *Platyzosteria* Brunner von Wattenwyl, but the posterior meta-tarsus long and biseriately spined beneath, its pulvillus apical; remaining tarsal joints unarmed beneath, their pulvilli occupying the entire joints. Tegminal rudiments present. In all but one species the posterior angles of the distal abdominal tergites strongly produced backwards. Supra-anal lamina ($\male$) quadrate.

Geographical distribution of species. — Formosa, Malay Archipelago, Torres Straits, Australia, New Zealand.

1. *C. nitida*, Brunner von Wattenwyl, Nouv. Syst. des Blatt. p. 214   Formosa, Malay Archipel-
   (1865).   ago, New S. Wales.
      Periplaneta polita, Walker, Cat. Blatt. Brit. Mus. p. 139 (1868).
      Cutilia tartarea, Stål, Oefv. Vet.-Akad. Förh. Vol. 34, n° 10, p. 36 (1877).
      ? *Blatta aterrima*, Eschscholtz, Entomographien, p 89 (1822).
2. *C. melanesiae*, Shelford, Trans. Ent. Soc. Lond. p. 291 (1909).   Torres Straits.
3. *C. triangulata*, Brunner von Wattenwyl, Ann. Mus. Stor. Nat. Genova,   Queensland, Thursday Isl.
   Vol. 13, p. 33 (1893), footnote.
      C. triangulata, Krauss, Denkschr. Med.-nat. Ges. Jena, Vol. 8, p. 750,
      pl. 67, f. 1 (1903).
      Leptozosteria secunda, Tepper, Trans. Roy. Soc. S. Austral., Vol. 18,
      p. 183 (1894).
4. *C. heydeniana*, Saussure, Rev. Zool. (2), Vol. 16, p. 317 (1864).   West Australia.
      Periplaneta marginifera, Walker, Cat. Blatt. Brit. Mus. p. 144 (1868).
5. *C. sedilloti*, Bolivar, Ann. Soc. Ent. Fr. (6), Vol. 2, p. 459 (1882). —   New Zealand.
   Pl. I, Fig. 5.
6. *C. brunni*, Alfken, Abhandl. Ver. Bremen, Vol. 17, p. 142 (1901).   Chatham Isl.

6. Genus ZONIOPLOCA, Stål

Zonioploca. Stål, Bih. Svensk. Akad., Vol. 2, n° 13, p. 13 (1874).
Knephasia. Tepper, Trans. Roy. Soc. S. Austral., Vol. 17, p. 99 (1893).

Characters. — Ocelli absent. Lateral margins of pronotum incrassated. Dorsal surface granulate, or with shallow punctures. Tegminal rudiments absent. Posterior angles of abdominal tergites 5-7 strongly produced. Supra-anal lamina : ($\male$) quadrate, angles obtuse, lateral margins entire, ($\male$) triangular, apex emarginate. Sub-genital lamina ($\male$) trapezoidal, styles lateral. Posterior metatarsus unarmed beneath, equal to the remaining joints in length, its pulvillus apical.

Geographical distribution of species. — Australia.

1. *Z. medilinea*, Tepper, Trans. Roy. Soc. S. Austral., Vol. 17, p. 100   Victoria, South and West
   (1893). — **Pl. I, Fig. 4.**   Australia.
2. *Z. alutacea*, Stål, Bih. Svensk. Akad., Vol. 2, n° 13, p. 13 (1874).   South Australia, Queens-
      Platyzosteria ardrossanensis, Tepper, Trans. Roy. Soc. S. Austral.,Vol. 17,   land.
      p. 92 (1893).
3. *Z. pallida*, Shelford. Blattidæ, in Fauna Südwest Austral.,Vol. 2. Lief. 9,   West Australia.
   p. 138, pl. 13, f. 7 (1909).
4. *Z. eastii*, Tepper, Trans. Roy. Soc. S. Austral.. Vol. 17, p. 92 (1893).   Central Australia.
5. *Z. robusta*, Shelford, Trans. Ent. Soc. Lond. p. 294 (1909).   Central Australia.

7. Genus COSMOZOSTERIA, Stål

Cosmozosteria. Stål, Bih. Svensk. Akad., Vol. 2, n° 13, p. 13 (1874).

Characters. — Ocelli present. Tegminal rudiments absent. Abdomen broader than thorax. Posterior angles of abdominal tergites 5-6 not or scarcely produced, of tergite 7 produced. Angles of ninth abdominal tergite lobiform. Dorsal surface of abdomen scabrous. Supra-anal and sub-genital laminæ (♂) quadrate. Cerci short. Posterior metatarsus very short, unarmed beneath, its pulvillus occupying the greater part of the joint.

Geographical distribution of species. — Australia.

1. *C. froggatti*, Shelford, Trans. Ent. Soc. Lond. p. 295 (1909).   ,Queensland.
2. *C. zonata*, Walker, Cat. Blatt. Brit. Mus. p. 159(1868). — **Pl. I, Fig. 6.** Queensland, South Austra-
   Polyzosteria quadrifascia. Walker, ibidem. p. 160 (1868).   [lia.
   Polyzosteria pectoralis, Walker, ibidem, p. 160 (1868).
   Platyzosteria trifasciata, Tepper, Trans. Roy. Soc. S. Austral.,Vol. 17, p. 91
   (1893).
3. *C. maculimarginata*, Tepper, ibidem. Vol. 19, p. 160 (1895).   ·Queensland.
4. *C. bicolor*, Saussure, Rev. Zool. (2), Vol. 16, p. 307 (1864).   Queensland, Victoria, New
   Polyzosteria ligata, Brunner von Wattenwyl, Nouv. Syst. des Blatt. p. 220   S. Wales.
   (1865).
   Platyzosteria subzonata, Tepper, Trans. Roy. Soc. S. Austral., Vol. 18,
   p. 181 (1894).
5. *C. gloriosa*, Shelford, Trans. Ent. Soc. Lond. p. 296 (1909).   Queensland.
6. *C. lateralis*, Walker, Cat. Blatt. Brit. Mus. p. 154 (1868).   Australia.
   Polyzosteria ferruginea, Walker, ibidem, p. 158 (1868).
7. *C. picta*, Tepper, Trans. Roy. Soc. S. Austral., Vol. 18, p. 182 (1894).   Queensland.

8. Genus ANAMESIA, Tepper

Anamesia. Tepper, Trans. Roy. Soc. S. Austral., Vol. 17, p. 69 (1893).
Pseudolampra. ·Tepper, ibidem, p. 96 (1893).

Characters. — Ocelli present or absent. Pronotum with margins not reflexed nor incrassated. Tegminal rudiments absent. Dorsal surface of abdomen not scabrous, with shallow punctures. Posterior angles of none of the abdominal tergites produced, angles of ninth abdominal tergite often lobiform. Cerci short, flattened. Supra-anal lamina : (♂) quadrate, (♀) trigonal, sub-cucullate. Tibiæ with spines on outer aspect triseriately arranged. Posterior metarsus shorter than remaining joints, not spined beneath, its pulvillus occupying the greater part of the joint.

Geographical distribution of species. — Australia.

1. *A. polyzona*, Walker, Cat. Blatt. Brit. Mus. p. 159 (1868). — **Pl. I,** West Australia.
   Fig. 7a.
   A. polyzona, Shelford, Blattidæ, in Fauna Südwest Austral.,Vol. 2, Lief. 9,
   p. 139, pl. 13, f. 10 (1909)
2. *A. lambii*, Tepper. Trans. Roy. Soc. S. Austral., Vol. 17, p. 70 (1893). Central Australia.
3. *A. frenchii*. Tepper, ibidem, p. 72 (1893). — **Pl. I, Fig. 7.**   Queensland, West Austra-
4. *A. lindsayi*, Tepper. ibidem, p. 71 (1893).   West Australia.   [lia.
5. *A. punctata*, Tepper, ibidem, p. 97 (1893).   West Australia.   ·
6. *A. rothei*, Tepper, ibidem, p. 98 (1893).   South Australia.
7. *A. walkeri*, Shelford. Trans. Ent. Soc. Lond. p. 301 (1909).   New S. Wales.
8. *A. circumcincta*, Walker. Cat. Derm. Salt. Brit. Mus., Vol. 5, Suppl. Australia.
   Blatt. p. 36 (1871).

Doubtful species :

9. *A. fulvornata*, Tepper, Trans. Roy. Soc. S. Austral.,Vol.18, p. 177 (1894). Victoria.
10. *A. ornata*, Tepper, ibidem, Vol. 17, p. 98 (1893).   South Australia.

9. Genus DESMOZOSTERIA, Shelford

Desmozosteria. Shelford, Blattidæ, in Fauna Südwest Austral., Vol. 2, Lief. 9, p. 139 (1909).

Characters. — Allied to *Zonioploca*, but the angles of none of the abdominal tergites backwardly produced. Lateral margins of the pronotum incrassated. Tegminal rudiments absent. Dorsal surface punctate or smooth. Supra-anal lamina : (♂) quadrate, margins entire, (♀) trigonal, cucullate. Cerci short, flattened. Posterior metatarsus very short, not spined beneath.

Geographical distribution of species. — Australia.

1. *D. grosse-punctata*, Shelford, Trans. Ent. Soc. Lond. p. 303 (1909).   Australia.
2. *D. michaelseni*. Shelford, Blattidæ, in Fauna Südwest Austral., Vol. 2,   West Australia.
   Lief. 9. p. 139, pl. 13, f. 9 (1909).
3. *D. rufescens*, Shelford, ibidem, p. 140 (1909).   West Australia.
4. *D. cincta*, Shelford, Trans. Ent. Soc. Lond. p. 303 (1909).   Central Australia.

10. Genus TEMNELYTRA, Tepper

Temnelytra. Tepper, Trans. Roy. Soc. S. Austral., Vol. 17, p. 38 (1893).

Characters. — Body flattened and depressed. Antennæ longer than the body. Pronotum anteriorly parabolic, posteriorly truncate, exposing the large scutellum. Tegmina quadrate or sub-quadrate, extending to the first abdominal tergite. Wings entirely absent. First abdominal tergite (♂) with scent-gland opening. Posterior angles of distal abdominal tergites produced (*T. undulivitta* Walker, ♂, is an exception). Supra-anal lamina : (♂) quadrate, margins entire, (♀) triangular, apex emarginate. Cerci longer than the lamina in both sexes. Posterior metatarsus very short, spined beneath.

Geographical distribution of species. — Australia, New Zealand.

1. *T. undulivitta*, Walker, Cat. Blatt. Brit. Mus. p. 144 (1868).   New Zealand.
2. *T. truncata*, Brunner von Wattenwyl, Nouv. Syst. des Blatt. p. 217   New S. Wales, South Aus-
   (1865). — **Pl. 1, Figs. 8a, 8b.**   tralia.
        T. harpuri, Tepper, Trans. Roy. Soc. S. Austral., Vol. 17, p. 39 (1893).
3. *T. subtruncata*, Tepper, ibidem, Vol. 19, p. 164 (1895).   Victoria.

11. Genus SCABINA, Shelford

Scabina. Shelford, Trans. Ent. Soc. Lond. p. 305 (1909).

Characters. — Eyes and antennal sockets equally far apart. Ocelli present. Antennæ robust. Pronotum parabolic, posteriorly truncate, exposing the scutellum. Tegmina quadrate, corneous, not extending beyond the first abdominal tergite. Wings rudimentary, squamiform. Posterior angles of abdominal tergites strongly produced backwards. Supra-anal lamina (♂) quadrate, entire. Cerci exceeding the lamina. Styles long, slender. Posterior metatarsus shorter than succeeding joints, not spined beneath, its pulvillus apical.

Geographical distribution of species. — Queensland.

1. *S. antipoda*, Kirby, Ann. Mag. Nat. Hist. (7), Vol. 12, p. 376 (1903). —   Queensland.
   Pl. 2, Fig. 9.

12. Genus METHANA, Stål

Methana. Stål. Oefv. Vet. Akad. Förh., Vol. 34, nº 10, p. 36 (1877).
Wodongia. Tepper, Trans. Roy. Soc. S. Austral., Vol. 19, p. 155 (1895).

Characters. — Antennæ longer than body. Pronotum anteriorly parabolic, almost covering vertex of head, posteriorly very obtusely angled; Scutellum not exposed. Tegmina and wings fully developed, at least as long as the abdomen, generally longer. Supra-anal lamina : (♂) quadrate, margins not serrate, (♀) triangular, apex emarginate. Cerci long, acuminate. Femora heavily spined. Posterior metatarsus about equal in length to remaining joints, biseriately spined beneath, its pulvillus apical; remaining joints of tarsus with large pulvilli, not spined beneath.

Geographical distribution of species. — Borneo, New Guinea, Australia.

1. *M. magna*, Shelford, Trans. Ent. Soc. Lond. p. 307 (1909).   Borneo.
2. *M. hosei*, Shelford, ibidem, p. 309 (1909).   Borneo.
3. *M. papua*, Shelford, Mém. Soc. Ent. Belg., Vol. 15, p. 234 (1908).   New Guinea.
4. *M. convexa*, Walker, Cat. Derm. Salt. Brit. Mus. Suppl. Blatt. p. 152 (1869).   Queensland, New S. Wales.
     M. rufescens, Kirby, Ann. Mag. Nat. Hist. (7), Vol. 12, p. 374 (1903).
5. *M. curvigera*, Walker, Cat. Blatt. Brit. Mus. p. 134 (1868).   Queensland.
6. *M. marginalis*, Saussure, Rev. Zool. (2), Vol. 16, p. 319 (1864) — **Pl. 2,**   Queensland, New S. Wales.
     Fig. 10.
     Periplaneta ligata, Brunner von Wattenwyl, Nouv. Syst. des Blatt. p. 234
     (1865).
7. *M. soror*, Saussure. Rev. Zool. (2), Vol. 16, p. 319 (1864).   Australia.
     Periplaneta biquadrata, Walker, Cat. Blatt. Brit. Mus. p. 134 (1868).
     Periplaneta oculata, Walker, Cat Derm. Salt. Brit. Mus. Suppl. Blatt. p. 152
     (1869).
     Wodongia lunata, Tepper, Trans. Roy. Soc. S. Austral. Vol. 19, p. 155 (1895).

Doubtful species :

8. *M. pallipalpis*, Serville, Hist. Nat. Ins. Orth. p. 71 (1839).   Java, Sumatra, Australia.

13. Genus PARAMETHANA, Shelford

Paramethana. Shelford, Sjöstedt's Kilimandjaro-Meru Exped. Blatt. p. 31 (1907).

Characters. — Differs from *Methana* in the short tegmina and wings of the female, which do not extend beyond the fifth abdominal tergite and in the discoidal pronotum. Third antennal joint nearly three times longer than the second

Geographical distribution of species. — East Africa.

1. *P. robusta*, Shelford, Sjöstedt's Kilimandjaro-Meru Exped. Blatt. p. 31.   German E. Africa.
     pl. 2, f. 7 (1907).
2. *P. buyssoni*, Shelford, Deutsche Ent. Zeitschr. p. 618 (1909). — **Pl. 2,**   German E. Africa.
     Fig. 11.

14. Genus THYRSOCERA, Burmeister

Thyrsocera. Burmeister, Handb. Ent., Vol. 2, p. 498 (1838).

Characters. — Sexes similar, completely winged. Antennæ incrassated in basal half and plumose. Pronotum trapezoidal, sides deflexed. Tegmina and wings exceeding the apex of the abdomen.

Cerci moderately long, flattened, spatulate. Femora sparsely armed. Tibial spines on outer aspect tri-seriately arranged. Posterior metatarsus equalling the length òf the remaining joints, spined beneath, its pulvillus small, apical; pulvilli of second and third joints larger, occupying the greater extent of the joint.

Geographical distribution of species. — India, Ceylon, Malay Peninsula.

1. *T. spectabilis*, Burmeister, Handh. Ent., Vol. 2, p. 498 (1838).   India, Ceylon.
2. *T. speciosum*, Walker, Cat. Blatt. Brit. Mus. p. 214 (1868).   Malay Peninsula.
       T. speciosum, Shelford, Trans. Ent. Soc. Lond. p. 250, pl. 14, f. 5 (1906).

15. Genùs EURYCOTIS, Stål

Eurycotis. Stål, Bih. Svensk. Akad , Vol. 2, n° 13, p. 13 (1874).

Characters. — Eyes on vertex of head further apart than the antennal sockets. Pronotum trapezoidal, not covering vertex of head. Tegmina squamiform or quadrate and not extending beyond the metanotum. Wings absent or squamiform. Tibial spines on outer aspect tri-seriately arranged. Tarsi as in *Polyzosteria, Platyzosteria*, etc.

Geographical distribution of species. — Florida, Central and South America, West Indies.

1. *E. floridana*, Walker, Cat. Blatt. Brit. Mus. p. 135 (1868). .— **Pl. 2,**   Florida.
   Fig. 12.
       Platyzosteria sabalianus, Scudder, Proc. Boston Soc. Nat. Hist. Vol. 19,
       p. 93 (1877). —
2. *E. ingens*, Scudder, ibidem, p. 92 (1877).   Florida.
3. *E. semipicta*, Walker, Cat. Blatt. Brit. Mus. p. 141 (1868).   Florida.
4. *E. mexicana*, Saussure, Rev. Zool. (2), Vol. 14, p. 163 (1862).   Mexico.
       Polyzosteria azteca, Saussure, ibidem, p. 163 (1862).
5. *E. mysteca*, Saussure, ibidem, p. 170 (1862).   Mexico.
       Polyzosteria rufovittata, Brunner von Wattenwyl, Nouv. Syst. des Blatt. p. 215
       (1865).
6. *E. vittifrons*, Saussure & Zehntner, Biol. Centr. Amer. Orth., Vol. 1, Guatemala.
   p. 71 (1893).
7. *E. quadrisquamata*, Saussure & Zehntner, ibidem, p. 71, pl. 4, f. 40 (1893).   Guatemala.
8. *E. subalata*. Saussure & Zehntner, ibidem, p. 72 (1893).   Colombia.
9. *E. cothurnata*, Giglio-Tos, Boll. Mus. Zool. Anat. Torino, Vol. 13,   Ecuador.
   n° 311, p. 11 (1898).
10. *E. occidentalis*, Saussure, Rev. Zool. (2), Vol 16, p. 318 (1864).   West Indies.
11. *E. opaca*, Brunner von Wattenwyl, Nouv. Syst des Blatt. p. 216 (1865). Cuba.
12. *E. dimidiata*, Bolivar, Mém. Soc. Zool. Fr., Vol. 1, p. 125 (1888).   Cuba.
13. *E. caraibea*, Bolivar, ibidem, p. 126 (1888).   Cuba.
14. *E. flavipennis*, Saussure & Zehntner, Biol. Centr. Amer. Orth. Vol. 1, Cuba.
    p. 71 (1893).
15. *E. finschiana*, Saussure, Mém. Soc. Sc. Phys. Nat. Genève,, Vol. 23,   Cuba.
    p. 111 (1873).
       Polyzosteria cabrerae, Bolivar, An. Soc. Esp. Hist. Nat. p. 355, pl. 8, f. 3
       (1881).
16. *E. bahamensis*, Rehn, Bull. Amer. Mus. Nat. Hist., Vol. 22, p. 110 (1906).   Bahamas.

Doubtful species :

17. *E. australis*, Burmeister, Handb. Ent., Vol. 2, p. 483 (1838).   Brazil.

16. Genus PELMATOSILPHA, Dohrn

Pelmatosilpha. Dohrn, Stett. Ent. Zeit., Vol. 48, p. 410 (1887).

Characters. — Eyes on vertex of head further apart than the antennal sockets. Pronotum trapezoidal, not covering vertex of head. Tegmina and wings completely developed but not exceeding the apex of the abdomen, or tegmina reduced, not surpassing the fifth abdominal tergite, and wings reduced or rudimentary. Tibial spines on outer aspect triseriately arranged. Tarsi as in *Polyzosteria, Platyzosteria,* etc.

Geographical distribution of species. — Texas, Central and South America, Ceylon.

1. *P. rotundata,* Scudder, Proc. Davenport Acad. Nat. Sc., Vol. 8, p. 93,   Texas, Panama.
   pl. 2, f. 5 (1900).
2. *P. villana,* Saussure & Zehntner, Biol. Centr Amer. Orth., Vol. 1, p. 72,   Panama.
   pl. 4, ff. 41, 42 (1893).
3. *P. alaris,* Saussure, Rev. Zool. (2), Vol. 16, p. 319 (1864).   Brazil.
4. **P. convexa, nov. sp.** (1).   Brazil.
5. *P. praestans,* Dohrn, Stett. Ent. Zeit., Vol. 48, p. 411 (1887).   Peru.
   P. aterrima, Walker, Cat. Derm. Salt. Brit. Mus. Suppl. Blatt. p. 151 (1869).
6. *P. marginalis,* Brunner von Wattenwyl, Proc. Zool. Soc. Lond. p. 603,   Grenada.
   pl. 52, f. 2 (1893).
7. *P. purpurascens,* Kirby, Ann. Mag. Nat. Hist. (7), Vol. 12, p. 375   Dominica.
   (1903). — **Pl. 2, Fig. 15.**
8. *P. decipiens,* Kirby, ibidem, p. 376 (1903).   Trinidad.
9. *P. coriacea,* Rehn. Trans. Amer. Ent. Soc., Vol. 29, p. 278 (1903).   Porto Rico.
10. *P. sinhalensis,* Shelford, Jahrb. Ver. Naturk. Wiesbaden, Vol. 61, p. 33   Ceylon.
    (1908).

Doubtful species :

11. *P. occidentalis,* Burmeister, Handb. Ent., Vol. 2, p. 483 (1838).   Colombia.

17. Genus DORYLÆA, Stål

Dorylæa. Stål, Oefv. Vet -Akad. Förh., Vol. 34, n° 10. p. 36 (1877).

Characters. — Sexes similar. Pronotum anteriorly arcuate, posteriorly truncate. Tegmina semi-corneous, venation obsolete not extending beyond the fourth or fifth abdominal tergite. Wings reduced or fully developed. Tibial spines triseriately arranged on the outer aspect of the tibiæ. Posterior metatarsi exceeding the following joints in length. armed beneath; second joint short armed beneath, third joint unarmed; pulvilli moderately enlarged.

Geographical distribution of species. — Malay Archipelago, Madagascar.

1. *D. flavicincta.* de Haan, in Temminck, Verhand. Nat. Ges. Orth. p. 50   Borneo, Java, Sumatra,
   (1842).   Madagascar.
   Methana zehntneri, Kirby, Ann. Mag. Nat. Hist. (7), Vol. 12, p. 374 (1903).

---

(1) **P. convexa, nov. sp.** — *Female.* — Convex, nitid. Head, pronotum, anal field of left tegmen, a triangular marking at base of right tegmen, abdomen and legs, castaneous. Pronotum parabolic. posteriorly truncate. Tegmina ovate, extending to base of supra-anal lamina, corneous, ochreous except for the castaneous areas and for some castaneous points between the obsolete veins, anal vein absent. Wings equal in length to tegmina, semi-corneous, anterior part densely flavo-reticulate. Supra-anal lamina produced, cucullate, posteriorly faintly emarginate. Abdomen piceous at base beneath. Posterior metatarsus much shorter than the succeeding joints. — Total length 21 mm.; length of tegmina 12.5 mm.; pronotum 6 mm. × 9 mm. — Espirito Santo.

2. *D. brunneri*, Stål, Oefv. Vet.-Akad. Förh., Vol. 34, n⁰ 10, p. 37 (1877).   Philippines.
3. **D. unicolor, nov. sp.** (1).   Talaut Isl.

18. Genus STYLOPYGA, Fischer von Waldheim

Stylopyga. Fischer von Waldheim, Orth. Ross. p. 68 (1846); Brunner von Wattenwyl, Nouv. Syst. des Blatt. p. 222 (1865).

Characters. — Sexes similar. Tegmina reduced to squamiform lobes, wings absent. Sixth abdomina tergite not enlarged nor declivous. Tibial spines on outer aspect triseriately arranged. Posterior metatarsus longer than the succeeding joints, spined beneath, its pulvillus small, apical; second and sometimes the third joint spined beneath, all the pulvilil small, apical.

Geographical distribution of species. — Cosmopolitan.

1. *S. rhombifolia*, Stoll, Spectres, Blatt. etc. p. 5, pl. 3*d*, f. 13 (1813).   Cosmopolitan.
   Periplaneta histrio, Saussure, Rev. Zool. (2), Vol. 16, p. 318 (1864).
   Periplaneta decorata, Brunner von Wattenwyl, Nouv. Syst. des Blatt. p. 224 (1865).
   Polyzosteria heterospila, Walker, Cat. Derm. Salt. Brit. Mus. Vol. 5, Suppl. Blatt. p. 35 (1871).
2. *S. ornata*, Brunner von Wattenwyl, Nouv. Syst. des Blatt. p. 225 (1865).   India.
   — **Pl. 2, Fig. 13.**
3. *S. sex-pustulata*, Walker, Cat. Derm. Salt. Brit. Mus. Vol. 5, Suppl.   India.
   Blatt. p. 36 (1871)
   Blatta bioculata, Paiva, Journ. Proc. Asiat. Soc. Bengal. Vol. 2, p. 346 (1906).
4. *S. parallela*, Bolivar, Ann. Soc. Ent. Fr. p. 299 (1897).   South India.
5. *S. picea*, Brunner von Wattenwyl, Nouv. Syst. des Blatt. p. 223 (1865).   Nicobar Isl.
6. *S. semoni*, Krauss, Denkschr. Med. nat. Ges. Jena, Vol. 8, p. 751 (1903).   Java.
7. *S. quadrilobata*, Brunner von Wattenwyl, Abhandl. Senckenb. Ges.   Celebes.
   Prankf., Vol. 24, p. 209 (1898).
8. *S. coxalis*, Walker, Cat. Blatt. Brit. Mus. p. 138 (1868).   Ceram, New Guinea.
9. **S. salomonis, nov. sp.** (2).   Solomon Isl.
10. *S. manca*, Gerstäcker, Mitt. Ver. Neuvorpomm. u. Rügen, Vol. 14,   Kamerun.
    p. 48 (1883).
11. *S. anthracina*, Gerstäcker, ibidem, p. 49 (1883).   Kamerun.
12. *S. furcifera*, Shelford, Jahrb. Ver. Naturk. Wiesbaden, Vol. 61, p. 31,   Kamerun.
    pl. 1, f. 1 (1908).
13. *S. assimilis*, Shelford, ibidem, p. 31, pl. 1, f. 2 (1908).   Kamerun.
14. *S. nigerrima*, Shelford; ibidem, p. 31, pl. 1, f. 3 (1908).   Kamerun.
15. *S. spinulifera*, Krauss, Zool. Jahrb. Abt. f. Syst., Vol. 5, p. 650, pl. 45,   San Thomé.
    f. 1 (1891).
16. *S. hottentota*, Saussure, Abhandl. Senckenb. Ges. Frankf., Vol. 21, p. 578   South Africa.
    (1899).
17. *S. tetra*, Walker, Cat. Blatt. Brit. Mus. p. 138 (1868).   South Africa.

---

(1) **D. unicolor, nov. sp.** — *Female.* — Unicolorous castaneous. Antennæ except at base rufous; clypeus rufous. Tegmina and wings extending to base of supra-anal lamina. Penultimate abdominal tergite produced, emarginate in the middle. Supra-anal lamina triangular, apex deeply cleft. Cerci moderate, exceeding the supra-anal lamina. Posterior metatarsus equal in length to succeeding joints spined beneath, its pulvillus smal apical; second tarsal joint spined beneath, its pulvillus occupying half the joint; remaining pulvilli large. — Total length 24 mm.; length of tegmina 14.5 mm.; pronotum 8.5 mm × 10 mm. — Talaut Isl. (Type in Oxford Museum.)

(2) **S. salomonis, nov. sp.** — *Male* — Allied to *S. quadrilobata* Brunner von Wattenwyl, but with the pronotum and tegminal rudiments outwardly margined with ochreous. Tegminal rudiments punctate. Wings-rudiments impunctate. Supra anal lamina trapezoidal, sub-cucullate, posteriorly faintly emarginate. Sub-genital lamina sub-quadrate, some fine spiniform setæ situated on the posterior margin at the base of the styles which are stout. Front coxæ testaceous, mid- and hind-coxæ outwardly margined with testaceous. — Total length 20 mm.; length of tegmina 3.5 mm; pronotum 7.5 mm. × 10 mm. — Solomon Isl. (Type in coll. W. W. Froggatt.)

18. *S. senecta*, Rehn, Proc. U. S. Nat. Mus., Vol. 27, p. 554 (1904).   South Africa.
19. *S. bimaculata*, Walker, Cat. Blatt. Brit. Mus. p. 139 (1868).   Natal.
20. *S. voeltzkowi*, Saussure, Abhandl. Senckenb. Ges. Frankf.,Vol. 21, p. 579   Madagascar.
    (1899).
21. *S. nossibei*, Saussure, ibidem, p. 580 (1899).   Madagascar.
22. *S. zamorensis*, Giglio-Tos, Mus. Boll. Zool. Anat. Torino, Vol. 13,   Ecuador.
    n⁰ 311, p. 10 (1898).
23. *S. antillarum*, Brunner von Wattenwyl, Proc. Zool. Soc. Lond. p. 204,   St. Vincent.
    pl. 15, f. 5 (1892).
24. *S. meridionalis*, Bruner, Journ. New York Ent. Soc.,Vol.14, p. 141 (1906).   Trinidad.

Doubtful species :

25. *S. signata*, Eschscholtz, Entomographien, p. 88 (1822)   Philippines.

19. GENUS BLATTA, LINNÆUS

Blatta. Linnæus. Syst. Nat. (ed. 10), Vol. 1, p. 424 (1758).
Kakerlac. Latreille, Fam. Nat. Règne Anim. p. 411 (1825).
Steleopyga. Fischer von Waldheim, Bull. Soc. Nat. Moscou, Vol. 6, pp. 356, 366 (1833).

Characters. — Sexes dissimilar. Antennæ long, setaceous. Pronotum trapezoidal, not covering vertex of head. Tegmina and wings of ♂ variable, not attaining the apex of the abdomen. Wings of ♀ absent, tegmina squamiform or quadrate. Femora strongly armed; tibial spines on outer aspect triseriately arranged. Tarsi elongate, metatarsi longer than the succeeding joints, spined beneath, second joint long and spined beneath, third and fourth joints shorter, spined beneath; all the pulvilli minute, apical.

Geographical distribution of species. — Cosmopolitan.

1. *B. orientalis*, Linnæus, Syst. Nat. (ed. 10), Vol. 1, p. 424 (1758).   Palæarctic region.
    Blatta culinaris, De Geer, Mém. Ins. Vol. 3, p. 530, pl. 25, ff. 1-7 (1773).
    Blatta ferrugineofusca, Gronovius, Zoophylacium, Vol. 2, p. 174 (1774).
    Blatta ferruginea, Thunberg, Vet.-Akad. nya Handl.,Vol. 31, p. 187 (1810).
    Kakerlak castanea, Blanchard, *in* Gay, Hist. fis. Chile, Zool., Vol. 6, p. 18,
      Orth. pl. 1, f. 2 (1852).
    Kakerlak platystetho, Philippi, Zeitschr. ges. Naturw.,Vol. 21, p. 221 (1863).
    Blatta badia, Saussure, Mém. Soc. Sc. Phys. Nat. Genève, Vol. 17, p. 150,
      pl. 1, f. 15 (1863).
    Periplaneta lateralis, Walker, Cat. Blatt. Brit. Mus. p. 136 (1868).
2. *B. sinuata*, Brunner von Wattenwyl, Ann. Mus. Stor. Nat. Genova,   Burma.
    Vol. 32. p. 35, pl. 1, f. 12 (1893).
3. **B. speciosa, nov. sp. (1).**   India.
4. *B. concinna*, de Haan, *in* Temminck, Verhand. Nat. Ges. Orth. p. 50   Japan, Hong-Kong, Malay
    (1842).   Archipelago, Australia.
    Periplaneta borrei, Saussure, Mém. Soc. Sc. Phys. Nat. Genève, Vol. 23,
      p. 113, pl. 10, f. 38 (1873).
    Blatta brunneri, Kirby, Ann. Mag. Nat. Hist. (7), Vol. 12, p. 375 (1903).

---

(1) **B. speciosa, nov. sp.** — *Female.* — Head, pronotum and tegmina rufo-castaneous. Pronotum laterally margined with paler colour, the bands expanding and extending inwards at the posterior angles. Tegmina quadrate, not extending beyond the thorax, overlapping at the sutural margins, posterior margins concave, anal vein impressed, its apex reaching the inner posterior angle of the tegmen. Abdomen above piceous, fourth to sixth tergites with an ochreous macula at each side, seventh tergite very large, eighth tergite produced in the middle. Supra-anal lamina tectiform, apex triangularly emarginate. Abdomen beneath castaneous. Anterior coxæ testaceous; legs castaneous. — Total length 34 mm.; length of tegmina 8.5 mm.; pronotum 11 mm. × 14 mm. — India, Sangli. (Type in Oxford University Museum.)

5. *B. agaboides.* Gerstäcker, Mitt. Ver. Neuvorpomm. u. Rügen, Vol. 14,   Kamerun, Assinie.
   p. 47 (1883).
       Periplaneta assiniensis, Bolivar, Ann. Soc. Ent. Fr. p. 172, pl. 1ˈ f. 1 (1893).
6. *B. flavilatera,* Saussure, Ann. Mus. Stor. Nat. Genova, Vol. 35, p. 76   Gallaland.
   (1895).
7. *B. ugandana,* Giglio-Tos, Boll. Mus. Zool. Anat. Torino, Vol. 22, n° 556,   Uganda.
   p. 2 (1907).
8. *B. montana,* Kirby, Trans. Zool. Soc. Lond., Vol. 19, p. 63 (1909).   Ruwenzori.
9. *B. propinqua.* Shelford, Sjöstedt's Kilimandjaro-Meru Exped., Blatt.   Kilimandjaro.
   p. 31 (1907).
10. *B. hova,* Saussure, Soc. Ent. Zurich, Vol. 6, p. 17 (1891).   Madagascar.
11. *B. meridionalis,* Saussure, Rev. Zool. (2), Vol. 16, p. 306 (1864).   South Africa.
       Deropeltis bivittata, Brunner von Wattenwyl, Nouv. Syst. des Blatt. p. 247
       (1865).
       Deropeltis distanti, Kirby, Ann. Mag. Nat. Hist. (7), Vol. 5, p. 284 (1900).
12. *B. rufa,* Tepper, Trans. Roy. Soc. S. Austral., Vol. 17, p. 101 (1903).   Central Australia.
13. *B. rotundata,* Brunner von Wattenwyl, Nouv. Syst. des Blatt. p. 230 (1865).   Fiji.
14. *B. pallipes,* Philippi, Zeitschr. f. Naturw., Vol. 21, p. 222 (1863).   Chili.
15. *B. brevipes.* Philippi, ibidem, p. 223 (1863).   Chili.

20. Genus CARTOBLATTA, Shelford

Cartoblatta. Shelford, Sjöstedt's Kilimandjaro-Meru Exped., Blatt., p. 33 (1907).

Characters. — Allied to *Blatta* Linnæus and *Pseudoderopeltis* Krauss. Pronotum (♂) transversely elliptical, its anterior border truncate, its posterior border slightly produced. Meso- and metanotum (♂) without backwardly-directed membranous processes. Tegmina and wings (♂) considerably exceeding the apex of the abdomen. Tegmina (♀) short and quadrate, not covering the first abdominal tergite, their sutural margins touching; wing-rudiments present. No scent-gland opening on dorsum of abdomen (♂). Tarsi as in *Blatta*.

Geographical distribution of species. — East Africa.
1. *C. pulchra,* Shelford, Sjöstedt's Kilimandjaro-Meru Exped., Blatt. p. 33,   Kilimandjaro.
   pl. 2, f. 4 (1907).

21. Genus PSEUDODEROPELTIS, Krauss

Pseudoderopeltis. Krauss, Zool. Jahrb. Abt. f. Syst., Vol. 5, p. 652 (1891).

Characters. — Resembles *Periplaneta* Burmeister, but male with the posterior angles of the meso- and metanotum produced as slender, membranous processes; a scent-gland opening on the first abdominal tergite. Female with lobiform tegmina, the sixth and seventh abdominal tergites declivous forming an angle with the preceding tergites and enlarged. Tarsi as in *Blatta*.

Geographical distribution of species. — Africa.
1. *P. adelungi,* Werner, Sitzungsb. Akad. Wiss. Wien, Vol. 116, Abt. 1,   Egyptian Sudan.
   p. 11 (1907).
2. *P. discrepans,* Adelung, Ann. Mus. Zool. St-Pétersb., Vol. 8, p. 312,   Abyssinia.
   pl. 20, f 14 (1903).
3. *P. gildessa,* Adelung, ibidem, p. 314. pl. 20, f. 4 (1903).   Abyssinia.
4. *P. saussurei,* Adelung, ibidem, p. 316, pl. 20. f. 5 (1903).   Abyssinia.
5. *P. conspersipennis,* Adelung, ibidem, Vol. 9, p. 448 (1905).   Abyssinia.

6. *P. spectabilis*, Adelung, ibidem, p. 451 (1905). Abyssinia.
7. *P. brunneriana*, Schulthess, Ann. Mus. Stor. Nat. Genova, Vol. 39, Somaliland.
   p. 167. pl. 2, f. 1 (1898).
8. *P. guttata*, Saussure, ibidem, Vol. 35, p. 75 (1895). Gallaland, Rhodesia.
9. *P. rothschildi*, Shelford, Ann. Mag. Nat. Hist. (7), Vol. 19, p. 39 (1907). British E. Africa.
10. *P. fulvornata*, Shelford, Sjöstedt's Kilimandjaro-Meru Exped., Blatt. Kilimandjaro.
   p. 34, pl. 2, f. 9 (1907).
11. *P. petrophila*, Shelford, ibidem, p 34, pl. 2, ff. 5, 6 (1907). Kilimandjaro.
12. *P. granulifera*, Krauss, Zool. Jahrb. Abt. f. Syst., Vol. 5, p. 653 (1891). Rhodesia.
13. *P. bicolor*, Thunberg, Vet.-Akad. nya Handl., Vol. 31, p. 187, pl. 5, f. A South Africa.
   (1810).
     Periplaneta orba, Stål, Oefv. Vet.-Akad. Förh. Vol. 13, p. 167 (1856).
     Ischnoptera juncea, Saussure, Rev. Zool. (2), Vol. 16, p. 314 (1864).
     Nauphoeta foveolata, Walker, Cat. Blatt. Brit. Mus. p. 42 (1868)
14. *P. similis*, Saussure, Rev. Zool. (2), Vol. 16, p. 314 (1864). South Africa.
     ? *Ischnoptera longipennis*, Walker, Cat. Blatt Brit. Mus. p. 117 (1868).
15. *P. antennata*, Saussure, Mém. Soc. Sc. Phys. Nat. Genève, Vol. 23, South Africa.
   p. 116, pl. 10, f. 39 (1873).
16. *P. longipennis*, Saussure, ibidem, p. 117 (1873). South Africa.
     Deropeltis saussurei, Kirby, Ann Mag. Nat. Hist. (7), Vol. 12, p. 377 (1903).
17. *P. anthracina*, Brancsik, Jahresh. Ver. Trencsin. Gomit. Vol. 17-18, Zambesi.
   p. 244, pl. 7, f. 2 (1897).
     Stylopyga brancsiki, Shelford, Sjöstedt's Kilimandjaro-Meru Exped. Blatt.
     p. 32 (1907).
18. *P. albilatera*, Stål, Oefv. Vet.-Akad. Pörh., Vol. 13, p. 167 (1856). South Africa.
     Polyzosteria capensis, Saussure, Rev. Zool. (2), Vol. 16, p. 307 (1864).
     Deropeltis flavomarginata, Brunner von Wattenwyl, Nouv. Syst. des Blatt.
     p. 247 (1865).
     Periplaneta collaris, Walker, Cat. Blatt. Brit. Mus. p. 142 (1868).
     Periplaneta decorata, Walker, ibidem, p. 142 (1868).
19. *P. diluta*, Stål, Oefv. Vet.-Akad. Förh. Vol. 13, p. 167 (1856). South Africa.
     Periplaneta (1) *africana*, Karny, Denkschr. Med.-nat. Ges. Jena, Vol. 13,
     p. 380, pl. 21, ff. 25, 26 (1908).
20. *P. flavescens*, Krauss, Zool. Jahrb. Abt. f. Syst., Vol. 5, p. 654 (1891). — Cape.
   Pl. 2, Fig. 14.
21. *P. prorsa*, Shelford, Mém. Soc. Ent. Belg., Vol. 15, p. 234 (1908). Congo.
22. *P. aethiopica*, Saussure, Rev. Zool. (2), Vol. 16, p. 317 (1864). Gaboon.

Doubtful species :

23. *P. brevicollis*, Serville, Hist. Nat. Ins Orth. p. 170 (1839). South Africa.
24. *P. dimidiata*, Walker, Cat. Blatt. Brit. Mus. p. 116 (1868). Natal.

22. GENUS PERIPLANETA, BURMEISTER

Periplaneta. Burmeister, Handh. Ent., Vol. 2, p. 502 (1838).
Cacerlaca. Saussure, Mém. Hist. Nat. Mexique, Blatt. p. 69 (1864).

Characters. — Sexes similar. Antennæ very long, slender. Pronotum trapezoidal, not covering vertex of head, sides deflexed, its greatest width behind the middle. Posterior angles of meso- and metanotum not produced as slender membranous processes. Tegmina and wings usually extending considerably beyond the apex of the abdomen, the former coriaceous. Cerci and genital styles long.

---

(1) *Periplaneta adelungi* Karny, is a species of *Ischnoptera*.

Legs long; femora and tibiæ strongly spined, tibial spines triseriately arranged. Tarsi long and slender, posterior metatarsus longer than remaining joints; all the joints spined beneath, their pulvilli minute, apical.

Geographical distribution of species. — Cosmopolitan.

1. *P. americana*, Linnæus. Syst. Nat. (ed. 10), Vol. 1, p. 424 (1758).   Cosmopolitan.
    Blatta hakkerlac, De Geer, Mém. Ins., Vol. 3, p. 535, pl. 44, ff. 1-3 (1773).
    Blatta aurelianensis, Fourcroy. Ent. Paris, Vol. 1, p. 177 (1785).
    Blatta siccifolia, Stoll, Spectres, Blatt. etc. p. 5, pl. 3*d*, ff. 10, 11 (1813).
    Blatta aurantiaca, Stoll, ibidem, p. 5, pl. 3*d*, f. 14 (1813).
    Periplaneta stolida, Walker, Cat. Blatt. Brit. Mus. p. 128 (1868).
2. *P. australasiae*, Fabricius, Syst. Ent. p. 271 (1775).   Cosmopolitan.
    Blatta domingensis, Beauvois, Insect. Afr. Amér. p. 182, Orth. pl. 1,
       f. 4 (1804).
    Periplaneta zonata, de Haan, *in* Temminck, Verhand. Nat. Ges. Orth.
       p. 49 (1842).
    Periplaneta repanda, Walker, Cat. Blatt. Brit. Mus. p. 125 (1868).
    Periplaneta subcincta, Walker, ibidem, p. 126 (1868).
    Periplaneta inclusa, Walker, ibidem, p. 126 (1868).
    Periplaneta emittens, Walker, Cat. Derm. Salt. Brit. Mus., Vol. 5, Suppl.
       Blatt. p 37 (1871).
    Polyzosteria subornata, Walker, ibidem, p. 35 (1871).
3. *P. furcata*, Karny, Wiss. Ergebn. Exped. Filchner China u. Tibet,   Asia Minor.
    Bd. 10, Teil 1, p. 19 (1908).
4. *P. tartara*, Saussure, *in* Fedtschenko, Reise Turkestan, Orth. p. 9   Turkestan.
    (1874).
5. *P. filchnerae*, Karny, Wiss. Ergebn. Exped. Filchner China u. Tibet,   China.
    Bd. 10, Teil, 1, pp. 18, 19, pl. 1, ff. 1-4 (1908).
6. *P. japonica*, Karny, ibidem, p. 18 (1908).   Japan.
7. *P. emarginata*, Karny, ibidem, p. 19 (1908).   Japan.
8. *P. picea*, Shiraki, Annot. Zool. Japon., Vol. 6. p. 26, pl. 2, f. 3 (1906).   Japan.
9. *P. striata*, Shiraki, ibidem, p. 27, pl. 2, f. 5 (1906).   Japan.
10. *P. lata*, Herbst, Fuessly Archiv, Vol. 7-8, p. 185, pl. 49, f. 7 (1786).   Borneo.
    — **Pl. 2, Fig. 16.**
11. *P. monochroma*, Walker, Cat. Derm. Salt. Brit. Mus., Vol. 5, Suppl.   Bombay.
    Blatt. p. 37 (1871).
12. *P. curta*, Walker, ibidem, p. 38 (1871).   Bombay.
13. *P. indica*, Karny, Wiss. Ergebn. Exped. Filchner China u. Tibet,   India.
    Bd. 10, Teil 1, p. 18 (1908).
14. *P. ceylonica*, Karny, ibidem, p. 18 (1908).   Ceylon.
15. *P. affinis*, Saussure, Mém. Soc. Sc. Phys. Nat. Genève, Vol. 20,   India (?).
    p. 261 (1869).
16. *P. valida*, Brunner von Wattenwyl, Ann. Mus. Stor. Nat. Genova,   Burma.
    Vol. 33, p. 36, pl. 1, f. 13 (1893).
17. *P. gracilis*, Brunner von Wattenwyl, ibidem, p. 36, pl. 1. f. 14 (1893).   Burma.
18. *P. regina*, Saussure, Rev. Zool. (2), Vol. 16, p 320 (1864). .   Malacca.
19. *P. malaica*, Karny, Wiss. Ergebn. Exped. Filchner China u. Tibet,   Banguey.
    Bd. 10, Teil 1, p. 19 (1908)
20. *P. crassa*, Karny, ibidem, p. 19, pl. 1, f. 5 (1908).   Borneo.
21. *P. spinosostylata*, Krauss, Denkschr. Med.-nat. Ges. Jena, Vol. 8, p. 752,   Java.
    pl. 67, f. 2 (1903).
22. *P. nitida*, Bolivar, An. Soc. Esp. Hist. Nat., Vol. 19. p. 302 (1890).   Philippines.
23. *P. methanoides*, Brunner von Wattenwyl, Abhandl. Senckenb. Ges.   Gilolo, Ambon.
    Frankf., Vol. 24, p. 209, pl. 16, f. 14 (1898).
24. *P. basedowi*, Tepper, Trans. Roy. Soc. S. Austral., Vol. 28, p. 162,   South Australia.
    pl. 32 (1904).

25. *P. savignyi*, Krauss, Verh. Zool.-bot. Ges. Wien, Vol. 40, p. 242 (1890).   Egypt.
26. *P. lebedinskii*, Adelung, Ann. Mus. Zool. St-Pétersb., Vol. 8, p. 305 (1904).   Abyssinia.
27. *P. vosseleri*, Shelford, Jahrb. Ver. Naturk. Wiesbaden, Vol. 61, p. 38   German E. Africa.
     (1908).
28. *P. atricollis*, Saussure, Abhandl. Senckenb. Ges. Frankf. Vol. 21. p. 580   South Africa.
     (1899).
29. *P. caffra*, Stål, Oefv. Vet.-Akad. Förh., Vol. 13, p. 166 (1856).   Natal.
30. *P. patens*, Walker, Cat. Blatt. Brit. Mus. p. 127 (1868).   Congo.
31. *P. funebris*, Shelford, Deutsche Ent. Zeitschr. p. 122 (1908).   Kamerun.
32. *P. bicolor*, Shelford, ibidem, p. 122 (1908).   Kamerun, Congo.
33. *P. stygia*, Shelford, ibidem, p. 619 (1909).   Kamerun.
34. *P. fuliginosa*, Serville, Hist. Nat. Ins. Orth. p. 70 (1839).   North America.
35. *P. insignis*, Serville, ibidem, p. 67 (1839).   Cayenne.
36. *P. brunnea*, Burmeister. Handb. Ent. Vol. 2, p. 503 (1838).   Demerara.
37. *P. truncata*, Krauss. Zool. Anzeig., Vol. 15, p. 165 (1892).   Cosmopolitan.

Doubtful species :

38. *P. heros*, Eschscholtz, Entomographien, p. 83 (1822).   Philppines.
39. P *australis*, MacLeay, in King, Survey Coasts Austral. Vol. 2, p. 454   N. Australia.
     (1827).
40. *P. cylindrica*, Thunberg, Mém. Acad. Sc. St-Péterb. Vol. 10, p. 279 (1826).   ? Hab.

23. GENUS HOMALOSILPHA, STÅL

Homalosilpha, Stål, Bih. Svensk. Akad., Vol. 2, n° 13, p. 13 (1874).

Characters. — Closely resembles *Periplaneta* Burmeister, but the pronotum discoïdal, its sides not deflexed, its greatest width at the middle.

Geographical distribution of species. — India to Sunda Islands, Philippines, Kamerun, Uganda.

1. *H. ustulata*, Burmeister, Handb. Ent., Vol. 2, p. 503 (1838).   India to Great Sunda Isl.
     Kakerlac thoracica, Serville, Hist. Nat. Ins. Orth. p. 69, pl. 2, f. 1 (1839).
     Periplaneta configurata, Walker, Cat. Blatt. Brit. Mus. p. 145 (1868).
2. **H. gaudens, nov. sp.** (1).   Tonkin.
3 *H. contraria*, Walker, Cat. Blatt. Brit. Mus. p. 131 (1868).   Philippines.
4. *H. decorata*, Serville, Hist. Nat. Ins. Orth. p. 99 (1839).   Borneo.
     H. decorata, Shelford, Trans. Ent. Soc. Lond. p. 270, pl. 14, f. 8 (1906).
5. *H. vicina*, Brunner von Wattenwyl, Nouv. Syst. des Blatt. p. 236 (1865).   Kamerun.
     Pl. 2, Fig. 17.
6. *H. cruralis*, Shelford, Deutsche Ent. Zeitschr. p. 121, pl. 2, f. 8c (1908).   Uganda.

24. GENUS EROBLATTA, NOV. GEN.

Characters. — Antennæ moniliform, shorter than the body. Pronotum almost rectangular, as long as broad, sides not deflexed. Tegmina and wings considerably exceeding the apex of the abdomen;

---

(1) **H. gaudens, nov. sp.** — *Male*. — Piceous. Pronotum broadly bordered anteriorly and laterally with ochreous, disc with obscure impressions. Tegmina unicolorous. Wings castaneous. Supra-anal lamina quadrate, the posterior angles acute, posteriorly concave, surpassing the sub-genital lamina which is quadrate, with the posterior angles acute. Genital styles slender. Cerci moderate. Coxæ and femora piceous, tibiæ and tarsi rufescent. — Total length 30 mm.; length of body 23 mm.; length of tegmina 23 mm.; pronotum 7 mm. X 9 mm. — Tonkin. (Type in Oxford Museum.)

the former narrow with the anal field long and pointed, the marginal field deflexed. Cerci long and pointed. Femora strongly armed beneath. Spines on outer aspect of tibiæ triseriately arranged. Posterior metatarsi longer than the succeeding joints, its pulvillus apical. Arolia moderate.

Geographical distribution of species. — Borneo.

1. *E. borneensis*, Shelford, Ann. Mag. Nat. Hist. (8), Vol. 1, p. 159, Borneo.
   pl. 9, f. 2 (1908).

25. GENUS DEROPELTIS, BURMEISTER

Deropeltis. Burmeister, Handb. Ent.. Vol. 2, p. 486 (1838).
Euryzosteria. Saussure, Rev. Zool. (2), Vol. 16, p. 316 (1864).

Characters. — Males with well-developed tegmina and wings; females entirely apterous. Vertex of head not hidden by pronotum Antennæ incrassated. Pronotum : (♂) discoidal, (♀) posteriorly truncate, posterior angles often produced. Posterior margin of fifth abdominal tergite sinuate. Supra-anal lamina : (♂) quadrate, (♀) triangular, cucullate. Legs long and slender; femora very sparsely armed; tibiæ with spines on outer aspect biseriately arranged; tarsi moderate. posterior metatarsi equal to the succeeding joints in length, armed beneath, pulvilli in the male small, in the female large.

Geographical distribution of species. — Africa and Madagascar.

1. *D. erythrocephala*, Fabricius, Spec. Ins., Vol. 1, p. 342 (1781).   S. Africa.
   Blatta capensis, Thunberg, Diss.Ent. Nov. Spec. Ins., Vol. 4, p. 77 (1784).
   Euryzosteria delalandii, Saussure, Rev. Zool. (2), Vol. 16. p. 316 (1864).
   ? *Perisphaeria verticalis*, Burmeister, Handb. Ent., Vol. 2, p. 486 (1838).
2. *D. gracilis*, Burmeister, ibidem. p. 500 (1838).   S. Africa.
3. *D. wahlbergi*, Stål, Oefv. Vet.-Akad. Förh., Vol. 13, p. 167 (1856).   S. Africa.
   Deropeltis atra. Brunner von Wattenwyl, Nouv. Syst. des Blatt. p. 244 (1865).
4. *D. intermedia*, Brunner von Wattenwyl. Nouv. Syst. des Blatt. p. 244   Natal.
   (1865).
5. *D. burmeisteri*, Saussure, Ann. Mus. Stor. Nat. Genova, Vol. 35. p. 77   S. Africa.
   (1895).
6. *D. péringueyi*, Saussure, ibidem, p. 77 (1895).   S. Africa.
7. *D. morio*, Karny, Denkschr. Med.-nat. Ges. Jena, Vol. 13, p. 378,   S. W. Africa.
   pl. 21, ff. 21, 22 (1908).
8. *D. paulinoi*, Bolivar, Journ. Sc. Lisboa, Vol. 8, p. 108 (1881); (2), Vol. 1,   S. W. Africa and Angola.
   p. 76 (1889).
9. *D. carbonaria*, Gerstäcker, Mitt. Ver. Neuvorpomm. u. Rügen, Vol. 14,   West Africa.
   p. 51 (1883).
10. *D. robusta*, Gerstäcker, ibidem, p. 52 (1883).   Kamerun.
11. *D. bueana*, Karsch, Berl. Ent. Zeitschr., Vol. 37, p. 65 (1892).   Kamerun.
12. *D. tullbergi*. Borg, Bih. Svensk. Akad., Vol. 28, n° 10, p. 16, pl. 2, f. 6   Kamerun.
    (1904).
13. *D. sculpturata*, Krauss, Zool. Jahrb. Abt. f. Syst., Vol. 5, p. 651, pl. 45,   San Thomé Isl.
    f. 2 (1891).
14. *D. trimpressa*, Krauss, ibidem, p. 656, pl. 45, f. 3 (1891).   San Thomé Isl.
15. *D. dichroa*, Gerstäcker, Mitt. Ver. Neuvorpomm. u. Rügen, Vol. 14,   Gold Coast.
    p. 50 (1883).
16. *D. gaboonica*, Rehn, Proc. U. S. Nat. Mus.. Vol. 27, p. 556 (1904).   Gaboon.
17. *D. autraniana*, Saussure, Ann. Mus. Stor. Nat. Genova, Vol. 35, p. 78   West Africa, Gallaland,
    (1895).   German E. Africa.

18. *D. melanophila,* Walker. Cat. Blatt. Brit. Mus. Suppl. p. 146 (1869).   E. Africa and Madagascar.
    Deropeltis madecassa, Saussure, Soc. Ent. Zurich, Vol. 6, p. 17 (1891);
      Saussure & Zehntner, in Grandidier, Hist. Nat. Madagascar, Orth.
      Vol. 1, p. 77, pl. 3, ff. 28, 29 (1895).
    Deropeltis speiseri, Brancsik, Jahresh. Ver. Trencsin. Com., Vol. 17-18,
      p. 245, pl. 7, f. 3 (1894).
19. *D. integerrima,* Brunner von Wattenwyl, Nouv. Syst. des Blatt. p. 245   E. Africa and Zanzibar.
    (1865). — **Pl. 2, Fig. 18.**
20. *D. nigrita,* Saussure, Ann. Mus. Stor. Nat. Genova, Vol. 35, p. 80 (1895).   Somaliland.
21. *D. barbeyana,* Saussure, ibidem, p. 79 (1895).   Somaliland.
22. *D. schweinfurthi,* Saussure, ibidem, p. 79 (1895).   Somaliland.
23. *D. dmitriewi,* Adelung, Ann. Mus. Zool. St-Pétersb., Vol. 9, p. 463 (1905).   Somaliland.
24. *D. kachovskii,* Adelung, ibidem, Vol. 8, p. 319, pl. 20, f. 6 (1903).   Abyssinia.
25. *D pallidipennis,* Adelung, ibidem. p. 327 (1903).   Abyssinia.
26. *D. negus,* Adelung. ibidem, Vol.·9, p. 458 (1905).   Abyssinia.
27. *D. erythropeza,* Adelung, ibidem, p. 460 (1905).   Abyssinia.
28. *D. adelungi,* Shelford, Sjöstedt's Kilimandjaro-Meru Exped., Blatt.   Abyssinia.
    p. 37 (1907).
      Deropeltis gracilis, Adelung, Ann. Mus. Zool. St-Pétersb. Vol. 9. p. 455 (1905).
29   *D. brevipennis,* Shelford, Deutsche Ent. Zeitschr. p. 619 (1909).   Erythræa.

26. Genus MIROBLATTA, Shelford

Miroblatta. Shelford, Trans. Ent. Soc. Lond. p. 271 (1906).

    Characters. — Pronotum sub-cucullate, anteriorly parabolic, covering vertex of head. posteriorly truncate, exposing the scutellum, disc with elevated ridges. Tegmina and wings not extending beyond the apex of the abdomen. Tegmina very broad, corneous, venation obscured, anal vein absent; mediastinal field on under surface elevated, keeled, the space between mediastinal and radial veins broad, inflexed, forming together with the mediastinal field an epipleuron. Wings broadly ovate, coriaceous, anterior part nearly twice as broad as posterior part, outer margin deeply indented at apex of dividing vein, posterior part not folding in fan-like manner. Genital styles minute. Cerci long, sharply pointed. Legs long, slender; femora unarmed beneath; spines on outer aspect of posterior tibiæ biseriately arranged. Posterior metatarsi longer than remaining joints, unarmed beneath; the pulvilli large, the second occupying the whole length of the joint.

    Geographical distribution of species. — Borneo.

1. *M. petrophila,* Shelford, Trans. Ent. Soc. Lond. p. 272, pl. 14. f. 4, 4a (1906).   Borneo.

27. Genus CATARA, Walker

Catara. Walker. Cat. Blatt. Brit. Mus. p. 52 (1868).

    Characters. — Male with tegmina and wings fully developed; female entirely apterous. Antennæ slightly incrassated. Pronotum rugose; sub-discoidal, anteriorly truncate in the male; sub-cucullate, posteriorly truncate and with the posterior angles produced in the female. Dorsal surface of female rugose, posterior angles of mesonotum produced. Supra-anal lamina of male sub-transverse; genital styles small. Cerci short, obtuse. Femora almost entirely unarmed. Tibial spines small and few in number, biseriately arranged on the outer aspect of the tibiæ. Tarsi unarmed beneath; posterior metatarsus equal in length to the remaining joints, its pulvillus apical, the remaining pulvilli large. Arolia small.

Geographical distribution of species. — Singapore, Java, Borneo.

1. *C. rugosicollis*, Brunner von Wattenwyl, Nouv. Syst. des Blatt. p. 245   Singapore, Borneo.
(1865). — **Pl. 2, Fig. 19.**
   Catara rugicollis, Walker, Cat. Blatt. Brit. Mus. p. 53 (1868).
   Archiblatta valvularia, Saussure, Mém. Soc. Sc. Phys. Nat. Genève,
   Vol. 23, p. 118, pl. 10, f. 40 (1873).
2. *C. minor*, Krauss, Denkschr. Med.-nat. Ges. Jena. Vol. 8. p. 753 pl. 67,   Java.
   f. 3 (1903).

28. Genus PROTAGONISTA, Shelford

Protagonista. Shelford, Ann. Mag. Nat. Hist. (8), Vol. 1, p. 158 (1908).

Characters. — Antennæ slightly incrassated. Eyes further apart than antennal sockets. True ocelli present. Pronotum almost rectangular, as long as broad, sides not deflexed, not covering vertex of head. Pronotum and tegmina with a fine erect pubescence. Tegmina and wings fully developed in the male (female unknown), exceeding the apex of the abdomen. Genital styles present. Cerci moderate. Legs slender; front femora with a complete row of spines on anterior margin beneath, none on posterior margin; mid and hind femora with only one spine on each margin. Spines on posterior tibiæ on outer aspect biseriately arranged. Posterior metatarsi very long, considerably exceeding the remaining joints in length; all the pulvilli apical; arolia minute.

Geographical distribution of species. — Tonkin.

1. *P. lugubris*, Shelford, Ann. Mag. Nat. Hist. (8), Vol. 1, p. 158, pl. 9, f. 1   Tonkin.
   (1908).

29. Genus ARCHIBLATTA, Vollenhoven

Archiblatta. Vollenhoven, Tijdschr. v Ent., Vol. 5, p. 106 (1862); Brunner von Wattenwyl, Nouv. Syst. des Blatt. p. 248 (1865).
Planetica. Saussure, Mém. Soc. Sc. Phys. Nat. Genève, Vol. 17, p. 164 (1864).

Characters. — Sexes dissimilar. Antennæ elongate. Pronotum slightly longer than broad, trapezoidal, anteriorly emarginate, not covering vertex of head, disc rugose. Male with fully-developed tegmina and wings considerably exceeding apex of abdomen. Tegmina with long anal field; mediastinal area deflexed. Wings with posterior part not broader than anterior part, outer margin deeply indented at apex of dividing vein. Female entirely apterous, with the abdomen ample. Genital styles small. Cerci moderate. Femora unarmed beneath. Tibiæ very sparsely armed, the spines arranged on the outer aspect in a single row. Posterior metatarsus shorter than the succeeding joint, unarmed beneath; all the pulvilli large.

Geographical distribution of species. — Singapore, Penang, Great Sunda Islands.

1. *A. hoevenii*, Vollenhoven, Tijdschr. v. Ent., Vol. 5, p. 106, pl. 6, ff. 1, 2   Penang, Singapore and
   (1862).   Great Sunda Isl.
   Planetica aranea, Saussure, Mém. Soc. Sc. Phys. Nat. Genève, Vol. 17,
   p. 166, pl. 1, f. 23 (1864).
2. *A. phalangium*, Saussure, Rev. Zool (2), Vol. 16, p. 344 (1864).   « India orientalis ».

Doubtful species :

3. *A. parva*, Shelford, Ann. Mag. Nat. Hist. (8), Vol. 1. p. 160 (1908).   West Australia.

30. GENUS NOCTICOLA, BOLIVAR

Nocticola. Bolivar, Ann. Soc. Ent. Fr., Vol. 61, p. 29 (1892).

Characters. — Size small. Eyes simple or absent. Antennæ very long. Third joint of palpi with obtuse apex. Pronotum more or less truncate anteriorly and posteriorly. Tegmina (♂) ovate, not exceeding the fourth abdominal tergite, corneous, ciliate; wings rudimentary. Tegmina and wings (♀) absent. Tibiæ scarcely longer than the femora, sparsely spined, the spines biseriately arranged. Tarsi very long, without pulvilli or arolia. Supra-anal lamina (♂ and ♀) triangular. Sub-genital lamina : (♂) with the apex emarginate, styles absent (?), (♀) large, compressed at the apex, divided by a longitudinal groove.

Geographical distribution of species. — Philippines.
1. *N. simoni.* Bolivar, Ann. Soc. Ent. Fr., Vol. 61, p. 32, pl. 1 (1892).   Philippines.
2. *N. cæca*, Bolivar, ibidem, p. 33 (1892).   Philippines.

31. GENUS SPELÆOBLATTA, BOLIVAR

Spelæoblatta. Bolivar, Ann. Mus. Stor. Nat. Genova, Vol. 38, p. 32 (1897).

Characters. — Size small. Head oblong, elongate. Eyes absent. Antennæ very long. Last joint of maxillary palpi incrassate towards the apex, which is truncate. Pronotum anteriorly arcuate, posteriorly truncate. Tegmina (♀) squamiform, obliquely truncate; wings absent. Tibiæ strongly spined, the spines biseriately arranged on the outer aspect. Tarsi very long, pulvilli and arolia absent. Supra-anal lamina (♀) triangular, apex rounded. Sub-genital lamina valvular. Cerci elongate, imperfectly articulate, pointed at the apex.

Geographical distribution of species. — Burma.
1. *S. gestroi*, Bolivar, Ann. Mus. Stor. Nat. Genova, Vol. 38, p. 32 (1897).   Burma.

INDEX

EXPLANATION OF THE PLATES

PLATE 1

Fig. 1. *Polyzosteria cuprea*, Saussure.

— 1a. — *pubescens*, Tepper. Apex of abdomen, ♀, dorsal view.

— 2. *Euzosteria mitchellii*, Angas.

— 2a. — *patula*, Walker. Apex of abdomen, ♀, dorsal view.

— 3. *Platyzosteria bicolor*, Kirby.

— 3a. — *ferox*, Shelford. Apex of abdomen, ♂, dorsal view.

— 3b. — *coolgardiensis*, Tepper. Apex of abdomen, ♂, dorsal view.

— 3c. — *melanaria*, Erichson. Apex of abdomen, ♂, dorsal view.

— 3d. — *semivitta*, Walker. Hind-leg of ♂.

— 4. *Zonioploca medilinea*, Tepper.

— 5. *Cutilia sedilloti*, Bolivar.

— 6. *Cosmozosteria zonata*, Walker.

— 6a. — — — Apex of abdomen, ♂, dorsal view.

— 7. *Anamesia frenchii*, Tepper.

— 7a. — *polyzona*, Walker. Apex of abdomen, ♂, dorsal view.

— 8a. *Temnelytra truncata*, Brunner von Wattenwyl. First abdominal tergite of ♂.

— 8b. — — — Apex of abdomen, ♂, dorsal view.

PLATE 2

Fig. 9. *Scabina antipoda*, Kirby.

— 10. *Methana marginalis*, Saussure.

— 11. *Paramethana buyssoni*, Shelford, ♀.

— 12. *Eurycotis floridana*, Walker.

— 13. *Stylopyga ornata*, Brunner von Wattenwyl.

— 14. *Pseudoderopeltis flavescens*, Krauss.

— 15. *Pelmatosilpha purpurascens*, Kirby.

— 16. *Periplaneta lata*, Herbst.

— 17. *Homalosilpha vicina*, Brunner von Wattenwyl.

— 18. *Deropeltis integerrima*, Brunner von Wattenwyl, ♀.

— 19. *Catara rugosicollis*, Walker, ♀.

Oxford, July 15, 1910.

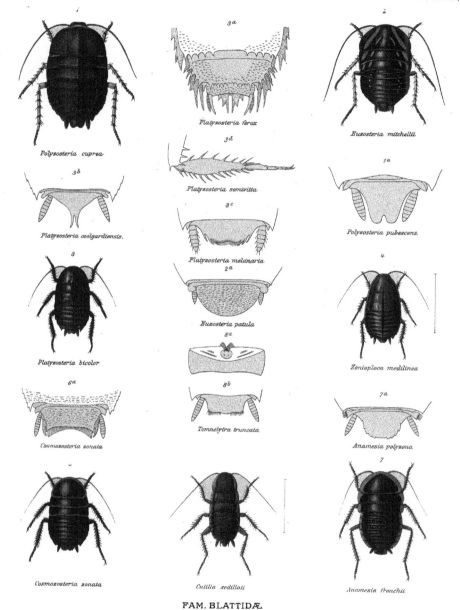

Polyzosteria cuprea

Platyzosteria ferax

Euzosteria mitchellii

Platyzosteria coolgardiensis.

Platyzosteria semivitta

Polyzosteria pubescens.

Platyzosteria melanaria

Platyzosteria bicolor

Euzosteria patula

Zonioploca medilinea

Cosmozosteria zonata

Temnelytra truncata

Anamesia polyzona.

Cosmozosteria zonata

Cutilia sedilloti

Anamesia frenchii

FAM. BLATTIDÆ

SUBFAM. BLATTINÆ (PERIPLANETINÆ)

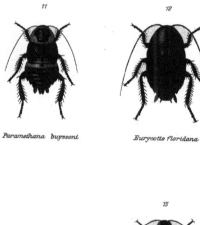

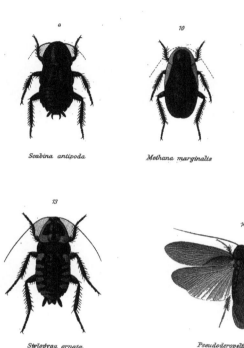

Scabina antipoda   *Methana marginalis*   *Paramethana buyssoni*   *Eurycotis floridana*

Stylopyga ornata   *Pseudoderopeltis flavescens.*   *Pelmatosilpha purpurascens*

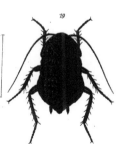

Periplaneta lata.   *Homalosilpha vicina*   *Deropeltis integerrima*   *Catara rugosicollis*

COLEOPTERA

FAM. APHODIIDÆ

COLEOPTERA LAMELLICORNIA

FAM. APHODIIDÆ [1]

von ADOLF SCHMIDT

MIT 3 COLORIERTEN TAFELN

EINLEITUNG.

 IE Aphodiinen sind eine Abteilung der coprophagen Lamellicornier und unterscheiden sich von den Copridæ durch die Zahl der Enddorne an den Hintertibien; die Aphodiinen haben deren zwei, die Copridæ nur einen. Sie werden von den Ægialiidæ, Hybosoridæ und Geotrupidæ dadurch getrennt, dass bei den drei letzteren die Mundwerkzeuge mehr oder weniger sichtbar sind, während dieselben bei den Aphodiinen vollständig unter dem Kopfschilde verborgen liegen.

Die älteste Gattung der Aphodiinen ist *Aphodius;* sie wurde von Illiger 1798 gegründet (Illiger, *Käfer Preussens*, p. 15). Die sechs Arten dieser Gattung, die Linné bekannt waren, führt letzterer in seinem Werke *Systema Naturae* 1758 als Scarabæiden auf. Es sind folgende Arten : *Scarab. subterraneus, erraticus, fossor, fimetarius, haemorrhoidalis, conspurcatus.* Eine siebente Art, die auch zu den Aphodiinen gehört, nämlich *Rhyssemus germanus,* führte Linné in der Gattung *Ptinus* auf. Illiger vereinigte in seiner neuen Gattung zweiunddreissig Arten, davon gehören aber *porcatus* zu *Oxyomus, sabuleti* und *globulus* zu *Ægialia, asper* zu *Rhyssemus.*

Dieser ersten Gattung fügte Serville in seiner *Encyclopédie Méthodique,* Vol. 10, p. 357 (1825) die Gattung *Euparia* zu; dann folgen 1840 *Oxyomus* Castelnau, 1841 *Psammobius* Heer, 1842 *Diastictus, Rhyssemus, Pleurophorus* und *Heptaulacus* Mulsant, 1843 *Rhyparus* Westwood, 1845 *Corythoderus* Klug, 1857 *Chaetopisthes* Westwood, *Sybax* Boheman, 1858 *Saprosites* Redtenbacher, 1859 *Coptochirus* Harold, 1861 *Harmogaster* und *Proctophanes* Harold, 1867 *Ataenius* Harold, 1868 *Cnemisus* Motschulsky, 1869 *Dialytes* Harold, 1871 *Simogonius* Harold, 1876 *Oxycorythus* Solsky, 1877 *Odochilus* Harold, 1884 *Notocaulus* G. Quedenfeldt, 1886 *Phycochus* Broun, 1891 *Rhyssemodes* Reitter, 1894 *Sugrames* Reitter und *Termitodius*

---

1) Wenn die Gruppe der Aphodiinen in dieser Arbeit als Familie bezeichnet wird. so geschieht es analog den andern Gruppen, wie z. B. der Geotrupidæ, und weil es bisher noch an einer genauen systematischen Benennung der einzelnen Gruppen fehlt.

COLEOPTERA LAMELLICORNIA

Wasmann, 1895 *Caelius* Lewis, 1896 *Sicardia* Reitter, *Didactylia* d'Orbigny und *Sybacodes* Fairmaire, 1900 *Odontoderus* und *Rhyssemorphus* Clouët, 1901 *Trichiorhyssemus* Clouët und *Aphodobius*, *Drepanocanthus*, *Harmodactylus*, *Lorditomaeus* Péringuey, 1905 *Stereomera* Arrow und *Turanella* Semenow, 1908 *Macroretrus* Péringuey, 1909 *Acanthaphodius* 1) A. Schmidt.

Somit ist die Anzahl der Gattungen auf 42 gestiegen, die zusammen 1152 Arten mit 277$\frac{1}{}$ Varietaten enthalten.

ALLGEMEINE KENNZEICHNUNG DER APHODIINEN

Farbe und Körperbau. — Die Aphodiinen sind in ihrem meist einfarbigen, helleren oder · dunkleren, seltener durch anders gefärbte Flecke, Makeln oder Binden etwas belebteren Kleide weit entfernt, das Auge zu entzücken und so die Aufmerksamkeit auf sich zu ziehen. Wer aber diese Gruppe der grossen Insektenwelt doch näher betrachtet, dabei die mannigfaltigen Abänderungen im Bau und der Skulptur beobachtet, der findet bald heraus, dass auch diese unscheinbaren Tierchen, abgesehen von dem Nutzen, den sie durch ihre Ernährungsweise schaffen, wert sind, Interesse zu beanspruchen und sich ihrem Studium hinzugeben.

Ihr Körper ist immer länglich, mehr oder weniger gewölbt. Die Oberfläche ist bald glanzend, bald matt, behaart oder nackt, glatt oder rauh.

Der Kopf ragt immer aus dem Halsschilde heraus, er ist nur geneigt oder stark herabgewölbt, seine Oberfläche ist entweder ganz glatt, punktiert, gehöckert oder mit Längs- oder Querleisten, zuweilen auch mit Haarbüscheln versehen.

Der Clipeus ist meistens durch eine vertiefte oder erhabene Linie von der Stirn getrennt, er ist dreieckig zugespitzt (*Oxycorythus*, *Corythoderus*), abgerundet, abgestutzt oder ausgerandet, an seinem Vorderrande ohne oder mit zwei oder vier Zähnchen besetzt.

Die Augen sind mittelgross, meistens etwas gewölbt, nur bei *Corythoderus* sind dieselben ganz flach; sie sind von oben fast immer, wenn auch nur zum Teil, sichtbar.

· Die Wangen sind in ihrer Grösse und Form sehr verschieden, aber immer etwas vertieft.

Die Fühler sind auf der Unterseite des Kopfes eingefügt und überragen kaum den letzteren. Sie sind aus neun Gliedern zusammengesetzt, nur in der Gattung *Phycochus* sind sie achtgliedrig. Das erste Glied ist immer das längste, das zweite und dritte sind wenig, das vierte bis sechste viel kürzer, die drei letzten Glieder bilden eine blättrige, mit dichtem Haarfilz überzogene Keule.

Die Mundwerkzeuge werden vollständig vom Kopfschilde bedeckt. Dieselben bestehen aus der häutigen Oberlippe, den beiden an der Basis hornigen, nach der Spitze zu häutigen Oberkiefern, aus den beiden Unterkiefern, die mehrere Teile aufweisen und die viergliedrigen Kiefertaster tragen, und zuletzt aus der Unterlippe mit den dreigliedrigen Lippentastern. Bei der Untersuchung der Mundwerkzeuge stellte sich heraus, dass dieselben bei einigen Gattungen kaum nennenswerte Unterschiede aufweisen, deshalb können sie auch im allgemeinen zur Gattungsunterscheidung nicht verwendet werden, und es kann um so leichter darauf vorzichtet werden, da genügend äussere Merkmale vorhanden sind, die eine sichere Trennung der Gattungen ermöglichen.

Das Halsschild ist meistens quer, mehr oder weniger stark herabgewölbt, an den Seiten fast immer, an der Basis oft gerandet; es ist meistens punktiert, glatt oder mit Quer- oder Längseindrücken versehen, zuweilen sind die Seiten und die Basis, seltener ist die ganze Oberfläche behaart.

Das Schildchen ist meistens sichtbar, von grösserer oder kleinerer, meistens dreieckiger Gestalt; es fehlt nur bei wenigen Gattungen, z. B. *Sybax*, *Rhyparus*, *Corythoderus*.

---

1) Die Gattung *Sabrus* Blackburn (*Proc. Roy. Soc. Victoria*, Vol. 17, p. 150, 1904) zählt der Autor auch zu den Aphodiinen. Da dieselbe aber hervorragende Mundwerkzeuge besitzt, so ist sie in dieser Arbeit nicht berücksichtigt worden.

FAM. APHODIIDÆ

Die Flügeldecken sind bei fast allen Arten deutlich länger als Kopf und Halsschild zusammen, sie sind gleichmässig gewölbt oder auf dem Rücken etwas abgeflacht (*maculicollis*, *erraticus*), meist das Pygidium bedeckend, ihre Oberfläche hat fast immer deutliche Punktstreifen, seltener zeigt sie statt derselben Längsrippen, dieselbe ist entweder nackt oder mit Haaren bekleidet, zum grössten Teil sind die Flügeldecken nach hinten mehr oder weniger spitz verrundet, nur sehr selten etwas abgestutzt (*contractus* Klug).

Die Unterseite ist fast immer glänzend und meistens behaart. Das Prosternum ist vor den Vorderhüften der Länge nach dachförmig zusammengedrückt, hinter denselben bildet es gewöhnlich einen deutlichen, verschieden gestalteten, oft mit langen Haaren bewachsenen Höcker, der mehr oder weniger deutlich hervorragt. Das Mesosternum ist grösstenteils deutlich punktiert, glänzend oder matt, im letzten Falle aber gewöhnlich die Mitte glatt und glänzend, zwischen den Mittelhüften ist dasselbe breiter oder schmaler, mit oder ohne Kiel. Das Metasternum ist seitlich fast immer punktiert und behaart, die Mitte desselben ist abgeplattet, vertieft, fast immer mit deutlicher Mittelfurche, punktiert oder ohne Punkte, oft auch behaart. Die Bauchsegmente sind mehr oder weniger flach, meistens punktiert und behaart, an den Rändern zuweilen gerieft, sehr selten in der ganzen Länge (*Odontoderus*), sie sind meistens frei, von gleicher Länge, nur bei *Sybacodes*, *Corythoderus* ist der fünfte Bauchring länger als die übrigen; zuweilen haben die Segmente an den Seiten starke Quereindrücke (*Rhyparus*). Die Epipleuren sind nur bei der Gattung *Lorditomaeus* sehr breit, sonst immer ziemlich schmal, von oben nicht sichtbar. (Die Gattung *Macroretrus* bildet darin eine Ausnahme.)

Die Vorder- und Hinterschenkel stehen dicht zusammen, die Mittelschenkel hingegen zuweilen weit entfernt (*Odontoderus*).

Die Beine sind gewöhnlich kurz und kräftig, ihre Hinterschenkel zuweilen stark verdickt (*Cnemisus*, *Ammoecius*), seltener sehr lang, dünn und gebogen (*Corythoderus*). Die Mittel- und Hinterschienen zeigen gewöhnlich am Aussenrande zwei mit Borsten besetzte Querleisten, die nur in einigen Gattungen fehlen oder nur angedeutet sind; die Schienen sind meistens gerade, nach der Spitze nur wenig verbreitert, zuweilen aber ganz bedeutend und dann auch gebogen (*Euparia*), manchmal sind dieselben parallelseitig, dann aber seitlich stark zusammengedrückt (*Chaetopisthes*). Am untern Spitzenrande sind die Schienen mit einem Borstenbesatz und zwei Enddornen versehen, die letzteren können aber auch fehlen (*Corythoderus*). Die Vordertibien sind in ihrer Form ebenfalls veränderlich. Bei den meisten Arten sind sie nach vorn gleichmässig verbreitert, bei wenigen mehr gleichseitig, denn aber gerade oder einwärts gekrümmt, der Aussenrand zeigt ein bis vier grössere Zähne, zuweilen nur mehrere kleine Kerbzähnchen (*Dialytes*), der Vorderrand ist entweder abgeschrägt oder abgestutzt (*Simogonius*), zuweilen mit einem Zahn versehen (*Sybacodes*), der innere Spitzenwinkel trägt neben der Einlenkung der Tarsen einen Enddorn, der selten fehlt (*Coptochirus*). Die Füsse sind fünfgliedrig, das letzte Tarsenglied aller Beine hat immer zwei Klauen.

Die Grösse. — Die meisten Arten sind nur kleine oder mittelgrosse Tiere, wenige gehen über dieses Mass hinaus. Die Grösse schwankt zwischen 1 1/2 und 15 mm.

Die Verbreitung. — Die Aphodiinen sind in ihrer Gesamtheit über die ganze Erde verbreitet. An dieser gewaltigen Ausbreitung partizipieren aber nur einzelne Gattungen, z. B. *Aphodius*, *Psammobius*, *Rhyssemus*, *Oxyomus*, *Ataenius*. Von ihnen kommt *Aphodius* nicht nur in allen Erdteilen vor, sondern ihr Verbreitungsgebiet ist sowohl im Norden (bis zum 70°), wie auch im Süden (bis zum 45°), hier mit *Ataenius*, *Psammobius* und *Saprosites*, am weitesten vorgeschoben. Zu den am weitesten nach Norden vorgedrungenen Arten gehören *Aphodius lapponum*, *piceus*, *borealis* Gyllenhal, *fimetarius*, *rufipes* Linné, *nemoralis* Erichson, *putridus* Herbst, *depressus* Kugelann. Von der Insel Island ist bisher nur ein einziger Vertreter, nämlich *Aphodius alpinus* Scopoli, bekannt. Auf Grönland scheint *Aphodius* zu fehlen. Wie die Gattung *Aphodius* überhaupt, so sind auch einzelne Arten derselben weit verbreitet. *Aphodius* *granarius* Linné und *lividus* Olivier sind Kosmopoliten, *amoenus* Boheman findet sich in Südafrika, Deutsch-Ostafrika, Aegypten, Ceylon, Malabar, Britisch-Indien, Sumatra, Japan, China, *urostigma* Harold ist in Transvaal, Madagaskar, Natal, Angola, Kongo, Kilimandjaro, Britisch-Indien, Sumatra, ebenso ist *Aph. nigrita* Fabricius in Afrika, Madagaskar und Amerika, *Aph. sorex* Fabricius in Abessinien, Natal, Kapland, Australien, Britisch-Indien, China einheimisch. Andere Gattungen dagegen sind wieder nur auf ein einziges Gebiet beschränkt, so kommen *Chaetopisthes* und *Sybacodes* in Indien, *Drepanocanthus*, *Harmogaster*, *Lorditomaeus*, *Odontoderus* in Afrika, *Phycochus* und *Proctophanes* nur in Australien vor.

Die folgende Tabelle gibt Aufschluss über das Verbreitungsgebiet aller Gattungen :

Die Verbreitung der einzelnen Gattungen

GRUPPE —	GATTUNG —	Palæarktisch. Gebiet	Afrikanisch. Gebiet	Indischen Gebiet	Amerikanisch. Gebiet	Australisch Gebiet	Gesamtzahl —
		ANZAHL DER ARTEN IM					
	Oxycorythus. . . .	2	—	—	—	—	2
	Turanella.	1	—	—	—	—	1
	Cnemisus.	6	—	—	—	—	6
	Aphodobius	—	2	—	—	—	2
	Acanthaphodius . .	—	—	—	1	—	1
	Sugrames.	2	—	—	—	—	2
	Aphodius.	367	159	44	130	15	715
	Oxyomus.	3	8	3	2	2	18
	Heptaulacus. . . .	7	1	2	—	1	11
Aphodiina . . .	Lorditomæus . . .	—	10	—	—	—	10
	Harmodactylus. . .	—	1	—	—	—	1
	Sybax	—	2	—	—	—	2
	Proctophanes . . .	—	—	—	—	2	2
	Macroretrus	—	1	—	—	—	1
	Didactylia	—	5	—	5	—	10
	Cælius.	1	—	—	—	—	1
	Coptochirus	2	7	—	—	—	9
	Drepanocanthus . .	—	6	—	—	—	6
	Harmogaster . . .	—	6	—	—	—	6
	Euparia	—	2	—	10	1	13
	Atænius	3	3	2	89	25	122
Eupariina . . .	Saprosites	2	7	6	15	15	45
	Simogonius	—	1	—	—	—	1
	Dialytes	1	—	1	3	1	6
	Odontoderus. . . .	—	5	—	—	—	3
	Phycochus	—	—	—	—	5	5
	Odochilus	—	—	1	—	—	1
Psammobiina . .	Psammobius. . . .	13	4	3	15	5	40
	Diastictus.	1	—	—	—	—	1
	Sicardia	1	—	—	—	—	1
	Zu übertragen . .	412	228	62	270	70	1042

GRUPPE —	GATTUNG	ANZAHL DER ARTEN IM					
		Palæarktisch. Gebiet	Afrikanisch. Gebiet	Indischen Gebiet	Amerikanisch. Gebiet	Australisch. Gebiet —	Gesamtzahl —
	Uebertrag . . .	412	228	62	270	77	1042
	Rhyssemus. . . .	13	27	4	3	2	50 1)
	Rhyssemodes . . .	4	—	1	—	—	5
Psammobiina . .	Rhyssemorphus . .	—	1	—	—	—	1
	Trichiorhyssemus. .	2	—	2	2	—	6
	Pleurophorus . . .	7	4	2	2	—	15
	Stereomera	—	—	1	—	—	1
	Termitodius . . .	—	—	—	1	—	1
Rhyparina . . .	Rhyparus	—	2	14	—	—	16
	Sybacodes	—	—	2	—	—	2
	Notocaulus. . . .	—	4	—	—	—	4
Corythoderina . .	Corythoderus . . .	—	2	1	—	—	3
	Chætopisthes . . .	—	—	6	—	—	6
	Zusammen. . .	438	268	95	278	72	1152

1151 1)

Manche der vorstehenden Arten kommen in mehreren Gebieten vor, sie wurden aber nur in dem gezählt, in welchem sie zuerst bekannt wurden. So leben z. B. *Aphodius fossor, erraticus, fimetarius, rufipes* Linné, *putridus* Herbst, *distinctus* Müller, *depressus* Kugelann, *prodromus* Brahm, *vittatus* Say, *Pleurophorus caesus* im palæarktischen und amerikanischen Gebiet, *Rhyssemus Mayeti* Clouët im palæarktischen und afrikanischen, *Aphodius urostigma* Harold und *Rhyssemus granosus* Klug im palæarktischen, afrikanischen und indischen, *Aphodius parvulus* Harold, *dorsalis* Klug und *Rhyssemus Reitteri* Clouët im afrikanischen und indischen, *Aphodius nigrita* Fabricius im afrikanischen und amerikanischen, *Aphodius ambiguus* Boheman im afrikanischen und australischen, *Aphodius australasiae* Boheman im indischen und australischen, *Aphodius marginellus* Fabricius und *Rhyssemus tarsalis* Waterhouse im afrikanischen, australischen und indischen Gebiet, *Aphodius granarius* Linné und *lividus* Olivier finden sich in allen Gebieten.

Die Lebensweise und Nahrung. — Die Lebensbedingungen, die Entwicklung und Ernährung der Aphodiinen sind bisher recht wenig bekannt geworden. Von den Aphodien oder Dungkäfern weiss man, dass sie ihre Eier an oder in den Dung legen, dass sich ihre Larven sowohl wie das entwickelte Insekt von ihm ernähren, und dass erstere sich in oder unter ihm verpuppen. Manche Aphodien scheinen nur die Exkremente einer bestimmten Tierart aufzusuchen, so leben im Hirsch- oder Rehkot *Aphodius cervorum* Fairmaire, *corvinus* Erichson, *depressus* Kugelann, *maculatus* Sturm, *nemoralis* Erichson, *putridus* Herbst, *Zenkeri* Germar, im Kuhdung hauptsächlich *Aphodius fossor* Linné, *pusillus* Herbst, *rufus* Moll, *scrofa* Fabricius, *serotinus* Panzer, *tirolensis* Rosenhauer, im Pferdekot *Aphodius affinis* Panzer, *contaminatus* Herbst, *sticticus* Panzer, im Kuh- und Pferdekot *Aphodius scrutator* Herbst, im Schafdung *Aphodius immundus* Fabricius, *montanus* Erichson, *nitidulus* Fabricius, *praecox* Erichson, *Aphodius piceus* Gyllenhal scheint die Exkremente des Menschen zu bevorzugen. *Aphodius troglodytes* lebt nach Hubbard in den Erdhöhlen einer Landschildkröte (*Gopherus polyphemus*) in Florida und *porcus* Fabricius legt nach Chapman (*Ent. M. Mag.* Vol. 5, p. 275, 1869) seine Eier in die Brutgänge von *Geotrupes stercorarius* Linné. Es ist also anzunehmen, dass sich seine Larve von den Exkrementen der *Geotrupes*-Larve nährt oder den

1) Wegen des Vaterlandes von *Rhyssemus Horni* Clouët siehe Anmerkung p. 126.

für letztere bereitgehaltenen Dungstoff verzehren hilft, *Aphodius cuniculorum* Mayet (*Bonnairei* Reitter) lebt von den Exkrementen der wilden Kaninchen. *Heptaulacus sus* Herbst fand ich bisher nur im Schweinedug. Andere Arten sind weniger wählerisch, sie begnügen sich mit dem Dung, der ihnen gerade erreichbar ist. So ernähren sich die zwölf auf Helgoland vorkommenden Arten ausschliesslich von Schafdung in Ermangelung anderer Nahrung. Ueber die Ernährungsverhältnisse der *Psammobius*- und *Rhyssemus*-Arten, die sandige Gegenden bevorzugen, sind authentische Beobachtungen bisher nicht gemacht worden. Von *Rhyssemus* nimmt man an, dass einzelne Arten vegetabilische Stoffe. andere wieder tierische Exkremente aufsuchen. *Ataenius* hat Dr. Ohaus sowohl unter Dung, als auch im Mulm alter Bäume (daselbst auch die Larven), ja selbst unter der Rinde derselben gefunden, wo sie sich nach Art der Scolytiden Gänge hergestellt hatten, die aber nicht die Regelmässigkeit wie bei den schädlichen Forstkäfern aufweisen. Von *Euparia castanea* Serville und *Friedenreichi* Harold ist bekannt, dass sie bei Ameisen leben, während *Chaetopisthes, Corythoderus* und *Termitodius* Bewohner der Termitenbauten sind.

Die Entwicklungsstufen folgender Arten sind bisher bekannt geworden : *Aphodius alpinus* Scopoli, *ater* De Geer, *brevis* Erichson, *conjugatus* Panzer, *constans* Duftschmid, *fimetarius* Linné, *fossor* Linné. *granarius* Linné, *haemorrhoidalis* Linné. *distinctus* Müller (*inquinatus* Herbst), *lividus* Olivier, *luridus* Fabricius, *merdarius* Fabricius, *mixtus* Villa, *porcus* Fabricius, *putridus* Herbst, *rufipes* Linné, *rufus* Moll, *satellitius* Herbst, *scrutator* Herbst, *scybalarius* Fabricius. *striatulus* Waltl, *subterraneus* Linné, *tunicatus* Reitter, *varians* Duftschmid, *Heptaulacus testudinarius* Fabricius, *villosus* Gyllenhal, *Oxyomus silvestris* Scopoli, *Pleurophorus caesus* Panzer.

Die Larve. — Die Larven haben eine halbwalzenförmige, etwas gekrümmte Gestalt. Der Kopf ist hell braunrot, die Oberkiefer schwarz, der Hinterleib mehr gelblichweiss gefärbt. Die Fühler reichen bis zur Spitze der Mandibeln und bestehen aus fünf Gliedern. Das erste Glied ist kurz, die drei folgenden sind an der Spitze verdickt, das fünfte ist klein und spitz. Die Oberlippe ist teils rund, teils ausgebuchtet. Die Oberkiefer haben eine stumpf dreizähnige Spitze und am Grunde einen Mahlzahn. Die Kiefertaster sind kurz und viergliedrig, die Lippentaster nur zweigliedrig. Die Beine bestehen aus fünf Gliedern, von denen das letzte klein und klauenförmig ist.

Der Nutzen. — Wie die Totengräber, die Aaskäfer, so leisten auch die Aphodien der Natur in ökonomischer und hygienischer Beziehung unschätzbare Dienste trotz ihrer Unscheinbarkeit. Ueberall, wo sich auf Strassen und Wegen, in Wald und Feld ein Dunghäufchen befindet, da führt ihr spürender Geruch die Tierchen herbei. Sie lassen sich, wie auch später ihre Larven, diese übelriechenden Stoffe wohlschmecken. Dabei durchwühlen, zerteilen und vermengen sie dieselben teilweise auch mit den benachbarten erdigen Teilen des Bodens und bringen auch auf diese Weise die Quelle schlechter Gerüche zum Verschwinden. Ihre Kleinheit wird bei dieser Reinigung der Luft durch ihre grosse Zahl aufgewogen.

Die Geschlechtsunterschiede. — Die Unterschiede zwischen den beiden Geschlechtern sind sehr mannigfaltiger Art, sie zeigen sich in der verschiedenen Grösse der Stirnhöcker, der verschiedenen Grösse und Breite des Halsschildes im Verhältnis zu den Flügeldecken und seiner Punktierung, ferner in der Skulptur und Behaarung der Flügeldecken, in der verschiedenen Bildung der Vorder- und Hintertibien, der verschiedenen Form des Enddorns an den Tibien, auch in der verschiedenen Länge der Hintertarsen, ebenso auch in der abweichenden Skulptur der Metasternalplatte und anderer Merkmalen.

Nähere Angaben werden, soweit sie bisher bekannt sind, bei den einzelnen Gattungen gemacht werden.

Literatur :

Schmidt, W., Revision der deutschen Aphodien-Arten. (*Germars Zeilschr. f. Ent.* Vol. 2, 1840.)
Mulsant, Histoire Naturelle des Coléoptères de France, Lamellicornes, 1842, 1871.

FAM. APHODIIDÆ

Erichson, Naturgeschichte der Insecten Deutschlands, Vol. 3. 1848.

Boheman. Insecta Caffrariæ, Vol. 2,-1857.

Harold, 1º Beiträge zur Kenntnis coprophager Lamellicornier. (*Berl. Ent. Zeitschr.* 1859, 1861, 1862, 1863, 1866, 1867, 1871, 1874.)

    2º Die Gattung *Euparia*. (*Coleopt. Hefte*, Vol. 6, 1870.)

    3º Die Untergattung *Ammoecius*. (*Coleopt. Hefte*, Vol. 7, 1871.)

    4º Die *Ataenius*-Arten mit gezähntem Clipeus. (*Coleopt. Hefte*, Vol. 12, 1874.)

Redtenbacher, Fauna Austriaca, Vol. 1. 1874.

Waterhouse, Aphodien Japans. (*Trans. Ent. Soc. Lond.* 1875.)

Burmeister, Aphodien Argentiniens. (*Stett. Ent. Zeit.* 1877.)

Horn, Aphodien Nordamerikas. (*Trans. Amer. Ent. Soc.* Vol. 3, 1870-71 ; Vol. 14, 1887.)

Bates, Aphodien Mittelamerikas. (*Biol. Centr. Amer. Coleopt.* Vol. 2. 1887.)

Schilsky, *Aphodius*-Varietäten. (*Deutsche Ent. Zeitschr.* 1888.)

Seidlitz, 1º Fauna Baltica. 1891.

    2º Fauna Transsylvanica, 1891.

Reitter, 1º Aphodiinen der palæarktischen Zone. (*Verhandl. d. Naturf. Vereines in Brünn*, Vol. 30, 1892; Vol. 31, 1893.)

    2º Aphodiinen der palæarktischen Zone. (*Bestimmungs-Tabelle Europ. Coleopt.* Vol. 24, 1892.)

    3º Die Untergattung *Melinopterus* Mulsant. (*Deutsche Ent. Zeitschr.* 1906.)

Wickham, Aphodiinen Kanadas. (*The Canad. Entom.* Vol. 16, 1894.)

d'Orbigny, Synopsis des Aphodiens. (*L'Abeille*, Vol. 18, 1896.)

Clouët des Pesruches : 1º Die Gattung *Odontoderus*. (*Ann. Soc. Ent. Belg.* 1900.)

    2º Die Gattung *Rhyssemus*. (*Mém. Soc. Ent. Belg.* Vol. 8, 1901.)

Péringuey. Aphodiinen Südafrikas. (*Trans. S. Afric. Philos. Soc.* Vol. 12, 1901-03, Cat. 1901; Vol. 13, 1904-08, Cat. 1908.)

Daniel. J., Die Untergattung *Agolius*. (*Münchener Koleopt. Zeitschr.* Vol. 1. 1902.)

Blackburn, Aphodiinen Australiens. (*Proc. Roy. Soc. Victoria*, Vol. 17, 1904.)

Fall, Aphodiinen Neu-Mexikos. (*Trans. Amer. Ent. Soc.* Vol. 33, 1907.)

Schmidt, A. : 1º Aphodien des Kilima-Ndjaro-Gebietes. (Sjöstedt. *Ergebnisse der Expedition nach dem Kilima-Ndjaro*, Vol. 7 (5), 1908.)

    2º Indische Aphodiinen-Fauna. (*Ent. Wochenbl.* Vol. 25. 1908.)

    3º Die Gattung *Lorditomaeus*. (*Stett. Ent. Zeit.* 1908.)

Biologie :

Chapuis & Candèze, Catalogue des larves des Coléoptères, 1853.

Perris, Larves des Coléoptères. (*Ann. Soc. Linn. Lyon*, 1875 [1876].)

Rupertsberger, Catalog europäischer-Larven. (*Stett. Ent. Zeit.* 1879.)

Rupertsberger, Biologie der Käfer Europas, 1880.

Rupertsberger. Die biologische Literatur über die Käfer Europas von 1880 an.

Rosenhauer, Käfer-Larven. (*Stett. Ent. Zeit.* 1882.)

Seidlitz, Berichte über die wissenschaftlichen Leistungen in der Entomologie.

Kataloge :

Gemminger & Harold, Catalogus Coleopterorum, Vol 4, 1869.

Heyden, Reitter, Weise, Catalogus Coleopterorum Europ. 1906.

A. Schmidt, Aphodiinen-Zusammenstellung. (*Beih. Deutsche Ent. Zeitschr.* 1907-08.)

Schilsky, System. Verzeichnis der Käfer Deutschlands und Deutsch-Oesterreichs, 1909.

Einteilung der Aphodiinen. → Ohne auf die Fresswerkzeuge Rücksicht zu nehmen, lassen sich die Aphodiinen nach rein äusserlichen Merkmalen zur leichteren Uebersicht zunächst in folgende fünf Gruppen bringen : 1° Aphodiina, 2° Eupariina, 3° Psammobiina, 4° Rhyparina, 5° Corythoderina.

Zu ihrer Charakterisierung dient folgende Tabelle : 1)

GRUPPEN-TABELLE

1. *Hinterschenkel kurz und kräftig, zuweilen länger und mehr schlank, dann aber niemals stark gebogen und das Abdomen überragend. Halsschild an der Basis nie tomentiert, nie mit einer mittleren und zugleich je einer tiefen seitlichen Furche. Schildchen vorhanden oder fehlend, Mittel- und Hintertibien fast immer deutlich zur Spitze verbreitert, nie stark seitlich zusammengedrückt, am Spitzenrande immer mit Borsten besetzt, meistens auch mit zwei kräftigen Enddornen. Flügeldecken nie mit nach hinten divergierenden, sich verbreiternden flachen Rippen.*

2. *Kopf glatt, gehöckert oder mit einem Querkiel, nie mit mehreren Längs- oder Querleistchen oder Haarbüscheln. Halsschild eben, der Rand zuweilen breit verflacht und bewimpert, aber nie mit Quer- oder Längsrippen, höchstens mit kurzer Längsfurche oder flacher Quervertiefung in der Mitte. Schildchen immer vorhanden. Flügeldecken mit ebenen, konvexen oder gerippten Zwischenräumen. Vordertibien mit Enddorn, derselbe fehlt höchst selten beim ♂, am Aussenrande mit zwei oder drei deutlichen Zähnen oder vielen kleinen Kerbzähnchen, zuweilen aber auch am Vorderrande mit einem Zahn (Megatelus contractus Klug), nie aber am innern Spitzenwinkel zahnförmig ausgezogen. Mittel- und Hinterschenkel kurz und kräftig, Mittel- und Hintertibien mit oder ohne Querleisten, stets aber mit zwei deutlichen Enddornen.*

3. *Kopf etwas geneigt, glatt, oft mit drei kleinen Höckerchen oder einem Querkiel. Halsschild eben, höchstens mit einer kurzen Längsfurche, nie seitlich breit verflacht. Flügeldecken mit ebenen oder konvexen, seltener mit gerippten Zwischenräumen. Vordertibien mit Enddorn (fehlt nur bei Coptochirus ♂), nie am Innen- oder Vorderrande mit zwei oder drei grösseren Zähnchen. Mittel- und Hintertibien stets mit zwei deutlichen Querleisten am Aussenrande (bei* Didactylia *fehlend) und zwei kräftigen Enddornen am Spitzenrande* . . . . 1. Gruppe Aphodiina, p. 9

3'. *Kopf gross, stark herabgewölbt, höchst selten mit Querkiel, nie mit drei Höckerchen. Halsschild eben, Aussenrand zuweilen verflacht und dicht bewimpert. Flügeldecken meistens mit ebenen oder konvexen Zwischenräumen, zuweilen sind dieselben auch rippenförmig. Vordertibien mit einem Enddorn und drei Aussenzähnen, ihr Vorderrand manchmal breit abgestutzt, hier mit oder ohne Zahn. Mittel- und Hintertibien entweder ganz ohne oder mit schwachen Spuren von Querleisten, aber mit zwei deutlichen Enddornen* . . . . . 2. Gruppe Eupariina, p. 102

2'. *Kopf gehörnt oder mit mehreren Leistchen oder zwei Haarbüscheln. Halsschild mit Quer- oder Längsrippen. Schildchen fehlend oder vorhanden. Flügeldecken zuweilen mit Längsrippen. Enddorn an den Vordertibien fehlend oder vor-*

---

1) Folgende Gattungen habe ich nicht gesehen : *Aphodobius, Caelius, Oxycorythus, Sicardia, Stercomera, Sugrames.*

handen, der Innenwinkel derselben zuweilen zahnartig ausgezogen, Vorderrand manchmal gezahnt, Aussenrand mit ein bis drei Zähnen. Mittel- und Hintertibien stets ohne Querleisten, zuweilen aber mit Enddornen.

4. *Kopf gehörnt, Halsschild mit einer Längs- und mehreren Querfurchen, die durch Querwülste getrennt werden und sich über die ganze Scheibe ausdehnen, zuweilen aber auch nur mit Längsfurche und zwei seitlichen kurzen Eindrücken, seltener ganz ohne Längsfurche und nur mit einem schwachen Eindruck an der Basis. Schildchen immer vorhanden. Flügeldecken meist mit konvexen oder gerippten Zwischenräumen. Vordertibien mit Enddorn und drei Aussenzähnen. Mittel- und Hinterschenkel kurz und meist kräftig. Mittel- und Hintertibien mit zwei deutlichen Enddornen, die zuweilen blattartig verbreitert sind; das erste Glied der Hintertarsen oft zur Spitze dreieckig verbreitert* . 3. Gruppe PSAMMOBIINA, p. 115

4'. *Kopf nicht gehörnt, aber mit Längs- oder Querleistchen oder Haarbüscheln. Thorax und Flügeldecken stets mit Längsrippen. Schildchen meistens fehlend. Vordertibien fast immer ohne Enddorn, aber oft am Innen- und Vorderrande mit einem, am Aussenrande mit ein oder zwei Zähnen. Mittel- und Hinterschenkel schmaler, länger und etwas gebogen. Enddorne an den Mittel- und Hintertibien fehlen oft* . . . 4. Gruppe RHYPARINA, p. 130

1'. *Hinterschenkel schmal, sehr lang und stark gebogen, die Spitze des Abdomens überragend. Halsschild an der Basis tomentiert, mit einer mittleren und zwei seitlichen, tiefen Längsfurchen. Ein deutliches Schildchen fehlt. Mittel- und Hintertibien nie zur Spitze verbreitert, am Innenrande oft gebuchtet, oder dieser ist dem Seitenrande parallel, meistens sind sie seitlich stark zusammengedrückt und sehr breit, am Endrande fehlt die Beborstung. Enddorne sehr kurz und fein, wenig bemerkbar, oder sie fehlen ganz. Flügeldecken stets mit flachen, nach hinten divergierenden und sich verbreiternden Rippen* . . . . . 5. Gruppe CORYTHODERINA, p. 137

I. GRUPPE APHODIINA

Charaktere. — Diese Gruppe umfasst die bekanntesten und am weitesten verbreiteten Arten. Ihr Körper ist auf der Oberseite meistens nackt, seltener behaart.

Der Kopf ist fast immer nur etwas geneigt, glatt oder mit einem oder drei Höckerchen versehen, ist er stark herabgewölbt, dann schmückt ihn zuweilen ein Querkiel; der Clipeus ist ein- bis vierzähnig; die Wangen überragen die Augen bald stärker, bald schwächer, zuweilen gar nicht.

Das Halsschild ist eben, höchstens mit kurzer Längsfurche versehen.

Ein sichtbares Schildchen ist stets vorhanden.

Die Flügeldecken sind meistens von der Breite des Halsschildes, sie haben ebene oder konvexe Zwischenräume, die durch vertiefliegende Punktstreifen getrennt werden, seltener sind letztere in scharfe Rippen umgewandelt (*Oxyomus*).

Die Vordertibien haben einen Enddorn, der höchst selten beim ♂ fehlt (*Coptochirus*), am Aussenrande sind zwei bis drei kräftige Zähne, darüber zuweilen noch mehrere Kerbzähnchen.

Mittel- und Hinterschenkel sind meistens kurz und kräftig, Mittel- und Hintertibien haben am Aussenrande zwei meistens sehr deutliche Querleisten, die nur bei der Gattung *Didactylia* fehlen, und am Spitzenrande einen Borstenbesatz und zwei kräftige Enddorne.

BESTIMMUNGS-TABELLE DER GATTUNGEN

1. *Kopf gross, halbkreisförmig, Clipeus in der Mitte in eine zahn-*
    förmige Spitze ausgezogen, Oberfläche behaart . . . .   1. Genus OXYCORYTHUS, Solsky.

1'. *Kopf weniger gross, Clipeus in der Mitte nicht zahnförmig,*
    Oberfläche nackt oder behaart.

2. *Clipeus am Vorderrande mit zwei genäherten Zähnchen, Taster*
    sehr lang . . . .   2. Genus TURANELLA, A. Semenow.

2'. *Clipeus ohne zwei genäherte Zähnchen, Taster normal.*

3. *Clipeus mit vier Zähnchen, Kopf granuliert, Schenkel und*
    Schienen stark verbreitert, Enddorne blattförmig oder einfach.   3. Genus CNEMISUS, Motschulsky.

3'. *Clipeus gerundet, abgestutzt oder ausgerandet, zuweilen mit*
    zwei entfernten Zähnchen, selten mit vier, dann aber der
    Kopf nicht granuliert.

4. *Enddorn an den Vordertibien beim ♂ und ♀ einwärts gebogen.*   4. Genus APHODOBIUS, Péringuey.

4'. *Enddorn nicht einwärts gebogen, höchstens zuweilen beim ♂.*

5. *Pygidium bedeckt.*

6. *Vordertibien am Vorderrande schräg, nie quer abgestutzt.*

7. *Vordertibien von der Basis nach vorn geradlinig verbreitert,*
    Aussenrand mit drei Zähnen.

8. *Flügeldecken mit zehn Zwischenräumen.*

9. *Die Zwischenräume flach oder konvex, durch vertiefte und*
    punktierte Streifen voneinander getrennt.

10. *Hinterschenkel nahe der Basis mit langem Dorn* . . . .   5. Genus ACANTHAPHODIUS, A. Schmidt.

10'. *Hintersohenkel nahe der Basis ohne langen Dorn.*

11. *Tarsen sehr kurz und dünn, Klauen haarförmig* . . . .   6. Genus SUGRAMES, Reitter.

11'. *Tarsen und Klauen normal* . . . .   7. Genus APHODIUS, Illiger.

9'. *Flügeldecken ohne vertiefte Streifen, mit zehn scharfen Rippen.*
    Halsschild vor dem Schildchen mit kurzer Längsfurche. .   8. Genus OXYOMUS, Castelnau.

8'. *Flügeldecken mit weniger als zehn Zwischenräumen.*

12. *Flügeldecken mit fünf bis neun meist zweistreifigen Zwischen-*
    räumen, die durch Rippen getrennt werden, Oberfläche
    behaart, Epipleuren schmal. . . . .   9. Genus HEPTAULACUS, Mulsant.

12'. *Flügeldecken mit acht oder neun Zwischenräumen, dieselben*
    werden durch Punktstreifen getrennt, alle Streifen reichen
    bis zur Basis, der Körper ist meist sehr breit und flach,
    Seitenrand mehr oder weniger flach ausgebreitet, Epipleuren
    sehr breit. . . . .   10. Genus LORDITOMÆUS, Péringuey.

7'. *Vordertibien schlank, nicht zur Spitze verbreitert. Aussenrand*
    nur mit zwei Zähnen . . . .   11. Genus HARMODACTYLUS, Péringuey.

6'. *Vordertibien vorn breit abgestutzt, nicht abgeschrägt.*

13. *Vordertibien am Aussenrande mit drei Zähnen, die entweder*

> *getrennt oder von denen die zwei unteren verbunden sind,
> Halsschild in der Mitte mit Längsfurche, jede Flügeldecke
> hat fünf Längsrippen* . . . . 12. Genus SYBAX, Boheman.

5'. *Pygidium unbedeckt* 1).

14. *Mesosternum zwischen den Mittelhüften breit.*

15. *Pygidium gross, senkrecht, Hintertibien mit deutlichen Querleisten am Aussenrande, alle Tarsen und Klauen beim ♂
normal, Epipleuren vorn nicht nach oben gerückt* . . . 13. Genus PROCTOPHANES, Harold.

15'. *Pygidium weniger senkrecht, Querleisten der Hintertibien
schwächer, Tarsen der Mitteltibien beim ♂ stark verdickt,
besonders das letzte Glied, Klauen blattartig verbreitert,
Epipleuren nach oben gerückt* . . . . 14. Genus MACRORETRUS, Péringuey.

14'. *Mesosternum zwischen den Mittelhüften schmal.*

16. *Querleisten an den Mittel- und Hintertibien fehlen, Tibien
nach der Spitze stark verbreitert, Vordertibien beim ♂ lang
und schmal, meistens nur mit zwei grossen Aussenzähnen,
beim ♀ normal* . . . . 15. Genus DIDACTYLIA, d'Orbigny.

16'. *Querleisten an den Tibien vorhanden.*

17. *Thorax längs des Seitenrandes gekerbt, nach hinten zu grösser,
so dass derselbe um die Hinterwinkel gezahnt ist* . . . 16. Genus CÆLIUS, Lewis.

17'. *Seitenrand glatt, nicht gekerbt.*

18. *Vordertibien beim ♂ ohne Enddorn, Aussenrand mit zwei
Zähnen, der Endzahn sehr verlängert und an der Spitze
breit abgestutzt, Clipeus meist tief ausgebuchtet* . . . . 17. Genus COPTOCHIRUS, Harold.

18'. *Vordertibien in beiden Geschlechtern mit Enddorn und drei
Aussenzähnen, Endzahn einfach, zugespitzt, Clipeus nicht
tief ausgerandet.*

19. *Vordertibien beim ♂ in der Vorderhälfte innen plötzlich verbreitert, erstes Glied der Hintertarsen an der Spitze dorn-
förmig verlängert, Flügeldecken mit zehn Zwischenräumen* . 18. Genus DREPANOCANTHUS, Péringuey.

19'. *Vordertibien innen nicht plötzlich verbreitert, normal, Metatarsus ohne Dorn, Flügeldecken mit mehr als zehn
Zwischenräumen.* . . . . 19. Genus HARMOGASTER, Harold.

I. GENUS OXYCORYTHUS, SOLSKY

Oxycorythus. Solsky, Fedtschenko, Turkest. Col. Vol. 2, p. 395 (1876).

Caraktere. — Diese Gattung unterscheidet sich von allen andern der ersten Gruppe durch den vorn in eine mehr oder weniger starke Spitze ausgezogenen Clipeus.

Der Körper ist länglich, ziemlich parallel, wenig gewölbt, die ganze Oberfläche behaart.

Der grosse, halbkreisförmige Kopf ist eben, nur in der Mitte mit einem kleinen Tuberkel geschmückt; die Wangen sind gross und eckig.

---

1) Die Grösse des freien Pygidiums ist nicht immer dieselbe bei den Arten einer Gattung, auch nicht bei mehreren Stücken derselben Species. Dieselbe hängt ab von der stärkeren oder geringeren Kontraktion des Hinterleibes nach dem Tode. Diese Zusammenziehung kann eine so grosse sein, dass das Pygidium von hinten nicht sichtbar ist; dann ragt es aber wenigstens auf der Bauchseite gegen die Bauchsegmente mehr hervor. Es liegt also nicht in gleicher Ebene mit denselben.

Das Halsschild ist wie der Kopf punktiert, es hat vor der Basis in der Mitte eine punktfreie und erhabene Mittellinie, seine Seiten und die Hinterwinkel sind gerundet und wie die Basis gerandet.

Das Schildchen ist länglich-dreieckig.

Die Flügeldecken sind von der Breite des Halsschildes, in den Streifen punktiert, die seitlichen sind vorn abgekürzt, die Zwischenräume eben.

Alle Schenkel stehen zusammen. Die Vordertibien haben am Aussenrande drei kräftige Zähne und einen Enddorn am innern Spitzenwinkel neben der Einlenkung der Tarsen. Die Mittel- und Hintertibien haben am Aussenrande zwei Querleisten, am Endrande einen Borstenkranz und zwei Enddorne; die Tarsen sind lang und schlank, das letzte Glied trägt zwei normale Klauen.

Die hierhergehörigen Arten sind rotbraun oder schwarz gefärbt, 3 1/2 bis 4 1/3 mm lang.

Geographische Verbreitung der Arten. — Die Gattung ist bisher nur aus Turkestan bekannt.

1. *O. Morawitzi*, Solsky, Fedtschenko, Turkest. Col. Vol. 2, p. 397, t. 2,   Syr-darja.
   f. 2 (1876).
           Morawitzi, Reitter 1), Tab. p. 32; Brünn, 30, p. 170.   Turkestan.
2. *O. Solskyi*, Dokhtouroff, Hor. Soc. Ent. Ross. Vol. 21, p. 345 (188).   Taschkent.

2. Genus TURANELLA, Semenow

Turanella. Semenow, Rev. Russe d'Ent. Vol. 5, p. 140 (1905).

Isochirus ‖ Reitter 1), Verh. Nat. Ver. Brünn, 1891, Vol. 30, p. 171 (1892); 1) Best. Tab. Eur. Col. Heft 24, p. 33 (1892).

Charaktere. — Die am vorderen Kopfrande genäherten beiden Zähnchen, die langen Kiefertaster und der sehr kurze Enddorn an den Vordertibien unterscheiden diese Gattung von allen übrigen.

Der Körper ist länglich, konvex, unbehaart.

Der Kopf ist eben, ohne Höcker, nach vorn verlängert, der deutlich aufgebogene Vorderrand zeigt in der Mitte zwei genäherte Zähnchen; die Wangen sind klein, sie überragen nur wenig die Augen; die Kiefertaster sind auffallend lang, das vorletzte Glied derselben ist länger als breit, das letzte ist nach der Spitze verbreitert und dann abgestutzt, es ist doppelt so lang als das vorhergehende.

Das Halsschild ist quer, herabgebogen, die Seiten und Basis sind gerandet, die Hinterwinkel im flachen Bogen verrundet. Kopf und Halsschild sind deutlich, etwas dicht punktiert.

Das Schildchen ist an der Basis parallel, dann zugespitzt.

Die Flügeldecken haben die Breite des Halsschildes, sie sind nach der Spitze kaum verbreitert, sehr fein punktiert-gestreift; die Zwischenräume sind eben.

Die Vordertibien haben drei grosse Aussenzähne, die fast die ganze Länge der Tibie einnehmen.

Die Schenkel, besonders die vorderen und hinteren, sind stark und kräftig, Mittel- und Hintertibien sind mit zwei Querleisten versehen, am Endrande haben sie einen Kranz kurzer Borsten und zwei kräftige Enddorne.

Die Tarsen sind sehr lang, auch die vorderen, das zweite Glied derselben ist bedeutend länger als das erste.

Die Metasternalplatte ist in der Mitte flach längsvertieft.

Die Bauchsegmente sind frei, punktiert und behaart.

---

1) Der Kürze wegen wird für Reitters Arbeit über coprophage Lamellicornier in den *Verhandlungen des Naturf. Vereins in Brünn*, Vol. 30 und 31, und in seiner *Bestimmungs-Tabelle*, Heft 24, nur Tab. p. ... oder Brünn, 30, oder Brünn, 31, p. ... angegeben.

Der einzige Vertreter dieser Gattung ist eine kleine. 2 1/2 bis 4 mm lange, schwarzgefärbte Art, deren Flügeldecken eine rote Längsbinde auf dem Rücken haben.

Geographische Vebreitung der Art. — Bisher nur aus Turkestan und Transkaspien bekannt.

1. *T. latevittis*, Reitter, Deutsche Ent. Zeitschr. p. 509 (1887); Tab. p. 33:   Turkestan und Transkas-
 Brünn, 30, p. 171. — **Taf. I, Fig. I.** pien.

3. GENUS ONEMISUS, MOTSCHULSKY

Cnemisus. Motschulsky, Hor. Soc. Ent. Ross. Vol, 6, Suppl. p. 63 (1868).

Ahermes. Reitter, Wien. Ent. Zeit. p. 254 (1891).

Cnemargus ‖ Motschulsky, Bull. Soc. Nat. Mosc. p. 56 (1845).

Cnemargulus. Semenow, Rev. Russe d'Ent. Vol. 3, p. 354 (1903).

Charaktere.—Die Arten dieser Gattung gleichen in ihrem Aussehen ganz einem echten *Aphodius*.

Der Körper ist gedrungen, gewölbt, meistens gelbbraun gefärbt, glänzend und an den Rändern des Kopfes, Halsschildes und der Flügeldecken bewimpert.

Der Kopf ist deutlich granuliert-punktiert, er hat eine glatte und erhabene Querlinie zwischen den Augen, die zuweilen schwach gehöckert ist; die Wangen überragen als rundliche Lappen die Augen; der Vorderrand des Clipeus zeigt vier spitze Zähnchen, denen bei manchen Arten je ein kleineres vor den Augen noch beigesellt ist.

Das Halsschild ist quer herabgewölbt, die Seiten desselben sind mehr oder weniger stark gerundet, die Hinterwinkel sind mehr verrundet, Basis und Seiten gerandet, die Oberfläche ist ohne Längslinie, wohl aber punktiert.

Das Schildchen ist länglich-dreieckig, klein und nicht sehr breit.

Die Flügeldecken sind an der Schulter ohne Dorn, nach hinten etwas erweitert, schwach punktiertgestreift, ihre Zwischenräume sind eben und punktiert, besonders die Spitze.

Die Unterseite ist mit der Oberseite gleichfarbig, sie ist glänzend und mehr oder weniger lang und dicht behaart.

Die Mittelschenkel stehen dicht zusammen, sie sind die schwächsten. Die Hinterschenkel sind sehr stark verbreitert. Die Vordertibien haben innen einen Enddorn und aussen drei kräftige Zähne, über denselben sind sie zuweilen gekerbt. Die Mittel- und Hintertibien zeigen am Aussenrande zwei Querleisten, ihr Spitzenrand ist beborstet und mit zwei Enddornen versehen, die an den stark verbreiterten Hintertibien blattartig sind. Zuweilen sind die Hinterschenkel und Hintertibien weniger verbreitert, ihre Enddorne mehr schlank (Gattung *Cnemargulus* Semenow). Die Tarsen sind verhältnismässig kurz, das erste Glied an den Vordertarsen ist kürzer, an den Mittel- und Hintertarsen dagegen länger als das zweite Glied. Die Klauen sind mehr oder weniger lang und dünn.

Die Grösse der Arten schwankt zwischen 4 und 9 mm.

Geographische Verbreitung der Arten. — Die Gattung ist bisher nur aus der Mongolei und Russland bekannt.

1. *C. Ahngeri*, Semenow, Rev. Russe d'Ent. Vol. 3 (1), p. 9, 28 (1903).   Transkaspien.
2. *C. Kasnakovi*, Semenow, ibidem, p. 27 (1903).   Mongolei.
3. *C. Kozlovi*, Semenow. ibidem, p. 27 (1903).   Mongolei.
4. *C. Krulikovskyi*, Semenow, ibidem, p. 354 (1903).   Transkaspien.
5. *C. pusio*, Semenow, ibidem, p. 355 (1903)   Transkaspien.
6. *C. rufescens*, Motschulsky, Bull. Soc. Nat. Mosc. Vol. 1, p. 56 (1845).   Wolga.
  rufescens, Reitter, Deutsche Ent. Zeitschr. p. 425 (1888); Tab. p. 33;   Astrachan.
  Brünn, 30, p. 171.
  Semenow, Rev. Russe d'Ent. Vol. 3, p. 26 (1903).

4. Genus APHODOBIUS, Péringuey

Aphodobius. Péringuey, Trans. S. Afric. Philos. Soc. (1901-03), Vol. 12, Cat. p. 369, 420 (1901).

Charaktere. — Die beiden Arten dieser Gattung stimmen im äussern Bau vollständig mit *Aphodius* überein, sie unterscheiden sich von letzteren nur dadurch, dass bei *Aphodobius* der innere Dorn an den Vordertibien in beiden Geschlechtern einwärts gebogen ist.

Es sind kleine Arten von 3 1/2 bis 4 mm Länge, hellbrauner Farbe und behaarter Oberfläche.

Der Kopf ist nach vorn rundlich verschmälert und am Vorderrande abgestuzt; zwischen den Augen befindet sich eine deutliche Stirnlinie, die aber ungehöckert ist; die Wangen sind klein und rundlich.

Das Halsschild ist ohne Längsfurche, an den Seiten gerandet, der Basalrand fehlt; die Oberfläche ist wenig konvex, nicht sehr dicht punktiert.

Das Schildchen ist klein, vorn parallel.

Die Flügeldecken haben deutliche Punktstreifen, die seitlichen sind vorn abgekürzt; die Zwischenräume sind mehr oder weniger konvex, punktiert und behaart.

Die Mitteltibien sind stark zur Spitze verbreitert, sie haben wie die Hintertibien zwei deutliche Querleistchen.

Das erste Glied der Hintertarsen ist so lang wie die drei folgenden zusammen; die Vordertibien sind dreizähnig.

Geographische Verbreitung der Arten. — Die Arten bewohnen das südliche Afrika.

1. *A. misellus*, Boheman, Ins. Caffr. Vol. 2, p. 356 (1857).   Orange.
     misellus, Péringuey, Trans S. Afric. Philos. Soc. Vol. 12 (1901-03); Cat.   Natal, Südrhodesia.
     p. 420 (1901).
2. *A. villosulus*, Péringuey, ibidem (1901-03); ibidem, p. 421 (1901).   Südrhodesia.

5. Genus ACANTHAPHODIUS, A. Schmidt

Acanthaphodius. A. Schmidt, Soc. Ent. Zürich, Vol. 24, p. 67 (1909-10 [1909]).

Charaktere. — Die bisher einzige Art dieser neuen Gattung gewährt ganz den Anblick eines echten *Aphodius*, sie unterscheidet sich aber von allen Aphodiinen durch die Bewaffnung der Hinterschenkel.

Der Körper ist länglich, gewölbt, glänzend, von gelblicher Färbung und mit schwärzlichen Zeichnungen.

Der Kopf ist hinten breit, nach vorn schwachbogig verschmälert, daselbst ausgerandet; zwischen den Augen befindet sich eine vertiefte Linie, vor ihr, in der Mitte des Kopfes, eine stumpfe Erhöhung; die Wangen sind schwach und abgerundet; die Oberfläche ist punktiert.

Das Halsschild ist ebenfalls punktiert, nach hinten wenig verengt, an den Seiten und der Basis gerandet, in der Mitte vor dem Schildchen mit kurzer Längsfurche und an den Seiten mit zwei schwachen Quereindrücken und dunkler Querbinde.

Das Schildchen ist klein und dreieckig.

Die Flügeldecken haben einen kleinen Schulterzahn, sie sind nach hinten etwas erweitert und punktiert-gestreift, die Seiten und die Spitze sind dunkel gefärbt.

Das Mesosternum ist zwischen den Mittelhüften stumpf gekielt.

Das Metasternum ist bis auf die schmale glatte Mitte punktiert und vertieft.

Die Mittel- und Hintertibien sind an der Aussenseite mit zwei Querleisten, am Spitzenrande mit Borstenbesatz und zwei Enddornen versehen.

Die Hinterschenkel haben in der Nähe der Basis einen langen dornförmigen Zahn.

An dem Aussenrande der Vordertibien sind nur zwei Zähne, ein dritter befindet sich an der Vorderkante, er ist mehr spitz und dornförmig, am innern Rande fehlt der Enddorn neben der Einlenkung der Tarsen.

Alle Tarsen sind fünfgliedrig, sie haben zwei normale Klauen.

Geographische Verbreitung der Art. — Die Art kommt in Südamerika vor.

1. *A. Bruchi.* A. Schmidt, Soc. Ent. Zürich, Vol. 24, p. 67 (1909-10). — Rio Negro.
   Taf. I, Fig. 2, 2a.

6. Genus SUGRAMES, Reitter

Sugrames. Reitter, Ent. Nachr. p. 184 (1894).

Charaktere. — Diese Gattung ist ebenfalls sehr dicht mit *Aphodius* verwandt, hauptsächlich mit der Untergattung *Mendidius* Reitter, und zwar durch den gekörnten Kopf und den gezähnten Clipeus, unterscheidet sich aber von dieser durch die Form der Wangen und Bildung der Tibien und Tarsen.

Die Wangen sind entweder halbkreisförmig, senkrecht nach aussen abstehend oder mehr lang und schmal, schief nach vorn den Kopfrand überragend.

Der Kopf ist hinten glatt, der übrige Teil gekörnt, in der Mitte mit einem Höckerchen.

Das Halsschild ist quer, punktiert, seine Basis ist gerandet und die Hinterwinkel sind abgerundet.

Die Flügeldecken sind nach hinten wenig verbreitert, ihre Oberfläche ist punktiert-gestreift.

Die Vordertibien haben innen einen Enddorn und drei starke Aussenzähne.

Die Mittel- und Hinterschienen sind zur Spitze stark verbreitert, am Aussenrande mit zwei deutlichen Querleisten versehen, ihr Apikalrand hat einen Borstenkranz und zwei deutliche Enddorne.

Die Tarsen sind fünfgliedrig, sehr kurz und dünn, die einzelnen Glieder nehmen allmählich an Länge und Breite ab, das Klauenglied selbst ist sehr klein und trägt zwei haarförmige, kurze Klauen.

Es sind kleine gelbbraune, glänzende Arten mit dunklem Kopfe und Halsschilde, zuweilen ist auch die Naht gebräunt.

Ihre Länge beträgt 3,5 bis 4,2 mm.

Geographische Verbreitung der Arten. — Die Gattung bewohnt Turkestan und Afghanistan.

1. *S. auriculatis*, Reitter, Tab. p. 43; Brünn, 30, p. 181.   Margljan.
2. *S. Hauseri*, Reitter, Ent. Nachr. p. 185 (1894).   Sefir-Kuh, Herat.

7. Genus APHODIUS, Illiger

Aphodius. Illiger, Verzeichn. der Käfer Preuss. p. 15 (1798).

Charaktere. — Die Arten dieser Gattung sind von länglicher, gleichbreiter oder nach hinten etwas erweiterter, mehr oder weniger stark konvexer Gestalt, ihre Oberfläche ist meistens glänzend, zuweilen mehr matt, meistens feiner oder stärker punktiert, sehr selten fast ohne Punkte.

Der Kopf ist geneigt, nur bei *Ammoecius* stärker herabgebogen, dann aber mit sehr deutlichem

Querkiel; zwischen den Augen zeigt derselbe oft eine deutlich vertiefte oder erhöhte Stirnlinie, die meistens mit drei Höckerchen besetzt ist, zuweilen ist der Kopf ganz glatt, oder er zeigt in der Mitte eine stumpfe Beule oder ein zugespitztes, etwas nach hinten gebogenes Höckerchen (*rhinocerus* Reiche, *magnificus* m.), seine Oberfläche ist feiner oder stärker punktiert, seltener runzlig granuliert oder ganz glatt; der Clipeus ist abgerundet, abgestutzt, ausgerandet, ohne oder mit zwei bis vier Zähnchen; die Wangen überragen meistens die Augen, bald mehr, bald weniger, sie sind rundlich oder mehr spitzwinklig (*Acrossus*); die Augen sind gewölbt, meistens ganz sichtbar.

Das Halsschild ist fast immer deutlich breiter als der Kopf mit den Augen, es ist gewöhnlich quer, mehr oder weniger stark herabgewölbt, an den Seiten parallel oder gerundet, zuweilen vorn breiter als hinten (*A. cribratus* Le Conte), die Seiten sind immer, der Vorder- und Hinterrand nur zuweilen gerandet, die Hinterwinkel sind stumpfwinklig, abgestutzt, ausgerandet oder abgerundet.

Das Schildchen ist von verschiedener Grösse und Form, bei den meisten Arten beträgt es ungefähr ein Zehntel, bei wenigen nur ein Fünftel bis ein Drittel der Flügeldeckenlänge (*Teuchestes*, *Megatelus*), es ist dreieckig oder an der Basis parallel und dann erst zugespitzt, meistens in der Höhe der Flügeldecken, zuweilen tiefer liegend (*Colobopterus*).

Die Flügeldecken sind an der Basis mehr oder weniger ausgerandet, seltener nur abgestutzt, sie sind parallel oder nach hinten verbreitert, dann gerundet zugespitzt, seltener an der Spitze abgestutzt (*A. erraticus* Linné, *maculicollis* Reiche), ihre Oberfläche ist immer punktiert-gestreift, die Streifen laufen entweder nach der Spitze frei aus oder verbinden sich untereinander in mannigfachen Abänderungen, der achte und neunte sind immer vorn verkürzt, zuweilen sind beide gleichlang, meistens aber verbindet sich der neunte unter der Schulter mit dem zehnten; letztere ist mehr oder weniger deutlich, seltener mit kleinem Dörnchen versehen; die Zwischenräume sind eben oder konvex, feiner oder stärker punktiert, zuweilen auch behaart.

Die Unterseite ist oft heller als die Oberseite, sie ist glänzend, meistens punktiert und behaart. Die Epipleuren sind immer nur schmal. Das Mesosternum ist oft durch dichte Punktierung matt, zwischen den Mittelhüften zuweilen gekielt. Das Metasternum ist in der Mitte mehr oder weniger abgeflacht, mit breiterer oder schmalerer Vertiefung, oft auch nur gefurcht. Die Bauchsegmente sind frei beweglich, nicht miteinander verbunden, das letzte Segment fast immer unter den Flügeldecken verborgen.

Vorder- und Hinterschenkel sind zusammenstehend, die Mittelschenkel etwas voneinander entfernt. Mittel- und Hinterschenkel oft schlanker als die stets kurzen, robusten Vorderschenkel. Die Vordertibien sind nach der Spitze meistens gleichmässig erweitert, an dem innern Spitzenwinkel mit Enddorn, am Aussenrande mit drei deutlichen Zähnen versehen, darüber oft noch gekerbt, diese Kerbzähnchen sind meistens klein und undeutlich, höchst selten kräftiger und länger, wie z. B. bei *Aph. rugosiceps*, von dem Harold in seiner Beschreibung die Vordertibien als fünfzähnig bezeichnet; nur sehr vereinzelt haben die Vordertibien am Vorderrande neben den Taisen einen Zahn (*Megatelus contractus* Klug).

Mittel- und Hintertibien sind gleichfalls nach der Spitze verdickt, sie haben an der Aussenseite zwei mehr oder weniger deutliche Querleisten, am Endrande einen Borstenbesatz und zwei Enddörne.

Alle Füsse haben fünf Glieder, das erste its meistens stark verlängert, das letzte trägt zwei normale Klauen.

Farbe. — Die Arten zeigen in ihrer Pärbung die grössten Unterschiede, sie weisen Uebergänge vom hellsten Braun bis zum tiefsten Schwarz auf. Bald ist die Oberseite einfarbig, bald von helleren oder dunkleren Flecken, Makeln oder Bändern unterbrochen.

Grösse. — Wie schon weiter oben erwähnt, ist auch die Grösse der Arten sehr veränderlich, sie schwankt zwischen 1 1/2 und 15 mm.

Geschlechtsunterschiede. — Die Unterschiede in den Geschlechtern beruhen auf der Form und

Bewaffnung des Kopfes, der Bildung des Halsschildes, der Behaarung der Flügeldecken, der Form des Enddorns an den Vorder- und Hintertibien und der beiden letzteren selbst.

Bei den Männchen ist der Kopf am Vorderrande breiter (*Aphodius prodromus* Brahm), mit einem (*Aphodius rhinocerus* Reiche) oder drei stärkeren Höckerchen geschmückt.

Das Halsschild überragt zuweilen die Breite der Flügeldecken beträchtlich und ist dann seitlich stärker gerundet (*Aphodius scuticollis* Semenow), oder es hat am Vorderrande einen rundlichen Eindruck (*Aphodius fimetarius* Linné), oder die vordere Hälfte ist abgeplattet (*Aphodius planatus* A. Schmidt), auch nach hinten von einem grössern Tuberkel überragt (*Aphodius magnificus* A. Schmidt).

Die Flügeldecken sind bisweilen viel stärker punktiert und behaart (*Aphodius Bolassogloi* König. *punctalosulcatus* Sturm).

Die Vordertibien einzelner Arten sind mehr schlank, gerade oder gebogen (*Aphodius peruanus* Erichson), zuweilen innen in der vordern Hälfte winklig erweitert (*Aphodius Walshi* Horn), ihr Enddorn ist bei einzelnen Arten länger, manchmal löffelförmig (*Aphodins hamatus* Say) oder mit der Spitze plötzlich nach innen gebogen, so dass er von vorn gesehen stumpf erscheint (*Aphodius prodromus* Brahm, *Heydeni* Harold, *pollicatus* Erichson), bei andern Arten ist er zugespitzt und nach innen gebogen.

Die Hintertibien sind zuweilen stark verbreitert (*Aphodius sorex* Fabricius, *tristis* Zenker, *tersus* Rosenhauer), ihr erstes Tarsenglied manchmal verdickt (*Aphodius tristis* Zenker) oder hakenförmig gestaltet (*Aphodius hamatus* Say).

Die Metasternalplatte ist fast immer grubig vertieft, meistens auch deutlich punktiert und zuweilen dicht behaart, entweder über der ganzen Mitte oder nur am Rande.

Die Weibchen zeigen obige Auszeichnungen nicht. Ihre Kopfhöckerchen sind immer schwächer oder fehlen ganz.

Das Halsschild ist immer schmaler als die Flügeldecken, stets viel deutlicher und dichter punktiert, auch auf der Scheibe.

Die Vordertibien sind immer schwach dreieckig, am Aussenrande immer mit drei Zähnen und neben den Tarsen mit zugespitztem, gerade nach vorn gerichteten Enddorn.

Die Hintertibien und ihr erstes Fussglied sind stets normal.

Das Metasternum ist in der Mitte meistens unpunktiert, nur mit vertiefter Linie versehen.

Geographische Verbreitung der Arten. — In allen bisher durchforschten Teilen der Erde sind Aphodien gefunden worden, sie haben unter den Aphodiinen die weiteste Verbreitung sowohl nach Norden als nach Süden.

A. — Aphodien des palæarktischen Gebietes

BESTIMMUNGS-TABELLE DER UNTERGATTUNGEN

1. *Hintertibien sehr kurz, dick, nach der Spitze stark verbreitert, Tarsen dünn und kurz, Klauen haarförmig* . .   1. Subgenus SITIPHUS, Fairmaire.

1'. *Hintertibien länger, nicht besonders stark nach der Spitze verbreitert, Tarsen schlanker, Klauen normal.*

2. *Schildchen ziemlich scharf zugespitzt, lang, ein Fünftel bis ein Drittel der Flügeldeckenlänge erreichend.*

3. *Flügeldecken auf dem Rücken abgeflacht, an der Spitze breit verrundet oder abgestutzt. Pygidium zum Teil unbedeckt, Schildchen tieferliegend.* . . . . . .   2. Subgenus COLOBOPTERUS, Mulsant.

3'. *Flügeldecken nicht verflacht, nach hinten mehr spitz ver-*

rundet, Schildchen liegt in gleicher Höhe mit den Flügeldecken.

4. *Flügeldecken bedeutend länger als das Halsschild, Schildchen mehr lang und schmal, Kopfschild mit drei deutlichen, beim ♀ etwas schwächeren Höckern* . . . .   3. Subgenus TEUCHESTES, Mulsant.

4'. *Flügeldecken kaum länger als Halsschild (nur bei A. confusus Harold etwas länger). Schildchen mehr breitdreieckig, Kopfschild mit drei Höckerchen oder einem queren, auch ganz ohne Höcker; Flügeldecken rötlichgelb, mit schwarzen Makeln oder Längsstrichen (confusus), Pygidium stets deutlich frei* . . . . . .   4. Subgenus MEGATELUS, Reitter.

2'. *Schildchen kleiner, ein Zehntel so lang als Flügeldecken, breiter oder schmaler dreieckig oder an der Basis parallel und dann zugespitzt.*

5. *Kopf gehörnt, Clipeus stets ohne Querkiel, am Vorderrande mit zwei Zähnchen oder ohne dieselben, zwischen den Augen mit erhöhter, selten gehöckerter Querlinie, Basis des Halsschildes stets gerandet. Flügeldecken gelb, rotbraun oder schwarz, bei den helleren Arten ist die Naht meist dunkler* . . . .   5. Subgenus MENDIDIUS, Reitter.

5'. *Kopf glatt, feiner oder stärker punktiert, zuweilen fein gehörnt, dann aber mit deutlichem Querkiel, Halsschild mit oder ohne Rand.*

6. *Hinterschienen am Spitzenrande mit kurzen, starken, gleichlangen Borsten, höchstens nach der obern Kante einzelne längere untermischt.*

7. *Basis des Halsschildes mehr oder weniger deutlich gerandet.*

8. *Kopf stark herabgewölbt, gross, mit Querkiel, der Raum zwischen ihm und dem Vorderrande senkrecht, Stirnlinie schwach, stets ohne Höcker. Die Arten sind schwarz, hochgewölbt, nach hinten verbreitert, Flügeldecken sind sehr deutlich punktiert-gestreift.* . . . .   6. Subgenus AMMŒCIUS, Mulsant.

8'. *Kopf weniger stark herabgewölbt, flacher, zuweilen mit kurzem Querkiel, dann ist aber die Stirnlinie gehöckert.*

9. *Halsschild beim Männchen vorn mit rundlichem Eindruck, die Hinterwinkel sind in beiden Geschlechtern kurz abgeschrägt und schwach ausgerandet. Der Kopf ist sehr deutlich gehöckert, das mittelste Höckerchen beim Männchen viel stärker, Flügeldecken meistens rotbraun, einfarbig oder mit dunklen Querbinden oder ebensolchem Längsfleck oder ganz schwarz, Vorderwinkel des Halsschildes fast immer mit heller Makel* . . . . . .   7. Subgenus APHODIUS, i. sp.

9'. *Halsschild in beiden Geschlechtern ohne Eindruck.*

10. *Hinterwinkel des Halsschildes lang abgeschrägt. Stirnnaht kaum gehöckert. Hierher gehören zwei Arten mit rotbraunen Flügeldecken* . . . .   8. Subgenus LORAPHODIUS, Reitter.

10'. *Hinterwinkel nicht abgeschrägt, dieselben sind entweder
    sumpf oder verrundet.*

11. *Schildchen schmal, vorn parallel, dann zugespitzt, Basis
    des Halsschildes immer gerandet, zuweilen aber sehr fein.*

12. *Tarsen nicht länger als die Schienen. Stirn deutlich gehöc-
    kert, Körper stark gewölbt, schwarz, Flügeldecken
    zuweilen rötlich oder gelblich, manchmal der ganze
    Körper bräunlich* . . . . 9. Subgenus CALAMOSTERNUS, Motschulsky.

12'. *Tarsen viel länger als die Schienen, Stirn nicht oder
    schwach gehöckert. Der Körper ist mehr flach, lang-
    gestreckt, gelb oder gelbrot* . . . . 10. Subgenus ERYTUS, Mulsant.

11'. *Schildchen breiter, dreieckig, vorn nicht parallel.*

13. *Ober- und Unterseite hell gelbbraun oder rotbraun, Kopf
    und Scheibe des Halsschildes manchmal dunkler, Seiten
    stets heller* . . . . 11. Subgenus BODILUS, Mulsant.

13'. *Ober- und Unterseite schwarz, Seiten des Halsschildes
    selten heller, Flügeldecken zuweilen rot oder rotgefleckt.* 12. Subgenus AGRILINUS, Mulsant.

7'. *Basis des Halsschildes ungerandet, wenigstens in der Mitte.*

14. *Schildchen dreieckig, Halsschild in den Vorderwinkeln
    gerandet, Körper schwarz, stark gewölbt, nach hinten
    verbreitert, Flügeldecken manchmal rot* . . . . 13. Subgenus OROMUS, Mulsant.

14'. *Schildchen parallel, Halsschild in den Vorderwinkeln
    nicht gerandet, Körper parallel, schwarz, Flügeldecken
    schwarz, zuweilen rotgefleckt, seltener sind dieselben gelb-
    braun mit dunkler Längsmakel, oder die ganze Oberseite
    ist gelblich oder braunrot* . . . . 14. Subgenus LIOTHORAX, Motschulsky.

6'. *Hinterschienen mit feineren Borsten am Spitzenrande, die-
    selben sind von verschiedener Länge.*

15. *Halsschild an der Basis stärker oder feiner gerandet,
    zuweilen wenig sichtbar.*

16. *Der siebente und neunte Zwischenraum nach hinten ver-
    einigt und als rippenartiger Wulst nach der Spitze
    verlängert. Der Nahtstreif ist vor der Spitze stark
    niedergedrückt. Kleine schwarze Arten, die Flügeldecken
    sind gelb oder bräunlich.* . . . . 15. Subgenus PLAGIOGONUS, Mulsant.

16'. *Flügeldecken ohne solchen Wulst vor der Spitze.*

17. *Halsschild mit schief abgestutzten Hinterwinkeln. Kopf-
    schild fein gerunzelt, Stirn beim Männchen mit einem
    undeutlichen Höckerchen. Der Körper ist schwarz, wenig
    stark gewölbt und nach hinten nicht verbreitert. Flügel-
    decken manchmal gelbbraun oder gelb mit schwarzem
    Fleck auf der Scheibe* . . . . 16. Subgenus PHÆAPHODIUS, Reitter.

17'. *Hinterwinkel des Halsschildes nicht abgestutzt.*

18. *Schildchen in der Vorderhälfte parallel.*

19. *Schwarze oder hellrotbraune Arten, deren Flügeldecken in
    Reihen behaart sind* . . . . 17. Subgenus TRICHONOTUS, Mulsant.

19'. *Flügeldecken unbehaart, gelb mit schwarzer Naht oder schwarz mit roten oder gelben Makeln.*

20. *Clipeus mit zwei Zähnchen, Flügeldecken gelb, Naht schmal angedunkelt* . . . . 18. Subgenus ESIMAPHODIUS, Reitter.

20'. *Clipeus ohne Zähnchen, mehr oder weniger gerundet, nur bei Orodalus striatulus Waltl im männlichen Geschlecht zahnartig, dann sind aber die Flügeldecken nicht gelb.*

21. *Flügeldecken rotgelb, braungelb oder blass weissgelb, Naht und erster Zwischenraum immer schwarz.* . . . . 19. Subgenus ESYMUS, Mulsant.

21'. *Flügeldecken niemals einfarbig gelblich.*

22. *Flügeldecken schwarz, mit roten oder gelben Makeln, zuweilen rot mit schwarzer Naht, Hinterwinkel deutlich.* 20. Subgenus ORODALUS, Mulsant.

22'. *Flügeldecken braunrot, Hinterwinkel breit verrundet* . . 21. Subgenus ORODALISCUS, Reitter.

18. *Schildchen breiter, an der Basis nicht parallel, gleich von hier aus verengt.*

23. *Flügeldecken schwarz oder dunkelbraun, selten heller, nie mit schwarzen Flecken oder einem dunklen Nebelfleck.*

24. *Oberseite sehr dicht punktiert, Zwischenräume der Flügeldecken zuweilen mattglänzend chagriniert, gerunzelt oder gestrichelt, Kopf höchstens schwach gehöckert, Oberseite schwarz oder braun, Flügeldecken zuweilen rot oder braungelb, selten fein behaart* . . . . 22. Subgenus AMIDORUS, Mulsant.

24'. *Oberseite weniger dicht, ungleich punktiert, Flügeldecken feiner und sehr vereinzelt, Körper langgestreckt, nach hinten verbreitert, flach gewölbt, schwarz, Flügeldecken manchmal braun oder rotgefleckt* . . . . 23. Subgenus PSEUDACROSSUS, Reitter.

23'. *Flügeldecken gelbbraun, mit schwärzlichen Flecken oder einem Nebelfleck auf der Scheibe, seltener sind dieselben einfarbig, zuweilen aber auch braunrot.*

25. *Flügeldecken mit kleinen schwärzlichen Makeln, nie mit Nebelfleck.*

26. *Flügeldecken gelblich oder rotbraun mit schwärzlichen Makeln, die zwei gebogene Querbinden formieren, zuweilen sind die Flecke beider Binden durch schwarze Längsstriche verbunden, seltener fehlen die Makeln fast ganz und die Streifen sind dann nur geschwärzt.* . 24. Subgenus CHILOTHORAX, Motschulsky.

26'. *Flügeldecken gelblich, mit dunklen nicht untereinander verbundenen Makeln, sie sind meistens stark behaart, Hinterwinkel sind sehr breit verrundet* . . . . . 25. Subgenus NIMBUS, Mulsant.

25'. *Flügeldecken gelblich oder braunrot, mit dunklem Nebelfleck oder ohne denselben, nie mit einzelnen schwarzen Makeln.*

27. *Basis des Halsschildes oft sehr fein gerandet, seltener ist der Rand in der Mitte unterbrochen, Flügeldecken beim Männchen dicht behaart, beim Weibchen nur um die Spitze sehr fein, seltener in beiden Geschlechtern kahl*

(*die Arten mit roten Flügeldecken*), *Stirn höchstens sehr
schwach gehöckert* . . . . 26. Subgenus MELINOPTERUS, Mulsant.

27'. *Basis deutlicher gerandet, Flügeldecken in beiden Geschlechtern kaum oder nicht behaart, Stirnnaht des Männchens
meist sehr deutlich gehöckert* . . . . 27. Subgenus MELAPHODIUS, Reitter.

15'. *Mitte der Basis stets, meistens aber die ganze Basis ungerandet* (*nur bei* Biralus Edgardi *deutlich gerandet*).

28. *Stirnlinie gehöckert.*

29. *Körper wenig gewölbt, schwarz, Flügeldecken entweder rot
mit schwarzen Flecken oder einfarbig braungelb, immer
dicht behaart, ihre Punktstreifen hinten nicht furchen-
artig, nicht frei auslaufend.* . . . . 28. Subgenus LIMARUS, Mulsant.

29'. *Körper stark gewölbt, dunkelvotbraun oder schwarz, Flügeldecken stark punktiert-gestreift, Streifen hinten furchenartig, frei auslaufend* . . . . 29. Subgenus PHARAPHODIUS, Reitter.

28'. *Stirnlinie ohne Höcker.*

30. *Clipeus mit zwei kleinen Zähnchen, Wangen die Augen
überragend, Flügeldecken braungelb, mit zwei dunklen
Querbinden* . . . . 30. Subgenus MENDIDAPHODIUS, Reitter.

30'. *Clipeus ohne Zähnchen.*

31. *Vorderwinkel des Halsschildes vorn ungerandet, Basis
neben der Mitte ausgebuchtet. Grosse, schwarze, abge-
flachte Arten* . . . . 31. Subgenus GONAPHODIUS, Reitter.

31'. *Vorderwinkel fein gerandet.*

32. *Erstes Glied der Vordertarsen kürzer als das zweite, Kopf
nicht sehr gross.*

33. *Wangen die Augen deutlich überragend.*

34. *Kopf nicht besonders klein, Wangen scharfeckig, die Augen
überragend, Flügeldecken braungelb mit schwarzen
Flecken, die sich zu Längs- oder Schrägbinden zusam-
mensetzen* . . . . 32. Subgenus CALAPHODIUS, Reitter.

34'. *Kopf sehr klein, abgerundet, Wangen mehr verrundet,
Flügeldecken schwarz, braun oder gelbrot, mit dunkleren
oder helleren Längsflecken auf der Scheibe* . . . . 33. Subgenus AGOLIUS, Mulsant.

33'. *Wangen die Augen nicht überragend, Basis des Halsschildes
zweibuchtig. Schwarze, etwas flache Arten, deren Flügeldecken einfarbig rot oder mit schwarzer, gemeinsamer
Dorsal- und mehr oder weniger deutlichen Seitenmakel;
zuweilen sind die Flügeldecken schwarz und die Basis
rotgelb* . . . . 34. Subgenus BIRALUS, Mulsant.

32'. *Erstes Glied der Vordertarsen länger als das zweite.*

35. *Kopfschild sehr gross, fast halbkreisförmig, Wangen sehr
gross, scharfwinklig. Seiten des Halsschildes sehr dick
gerandet, Schildchen bald breit-, bald schmal-dreieckig,
Flügeldecken schwarz, dann zuweilen mit hellerer Makel
oder einfarbig rot, manchmal gelbbraun mit schwarzen*

Flechen ; sie sind matt oder glänzend, höchst selten fein
behaart . . . . 35. Subgenus Acrossus, Mulsant.

35'. *Kopfschild nicht sehr gross, Wangen rund und klein, die*
Augen wenig überragend, Seiten des Halsschildes nur
fein gerandet, Schildchen schmal, Flügeldecken meistens
einfarbig schwarz, zuweilen Basis und Spitze heller, oder
die ganzen Flügeldecken gelbbraun, aber immer an den
Seiten und vor der Spitze langabstehend behaart. . . 36. Subgenus Aganocrassus, Reitter.

I. Subgenus SITIPHUS, Fairmaire

Sitiphus. Fairmaire, Ann. Soc. Ent. Belg. Vol. 38, p. 313 (1894).

Charaktere. — Die einzige Art dieser Untergattung ähnelt sehr einem *Mendidius* durch den gekörnten Kopf und die verbreiterten Hinterschenkel, ist aber durch die Form der Hintertibien und Hintertarsen deutlich verschieden.

Der Körper ist von länglicher, konvexer, fast paralleler Gestalt, glänzend braunrot gefärbt, auf dem Kopfe und Halsschilde wenig dunkler, unbehaart.

Der Kopf ist nach vorn verschmälert, ringsum gerandet, vorn sehr wenig ausgebogt und seitlich verrundet, ohne Clipealzähnchen, die Oberfläche desselben ist gekörnt, zwischen den Augen mit erhöhter Querlinie versehen, dieselbe ist ungehöckert.

Das Halsschild ist quer, gewölbt, dicht und gleichmässig punktiert, an den bewimperten Seiten und der Basis gerandet.

Das Schildchen ist klein, dreieckig, punktiert.

Die Flügeldecken sind punktiert-gestreift, sie haben fast ebene, fein und zerstreut punktierte Zwischenräume.

Die Vordertibien haben einen Enddorn neben den Tarsen und an der Aussenseite drei starke Zähne.

Die Hinterschenkel sind sehr verbreitert, die Mittel- und Hintertibien sind nach der Spitze sehr stark verdickt, sie haben am Endrande einen Borstenbesatz und zwei verdickte Enddorne.

Die Tarsen sind sehr kurz und dünn, ihre Klauen sind klein und haarförmig.

Geographische Verbreitung der Art. — Diese Untergattung ist bisher nur aus Nordafrika bekannt.

1. *S. brevitarsis*, Reitter, Ent. Nachr. Vol. 20, p. 186 (1894).   Algier.
     brevitarsis, d'Orbigny, L'Abeille, 1892-96, Vol. 28, p. 122 (1896).   Tunis.
     Brisouti, Fairmaire, Ann. Soc. Ent. Belg. p. 313 (1894).   Algier.
     sec. Reitter, Wien. Ent. Zeit. p. 253 (1894).

2. Subgenus COLOBOPTERUS, Mulsant

Colobopterus. Mulsant, Hist. Nat. Col. France, Lamell. p. 165 (1842); p. 153 (1871).

Coprimorphus. Mulsant, ibidem, p. 168 (1842); p. 155 (1871).

Eupleurus. Mulsant, ibidem, p. 170 (1842); p. 155 (1871).

Charaktere. — Diese Untergattung wird charakterisiert durch das verlängerte und tieferliegende Schildchen und die auf dem Rücken abgeflachten und an der Spitze meistens etwas abgestutzten Flügeldecken.

Der Körper ist oben unbehaart, glänzend, schwarz, Seiten des Halsschildes und die Flügeldecken manchmal bräunlich oder gelbrot, mit oder ohne Nebelfleck.

Der Kopf ist breit, am Vorderrande ausgebuchtet, punktiert, mit einem oder drei Höckern, von denen bei dem Männchen der mittelste stärker und mehr spitz ist; vor den Höckern befindet sich gewöhnlich ein Querkiel.

Das Halsschild ist quer, gewöhnlich deutlich, aber nicht dicht punktiert, die Hinterwinkel sind stumpf oder abgestutzt und dann schwach ausgerandet, die Seiten sind immer, die Basis zuweilen nicht gerandet.

Das Schildchen ist gross, zugespitzt, punktiert, tieferliegend.

Die Flügeldecken sind punktiert-gestreift, auf dem Rücken oft mehrstreifig.

Die Vordertibien haben über den drei grossen Aussenzähnen zuweilen noch einige kleine Kerbzähnchen.

Die Mittel- und Hintertibien sind am Aussenrande mit Querleisten, am Spitzenrande mit einem Kranze kurzer, gleichlanger Borsten versehen, die beiden Enddorne sind fast so lang als das erste, verlängerte Tarsenglied.

Die Klauen sind normal.

Geographische Verbreitung der Arten. — Hierher gehören grosse Arten, die Europa, Nordasien, Japan, Korea, den Kaukasus und Nordamerika bewohnen.

1. *C. antiquus** 1), Faldermann, Mem. Acad. Petr. Vol. 2, p. 367 (1835). Mongolei.
  antiquus, Harold, Berl. Ent. Zeitschr. p. 396 (1862); p. 387 (1863). Ostsibirien.
   . Reitter, Tab. p. 40; Brünn, 30, p. 178. Sibirien.
2. *C. apicalis*, Harold, Berl. Ent. Zeitschr. p. 93, 96 (1861). Japan.
  apicalis, Waterhouse, Trans. Ent. Soc. Lond. p. 80 (1875). China.
  Reitter, Tab. p. 40; Brünn, 30, p. 178. Ostsibirien, Korea.
3. *C. erraticus*, Linné, Syst. Nat. (ed. 10), Vol. 1, p. 348 (1758). Europa.
  erraticus, Paykull, Fauna Suec. Vol. 1, p. 16 (1798). Schweden.
  Erichson, Naturg. Ins. Deutschl. Vol. 3. p 794 (1848l. Deutschland.
  Horn, Trans. Amer. Ent. Soc. Vol. 14. p. 6 (1887). Mittelstaaten.
  Reitter, Tab. p. 40; Brünn, 30, p. 178. Asien, Nordamerika.
  sec. Bailey. Ent. M. Mag. p. 90 (1905). Insel Man.
  pensvallensis, Melsheimer, Proc. Acad. Nat. Sc. Philad.Vol. 2, p. 135 (1844). Pennsylvanien.
  unicolor,var., Dalla Torre,Ber.Ver.Naturk.Oberösterr.Vol.10.p.106 (1879). Oberösterreich.
  sec. Schilsky, Deutsche Ent. Zeitschr. p. 318 (1888).
  var. *striolatus*, Gebler, Nouv. Mém. Soc. Nat. Mosc. Vol. 2, p. 50 (1809). Ostsibirien.
  Harold, Berl. Ent. Zeitschr. p. 104 (1861). Spanien, Marokko.
  gonagricus, Fischer, Bull. Soc. Nat. Mosc. Vol. 17 (1), p. 45 (1844). Daurien.
  sec. Solsky, Fedtschenko Turkest. Col. p. 315 (1876).
  submaculatus, Mulsant, Hist. Nat. Col. France, Lamell. p. 166 (1842). Frankreich.
  bistrigatus, Dalla Torre, Ber. Ver. Naturk. Oberöster.Vol.10, p. 106 (1879). Oberösterreich.
  sec. Schilsky, Deutsche Ent. Zeitschr. p. 318 (1888).
  var. *nebulosus*, Mulsant, Hist. Nat. Col. France, Lamell. p. 166 (1842). Frankreich.
  sec. Dalla Torre,Ber.Ver.Naturk.Oberösterr.Vol.10,p.106(1879). Oberösterreich.
  var. *fumigatus*, Mulsant, Hist. Nat. Col. France, Lamell. p. 166 (1842). Frankreich.
  melancholicus, DallaTorre,Ber.Ver.Naturk.Oberösterr.Vol.10,p 106(1879). Oberösterreich.
  sec. Schilsky, Deutsche Ent. Zeitschr. p. 318 (1888).
  var. *lineatus*, Dalla Torre, Ber. Ver. Naturk. Oberösterr. Vol. 10, p. 106 (1879). Oberosterreich.
  taeniatus, Schilsky, Deutsche Ent. Zeitschr. p. 306 (1888). Oesterreich, Thüringen
  sec. Schilsky, ibidem, p. 318 (1888).
4. *C. indagator*, Mannerheim, Bull. Soc. Nat. Mosc. Vol. 22(1), p. 233 (1849) Irkutsk.
  indagator, Harold, Berl. Ent. Zeitschr. p. 93, 96 (1861). Sibirien.
  Reitter, Tab. p. 40; Brünn, 30, p. 178. Sibirien.
5. *C. major*, Waterhouse, Trans. Ent. Soc. Lond. p. 80 (1875). Japan.
  major, Reitter, Tab. p. 39; Brünn, 30. p. 177. Ostsibirien.

---

1) Die mit einem * versehenen Zitate habe ich nicht einsehen können.

6. *C. scrutator*, Herbst, Natursyst. Ins. Vol. 2, p. 161, t. 16, f. 6 (1789).　　Ungarn.
　　scrutator, Erichson, Naturg. Ins. Deutschl. Vol. 3, p. 796 (1848).　　　Oesterreich, Süddeutschland
　　　　Harold, Berl. Ent. Zeitschr. p. 93 (1861).
　　　　Reitter, Tab. p. 39; Brünn, 30, p. 177.　　　　　　　　　Mittel-und Südeuropa, Kaukasus.
　　brevicornis, Schrank, Naturf. Vol. 24, p. 62 (1789).　　　　　　Oesterreich.
　　rubidus, Olivier, Ent. Vol. 1 (3), p. 77, t. 26, f. 224 (1789).　　　Frankreich.
　　var. *aequinoctialis*, Harold, Berl. Ent. Zeitschr. p. 98 (1861).　　　Azoren.
　　var. *submaculatus*, Mulsant, Hist. Nat. Col. France, Lamell. p. 169 (1842).　Frankreich.
　　var. *nigricollis*, Mulsant, ibidem, p. 169 (1842).　　　　　　　Frankreich.
　　　tristissimus, Dalla Torre, Ber. Ver. Naturk. Oberösterr. Vol. 10, p. 106 (1879).　Oberösterreich.
　　　　sec. Schilsky, Deutsche Ent. Zeitschr. p. 318 (1888).
　　var. *brunnipes*, Mulsant, Hist. Nat. Col. France, Lamell. p. 169 (1842).　Frankreich.
　　var. *latemarginatus*, Dalla Torre, Ber. Ver. Naturk. Oberösterr. Vol. 10, p. 106　Oberösterreich.
　　　(1879).
　　var. *angustemarginatus*, Dalla Torre, ibidem, p. 106 (1879).　　　Oberösterreich.
　　var. *angulatus*, Dalla Torre, ibidem, p. 106 (1879).　　　　　　Oberösterreich.
　　Biologie : Xambeu, Rev. d'Ent. Caen, Vol. 20, p. 56 (1901). — Ei beschrieben.

7. *C. subterraneus*, Linné, Syst. Nat. (ed. 10), Vol. 1, p. 348 (1758).　　Europa.
　　subterraneus, Herbst, Natursyst. Ins. Vol. 2, p. 123, t. 11, f. 6 (1789).　　Berlin.
　　　　Erichson, Naturg. Ins. Deutschl. Vol. 3, p. 797 (1848).　　　Deutschland.
　　　　Harold, Berl. Ent. Zeitschr. p. 94 (1861).
　　　　Reitter, Tab. p. 40; Brünn, 30, p. 178.　　　　　　　　　Asien ·
　　　　sec. Beare, Ent. M. Mag (2), Vol. 5, p. 276 (1894).　　　　England.
　　var. *coerulescens*, Harold, Berl. Ent. Zeitschr. p. 103 (1861).　　　München.
　　var. *fuscipennis*, Mulsant, Hist. Nat. Col. France, Lamell. p. 171 (1842).　Frankreich.
　　　fuscus, Dalla Torre, Ber. Ver. Naturk. Oberösterr. Vol. 10, p. 106 (1879).　Oberösterreich.
　　　rufus, Dalla Torre, ibidem, p. 106 (1879).　　　　　　　　Oberösterreich.
　　　ruber, Dalla Torre, ibidem, p 106 (1879).　　　　　　　　Oberösterreich.
　　　　sec. Schilsky, Deutsche Ent. Zeitschr. p. 319 (1888).
　　Biologie : Xambeu, Rev. d'Ent. Caen, Vol. 17, p. 20 (1898). — Ei beschrieben.

3. SUBGENUS TEUCHESTES, MULSANT

Teuchestes. Mulsant, Hist. Nat. Col. France, Lamell. p. 176 (1842); p. 162 (1871).

Otophorus. Mulsant, ibidem, p. 172 (1842); p. 159 (1871).

Charaktere. — Die Arten haben ebenfalls ein grosses, schmal-dreieckiges Schildchen, dasselbe liegt aber nicht tiefer als die Flügeldecken, letztere sind auf dem Rücken nicht abgeflacht und an der Spitze nicht abgestutzt.

Der Körper ist länglich, stark gewölbt, schwarz, die Flügeldecken sind zuweilen rot- oder gelbgefleckt oder einfarbig gelb- oder rotbraun.

Der Kopf ist breit und kurz, punktiert, ausgerandet, mit drei deutlichen Höckern.

Das Halsschild ist breit, stark herabgewölbt, die Seiten und die Basis sind immer gerandet, die Hinterwinkel abgestutzt und ausgerandet.

Das Schildchen ist gross, langgestreckt, nicht vertieft.

Die Flügeldecken sind einfach punktiert-gestreift.

Die Vordertibien haben drei Aussenzähne, die Mittel- und Hintertibien zwei Querleisten, die Borsten am Spitzenrande der letzteren sind kurz und gleichlang, die Enddorne so lang oder länger als das erste Glied.

Die Männchen haben gewöhnlich einen stumpfen, nach der Spitze meist deutlich verbreiterten Enddorn an den Vordertibien. Das Halsschild zeigt hinter dem Vorderrande einen etwas länglichen Eindruck. Die Kopfhöcker sind stärker entwickelt, besonders der mittelste. Bei *sorex* Fabricius sind die Hinterschienen stark verbreitert.

Bei den Weibchen ist das Halsschild vorn ohne Eindruck und viel zahlreicher punktiert. Die Stirnhöcker sind schwächer. Der Enddorn der Vordertibien ist spitz, die Hintertibien sind normal.

Geographische Verbreitung der Arten. — Die Arten bewohnen Europa, Nordasien, China, Indien, Afrika und Australien.

1. *T. brachysomus*, Solsky, Col. Hefte, Vol. 12. p. 13 (1874).   Ostsibirien.
   brachysomus. Reitter, Tab. p. 41; Brünn, 3o, p. 179.   Ostsibirien.
        Jacobson, Hor. Soc Ent. Ross. 1896-97. Vol. 31, p. 88 (1898).

2. *T. fossor*, Linné, Syst. Nat. (ed. 10), Vol. 1, p. 348 (1758).   Europa.
   fossor, De Geer, Mém. Ins. Vol. 4, p. 264 t. 10, f. 7 (1774).
        Erichson, Naturg. Ins. Deutschl. Vol. 3, p. 799 (1848).   Deutschland.
        Harold, Berl. Ent. Zeitschr. p. 155, 166.(1862).   Nord-und Mitteleuropa, Sibirien.
        Horn, Trans. Amer. Ent. Soc. Vol. 14, p. 4 (1887).   Nordamerika.
        Reitter, Tab. p. 41; Brünn, 3o, p. 179.   Europa, Nordasien.
        Jacobson, Hor. Soc. Ent. Ross. Vol. 31, p. 88 (1898).
        sec. Clouët, Bull. Soc. Ent. Fr. p. 188 (1898).   Algier.
        sec. Bailey, Ent. M. Mag. p. 90 (1905).   Insel Man.
   triangulum, Piller & Mitterpacher, Iter per Poseganam (Scriba Journ.)   Slavonien.
        p. 97, t. 9, f. 15 (1783).
   var. silvaticus. Ahrens, Neue Schrift. Ges. Halle, Vol. 2 (2), p. 33 (1812).
   brunneus, Mulsant, Hist. Nat. Col. France, Lamell. p. 177 (1842).   Frankreich.
        sec. Schilsky, Deutsche Ent. Zeitschr. p 307 (1888).
   Biologie : Chapuis & Candèze, Cat. Larv. Col. p. 124, t. 4, f. 3 (1853). —
        Beschreibung und Abbildung der Larve.
   * Schioedte, Nat. Tidsskr.Vol.9, p 328(1874).—Beschreib. der Larve.
        Perris, Ann. Soc. Linn. Lyon, 1875, Vol. 22, p. 367 (1876). —
        Beschreibung der Larve.
        Perris, ibidem, 1876, Vol. 23, t. 3, f. 85-92 (1877). — Abbildung der
        Larve.
   * Kittel, Correspbl. Zool. Miner. Ver. Regensb. Vol. 32, p. 190 (1878).
        — Beschreibung der Larve.
        Xambeu, Ann. Soc. Linn. Lyon, Vol. 39, p. 157 (1892). — Beschrei-
        bung der Larve, Puppe.
        Xambeu, Rev. d'Ent. Caen, Vol. 19, p. 44 (1900). — Kopulation u.
        Eiablage.

3. *T. haemorrhoidalis*, Linné Syst. Nat. (ed. 10), Vol. 1, p. 348 (1758).   Europa.
   haemorrhoidalis, Herbst, Naturs. Ins. Vol. 2, p. 152, t. 12, f. 11 (1789).   Pommern.
        Erichson, Naturg. Ins. Deutschl. Vol. 3, p. 800 (1848).   Deutschland.
        Harold, Berl. Ent. Zeitschr. p. 155, 163 (1862).   Nord- und Mitteleuropa und Hi-
        Reiter, Tab. p. 41; Brünn, 3o, 179.   Europa, Sibirien.   [malaya.
        sec. Walker, Ent. M. Mag. (2), Vol. 3o, p. 115 (1894).   England.
   granarius, var. β, Fabricius, Syst. Ent. p. 16 (1775).   Europa.
   triplagiatus, Harold, Berl. Ent. Zeitschr. p. 163 (1862).   Sibirien.
   var. sanguinolentus. Herbst, Arch. Vol. 4, p. 6, t. 19, f. 4 (1783).   Berlin.
        Illiger, Verz. Käf. Preuss. p. 23 (1798).   Preussen.
   var. humeralis, Mulsant, Hist. Nat. Col. France, Lamell. p. 174 (1842).   Frankreich.
   var. rubidus, Mulsant, ibidem, p. 174 (1842).   Frankreich.
        sec. Harold, Brünn. Vol. 16, p. 187 (1877).   Kaukasus.
   Biologie : Xambeu, Ann. Soc. Nat. Linn. Lyon, Vol. 42, p. 68 (1895). —
        Larve und Puppe beschrieben.

4. *T. sorex*, Fabricius, Ent. Syst. Vol. 1, p. 23 (1792).   China, Ostindien.
   sorex, Harold, Berl. Ent. Zeitschr. p. 155, 167 (1862).   Australien, Caffrarien.
        Péringuey, Trans. S. Afric. Philos. Soc. 1901-1903, Vol. 12 ; Cat.   Natal. Kapkolonie.
        p. 425 (1901).
        Reitter, Tab. p. 41 ; Brünn, 3o, p. 179.   China.
        Jacobson, Hor. Soc. Ent. Ross. 1896-1897, Vol. 31, p. 88 (1898).   Ostindien.
        sec. Clouët, Bull. Soc. Ent. Fr. p. 187 (1898).   Abessinien.
   var. analis, Fabricius, Mant. Vol. 1, p. 8 (1787).   Ostindien.
        Harold, Berl. Ent. Zeitschr. p. 167 (1862).   China, Australien, Caffrarien.
   var. caffer, Wiedemann, Zool. Mag. Vol. 2 (1), p. 25 (1823).   Kap der gutten Hoffnung.
        Boheman, Ins. Caffr. Vol. 2, p. 328 (1857).   Limpopo.
        Harold, Berl. Ent. Zeitschr. p. 167 (1862).   Australien, Caffrarien.

5. *T. Troitzkyi*, Jacobson. Hor. Soc. Ent. Ross. 1896-97, Vol. 31, p. 87   Minussinsk.
   (1898).

4. SUBGENUS MEGATELUS, REITTER

Megatelus. Reitter, Verhandl. Naturf. Ver. Brünn. Vol. 3o, p. 179 (1891); Best.-Tab. Eur. Col. Heft 24, p. 41 (1892).

Charaktere. — Die Arten dieser Untergattung sind ausgezeichnet durch die äusserst kurzen Flügeldecken. Ihr Körper ist kurz und breit, konvex, schwarz, die Flügeldecken sind gelb mit dunklen Makeln.

Der Kopf ist schwarz, punktiert, mit drei Höckern oder einem queren, der Clipeus ist ausgerandet, zuweilen auch noch der Seitenrand; die Wangen sind klein.

Das Halsschild ist schwarz, gewölbt, punktiert, die Basis ist nur zuweilen, die Seiten sind immer gerandet, die Hinterwinkel sind abgeschrägt.

Das Schildchen ist breit-dreieckig, sehr gross.

Die Flügeldecken sind gelb, mit dunkler Basal- oder ebensolcher Seitenmakel, sie sind kaum länger als das Halsschild (nur bei *M. confusus* Harold etwas länger), ihre Punktstreifen sind deutlich, die Zwischenräume sind wenig gewölbt, schwach oder nicht punktiert.

Die Vordertibien haben drei kräftige Aussenzähne, nur bei *M. contractus* Klug sind es deren zwei, dafür befindet sich aber noch ein kleiner Zahn am Vorderrande neben den Tarsen.

Die Mittel- und Hintertibien haben zwei Querleisten, die Borstenkränze sind meistens gleichlang, die Enddornen sind kürzer als das erste verlängerte Tarsenglied.

Die Klauen sind normal.

Geographische Verbreitung der Arten. — Die Arten finden sich im paläarktischen und afrikanischen Gebiet.

1. *M. confusus*, Harold, Berl. Ent. Zeitschr. p. 154, 155 (1862).   Aegypten, Senegal.
2. *M. contractus*, Klug, Symb. Phys. Vol. 5, t. 42, f. 3 (1845).   Aethiopien.
     contractus, Harold, Berl. Ent. Zeitschr. p. 155, 157 (1862).   Aegypten, Nubien.
     Reitter. Tab. p. 42; Brünn 3o, p. 180.   Syrien.
3. *M. scolytiformis*, Reitter, ibidem, p. 41; ibidem, p. 179.   Syrien.
4. *M. scolytoides*, Lucas, Expl. Algér. Zool. Vol. 2, p. 259, t. 24, f. 2 (1846).   Algier.
     scolytoides, Harold, Berl. Ent. Zeitschr. p. 155, 159 (1862).   Algier.

5. SUBGENUS MENDIDIUS, HAROLD

Mendidius. Harold, Col. Hefte, Vol. 3, p. 86 (1868).
Cnemargus. Harold, Berl. Ent. Zeitschr. p. 123 (1866).

Charaktere. — Rotbraun gefärbte Arten mit braungelben, seltener ganz schwarzen Flügeldecken, deren Vorderkopf gekörnt ist, bilden diese Untergattung.

Der Körper ist gewölbt, glänzend, länglich, oft nach der Spitze verbreitert, an den Rändern mehr oder weniger lang behaart.

Der Kopf ist gekörnt oder wenigstens stark runzlig-punktiert, hinten mehr glatt, einfach punktiert, die Stirnlinie ist immer deutlich, zuweilen mit Spuren kleiner Höckerchen, der Clipeus ist in der Mitte ausgerandet. jederseits gezähnt, sehr selten ohne Zähnchen.

Das Halsschild ist immer breiter als der Kopf, die Seiten desselben sind gerandet, der Basalrand fehlt nur zuweilen, die Oberfläche ist immer punktiert.

Das Schildchen ist klein, dreieckig, seltener vorn parallel, immer punktiert.

Die Flügeldecken sind meistens nach hinten verbreitert, hellgelbbraun, mit oftmals angedunkelter Naht, sie sind punktiert-gestreift, ihre Zwischenräume sind selten deutlich punktiert.

Die Unterseite ist meistens etwas heller gefärbt als die Oberseite, sie ist punktiert und behaart. Die Hinterschenkel sind meistens stark verbreitert.

Die Vordertibien haben drei kräftige Aussenzähne und darüber öfter mehrere kleine Kerbzähnchen.

Die Mittel- und Hintertibien besitzen deutliche Querleisten, zwei Enddorne und meistens einen Kranz kurzer Borsten am Spitzenrande. Die Enddorne sind oft länger als das erste Glied, letzteres wenig verlängert.

Die Klauen sind normal.

Hierher gehören kleinere und mittelgrosse Arten.

Geographische Verbreitung der Arten. — Die Species dieser Untergattung wurden bisher in Südrussland, Sibirien, Mongolei, Persien, Turkestan, Armenien, Arabien und Nordafrika gefunden.

1. *M. Adolfischmidti,* Reitter, Wien. Ent. Zeit. Vol. 28, p. 75 (1909). — Uralsk.
2. *M. atricolor,* Reitter, Tab. p. 45; Brünn, 30, p. 183. — Südturkestan.
3. *M. bidens,* Solsky, Fedtschenko Turkest. Col. Vol. 2, p. 346 (1876). — Maracandam.
  bidens, Reitter, Tab. p. 43; Brünn, 30, p. 181. — Armenien, Nordpersien, Transkaspien, Turkestan.
  bispinifrons, Reitter, Brünn, 27, p. 103 (1888). — Transkaspien, Persien.
    sec. Reitter, Wien. Ent. Zeit. p. 228 (1891).
4. *M. Brancsiki,* Reitter. Deutsche Ent. Zeitschr. p. 200 (1899). — Transkaspien.
5. *M. breviciliatus,* Poppius, Ann. Mus. Zool. St. Pétersb. Vol. 8. p. 366 (1903). — Kaukasus.
  fimbriolatus, Reitter (nec Mannerheim), Tab. p. 44; Brünn, 30. p. 182. — Transkaspien, Turkestan.
6. *M. burgaltaicus,* Csiki, Zichy, 3. Asiat. Forschungsreise, Vol. 2, p. 107 (1901). — Mongolei.
7. *M. curtulus,* Harold, Berl. Ent. Zeitschr. p. 125 (1866). — Südöstl. Russland.
  curtulus, Reitter, Tab. p. 42; Brünn, 30 p. 180. — Südöstl. Russland.
8. *M. diffidens.* Reitter. Tab. p. 44; Brünn, 30, p. 182. — Ordubad.
9. *M. fimbriolatus,* Mannerheim, Bull. Soc. Nat. Mosc. Vol. 22 (1), p. 235 (1849). — Irkutsk.
  fimbriolatus, Harold, Berl. Ent. Zeitschr. p. 124 (1866). — Ostsibirien.
10. *M. granulifrons,* Fairmaire, C. R. Ann. Soc. Ent. Belg. p. 42, 157 (1883). — Algier.
  granulifer, Reitter, Ent. Nachr. p. 185 (1894); Wien. Ent. Zeit. p. 253 (1894). — Marokko.
11. *M. laevicollis,* Harold, Berl. Ent. Zeitschr. p. 123 (1866). — Aegypten.
  laevicollis, d'Orbigny, L'Abeille, Vol. 28, p. 201 (1896).
12. *M. multiplex,* Reitter. Wien. Ent. Zeit. p. 241 (1897) nom. nov.
  granulifrons ‖ Reitter (non Fairmaire), Hor. Soc. Ent. Ross. Vol. 21, p. 221 (1887); Tab. p. 44; Brünn, 30, p. 182. — Chines.-Turkestan, Turkestan.
  Reitteri ‖ Fairmaire (non Koshantschikow), Ann. Soc. Ent. Belg. p. 313 (1894).
  Reitterianus ‖ Heyden (non Schwarz), Col. Sib. 2. Nachr. p. 44 (1897).
13. *M. rutilinus,* Reitter. Tab. p. 44; Brünn, 30, p. 182. — Bou-Saada.
14. *M. rutilus,* Klug, Symb. Phys. Vol. 5, nᵒ 9, t. 42, f. 9 (1845). — Arabien.
  rutilus, Harold, Berl. Ent. Zeitschr. p. 257, 258 (1871). — Nubien, Aegypten.
15. *M. spinosus,* Koshantschikow. Hor. Soc. Ent. Ross. 1893-94, Vol. 28, p. 107 (1894). — Westturkestan.
16. *M. Willbergi,* Reitter. Wien. Ent. Zeit. p. 255 (1891); Tab. p. 43; Brünn, 30, p. 181. — Margljan.

6. Subgenus AMMŒCIUS, Mulsant

Ammœcius. Mulsant, Hist. Nat. Col. France, Lamell. p. 302 (1842); p. 356 (1871).

Charaktere. — Der Körper dieser Arten ist stark konvex, nach hinten gewöhnlich sichtbar verbreitert, schwarz oder schwarzbraun, glänzend, unbehaart.

Der Kopf ist gross, stark herabgewölbt, ohne sichtbare Stirnlinie und stets ohne Höckerchen, er ist bald glatt, bald nach vorn hin stärker, seltener runzlig punktiert, aber immer im vorderen Teile mit einer glatten Querleiste und von dieser nach dem Vorderrande senkrecht abfallend; der Clipeus ist stets ausgerandet, seitlich davon mit zwei deutlichen Zähnchen oder nur stumpfwinklig, nie breit verrundet; die Augen sind fast vollständig vom Vorderrande des Halsschildes bedeckt.

Das Halsschild ist stark gewölbt, zerstreuter oder dichter punktiert, der Seiten- und Basalrand sind immer vorhanden, zuweilen auch eine vertiefte Linie hinter dem Vorderrande.

Das Schildchen ist klein, dreieckig und punktiert.

Die Flügeldecken sind nach hinten meistens verbreitert, feiner oder stärker punktiert-gestreift, die Zwischenräume sind bei den meisten Arten nur vor der Spitze gewölbt.

Die Vordertibien haben drei Aussenzähne und einen Enddorn.

An den Mittel- und Hintertibien fehlen die Querleisten nie, die Borsten am Spitzenrande sind kurz und gleichlang; der obere Enddorn ist entweder etwas länger oder ebensolang als das wenig verlängerte erste Glied.

Die Klauen sind normal.

Geographische Verbreitung der Arten. — Die Arten leben in Europa, Turkestan und Nordafrika.

1. *A. angulatus*, A. Schmidt, Deutsche Ent. Zeitschr. p. 201 (1907), nom. nov.   Samarkand.
   discolor ‖ Solsky, Fedtschenko Turkest. Col. p. 345 (1876).
2. *A. brevis*, Erichson. Naturg. Ins. Deutschl. Vol. 3, p. 907 (1848).   Mittel- und Süddeutsch-
   brevis, Thomson, Skand. Col. Vol. 5, p. 67 (1863).   Schweden.   [land.
   Harold, Col. Hefte, Vol. 7, p. 4, 11 (1871).   N.- und Mitteleuropa, Kaukasus.
   Reitter, Tab. p. 46; Brünn, 30, p. 184.   N.- und Mitteleuropa, Kaukasas.
   elevatus, Paykull, Fauna Suec. Vol. 1, p. 28 (1798).   Schweden.
   Illiger, Olivier Entom. der Naturg. der Insecten, Vol. 1, p. 192 (1800).
   Panzer, Fauna Germ. p. 87 (1).
   sec. A. Schmidt, Aphodiinen-Zusammenst. Deutsche Ent. Zeitschr.
   Beih. p. 11, Anmerkung (1907-08).
   Sturm, Deutschl. Ins. Vol. 1, p. 170 (1805).   Deutschland.
   Duftschmid, Fauna Austr. Vol. 1, p. 129 (1805).   Oesterreich.
   Gyllenhal, Ins. Suec. Vol. 1, p. 6 (1820).   Schweden.
   Schmidt, Germars Zeitschr. f. Ent. Vol. 2, p. 171 (1840).   Deutschland, Oesterreich.
   Heer, Fauna Col. Helv. Vol. 1, p. 530 (1841).   Schweiz.
   Biologie : *Schioedte, Nat. Tidsskr. Vol. 9, p. 328, t. 15, f. 1-4, t. 19, f. 11 (1874).
   — Larve beschrieben und abgebildet.
3. *A. dentatus*, A. Schmidt, Deutsche Ent. Zeitschr. p. 504 (1908).   Tanger, Marokko.
4. *A. elevatus*, Olivier, Ent. Vol. 1 (3), p. 89, t. 21, f. 190 (1789).   Frankreich.
   elevatus, Fabricius, Ent. Syst. Vol. 1, p 37 (1792).   Frankreich.
   Erichson, Naturg. Ins. Deutschl. Vol. 3, p. 908 (1848).   Spanien.
   Harold, Col. Hefte, Vol. 7, p. 14, 16 (1871)   Südwesteuropa, Marokko.
   Reitter, Tab. p. 45; Brünn, 30, p. 183.   Pyrenäen, Portugal, Algier
   var. *edentulus*, Mulsant, Hist. Nat. Col. France, Lamell. p. 303 (1842).   Südfrankreich.
   var. *fusciventris*, Mulsant, ibidem, p. 303 (1842).   Südfrankreich.
   Biologie : Xambeu, Rev. d'Ent. Caen, Vol. 9, p. 61 (1890) ; Ann. Soc. Linn.
   Lyon, 39, p. 165 (1892). — Larve, Puppe und Lebensweise
   beschrieben.
5. *A. Felscheanus*, Reitter, Wien. Ent. Zeit. p. 255 (1904).   Algier.
6. *A. frigidus*, Brisout. Ann. Soc. Ent. Fr. p. 374 (1866).   Escorial.
   frigidus, Harold, Col. Hefte. Vol. 7, p. 4, 15 (1871).   Asturien.
   Reitter, Tab. p. 46; Brünn, 30, p. 184.   Spanien, Portugal.
7. *A. lusitanicus*, Erichson, Naturg. Ins. Deutschl. Vol. 3, p. 908 (1848).   Portugal.
   lusitanicus, Harold, Col. Hefte. Vol. 7, p. 4, 13 (1871).   Portugal.
   Reitter, Tab. p. 46; Brünn, 30, p. 184.   Spanien, Marokko
   elevatus, Illiger, Mag. Insekt. Vol. 2, p. 197 (1803).   Portugal.
8. *A. nitidus*, Küster, Käf. Europ. Vol. 18, p. 55.   Montenegro.

9. *A. numidicus*, Mulsant, Mém. 'Acad. Sc. Lyon, Vol. 1, p. 192 (1851).   Algier.
    numidicus, Harold. Col. Hefte. Vol. 14, p. 210 (1875).
10. *A. rugiceps*, Mulsant, Hist. Nat. Col. France, Lamell. p. 365 (1871).   Pyrenäen.
    rugiceps, A. Schmidt, Aphodiinen-Zusammenst. Deutsche Ent. Zeitschr.,
    Beih. p. 70, Anmerkung (1907-08).
11. *A. rugifrons*, Aubé. Ann. Soc. Ent. Fr. (2), Vol. 8, p. 335 (1850).   Algier.
    rugifrons, Harold, Col. Hefte, Vol. 7, p. 3, 10 (1871).   Algier.
    Reitter, Tab. p. 46; Brünn, 30, p. 184.   Sardinien.
    Levaillanti, Godart, Ann. Soc. Linn. Lyon, 1850-52, p. 297 (1852).   Algier.
    sec. Reiche, Bull. Soc. Ent. Fr. p. 59 (1852).

7. SUBGENUS APHODIUS, I. SP.

Aphodius. Mulsant. Hist. Nat. Col. France, Lamell. p. 168 (1871).
Loraspis. Mulsant, ibidem, p. 178 (1871).

Charaktere. — In der konvexen, etwas robusten Gestalt stimmen die Arten dieser Untergattung mit der vorigen überein, unterscheiden sich aber von ihnen durch den kleineren, mehr flachen und mit drei Höckern versehenen Kopf.

Der Körper ist schwarz. glänzend, unbehaart, die Flügeldecken sind rot- oder gelbbraun. zuweilen ganz gelb, einfarbig oder mit dunklem Längsfleck oder ebensolchen Querbinden, seltener schwarz.

Der Kopf ist breit, vorn ausgerandet, punktiert, die Stirnnaht ist immer sehr deutlich gehöckert, die Wangen sind stumpfwinklig.

Das Halsschild ist quer, herabgewölbt, an den Seiten und der Basis gerandet, seltener auch am Vorderrande (*Loraspis* Mulsant), mit gewöhnlich helleren Vorderwinkeln, die Hinterwinkel sind meistens deutlich abgeschrägt und schwach ausgerandet.

Das Schildchen ist klein, dreieckig, punktiert, schwarz.

Die Flügeldecken sind punktiert-gestreift, ihre Zwischenräume wenig gewölbt.

Die Unterseite ist gewöhnlich glänzend. behaart, einfarbig schwarz, seltener mit rötlichem Abdomen.

Im Fussbau stimmen die Arten mit denen der vorhergehenden Untergattung überein.

Die Männchen haben stärker entwickelte Kopfhöcker, davor oft einen stumpfen Querkiel, das Halsschild ist breiter als die Flügeldecken, nur zerstreut punktiert. hinter dem Vorderrande mit rundlichem Eindruck.

Die Weibchen haben nur schwach angedeutete Höckerchen, der Querkiel fehlt fast ganz, das Halsschild ist nur von der Breite der Flügeldecken, es ist ohne Eindruck und viel dichter, auch auf der Scheibe punktiert.

Hierher gehören grössere und mittlere Arten.

Geographische Verbreitung der Arten. — Europa, Kaukasus, Vorder-, Mittel- und Nordasien, Japan, Nordafrika. Indien, Nordamerika.

1. *A. chinensis*, Harold. Berl. Ent. Zeitschr. p. 105 (1861); p. 96, 112 (1866).   China.
2. *H. conjugatus*, Panzer, Ent. Taschenb. Addenda p. 364 (1795).   Deutschland.
    conjugatus, W. Schmidt, Germars Zeitschr. f. Ent. Vol. 2, p. 97 (1840).   Oesterreich.
    Harold, Berl. Ent. Zeitschr. p. 332, 347 (1863).   Mittel- und Südosteuropa. Südfrankreich, Südrussland.
    Erichson, Naturg. Ins. Deutschl. Vol. 3, p. 801 (1848).   Oesterreich.
    Reitter, Tab. p. 47; Brünn, 30, p. 185   Europa, Ungarn, Russland.
    fasciatus, Fabricius, Syst. Eleuth. p. 68 (1801).   Oesterreich.
    var. *fasciatus*, Mulsant, Hist. Nat. Col. France, Lamell. p. 182 (1842).   Frankreich.
    interruptus, Dalla Torre, Ber. Ver. Naturk. Oberösterr. p. 107 (1879).   Oberösterreich.
    angustifasciatus, Dalla Torre, ibidem, p. 107 (1879).   Oberösterreich.
    sec. Schilsky, Deutsche Ent. Zeitschr. p. 319 (1888).
    sec. Harold, Brünn, 16, p. 187 (1877).   Kaukasus.

Biologie : Koy, Anmerk. über ein. Ins. Col. (Naturforscher), p. 106 (1802). —
    Beschreibung der Larve.
    Sturm, Deutschl. Ins. Vol. 1, p. 85 (1805). — Kurze Beschreibung
      der Larve.
    De Haan, Nouv. Ann. Mus. Hist. Nat. Paris, Vol. 4, p. 147, t. 12,
      f. 5, t. 14, f. 9 (1835). — Beschreibung und Abbildung der
      Larve.
    Erichson, Naturg. Ins. Deutschl. Vol. 3, p. 802 (1848). — Beschrei-
      bung der Larve.

3. *A. elegans*, Allibert, Rev. Zool. p. 18 (1847).   China.
    elegans, Harold, Berl. Ent. Zeitschr. p. 332, p. 344 (1863).   Japan.
      Waterhouse, Trans. Ent. Soc. Lond. p. 81 (1875).   Japan.
    var. expletus, A. Schmidt, Soc. Ent. Zürich, 1909-10, Vol. 24, p. 20 (1909).   Yünnan.

4. *A. Emerichi*, Reitter, Tab. p. 49; Brünn, 30, p. 187.   Sibirien.

5. *A. fimetarius*, Linné. Syst. Nat. Vol. 1, p. 348 (1758).   Europa.
    fimetarius, Olivier, Ent. Vol. 1 (3), p. 78, t. 18, f. 167 (1789).   Europa
      Erichson, Naturg. Ins. Deutschl. Vol. 3, p. 805 (1848).   Deutschland.
      Harold, Berl. Ent. Zeitschr. p. 332, 338 (1863).   Asien, Nordküste Afrikas, Nord-
      Mulsant, Hist. Nat. Col. France, Lamell. p 159 (1842).   Frankreich.   [amerika.
      Horn, Trans. Amer. Ent. Soc. Vol. 14, p. 11 (1887).   Osthälfte der Vereinigten Staaten
      Reitter, Tab. p. 48; Brünn, 30, p. 186.   Kaukasus, Nord- und Mittelasien.
      sec. Wickham, The Canad. Entom. Vol. 26, p. 205 (1894).   Kanada.
      sec. Bailey, Ent. M. Mag. p. 80 (1905).   Insel Man.
      sec. A. Schmidt, Aphodiinen-Zusammenst. Deutsche Ent.   Kaschmir.
        Zeitschr. Beih. p. 25, Anmerkung 1 (1907-08).
    pedellus, De Geer, Mém. Ins. Vol. 4, p. 266, t. 10, f. 8 (1774).   Frankreich.
    bicolor, Fourcroy, Ent. Paris, Vol. 1, p. 9 (1785).   Kaschmir.
      A. Schmidt, Aphodiinen-Zusammenst. Deutsche Ent. Zeitschr.
        Beih. p. 25, Anmerkung 2 (1907-08).
    nodifrons*, Randall, Boston. Journ. Vol. 2, p. 20.   Nordamerika.
    var: autumnalis*, Naezen, Vet.-Akad. Handl. p. 167 (1792).   Schlesien.
    orophilus, Charpentier, Hor. Ent. p. 210 (1825).   Frankreich.
    imperfectus, Mulsant, Hist. Nat. Col. France, Lamell. p. 187 (1842); p. 178
      (1871).
    var. monticola, Heer, Fauna Helv. Vol. 1, p. 513 (1841).   Schweiz.
    var. maculipennis, Mulsant, Hist. Nat. Col. France, Lamell. p. 187 (1842).   Frankreich.
    var. punctulatus, Mulsant, ibidem. p. 187 (1842).   Frankreich.
    var. subluteus, Mulsant, ibidem. p. 187 (1842).   Frankreich.
    var. hypopygialis, Mulsant, ibidem, p. 187 (1842).   Frankreich.
    var. bicolor, Mulsant. ibidem. p. 187 (1842).
    var. cinnamomeus, Harold. Berl. Ent. Zeitschr. p. 338 (1863).
    var. cardinalis, Reitter, Tab. p. 48; Brünn, 30, p. 186.   Syrien, Algier, Andalusien.
      d'Orbigny, L'Abeille, Vol. 28, p. 205, 259 (1896).   Frankreich.
    Biologie : Frisch Beschreib. Ins. Teutsch. Vol. 4; p. 35, t. 19, f. 1 (1722).
      — Beschreibung und Abbildung der Larve und Puppe.
      Mulsant, Hist. Nat. Col France, Lamell. p. 159 (1842); p. 150
        (1871). — Larve beschrieben.
      Erichson, Naturg. Ins. Deutschl. Vol. 3, p. 806 (1848). — Larve
        beschrieben.
      *Targioni-Tozzetti, Ann. Agric. Firenze-Roma, t. 1, f. 10. — Larve
        abgebildet.
      Kambeu, Rev. d'Ent. Caen, Vol. 20, p. 9 (1901). — Ei und Puppe
        beschrieben.

6. *A. foetens*, Fabricius, Mant. Ins. Vol. 1, p. 8 (1787).   Halle.
    foetens, Erichson, Naturg. Ins. Deutschl. Vol. 3, p. 804 (1848).   Deutschland.
      Harold, Berl. Ent. Zeitschr. p. 332, 339 (1863).   Europa, Vorderasien.
      Reitter. Tab. p. 47; Brünn, 30, p. 185.   Europa.
    fimetarius, var. γ, Laicharting, Verz. Tyr. Ins. Vol. 1, p. 12 (1781).   Tirol.
    ochraceus*, Stephens, Ill. Brit. Ent. Vol. 3, p. 191 (1830) (pars.).   England.
    rufiventris, Preller, Käf. Hamb. p. 75 (1862).   Holstein.
    var. vaccinarius, Herbst, Naturs. Ins. Vol. 2, p. 138, t. 12, f. 5 (1789).
    var. scrutator, Marsham, Ent. Brit. Vol. 1, p. 11 (1802).   England.
    var. fuscipes, Mulsant, Hist. Nat. Col. France, Lamell. p. 184 (1842).   Frankreich.
    var. nigricollis, Mulsant, ibidem, p. 184 (1842).   Frankreich.

var. *sanguinipennis*, Mulsant, Hist. Nat. Col. France, Lamell. p. 184 (1842). Frankreich.
var. *limbatus*, Dalla Torre, Ber. Ver. Nat. Oberösterr. Vol. 10, p. 107 (1879). Oberösterreich.
 Biologie : Heeger, Sitzber. Acad. Wissensch. Wien, 1854, Vol. 14 (1), p. 30,
 t. 2 (1855). — Vollständ. Entwicklungsgeschichte und Abbildung aller
 Stufen.

7. *A. frater*, Mulsant & Rey, Opuso. Ent. Vol. 14, p. 203 (1870); Ann. Batum.
 Soc. Linn. Lyon 1870-71, p. 171 (1872).
  frater, A. Schmidt, Aphodiinen-Zusammenst. Deutsche Ent. Zeitschr.
   Beih. p. 28, Anmerkung (1807-08).

8. *A. nigerrimus*, Waterhouse, Trans. Ent. Soc. Lond. p. 83 (1875). Japan.
  nigerrimus, Reitter, Tab. p. 49; Brünn, 30, p. 187. Korea.

9. *A. scybalarius*, Fabricius, Spec. Ins. Vol. 1, p. 16 (1781). Deutschland.
  scybalarius, Herbst, Natursyst. Ins. Vol. 2, p. 133, t. 12, f. 2 (1789).
   Erichson, Naturg. Ins. Deutschl. Vol. 3, p. 803 (1848). Deutschland.
   Harold, Berl. Ent. Zeitschr. p. 332, 342 (1863). Europa, Mittelmeerküste
   Reitter, Tab. p. 48; Brünn, 30, p. 186. Nordafrika, Kaukasus.
  conflagratus, Olivier, Ent. Vol. 1 (3), p. 80, t. 26, f. 220 (1789). Deutschland.
  foetidus, Herbst, Fuessly, Arch. Ins. Vol. 4, p. 7, t. 19, f. 6 (1783). Berlin.
  coprinus, Marsham, Ent. Brit. Vol. 1, p 12 (1802). England.
  var. *conflagratus*, Fabricius, Ent. Syst. Vol. 1, p. 27 (1792). Deutschland.
   Panzer, Fauna Germ. p. 47 (2) (1797). Deutschland.
  scybalarius, Olivier, Ent. Vol. 1 (3), p. 79, t. 26, f. 226 (1789).
  var. *dichrous*, W. Schmidt, Germar Zeitschr. Ent Vol. 2, p. 134 (1840). Triest, Eckernförde.
  fimetarius, var. β, Linné, Syst. Nat. Vol. 1, p. 348 (1758). Europa.
  argillicolor, Mulsant, Hist. Nat. Col. France, Lamell. p. 180 (1842). Frankreich.
  testaceus, Dalla Torre, Ber. Ver. Naturk. Oberösterr. Vol. 10, p. 107 (1879). Oberösterreich.
  fusca, Dalla Torre, ibidem, p. 107 (1879). Oberösterreich.
  var. *nigricans*, Mulsant, Hist. Nat. Col. France, Lamell. p. 179 (1842). Frankreich.
  var. *pallipes*, Mulsant, ibidem, p. 180 (1842). Frankreich.
  Biologie : Rosenhauer, Stett. Ent. Zeit. p. 22 (1882). — Larve beschrieben.

10. *A. sulcatus*, Fabricius, Ent. Syst. Vol. 1, p. 24 (1792). Deutschland.
  sulcatus, Sturm, Deutschl. Ins. Vol. 1, p. 120, t. 14, f. A (1805).
   Erichson, Naturg. Ins. Deutschl. Vol. 3, p. 807 (1848). Oesterreich.
   Harold, Col. Hefte, Vol. 7, p. 4, 8 (1871). Schweiz, Kaukasus.
   Reitter, Tab. p. 49; Brünn, 30, p. 187. Ungarn, Rufsland.
   A. Schmidt, Aphodiinen-Zusammenst. Deutsche Ent. Zeitschr.
   Beih. p. 28, Anmerkung (1907-08).
  var. *erythropterus*, d'Orbigny, L'Abeille, Vol. 28, p. 205 (1896).

11. *A. swaneticus*, Reitter, Tab. p. 48; Brünn, 30, p. 186. Kaukasus.

8. Subgenus LORAPHODIUS, Reitter

Loraphodius. Reitter, Best.-Tab. Eur. Col. Heft 24, p. 49 (1892); Verh. Naturf. Ver. Brünn, 1891, Vol. 30, p. 187 (1892).

 Charaktere. — Von der vorhergehenden Untergattung unterscheidet sich diese hauptsachlich durch eine flachere Form und das Fehlen eines Eindruckes am Vorderrande des Halsschildes.

 Der Körper ist wenig gewölbt, glänzend, unbehaart, von schwarzbrauner Farbe, die Flügel-decken sind etwas heller braun.

 Der nach vorn verschmälerte Kopf zeigt einen schwach ausgebuchteten Vorderrand, seitlich davon ist derselbe entweder mit oder ohne Zähnchen, seine Oberfläche ist dicht und sehr deutlich punktiert, die Stirnlinie zeigt nur geringe Spuren von Höckerchen.

 Das Halsschild ist quer, wenig gewölbt, gerandet (Seiten und Basis) und sehr deutlich punktiert, die Hinterwinkel sind lang abgestutzt und ausgerandet.

 Die Flügeldecken verbreitern sich kaum nach hinten, sie zeigen deutlich punktierte Streifen und flache Zwischenräume, dieselben sind einzeln fein punktiert und nach der Spitze zuweilen konvex.

 Das Schildchen ist klein, dreieckig, grob oder fein punktiert.

Die Unterseite ist glänzend, punktiert und behaart.

Die Borsten an den Hinterschienen sind kurz und dicht, nach dem obern Rande mit wenigen längeren dazwischen.

Der obere Enddorn ist fast gleich dem verlängerten ersten Gliede.

Geographische Verbreitung der Arten. — Die Heimat dieser Untergattung ist Frankreich, das südöstliche Europa und das südwestliche Asien.

1 *L latisulcus*, Reitter, Tab. p. 5o; Brünn, 3o, p. 188.	Kaukasus..
2. *L. suarius*, Faldermann, Fauna Transcauc, Vol. 1, p. 254 (1836).	Kaukasus. Dalmatien.
suarius, Reiche, Ann. Soc. Ent. Fr. p. 392 (1856).	Orient.
Harold, Berl. Ent. Zeitschr. p. 92 (1866).	Griechenland, Rumelien, Konstantinopel, Smyrna.
Reitter, Tab. p. 5o; Brünn, 3o, p. 188.	Türkei, Kleinasien, Syrien.
sec. Sietti, Bull. Soc. Ent. Fr. p. 80 (1905).	Frankreich.

9. Subgenus CALAMOSTERNUS, Motschulsky

Calamosternus. Motschulsky, Etud. Ent. p. 156 (1859).

Charaktere. — Der Körper ist meistens stark gewölbt, kurz, einfarbig schwarz oder braunrot, zuweilen sind die Flügeldecken hellgelbbraun mit dunkler Naht oder schwarz mit roter Längsbinde auf der Scheibe.

Der Kopf ist punktiert, seine Stirnlinie ist immer deutlich und mit drei Höckern geschmückt; die Wangen sind klein; der Clipeus ist ausgerandet und daneben verrundet.

Das Halsschild ist stark gewölbt, quer. vereinzelt grösser punktiert, seltener dichter und feiner, die Seiten und Basis sind immer gerandet.

Das Schildchen ist klein, vorn parallel und dann zugespitzt.

Die Flügeldecken sind parallel, deutlich punktiert-gestreift, die Zwischenräume sind eben, meistens nur vereinzelt und sehr fein punktiert.

Die Unterseite ist glänzend wie die Oberseite, die Seiten der Brust und das Abdomen sind punktiert und behaart.

Die Schenkel sind fast immer etwas heller, unpunktiert.

Die Borstenkränze an dem Spitzenrande der Hinterschienen sind kurz, gleichlang.

Der obere Enddorn ist meistens so lang als das erste Fussglied, selten wenig länger.

Der Metatarsus ist kurz, nicht viel länger als das zweite Glied.

Geographische Verbreitung der Arten. — Die Arten leben, abgesehen von *granarius* Linné, der in der ganzen Welt vorkommt, in Frankreich, Spanien, Italien, Nordafrika, auf den Kapverdischen- und Kanarischen Inseln, in Arabien und Transkaukasien.

1. *C. basilicatus*, Fiori, Il Natural. Sicil. Vol. 19, p. 118 (1907).	Norditalien.
2. *C. Clermonti*, Reitter, Deutsche Ent. Zeitschr. p. 407 (1907).	Transkaukasien.
3. *C. ferrugineus*, Mulsant, Hist. Nat. Col. France, Lamell. p. 233 (1842); p. 273 (1871).	Südfrankreich.
ferrugineus, Harold, Berl. Ent. Zeitschr. p, 258, 276 (1871).	Andalusien, Algier.
Reitter, Tab. p. 52; Brünn, 3o, p. 191.	Frankreich, Spanien, Marokko.
cognatus, Fairmaire, Ann. Soc. Ent. Fr. p. 172 (1860) (pars.).	Tanger, Arabien, Senegal.
4. *C. granarius*, Linné, Syst. Nat. (ed. 2), Vol. 1, p. 547 (1767).	Kosmopolit.
granarius, Olivier, Ent. Vol. 1 (3), p. 82, t. 18, f. 172 (1789).	
Illiger, Magaz. Ins. Vol. 2, p. 192 (1803).	Portugal.
Erichson, Naturg. Ins. Deutschl. Vol. 3, p. 813 (1848).	Deutschland.
Harold, Berl. Ent. Zeitschr p. 332, 347 (1863).	Ganze Erde.

Burmeister, Stett. Ent. Zeit. p. 404 (1877). — Argentinien.
Reitter, Tab. p. 51; Brünn, 3o, p. 189. — Ganze Erde.
haemorrhoidalis, De Geer, Mém. Ins. Vol. 4, p. 271 (1774).
Marsham, Ent. Brit. Vol. 1, p. 19 (1802). — England.
4-tuberculatus, Fabricius, Ent. Syst. Suppl. p. 23 (1798).
niger, Creutzer, Ent. Versuche, p. 20 (1799). — Wien.
Sturm, Verzeichn. Vol. 1, p. 47 (1800). — Nürnberg.
inquinatus, var. ζ, Illiger, Magaz. Ins. Vol. 1, p. 24 (1802). — Preussen.
carbonarius, Sturm, Naturg. Ins. Deutschl. Vol. 1, p. 128, t. 14, f. C (1805). — Nürnberg.
ater*, Thunberg, Mem. Acad. Petr. Vol. 6, p. 400 (1818).
haemorrhous*, Stephens, Illustr. Brit. Ent. Vol. 3, p. 196 (1830). — England.
lucens, Stephens, ibidem, p. 196 (1830). — England.
elongatus, Ménétriés, Cat. Rais. p. 182 (1832). — Baku.
Faldermann, Fauna Transcauc. Vol. 1, p. 260 (1836). — Transkaukasien.
sec. Reiche & Saulcy, Ann. Soc. Ent. Fr. p. 394 (1856).
retusus, Waltl, Reise n. Spanien, Vol. 2, p. 67 (1839). — Andalusien.
adelaidae, Hope, Proc. Ent. Soc. Lond. Vol. 4, p. 146 (1846); Trans. Ent. — Adelaïde, Neu-Holland.
Soc. Lond. Vol. 4, p. 284 (1847).
aterrimus, Melsheimer, Proc. Acad. Nat. Sc. Philad. 1844-45, Vol. 2, — Maryland.
p. 136 (1846).
metallicus, Haldemann, Journ. Acad. Nat. Sc. Philad (2), Vol. 1. p. 105 (1848). — Maryland.
Pervzi, Harold, Berl. Ent. Zeitschr., Beih. : Heyden, Reise n. Spanien, — Malaga, Mittelmeerländer.
p. 113 (1870); ibidem, p. 252 (1871).
sec. Reitter, Tab. p. 51; Brünn, 3o, p. 189.
nama, Kolbe, jenaische Denkschr. Vol. 13, p 126 (1908). — Klein-Namaland.
var. *emarginatus*, Stephens, Illustr. Brit. Ent. Vol. 3, p. 198 (1830).
var. *melanopus*, Stephens, ibidem, p. 198 (1830).
var. *suturalis*, Faldermann, Fauna Transcaucas. Vol. 1, p 259 (1836). — Transkaukasien.
sec. Harold, Col. Hefte, Vol. 5, p. 69 (1869).
vagus, Marseul, Nouv. et Faits, l'Abeille (2), Vol. 14-15, p. 56 (1878). — Algier.
sec. d'Orbigny, L'Abeille, Vol. 28, p. 211 (1876).
var. *parcepunctatus*, ♂, Mulsant, Hist. Nat. Col. France, Lamell. p. 199 (1842). — Frankreich.
var. *cribratus*, ♀, Mulsant, ibidem, p. 199 (1842). — Frankreich.
var. *rugosulus*, Mulsant, ibidem, p. 199 (1842). — Frankreich.
var. *moestus*, Mulsant, ibidem, p. 199 (1842). — Frankreich.
basilaris, Dalla Torre, Ber. Ver. Naturk. Oberösterr. Vol. 10, p. 107 (1879). — Oberösterreich.
sec. Schilsky, Deutsche Ent. Zeitschr. p. 319 (1888).
concolor, Mulsant, Hist. Nat. Col. France, Lamell. p. 199 (1842). — Frankreich.
spretus, Haldemann, Journ. Acad Nat. Sc. Philad. (2), Vol. 1, p. 106 (1848). — Mittelstaaten.
sec. Horn. Trans. Amer. Ent. Soc. Vol. 14, p. 107 (1887).
var. *thoracicus*, Dalla Torre, Ber. Ver. Naturk. Oberösterr Vol. 10, p 107 (1879). — Guadeloupe.
var. *guadeloupensis*, Fleutiaux & Sallé, Ann. Soc. Ent. Fr. p. 396 (1889). — Araxes, Syrien, Ungarn.
var. *brunnescens*, Reitter, Tab. p. 51; Brünn, 3o, p. 189.
var. *Ragusanus*, Reitter, nom. nov. Catal. Col. Eur. p. 718 (1906).
apicalis || Ragusa, Il Natur. Sicil. Vol. 12, p. 8 (1892). — Sizilien.
Biologie : *Schioedte, Naturh. Tidsskr. Vol. 9. p. 327 (1874).—Larve beschrieben.
*Xambeu, L'Echange, Lyon, p. 1 (1892). — Larve und Puppe
beschrieben.
sec. Wiegmann, Arch. f. Naturg. Bericht 1894, p. 504 (1897).

5. **C. lucidus**, Klug, Symb. Phys. Vol. 5, n° 2, t. 42, f. 1 (1842). — Aegypten, Kapverdische
lucidus, Harold, Berl. Ent. Zeitschr. p. 253 (1871). — Nordküste Afrikas. [Inseln.
Reitter, Tab. p. 52; Brünn, 3o, p. 190. — Arabien, Turkestan.
taeniatus, Wollaston, Cat. Col. Canar. p. 189 (1864); Col. Atlant. p. 177 (1865). — Kanarische Inseln.
sec. Harold. Berl. Ent. Zeitschr. p. 254 (1871).

6. **C. tricornifrons**, Reitter, Wien. Ent. Zeit. Vol. 28, p. 76 (1909). — Uralsk.

7. **C. trucidatus**, Harold, Berl. Ent. Zeitschr. p. 332, 351 (1863). — Kurdistan.
trucidatus, Reitter. Tab. p. 51; Brünn, 3o, p. 189. — Syrien, Armenien, Astrachan.
sec. Heyden, Reise Spanien, Beih. Berl. Ent. Zeitschr. p. 113 — Griechenland, Spanien.
(1870).
sec. Harold, Berl. Ent. Zeitschr. p. 253 (1871). — Kleinasien, Cypern, Andalusien,
rutilipennis, Harold, ibidem, p. 253 (1871). — [Algier.
var. *suturifer*, Reitter, Tab. p. 51; Brünn, 3o, p. 189. — Transkaspien.

10. Subgenus ERYTUS, Mulsant

Erytus, Mulsant, Hist. Nat. Col. France, Lamell. p. 273 (1871).

Charaktere. — Die längliche, flache Gestalt und die verlängerten Tarsen zeichnen diese Untergattung aus.

Der Körper ist gelbbraun gefärbt, glänzend, seltener matt, er ist entweder unbehaart oder mit sehr feinen und kurzen Härchen an den Seiten und vor der Spitze besetzt.

Der Kopf ist flach, feiner oder stärker punktiert, am Vorderrande ausgebuchtet, seitlich davon verrundet, die Stirnlinie ist immer deutlich, sie zeigt zuweilen schwache Spuren von Höckern; die Wangen sind klein.

Das Halsschild ist quer, wenig herabgewölbt, stärker oder feiner punktiert. die Seiten und Basis sind gerandet, letztere zuweilen sehr fein, wenig sichtbar.

Das Schildchen ist klein, parallel an der Basis.

Die Flügeldecken sind langgestreckt. parallel, nur bei *sitiphoides* d'Orbigny kürzer und mehr konvex, sie sind meistens fein gestreift, selten stärker, dann aber mit deutlich punktierten Streifen, die Zwischenräume sind flach, zuweilen dicht und fein punktiert.

Die Unterseite ist fein punktiert, das Abdomen länger behaart als die Seiten.

Die Beine sind schlank, die Tarsen sind länger als die Schienen; die Borstenkränze an den Hinterschienen sind kurz und gleichlang.

Geographische Verbreitung der Arten. — Ural, Transkaukasien, Transkaspien, Turkestan, Persien, Syrien, Arabien, Nubien, Nordküste Afrikas.

1. *E. aequalis,* A. Schmidt. Deutsche Ent. Zeitschr. p 201 (1907), nom. nov.   Chodshent.
   nitidus || Ballion, Bull. Soc. Nat. Mosc. 1870. Vol. 43 (2), p. 333 (1871).   Sarafschan-Tal, Kisil-kum.
   Solsky, Fedtschenko Turkest. Col. p. 323 (1876).   Turke-tan, Transkaukasien, Sy-
   Reitter, Tab. 24, p. 53; Brünn, 30, p. 191.   Ural.   [rien.
   Reitter, Cat. Col. Europ. p. 718 (1906).
2. *E. Chobauti* 1), Clouët, Bull. Soc. Ent. Fr. p. 371 (1896).   Algier.
3. *E. opacior,* Koshantschikow. Hor. Soc. Ent. Ross. 1893-94, Vol. 28,   Algier.
   p. 102 (1894), nom. nov.   Tunis.
   opacus || Reitter, Tab. p. 53; Brünn, 30, p 191.
   d'Orbigny, L'Abeille, Vol. 28, p. 217 (1896).
4. *E. pruinosus,* Reitter, Tab. p. 53; Brünn, 30, p. 191.   Transkaspien, Turkestan,
   brunneus || Klug, Symb. Phys. Vol. 5, n° 6, t. 42, f. 6 (1845).   Nubien.   [Persien.
   Harold, Berl. Ent. Zeitschr. p. 258, 285 (1871).   Portugal, Andalusien, Algier,
            Aegypten, Arabien, Turkestan,
            Syrien.
   Reitter, Tab. p. 53, Brünn. 30, p. 191.   Nordafrika, Kaukasien, Trans-
   sec. Clouët, Bull. Soc. Ent. Fr. p. 187 (1898).   [kaspien, Türkei.
   sec. A. Schmidt, Deutsche Ent. Zeitschr. p. 201 (1907).
   unicolor, Lucas, Explor. Algér. Ent. Vol. 2, p. 264 (1849).   Oran.
   cognatus, Fairmaire, Ann. Soc. Ent. Fr. p. 172 (1860) (pars).   Tanger, Arabien, Senegal.
5. *E. sitiphoides,* d'Orbigny, Bull. Soc. Ent. Fr. p. 149 (1896).   Algier, Tunis.
   sitiphoides, d'Orbigny, L'Abeille, Vol. 28, p. 217 (1896).   Tunis.

11. Subgenus BODILUS, Mulsant

Bodilus. Mulsant, Hist. Nat. Col. France, Lamell. p. 278 (1871).

Charaktere. — Der Körper ist länglich, flach gewölbt, aber weniger schmal als bei der vorher-

---

1) Die Art ist vielleicht richtiger in der Untergattung *Mendidius* untergebracht.

gehenden Untergattung, er ist gleichmässig gelb- oder mehr rotbraun gefärbt, das Halsschild ist in der Mitte meistens dunkler, die Seiten bleiben immer breit heller, die Flügeldecken sind einfarbig, nur sehr selten mit einigen kleinen dunklen Flecken oder ebensolcher Längsmakel auf der Scheibe.

Die Oberfläche ist glänzend, sehr selten die ganzen Flügeldecken oder nur ihre Spitze matt, letztere und die Seiten zeigen manchmal eine äusserst kurze und feine Behaarung.

Der Kopf ist kurz und breit, wenig gewölbt und punktiert, die Stirnlinie zwischen den Augen ist deutlich, der schwach ausgerandete Clipeus zeigt abgerundete Ecken; die Wangen sind klein.

Das Halsschild ist quer, wenig herabgewölbt, mit Randung an den Seiten und der Basis. zuweilen auch am Vorderrande.

Das Schildchen ist klein, dreieckig, vorn nicht parallel, vereinzelt punktiert, dunker als die Grundfarbe.

Die punktiert-gestreiften Flügeldecken sind nach hinten wenig verbreitert, ihre Zwischenräume sind höchst selten deutlich gewölbt und stärker und dicht punktiert.

Die Unterseite ist glänzend, auch bei den matten Arten, die Seiten der Brust und die Bauchsegmente sind punktiert und behaart.

Die Borsten am Spitzenrande der Hinterschienen sind kurz und gleichlang; der obere Enddorn der letzteren ist etwas länger oder so lang als das erste Glied, dieses ist fast immer so lang als die drei folgenden Glieder.

Bei den Männchen ist der Kopf deutlich dreihöckerig, das Halsschild ist breiter als die Flügeldecken und in der Mitte fast unpunktiert.

Die Weibchen zeigen auf der Stirnnaht nur schwache Spuren von Höckerchen, das Halsschild ist von der Breite der Flügeldecken. viel dichter punktiert, auch auf der Scheibe.

Geographische Verbreitung der Arten. — Das ganze Europa, Kanarische Inseln, Madeira, Nordküste Afrikas, Choa, Kleinasien, Syrien, Nord- und Mittelasien. Japan, Yünnan.

1. *B. digitalis*, Koshantschikow, Hor. Soc. Ent. Ross. 1893-94, Vol. 28, p. 102 (1894), nom. nov.

    digitatus ‖ Reitter, Tab. p. 225; Brünn, 31, p. 104 (nec. Harold).   Turkestan

2. *B. Holderi*, Reitter, Wien. Ent. Zeit. p. 155, t. 1, f. 1 (1900).   Kuku-noor.

3. *B. hydrochoeris*, Fabricius, Ent. Syst. Suppl. p. 23 (1798).   Tanger.

    hydrochoeris, Ahrens, Neue Schrift. Naturf. Ges. Halle, Vol. 2, p. 26, t. 1, f. 13 (1812).   Magdeburg.

    Erichson, Naturg. Ins. Deutschl. Vol. 3, p. 820 (1848).   Mitteldeutschland.

    Harold, Berl. Ent. Zeitschr p. 97, 113 (1866).   Mittel- und Südeuropa.

    Reitter, Tab. p. 54; Brünn, 30, p. 192.   Nordafrika, Syrien, Kaukasus

    meridionalis*, Villa, Col Eur. Dupl. Suppl. p. 48 (1835).   Italien.   [bis Ostsibirien.

    sec. Harold, Col. Hefte, Vol. 6, p. 106 (1870).

    sec. Wollaston, Cat. Col. Canar. p. 187 (1864).   Kanarische Inseln.

    var. *tataricus*, Harold, Berl. Ent. Zeitschr. p 114, 115 (1866).   Krim.

    var. *coloratus*, Mulsant, Hist. Nat. Col France, Lamell. p. 218 (1842).   Frankreich.

    var. *discicollis*, Mulsant, ibidem, p. 218 (1842).

    var. *germanus*, Mulsant, ibidem, p. 218 (1842).

4. *B. immundus*, Creutzer, Ent. Versuche, p. 57, t. 1, f. 9 (1799).   Wien.

    immundus, Erichson, Naturg. Ins. Deutschl. Vol. 3, p. 827 (1848).   Deutschland.

    Harold, Berl. Ent. Zeitschr. p. 96, 112 (1866).   Mittel- und Südeuropa, Syrien, Kleinasien, Aegypten.

    Reitter, Tab. p. 57; Brünn, 30, p. 195.   Sibirien, Russland, Turkestan.

    var. *fulvicollis*, Mulsant, Hist. Nat. Col. France, Lamell. p. 227 (1842).   Frankreich.

    var. *melinopleurus*, Mulsant, ibidem, p. 227 (1842).   Frankreich.

5. *B. longeciliatus*, Reitter, Hor. Soc. Ent Ross. Vol. 21, p. 207, 222 (1887); Tab. p. 55; Brünn. 30, p. 193.   Tibet, Zentralasien.

6. *B. longispina*. Küster Käf. Europ. Vol. 28, p. 33 (1854).   Südspanien.

    longispina, Reitter, Tab. p. 56; Brünn, 30, p. 194.   Algier, Marokko.

beduinus, Reitter, Tab. p. 55; Brünn, 3o, p. 193.　　　　　　　Marokko, Sizilien.
　　　　sec. Clouët, Bull. Soc. Ent. Fr. p. 187 (1898).
　　　　sec. Maindron, ibidem, p. 314 (1904).　　　　　　　　　　Frankreich.
7. *B. lugens*, Creutzer, Ent. Versuche, p. 59, t. 1, f. 10 (1799).　　　Oesterreich.
　　　lugens, W. Schmidt, Germars Zeitschr. f. Ent. Vol. 2, p. 140 (1840).　Pommern, Bayern.
　　　　Erichson, Naturg. Ins. Deutschl. Vol. 3, p. 825 (1848).　Deutschland, Sizilien, Orient.
　　　　Harold. Berl. Ent. Zeitschr. p. 96. 107 (1866).　　　Europa, Nordafrika.
　　　　Reitter, Tab. p. 56; Brünn, 3o, p. 194.　　　　　　Kaukasus, Turkestan.
　　　*Faldermanni**. Sperk, Bull. Soc. Nat. Mosc. Vol. 8, p. 157 (1835).　Südrussland.
　　　nigriventris, Reitter, Tab. p. 56; Brünn, 3o, p. 194.　　Kuldscha.
　　　　sec. Clouët, Bull. Soc. Ent. Fr. p. 187 (1898).
　　　var. emarginalis, Mulsant, Hist. Nat. Col. France, Lamell. p. 225 (1842).　Frankreich.
　　　var. indecorus, Mulsant, ibidem, p. 225 (1842).　　　Frankreich.
8. *B. nasutus*, Reitter, Hor. Soc. Ent. Ross. Vol. 21, p. 221 (1887).　Tibet.
9. *B. nitidulus*, Fabricius, Ent. Syst. Vol. 1, p. 3o (1792).　　Europa.
　　　nitidulus, Sturm, Deutschl. Ins. Vol. 1, p. 95 (1805).　　Deutschland.
　　　　*Stephens, Illustr. Brit. Ent. Vol. 3, p. 192 (1830).　England.
　　　　Erichson, Naturg. Ins. Deutschl. Vol. 3, p. 826 (1848).·　Deutschland.
　　　　Harold. Berl. Ent. Zeitschr p. 97. 117 (1866) .　　Westasien, Nordafrika.
　　　　Reitter, Tab. p. 56; Brünn, 3o, p. 194.　　　　Syrien, Kaukasus.
　　　merdarius, Panzer, Fauna Germ. p 48 3) (1797).　　Deutschland.
　　　ictericus, Paykull, Fauna Suec. Vol. 1, p. 17 (1798).　Schweden.
　　　　Creutzer, Ent. Versuche. p. 52, t. 1, f. 8a (1799).　Oesterreich.
　　　　Duftschmid, Fauna Austr. Vol. 1, p 105 (1805).
　　　*sordidus**, Brullé, Webb & Bertholet, Canar. Ent. p. 60 (1838).　Canarische Inseln, Madeira.
　　　gilvus, W. Schmidt, Germar Zeitschr. f. Ent. Vol. 2, p. 136 (1840).　Pommern,.Sachsen, Hessen.
10. *B. obsoletus*, Waterhouse, Trans. Ent. Soc. Lond. p. 88 (1875).　China, Japan
11. *B. punctipennis*, Erichson, Naturg. Ins. Deutschl. Vol 3, p. 821　Südrussland, Aegypten.
　　　(1848).
　　　punctipennis, Harold, Berl. Ent. Zeitschr. p. 96, 104 (1866).　Kaukasus.
　　　　Reitter, Tab. p. 54; Brünn, 3o, p. 192.　　　　Ungarn, Derbent, Turkmenien.
　　　intermedius, Ballion, Bull. Soc. Nat. Mosc. 1870, Vol. 43 (2), p. 332 (1871).　Chodshent.　　　[Turkestan.
　　　incertus, Ballion, ibidem, Vol. 53 (1), p. 282 (1878).　Kuldsha.
　　　　sec. Reitter, Tab. p. 54; Brünn, 3o, p. 192.
12. *B. rufus*, Moll, Fuessly, Neu. Mag. Vol. 1, p. 372 (1782).　Salzburg.
　　　rufus, Reitter, Tab. p. 55; Brünn, 3o, p. 193.　　　Europa.
　　　rufescens, Fabricius, Syst. Eleuth. Vol. 1, p. 74 (1801).　Nordeuropa.
　　　　Erichson, Naturg. Ins. Deutschl. Vol. 3, p. 823 (1848).　Deutschland.
　　　　Harold, Berl Ent. Zeitschr p. 96, 101 (1866).　　Nord- und Mitteleuropa.
　　　sordidus. var. γ. Illiger, Verz. Käf. Preuss. p. 32 (1798).
　　　unicolor, Marsham, Ent. Brit. Vol. 1, p. 11 (1802).　　England.
　　　*ochraceus**. Stephens. Ill. Brit. Ent. Vol. 3, p. 191 (1830) (pars).　England.
　　　aurantiacus, Mulsant, Hist. Nat. Col. France, Lamell. p. 221 (1842).　Frankreich.
　　　*rufifrons**, Dufour, Actes Soc. Linn Bordeaux, p. 334 (1851).
　　　moscoviticus, Semenow, Hor. Soc. Ent. Ross. Vol. 34,·, p. 91 (1900).　Mittelrussland.
　　　　Semenow, Rev. Russe d'Ent. Vol. 4, p. 37 (1904).
　　　　sec. Reitter, Cat. Col. Eur. p. 719 (1906).
　　　var. arcuatus, Moll, Naturh Brief. üb. Oesterr. Vol. 1, p. 103, 160 (1785).　Alpen.
　　　foetens, Olivier, Ent. Vol. 1 (3), p. 85, t. 9, f. 71 (1789).　Südfrankreich.
　　　sordidus, var. δ, Illiger, Verz. Käf. Preuss. p. 22 (1798).　Argentinien.
　　　hypocyphthus. W. Schmidt, Germars Zeitschr. f. Ent Vol. 2, p. 139 (1840).　Yünnan.
　　　hypocophus, Heer, Fauna Col. Helv. Vol. 1 p 523 (1841).　Alpen.
　　　sordidus, var. H, Mulsant, Hist. Nat. Col. France, Lamell. p. 222 (1842).
　　　var. castaneus, Marsham, Ent Brit. p. 12 (1802).　　England.
　　　var. melanotus, Mulsant, Hist. Nat. Col. France, Lamell. p. 222 (1842).
　　　sordidus, var. ε, Illiger, Verz. Käf. Preuss. p. 33 (1798).
　　　var. piceola, Semenow, Hor. Soc. Ent. Ross. Vol 34, p. 92 (1900).
　　　　sec. Harold. Verh. Naturf. Ver. Brünn, Vol. 16, p, 188 (1877).　Kaukasus.
Biologie : Rosenhauer, Stett. Ent. Zeit. p. 19 (1882). — Larve und Puppe
　　　beschrieben.
　　　　Xambeu, Ann. Soc. Linn. Lyon, Vol. 42, p. 70 (1895). —Larve und
　　　Puppe beschrieben.

13. *B. sordescens,* Harold, L'Abeille, Vol. 5, p. 431 (1869); Berl. Ent.   Sibirien.
    Zeitschr. p. 255 (1871).
      sordescens, Reitter, Tab. p. 56; Brünn, 30, p. 194.   Kiachta.
14. *B. sordidus.* Fabricius, Syst. Ent. p. 16 (1775); Spec. Ins. Vol. 1, p. 17 (1781).   England.
     sordidus, Paykull, Fauna Suec. p. 12 (1798).   Schweden.
      Illiger, Verz. Käf. Preuss. p. 32 (1798).   Preussen.
      Erichson, Naturg. Ins. Deutschl. Vol. 3, p. 822 (1848).   Deutschland.
      Harold, Berl. Ent. Zeitschr. p. 96, 97 (1866).   Europa, Asien bis Sibirien.
      Reitter, Tab. p, 54; Brünn, 30, p. 192.   Kaukasus.
    var. quadripunctatus, Panzer, Einige selt. Ins. beschr. (Coleoptera) in Natur-   Deutschland.
      forscher, Stück 24, p. 4, t. 1, f. 4 (1789).
      Uddman, Nov. Ins. Spec. p. 6 (1753).
      Waterhouse, Trans. Ent. Soc. Lond. p. 83 (1875).   Japan.
     sordidus, var. ♂, Illiger, Verz. Käf. Preuss. p. 32 (1798).
    var. limbatellus, Mulsant, Hist. Nat. Col. France, Lamell. p. 221 (1842).   Frankreich.
    var. bipunctatellus, Mulsant, ibidem, p. 221 (1842).   Frankreich.
     sordidus, var. γ, Creutzer, Ent. Versuche, p. 51 (1799).
     Creutzeri, Dalla Torre, Ber. Ver. Oberösterr Vol. 10, p. 107 (1879).   Oberösterreich.
      sec. Schilsky, Deutsche Ent. Zeitschr. p. 319 (1888).
    var. nigromaculatus, A. Schmidt, Soc. Ent. Zürich, 1909-10, Vol. 24, p. 20 (1909).   Yünnan.
15. *B. tabaeus,* Peyerimhoff, L'Abeille, Vol. 31, p. 45 ( ).   Sinai.
16. *B. Wollastoni,* Harold, Berl. Ent. Zeitschr. p. 397 (1862).   Kanarische Inseln, Algier.
     Wollastoni, Wollaston, Cat. Col. Canar. p. 188 (1864).   Kanarische Inseln.

12. SUBGENUS AGRILINUS, MULSANT

Agrilinus. Mulsant, Hist. Nat. Col. France, Lamell. p. 179 (1871).

Planolinus. Mulsant. ibidem, p. 186 (1871).

Parammœcius. Seidlitz, Fauna Balt. p. 133 (1891) (pars).

    Charaktere. — Die Arten dieser Untergattung haben einen weniger verlängerten, meist kürzeren Körper von schwarzer Grundfarbe, das Halsschild ist selten an den Seiten etwas heller gefärbt, die Flügeldecken sind zuweilen rot oder rotgefleckt.

    Der Kopf ist nach vorn gerundet-verschmälert, punktiert, mit Stirnlinie und oft noch mit deutlichem Querkiel hinter dem Vorderrande, der Clipeus ist ausgerandet, jederseits abgerundet oder mit scharfer, aufgebogener Ecke.

    Das Halsschild ist quer, meistens deutlich herabgewölbt. an den Seiten und der Basis gerandet, zuweilen auch hinter dem Vorderrande, die Hinterwinkel sind stumpf, die Oberfläche ist feiner oder stärker punktiert. die Punkte sind entweder in der Grösse ziemlich gleich oder sehr verschieden.

    Das Schildchen ist dreieckig, vorn nicht parallel, punktiert, schwarz.

    Die Flügeldecken sind bald parallel, bald nach hinten deutlich verbreitert, meistens glänzend und fein punktiert-gestreift, die Zwischenräume sind eben oder schwach gewölbt, bald fein und einzeln, bald dichter und stärker punktiert, selten haben sie einen Schulterzahn.

    Die Unterseite ist schwarz und glänzend, die Seiten der Brust und der Bauch sind punktiert und behaart.

    Die Borsten an den Hinterschienen sind kurz und gleichlang.

    Der obere Enddorn ist meistens kaum so lang als das erste Glied, dieses ist verlängert und gewöhnlich die zwei folgenden Glieder an Länge überragend.

    Die Männchen haben entweder einen starken, oben ausgerandeten oder drei deutliche Höcker, seltener sind dieselben nur angedeutet, dann ist aber der Enddorn an den Vordertibien abgestutzt, die Metasternalplatte ist immer breit vertieft.

    Die Weibchen haben meistens nur sehr schwache Höckerchen, der Enddorn ist immer spitz und die Metasternalplatte ist nicht vertieft, höchstens mit feiner Mittellinie versehen.

Geographische Verbreitung der Arten. — Ganz Europa, Algier, Nord- und Mittelasien, Nordamerika, Mexiko.

1. *A. aleutus**, Eschscholtz, Entomographien, Vol. 1, p. 27 (1822).   Unalaschka.
   aleutus, Mannerheim, Bull. Soc. Nat. Mosc. Vol. 16 (2), p. 261 (1843).   Unalaschka.
     Harold, Berl. Ent Zeitschr. p. 333, 372 (1863).   Unalaschka.
     Horn, Trans. Amer. Ent. Soc. Vol. 14, p. 12 (1887).   Westliches Nordamerika.
   var. ursinus, Motschulsky, Bull. Soc. Nat. Mosc. Vol. 18 (4), p. 365, t. 6, f. 6 (1845).   Kamtschatka.
     Mannerheim, ibidem, Vol. 26 (2), p. 218 (1853).   Halbinsel Kenai.
     Harold, Berl. Ent. Zeitschr. p. 334, 386 (1863).   Jakutsk.
     Horn, Trans. Amer. Ent. Soc. p. 118 (1870); Vol. 14, p. 13 (1887).   Alaska.

2. *A. ascendens*, Reiche, Grenier, Cat. Col. France, p. 75 (1863).   Südfrankreich, Pyrenäen.
   ascendens, Mulsant, Hist. Nat. Col. France, Lamell. p. 182 (1871).   Südfrankreich, Pyrenäen.
   adscendens, var., Reitter, Tab. p. 59; Brünn, 30, p. 197.   Bosnien, Kaukasus.
     sec. Pauvel, Rev. d'Ent. Caen, p. 110 (1895).
     A. Schmidt, Aphodiinen-Zusammenst. Deutsche Ent.
     Zeitschr. Beih. p. 5, Anmerkung 2 (1907-1908).

3. *A. ater*, De Geer, Mém. Ins. Vol. 4, p. 270 (1774).
   ater, Fabricius, Ent. Syst. Vol. 1, p. 26 (1792) (pars).   Kiel.
     Illiger, Verz. Käf. Preuss p. 19 (1798).   Preussen.
     Sturm, Deutschl. Ins. Vol. 1, p. 122 (1805).   Deutschland.
     Erichson, Naturg. Ins. Deutschl. Vol. 3, p. 808 (1848).   Deutschland.
     Harold, Berl. Ent. Zeitschr. p. 333, 358 (1863).   Europa, Westasien.
     Reitter, Tab. p. 59; Brünn, 30, p. 197; Hor. Soc. Ent. Ross. Vol. 21,   Nord- und Mitteleuropa, Tibet,
       p. 206 (1887).   Amur.
   terrestris, Fabricius, Syst. Ent. p. 15 (1875).   England.
     Sturm, Deutschl. Ins. Vol. 1, p. 118, t. 13, f. C (1805).   Tuttlingen.
     W. Schmidt, Germar, Zeitschr Ent. Vol. 2, p. 97 (1840).   Pommern, Bayern, Oesterreich.
   obscurus, Marsham, Ent. Brit. Vol. 1, p. 18 (1802).   England.
     *Stephens, Ill. Brit. Ent. Vol. 3, p. 195 (1830).   England.
   var. convexus, Erichson, Naturg. Ins. Deutschl. Vol. 3, p. 810 (1848).   Oesterreich, Tirol, Erlangen.
     Harold, Berl. Ent. Zeitschr. p. 358 (1863).
     Mulsant, Hist. Nat. Col. France, Lamell. p. 182 (1871).   Oesterreich, Deutschland.
   var. Lucasi, Harold, Berl. Ent. Zeitschr p. 224 (1859).
   affinis ‖ Lucas, Explor. Algér. Ent. Vol. 2, p. 261, t. 24, f. 1 (1849).   Algier.
     Harold, Col. Hefte, Vol. 5, p. 69 (1869).
   var. pusillus, Mar ham, Ent. Brit. Vol. 1, p. 18 (1802).   England.
   terrenus, Stephens, Ill. Brit. Ent. Vol. 3, p. 195 (1830).   England.
     Mulsant, Hist. Nat. Col. France, Lamell. p. 196 (1842).   Frankreich.
   var. falsarius, Reitter, Tab. p. 59; Brünn, 30, p. 197.   Kaukasus.
     A. Schmidt, Aphodiinen-Zusammenst. Deutsche Ent. Zeitschr.
     Beih. p. 6, Anmerkung (1907-08).
   Biologie: °Xambeu, Mœurs et Métam. Ins. 6. Mém. Suppl. Echang. p. 14 (1894).
     — Beschreibung der Verwandlungsstadien.
     sec. Wiegmann, Arch. f. Naturg. Ber. 1894, p 504 (1897).

4. *A. borealis*, Gyllenhal, Ins. Suec. Vol. 4, p. 248 (1827).   Lappland.
   borealis, Harold, Berl. Ent. Zeitschr. p. 333, 365 (1863).   Sibirien.
     Reitter, Tab. p. 62; Brunn, 30, p. 200.   Nord- und Mitteleuropa, Kauka-
   putridus ‖ Sturm, Deutschl. Ins. Vol. 1, p. 125, t. 14, f. B (1805).   Wien.   [sus.
     Harold, Berl. Ent. Zeitschr. p. 333, 367 (1863).   Frankreich, Schweden, England.
     Erichson, Naturg. Ins. Deutschl. Vol. 3, p. 818 (1848).   Oesterreich.
   sedulus, Harold, Col. Hefte, Vol. 8, p. 119 (1871).
     sec. Reitter, Tab. p. 62; Brünn, 30, p. 200.
   var. Gyllenhali, Seidlitz, Fauna Transsylv. p. 143 (1891).   Europa.

5. *A. constans*, Duftschmid, Fauna Austr. Vol. 1, p. 94 (1805).   Wien.
   constans, Erichson, Naturg. Ins. Deutschl. Vol. 3, p. 811 (1848).   Oesterreich.
     Harold, Berl. Ent. Zeitschr. p. 333, 357 (1863).   Südeuropa.
     Reitter, Tab. p. 60; Brünn, 30, p. 199.   Mittel- und Südeuropa
   nitidus*, Stephens, Ill. Brit. Ent. Vol. 3, p. 196 (1830).   England.
   nomas, Kolenati, Melet, Ent. Vol. 5, p. 14 (1846).   Russisch-Armenien.
   melanopus, Hardy, Ann. Mag. Nat. Hist. Vol. 19, p. 382 (1847).   England.
   vernus, Mulsant, Hist. Nat. Col. France, Lamell. p. 193 (1842); p. 184 (1871).   Frankreich.
   exiguus, Mulsant, ibidem, p. 210 (1842).   Frankreich.
     sec. Reitter, Tab. p. 60; Brünn, 30, p. 199.

var. martialis, Mulsant, Hist. Nat. Col. France, Lamell. p. 193 (1842).   Frankreich.
    Biologie : Perris, Ann. Soc. Linn. Lyon. 1875, Vol. 22, p. 368 (1876). — Larve
        kurz erwähnt.
    Kambeu, Rev. d'Ent. Caen, Vol. 20, p. 27 (1901). — Ei von *vernus*
        Mulsant.
    Xambeu, Ann. Soc. Linn. Lyon, 1898, Vol. 45, p. 33 (1899). — Larve
        beschrieben.

6. *A. gibbus,* Germar, Fauna Ins. Europa, Vol. 3 (2) (1817).   Oesterreich.
    gibbus, W. Schmidt, Germar Zeitschr. Ent. Vol. 2, p. 111 (1840).   Oesterreich.
    Erichson, Naturg. Ins. Deutschl. Vol. 3, p. 908 (1848).   Oesterreich.
    Harold, Col. Hefte. Vol. 7, p. 3, 7 (1871).   Schweiz, Riesengebirge.
    Reitter, Tab. p. 59; Brünn, 30, p. 197.   Gebirge Mitteleuropas.
    sec. *Strand, Arch. Math. Nat. Vol. 24, p.? (1904) (Wiegm.   Norwegen.
        Bericht 1904, p. 227 [1906]).
    anthracinus, W. Schmidt, Germar Zeitschr. Ent. Vol. 2, p. 111 (1840).   Illyrien.
    transsylvanicus, Küster, Käf. Europ. Vol. 18, p. 54 (1849).   Siebenbürgen.
    sec. Reitter, Tab. p. 59; Brünn, 30, p. 197.

7. *A. lapponum,* Gyllenhal in Schönherr, Syn. Ins. Vol. 1, p. 72 (1806).   Lappland.
    lapponum, Harold, Berl. Ent. Zeitschr. p. 333, 369 (1863).   Sibirien, Nordschottland.
    Reitter, Tab. p. 62; Brünn, 30, p. 200.   Nordeuropa.
    subalpinus, Hardy, Ann. Mag. Nat. Hist. Vol. 19, p. 380 (1847).   England.
    var. axillaris,* Stephens, Man. Brit. Col. p. 162 (1839).   England.

8. *A. monticola,* Mulsant, Hist. Nat. Col. France, Lamell. p. 215 (1842).   Frankreich.

9. *A. nemoralis,* Erichson, Naturg. Ins. Deutschl. Vol. 3, p. 816 (1848).   Thüringen.
    nemoralis, Harold, Berl. Ent. Zeitschr. p. 334, 377 (1863).   Mittel- und Süddeutschland.
    Reitter, Tab. p. 58; Brünn, 30, p. 196   Deutschland, Oesterreichische
    var. ferrugineus, Schilsky, Deutsche Ent. Zeitschr. p. 309 (1888).   München.   [Alpen.
    Biologie : Rosenhauer, Stett. Ent.Zeit. p.22 (1882).—Larve, Puppe beschrieben.

10. *A. obliviosus,* Reitter, Tab. p. 61; Brünn, 30, p. 199.   Chinesisch-Turkestan.

11. *A. orophilus,* Mulsant & Rey, Opusc. Ent. Vol. 14, p. 206 (1870); Ann.   Kaukasus.
    Soc. Linn. Lyon, 1870-71, p. 174 (1872).

12. *A. piceus,* Gyllenhal, Ins. Suec. Vol. 1 (1), p. 21 (1808).   Lappland.
    piceus, W. Schmidt, Germar Zeitschr. Ent. Vol. 2, p. 114 (1840).   Passau.
    Heer, Fauna Col. Helv. Vol. 1, p. 515 (1841).   Schweiz. [Schweden, Finnland.
    Harold, Berl. Ent. Zeitschr. p. 334, 382 (1863).   Oesterr. - Schlesien, Savoyen,
    Reitter, Tab. p. 59; Brünn, 30. p. 197.   Nord- und Mitteleuropa.
    sec. A. Schmidt, Aphodiinen-Zusammenst. Deutsche Ent. Zeitschr.   Altai.
        Beih. p. 57 (1907-08).
    melanarius, Germar, Ins. Spec Nov. Vol. 1, p. 110 (1824).   Krim.
    alpicola, Mulsant, Hist. Nat. Col. France, Lamell. p. 191 (1842).   Frankreich.
    var. orobius, Mulsant, ibidem, p. 191 (1842).   Frankreich.
    Biologie : Xambeu, Ann. Soc. Linn. Lyon. Vol. 42, p. 74 (1895). — Puppe
        beschrieben.

13. *A. punctator,* Reitter, Tab. p. 58; Brünn, 30, p. 196.   Chinesisch-Turkestan.

14. *A. putridus,* Herbst, Natursyst. Ins. Vol. 2, p. 160, t. 12; f. 15 (1789).   Pommern.
    foetidus, Fabricius, Ent. Syst. p. 40 (1792)   Deutschland.
    sec. Harold, Col. Hefte, Vol. 8, p. 119 (1871).
    Erichson, Naturg. Ins. Deutschl. Vol. 3, p. 817 (1848).   Deutschland.
    Harold, Berl. Ent. Zeitschr. p. 333, 364 (1863).   Mittel- und Nordeuropa, Sibirien.
    Reitter, Tab. p. 62; Brünn, 30, p. 200.   Europa, Kaukasus bis Sibirien.
    Horn, Trans. Amer. Ent. Soc. Vol. 14, p. 13 (1887).   Ostküste bis Colorado, Mexiko.
    tenellus, Say, journ. Acad. Nat. Sc. Philad. Vol. 3, p. 213 (1823).   Vereinigte Staaten Nordamerika.
    var. sus, Kugelann, Verz. der in ein. Gegenden Preuss. entd Käferarten   Preussen.
        (Schneiders Mag. Heft 3. p. 267 [1792]).
    uliginosus, Hardy, Ann. Mag. Nat. Hist. Vol. 19, p. 382 (1847).   England.
    var. transitus, Reitter, Tab. p. 62; Brünn, 30, p. 200.   Bosnien, Ostsibirien.
    Biologie : *Xambeu, L'Echange, Suppl. p. 11 (1894). — Verwandlungsstufen
        von *Aph. foetidus* (sec. Wiegmann. Arch. f. Naturg. Ber. 1894,
        p. 504 (1897).

15. *A. pyrenaeus,* Jacquelin Du Val. Gen. Col. Eur. (Catal.), p. 130 (1863).   Pyrenäen.
    pyrenaeus, Harold, Col. Hefte, Vol. 7. p. 3, 4 (1871).   Pyrenäen.
    Reitter, Tab. p. 58; Brünn, 30, p. 196.   Pyrenäen.
    sec. Reitter, Ent. Nachr. p. 186 (1894).   Irkutsk.

jugicola, Harold, Berl. Ent. Zeitschr. p. 334, 379 (1863).   Piemont, Alpen.
    sec. Reitter, Tab. p. 58; Brünn, 3o, p. 196.
Reitterianus, Schwarz, Wien. Ent. Zeit. p. 32 (1897).   Mattmark.
    sec. J. Daniel. Münch.Koleopt.Zeitschr.Vol.1(2), p.251 (1903).

16. *A. satyrus*, Reitter, Tab. p. 60; Brünn, 3o, p. 198.   Bayern, Schweiz, Italien.
17. *A. Semenowi*, Reitter, Hor. Soc. Ent. Ross. Vol. 21, p. 220 (1887);   Tibet, Chinesisch - Turke-
    Tab. p. 57; Brünn. 3o. p. 195.   stan.
18. *A. virginalis*, Reitter, Wien. Ent. Zeit. p. 157 (1900).   Kuku-noor.   [amerikas.
19. *A. vittatus*, Say, Journ. Acad. Nat. Sc. Philad. Vol. 5, p. 191 (1825).   Vereinigte Staaten Nord-
    vittatus, Harold, Berl. Ent. Zeitschr. p. 333, 355 (1863).   Vereinigte Staaten Nordamerikas
    Bates. Biol. Centr. Amer. Col. Vol. 2 (2), p. 84 (1887).   Mexiko, Vera Cruz.
    Horn.Trans.Amer.Ent.Soc.Vol.3, p.120(1870); Vol.14, p.17 (1887).   Mittelstaaten bis Kansas.
    sec. *Wickham, The Canad. Entom. Vol. 26, p. 205 (1894).   Kanada.
    mundus, Reitter, Tab. p. 61; Brünn,,3o, p. 199.   Syrien, Kaukasus.
    sec. Clouët, Bull. Soc. Ent. Fr. p. 187 (1898).
    var. sellatus, Mannerheim, Bull. Soc. Nat. Mosc. Vol. 25 (4), p. 299 (1852).   Irkutsk.
    Harold, Berl. Ent. Zeitschr. p. 333, 355 (1863).   Sibirien.
    sec. Clouët, Bull. Soc. Ent. Fr. p. 187 (1898).
    Reitter, Tab. p. 61; Brünn, 3o, p. 199   Sibirien.
    semiruber, Motschulsky, Schrenck Reise, p. 131, t. 9, f. 1 (1860).   Amur.
    var. rufoplagiatus, Reitter, Tab. p. 60; Brünn, 3o, p. 198.   Chinesisch.-Turkestan.
    sec. Reitter, Ent. Nachr. p. 186 (1894).
    var. vitiosus, Reitter, Tab. p. 61; Brünn, 3o, p. 199.

13. SUBGENUS OROMUS, MULSANT

Oromus. Mulsant, Hist. Nat. Col. France, Lamell. p. 195 (1871).

Charaktere. — Hierher gehören nur wenige Arten, ihr Körper hat eine ziemlich stark konvexe, nach hinten verbreiterte Gestalt, er ist schwarz gefärbt, die Flügeldecken sind zuweilen rotbraun, einfarbig oder mit dunklen Längsflecken.

Der Kopf ist schwach gewölbt, nach vorn bogig verschmälert, punktiert, die Stirnlinie ist schwach gehöckert; die Wangen sind deutlich; der Clipeus ist ausgerandet, seine Ecken sind abgerundet.

Das Halsschild ist stark gewölbt, quer, ziemlich dicht mit verschieden grossen Punkten besetzt, die Seitenrandung setzt sich um die stumpfen Hinterwinkel fort und erlischt dann, der grösste Teil der Basis bleibt also ungerandet.

Das Schildchen ist klein, breit-dreieckig, vorn nicht parallel, punktiert.

Die Flügeldecken sind mässig stark punktiert-gestreift, die Zwischenräume sind eben oder schwach konvex, sie sind gewöhnlich nur fein punktiert.

Die Unterseite ist immer schwarz, an den Seiten der Hinterbrust und am Abdomen punktiert und behaart.

Die Borstenkränze an den Hinterschienen sind kurz und gleichlang.

Der obere Enddorn ist meistens nur fast so lang als das erste Tarsenglied, dieses so lang als die zwei oder drei folgenden Glieder.

Es sind kleine und mittelgrosse Arten, sie bewohnen die Gebirge.

Geographische Verbreitung der Arten. — Europa, Kaukasus.

1. *O. alpinus*, Scopoli, Ent. Carn. p. 9 (1763).   Alpen.
    alpinus, Harold, Berl. Ent. Zeitschr. p. 257, 272 (1871).   Schottland, Lappland. Island,
        Asturien, Pyrenäen, Apenninen.

    Erichson, Naturg. Ins. Deutschl. Vol. 3, p. 829 (1848).   Oesterreich.
    Reitter, Tab. p. 63; Brünn, 3o, p. 201.   Alpen Europas.
    constans, W. Schmidt, Germar Zeitschr. Ent. Vol. 2, p. 113 (1840).   Süddeutschland, Wien.
    Heer, Fauna Col Helv. Vol 1, p. 515 (1841).   Schweiz.
    var. rubens, Comolli. Coleopt. Nov prov. Novocomi, p. 23 (1837).   Alpen.
    W. Schmidt, Germars Zeitschr. f. Ent. Vol. 2, p. 134 (1840).   Bayern, Krain, Süddeutschland.
    Heer, Fauna Col. Helv. Vol. 1, p. 513 (1841).

rhenonum, Zetterstedt, Ins. Lappon. p. 114 (1840).   Lappland.
    Harold, Berl. Ent. Zeitschr. p. 371 (1863).
dilatatus 1), W. Schmidt, Germar Zeitschr. Ent. p. 105 (1840).
    Heer, Fauna Col. Helv. Vol. 1, p. 514 (1841).   Alpen.
Schmidti 1), Heer, ibidem. p. 514 (1841).   Alpen.
alpestris, Heer, Mitteil. Naturf. Ges. Zürich, Vol. 1, p. 158 (1849); Fauna   Alpen.
    Col. Helv. Vol. 1, p. 513 (1841).
carthusianus. Mulsant. Hist. Nat. Col. France, Lamell. p. 189 (1842).   Frankreich.
var. *asphaltinus*, Kolenati, Melet. Ent. Vol. 5, p. 15 (1846).   Cirkaukasien.
    Reitter, Tab. p. 63; Brünn. 30, p. 201.   Kaukasus.
var. *rupicola*, Mulsant, Hist. Nat. Col. France, Lamell. p. 189 (1842).   Frankreich.
nigerrimus, Dalla Torre, Ber.Ver. Naturk. Oberösterr.Vol. 10, p. 108(1879).   Oberösterreich.
var. *Mulsanti*, Dalla Torre, ibidem, p. 108 (1879).   Oberösterreich.
rubens, Mulsant, Hist. Nat. Col. France, Lamell. p. 189 (1842).   Frankreich.
    Biologie : Kambeu, Ann. Soc. Linn. Lyon, Vol. 39, p. 158 (1892). — Beschrei-
    bung der Larve und Puppe.
2. *O. corvinus*, Erichson, Naturg. Ins. Deutschl. Vol. 3, p. 831 (1848).   Thüringen, Tirol, Steier-
corvinus, Harold, Col. Hefte, Vol. 7, p. 3, 5 (1871).   Mitteleuropa. [mark.
    Mulsant, Hist. Nat. Col. France, Lamell. p. 198 (1871).   Frankreich.
    Reitter, Tab. p. 63; Brünn, 30, p. 201.   Mitteleuropa.

14. SUBGENUS LIOTHORAX, MOTSCHULSKY

Liothorax. Motschulsky, Etud. Ent. p. 156 (1859).
Nialus, Mulsant, Hist. Nat. Col. France, Lamell. p. 216 (1871).
Subrinus. Mulsant, ibidem, p. 271 (1871).
Labarrus. Mulsant, ibidem, p. 275 (1871).

Charaktere. — Der Körper ist konvex, glänzend, unbehaart, lang und schmal, parallel, er ist einfarbig schwarz oder gelbbraun gefärbt, die Flügeldecken der helleren Arten zeigen zuweilen dunkle Naht und dunklen Längsfleck auf der Scheibe, die der schwarzen Arten eine rote Basal- oder eine ebensolche Scheibenmakel.

Der Kopf ist meistens mehr geradlinig nach vorn verengt, er ist wenig gewölbt, immer deutlich punktiert, besonders in der vordern Hälfte, die Stirnlinie ist deutlich, sie trägt gewöhnlich einen Mittelhöcker, der Clipeus ist gewöhnlich deutlich ausgerandet, seitlich davon mehr oder weniger breit verrundet oder auch schwach gezähnt; die Wangen sind klein. abgerundet, sie überragen die Augen nur wenig.

Das Halsschild ist quer, gewölbt. seine Mitte bei den hellen Arten angedunkelt, auf der Oberfläche meistens nur zerstreut feiner und stärker punktiert, seltener gleichmässig und dichter, die Seiten sind bis um die stumpfen Hinterwinkel gerandet, die Basis bleibt ohne Rand.

Das Schildchen ist klein, vorn parallel, zuweilen längs eingedrückt.

Die Flügeldecken sind punktiert-gestreift, die Streifenpunkte oft wenig deutlich, die Zwischenräume fast immer nur vereinzelt und fein punktiert, meistens nur wenig oder garnicht gewölbt.

Die Borstenkränze an den Hinterschienen sind kurz und gleichlang.

Der obere Enddorn ist gewöhnlich so lang als das erste Tarsenglied, selten kürzer, dieses meistens nur den zwei folgenden Gliedern an Länge gleich.

Geographische Verbreitung der Arten. — Von *Aph. lividus* abgesehen, der in allen Erdteilen vorkommt, bewohnen diese Arten das ganze Europa, Nordafrika, Abessinien, Dar-es-Salâm, Senegal, Syrien, Kaukasus. Persien, Nord- und Centralasien, Japan.

1. *L. angustatus*, Klug, Symb. Phys. Vol. 5, No 8, t. 42, f. 8 (1845).   Aegypten.
2. *L. Kocae*, Reitter, Wien. Ent. Zeit. p. 204 (1897).   Slavonien.

---

1) *O. dilatatus* W. Schmidt und *Schmidti* Heer können nicht als Varietäten erhalten bleiben, da die ihnen zuerkannten Merkmale sich nicht als konstant erweisen, sie sind daher = var. *rubens* Comolli. Ueberhaupt ändert die Streifung und Punktierung der Flügeldecken bei *alpinus* Scopoli bei manchen Exemplaren bedeutend ab.

3. L. Kraatzi. Harold, Col. Hefte. Vol. 3, p. 84 (1868).

    Kraatzi, Harold, Berl. Ent. Zeitschr. p. 257, 269 (1871).

        Reitter, Tab. p. 65 ; Brünn, 3o, p. 2o3.

    Haagi, Becker, Bull. Soc. Nat. Mosc. Vol. 40 (1), p. 108 (1867).

        sec. Harold, Col. Hefte, Vol. 5, p. 69 (1869).

4. L. linearis. Reiche & Saulcy, Ann. Soc. Ent. Fr. p. 394 (1856).

    linearis, Reitter, Tab. p. 64; Brünn, 3o, p. 2o2.

    armiger, Harold, Berl. Ent. Zeitschr. p. 257, 259 (1871).

        sec. Reitter, Tab. p. 64; Brünn, 3o, p. 2o2.

    cylindricus, Reiche & Saulcy, Ann. Soc. Ent. Fr. p. 396 (1856).

        Reitter, Tab. p. 71; Brünn, 3o, p. 2o9.

        Mulsant, Hist. Nat. Col. France, Lamell. p. 217 (1871).

        sec. d'Orbigny, L'Abeille, Vol. 28, p. 215 (1896).

5. L. lividus, Olivier, Ent. Vol. 1 (3), p. 86, t. 26, f. 222 (1789).

    lividus, Creutzer, Ent. Versuche, p. 44, t. 1, f. 7 (1799).

        Heer, Fauna Col. Helv. Vol. 1, p. 524 (1841).

        Erichson, Naturg. Ins. Deutschl. Vol. 3, p. 837 (1848).

        Harold, Berl. Ent. Zeitschr. p. 258, 279 (1871).

        Reitter, Tab. p. 64; Brünn, 3o, p. 2o2.

    suturalis, Fabricius, Ent. Syst. Vol. 1, p. 28 (1792).

    vespertinus, Panzer, Fauna Germ. p. 67 (3) (1799).

    obsoletus, Fabricius, Syst. Eleuth. Vol. 1, p. 70 (1801).

    bilituratus, Marsham, Ent Brit. Vol. 1, p. 15 (1802).

    discus, Wiedemann, Zool. Mag. Vol. 2 (1), p. 28 (1823).

    cincticulus, Hope, Proc. Ent. Soc. Lond. p. 147 (1846); Trans. Ent. Soc. Lond. Vol. 4, p. 284 (1847).

    spilopterus*, Germar, Linn. Ent. Vol. 3, p. 189 (1848).

    scutellaris, Roth, Wiegmann, Arch. f. Naturg. Vol. 1, p. 132 (1851).

    sequens, Walker, Ann. Mag. Nat. Hist. (3), Vol. 2, p. 207 (1858).

    maculicollis, Montrouzier, Ann. Soc. Ent. Fr. p. 268 (1860).

    var. *limicola*, Panzer, Fauna Germ. p. 58 (6) (1798).

    var. *anachoreta*, Fabricius, Syst. Eleuth. Vol. 1, p. 74 (1801).

        Sturm, Deutschl. Ins. Vol. 1, p. 97 (1805).

        Duftschmid, Fauna Austr. Vol. 1, p. 108 (1805).

    limbatus, Wiedemann, Germars Mag. Vol. 4, p. 129 (1821).

    var. *innumerabilis*, A. Schmidt, Stett. Ent. Zeit. p. 31 (1911).

    Biologie : Bouché, Naturg. Ins. Vol. 1, p. 190 (1834). — Larve und Puppe beschrieben.

        Erichson, Naturg. Ins. Deutschl. Vol. 3, p. 838 (1848). — Larve beschrieben.

        Kambeu, Ann. Soc. Linn. Lyon, 1895 (sec. Wiegm. Bericht. 1895, p. 485 (1898).

6. L. Matthiesseni, Reitter, Deutsche Ent. Zeitschr. p. 407 (1907).

7. L. niger, Panzer, Fauna Germ. p. 37 (1), (1797).

    niger, Illiger, Verz. Käf. Preuss. p. 24 (1798).

        Thomson, Skand. Col. Vol. 5, p. 52 (1863).

        Erichson, Naturg. Ins. Deutschl. Vol. 3, p. 833 (1848).

        Harold, Berl. Ent. Zeitschr. p.257, 266 (1871).

        Reitter, Tab. p. 66; Brünn, 3o, p. 2o4.

        sec. Reitter, Hor. Soc. Ent. Ross. Vol 21, p. 206 (1887).

    terrestris, Paykull, Fauna Suec. Vol. 1, p. 22 (1798).

8. L. pallidicinctus, Waterhouse, Trans. Ent. Soc. Lond. p. 85 (1875).

    pallidicinctus, Reitter, Tab. p. 99; Brünn, 3o, p. 237.

9. L. plagiatus, Linné, Syst. Nat. (ed. 12), Vol. 1 (2), p. 559 (1766).

    plagiatus, Paykull, Fauna Suec. Vol. 1, p. 23 (1798).

        W. Schmidt, Germar Zeitschr. Ent. Vol. 2, p. 125 (1840).

        Erichson, Naturg. Ins. Deutschl. Vol. 3, p. 835 (1848).

        Thomson, Skand. Col. Vol. 5, p. 52 (1863).

        Harold, Berl. Ent. Zeitschr. p. 257, 264 (1871).

        Reitter, Tab. p. 66; Brünn, 3o, p. 2o4.

    longulus, Ménétriés, Mém. Acad. St-Pétersb. (6), Vol. 6, p. 60, t. 2, f. 11 (1849).

        sec. Harold, Berl. Ent. Zeitschr. p. 264 (1871).

Südrussland, Griechenland, Kreta.
Kaukasus, Centralasien, Slavo-Südrussland.   [nien.

Syrien.
Griechenland.
Griechenland.

Spanien, Frankreich.
Spanien, Frankreich.
Frankreich.

Kosmopolit.
Wien.
Schweiz.
Berlin.
Alle Weltteile.
Alle Weltteile.
Inseln Amerikas.
Wien.
Ostindien.
England.
Bengalen
Adelaide.

Adelaide.
Tigré.
Ceylon.
Neu-Kaledonien.
Schlesien.
Deutschland.
Wien.
Oesterreich.
Oesterreich.
Galla-Land.

Mittelpersien.
Braunschweig.
Preussen.
Schweden.
Deutschland.
Oesterreich, Russland.
Europa.
Turkestan, Altai, Tibet.
Schweden.

Japan, China.
Chinesisch-Turkestan.

Europa.
Schweden.
Deutschland.
Deutschland.
Schweden.
Europa, Vorderasien, Sibirien.
Zentralasien, Kaukasus, Syrien.
Buchara.

var. *elegantulus*, Hochhut, Bull. Soc. Nat. Mosc. p. 131 (1873).   Südwestrussland.
var. *immaculatus*, Dalla Torre, Ber. Ver. Naturk Oberösterr. Vol. 10, p. 108 (1879).   Oberösterreich.
  concolor, Schilsky, Deutsche Ent. Zeitschr. p. 311 (1888).   Mark Brandenburg.
  var. *discus*, Reitter, Tab. p. 66; Brünn, 30, p. 204.   Araxes.
10. *L. politus*, Mulsant & Rey, Opusc. Ent. Vol. 14, p. 204 (1870); Ann.   Syrien.
    Soc. Linn. Lyon, 1870-71, p. 172 (1872).
11. *L. Sturmi*, Harold, Col. Hefte, Vol. 6, p. 106 (1870), nom. nov.; Berl.   Südeuropa.
    Ent. Zeitschr. p. 258, 283 (1871).
     Sturmi, Reitter, Tab. p. 65; Brünn, 30, p. 203.   Armenien.
     rufus ‖ Sturm, Deutschl. Ins. Vol. 1, p. 144, t. 14, f. D (1805).   Wien.
       W. Schmidt, Germar Zeitschr. Ent. Vol. 2, p. 142 (1840).   Wien.
       Erichson, Naturg. Ins. Deutschl. Vol. 3, p. 836 (1848).   Oesterreich, Tirol.
     Illigeri, Mulsant, Hist. Nat. Col. France, Lamell. p. 271 (1871).   Frankreich.
12. *L. subtilis*, Koshantschikow, Hor. Soc. Ent. Ross. 1893-1894, Vol. 28,   Astrachan.
    p. 126 (1894).
13. *L. varians*, Duftschmid, Fauna Austr. Vol. 1, p. 93 (1805).   Oesterreich, Schanghai.
     varians, Harold, Berl. Ent. Zeitschr. p. 257, 262 (1871).   Europa, Vorderasien, Nordafrika
      Reitter, Tab. p. 65; Brünn, 30, p. 203.   Kaukasus, Armenien.
     niger, Sturm, Deutschl. Ins. Vol. 1, p. 127 (1805).   Nürnberg.
     bimaculatus, var. *ambiguus*, Mulsant, Hist. Nat. Col. France, Lamell.   Frankreich.
      p. 202 (1842).
    var. *Fabriciusi*, d'Orbigny, L'Abeille, Vol. 28, p. 215 (1896), nom. nov.
     bimaculatus ‖ Fabricius, Mant. Ins. Vol. 1, p. 8 (1787).   Deutschland.
       Herbst, Natursyst. Ins. Vol. 2, p. 159, t. 12, f. 14 (1789).
       Kugelann, Verz. Gegenden Preuss. Käferarten : Schneiders
        Mag. Vol. 1 (3), p. 266 (1792).
       Thomson, Skand. Col. Vol. 5, p. 53 (1863).
     terrestris, var. β, Illiger, Verz. Käf. Preuss. p. 24 (1798).
     varians, var. β, Duftschmid, Fauna Austr. Vol. 1, p. 93 (1805).
       Erichson, Naturg. Ins. Deutschl. Vol. 3, p. 832 (1848).   Deutschland.
    var. *punctatellus*, Mulsant, Hist. Nat. Col. France, Lamell. p. 202 (1842).   Frankreich.
    var. *punctulatus*, Mulsant, ibidem, p. 221 (1871).   Frankreich.
     Biologie : Mulsant, ibidem, t. 1, f. 8 (1842). — Abbildung der Larve.
14. *L. vitellinus*, Klug, Symb. Phys. Vol. 5, t. 42, f. 7 (1845).   Aegypten.
     vitellinus, Harold, Berl. Ent. Zeitschr. p. 258, 282 (1871).   Südfrankreich.
      Reitter, Tab. p. 65; Brünn, 30, p. 203.   Südeuropa, Nordafrika.
      sec. Harold, Col. Hefte, Vol. 8, p. 21 (1871).   Abessinien.
     nitens, Mulsant & Rey, Opuso. Vol. 14, p. 211 (1870); Ann. Soc. Linn.   Algier.
      Lyon, 1870-1871, p. 187 (1872).
      sec. d'Orbigny, L'Abeille, Vol. 28, p. 216 (1896).   Tunis, Syrien.

15. SUBGENUS PLAGIOGONUS, MULSANT

Plagiogonus. Mulsant, Hist. Nat. Col. France, Lamell. p. 306 (1842); p. 371 (1871).

    Charaktere. — Die Skulptur der Flügeldecken zeichnet diese Untergattung aus. Der Körper ist klein, meistens ist derselbe nur wenig gewölbt, seltener nach hinten verbreitert, glänzend, er ist schwarz oder schwarzbraun gefärbt, die Flügeldecken sind zuweilen heller, seltener gelblich, einfarbig oder mit schwarzer Naht und Spitze, auch wohl mit dunklem Längsfleck auf der Scheibe.

    Der Kopf ist wenig gewölbt, ohne Höcker, feiner oder stärker punktiert, zuweilen auf dem Vorderkopf ziemlich grob und hier meistens sehr deutlich behaart, der Clipeus ist ausgerandet, seitlich davon mehr stumpfwinklig als abgerundet, die Stirnlinie ist deutlich; die Wangen sind klein und rundlich.

    Das Halsschild ist quer, seitlich wenig gerundet, die Hinterwinkel sind stumpf, die Basis ist schwach zweibuchtig, sehr fein oder nicht gerandet, die Oberfläche ist feiner und stärker, ziemlich dicht punktiert.

    Das Schildchen ist klein, dreieckig.

    Die Flügeldecken sind seltener nach hinten verbreitert, sie sind deutlich punktiert-gestreift, der

Nahtstreif ist vor der Spitze meistens stark niedergedrückt, die Streifen sind vor der Spitze gewöhnlich tiefer, furchenartig, die Zwischenräume sind auf dem Rücken eben oder flach gewölbt, vor der Spitze stets viel stärker erhaben, hier verbindet sich gewöhnlich der siebente mit dem neunten zu einem gemeinschaftlichen rippenförmigen Wulst, zuweilen sind die Flügeldecken am Ende der Naht gemeinschaftlich winklig ausgeschnitten.

Die Unterseite ist glänzend, behaart, auch die Schenkel.

Die Schienen haben am Endrande ungleiche Borsten. Der obere Enddorn ist gewöhnlich so lang als das erste Glied, dieses entweder den zwei oder drei folgenden an Länge gleich.

Hierher gehören nur kleine Arten.

Geographische Verbreitung der Arten. — Europa, Nordafrika, Kleinasien, Syrien, Kaukasus, Mittelasien.

1. *P. arenarius*, Olivier, Ent. Vol. 1 (3), p. 96, t. 24, f. 206 (1789).   Paris.
    arenarius, Illiger, Verz. Käf. Preuss. p. 22 (1798).   Preussen.
    Erichson, Naturg. Ins. Deutschl. Vol. 3, p. 900 (1848).   Deutschland.
    A. Schmidt, Aphodiinen-Zusammenst. Deutsche Ent. Zeitschr.
    Beih. p. 5, Anmerkung 1 (1907-08).
    pusillus, Preyssler, Verz. böhm. Ins. Schneider Mag. Vol. 1, p. 104, t. 2,   Prag.
    f. 8 (1790).
    Panzer, Fauna Germ. Vol. 58, p. 8 (1798).
    rhododactylus, Marsham, Ent. Brit. Vol. 1, p. 29 (1802).   England.
    Reitter. Tab. p. 66; Brünn, 30. p. 204.   Europa, Kaukasus.
    var. *sabulicola*. Mulsant, Hist. Nat. Col. France, Lamell. p. 306 (1842).   Frankreich.
2. *P. culminarius*, Reitter, Wien. Ent. Zeit. p. 156 (1900).   Donkyr.
3. *P. esimoides*, Reitter, Tab. p. 226; Brünn, 31, p. 105.   Tunis.
    esimoides, A. Schmidt, Aphodiinen-Zusammenst. Deutsche Ent. Zeitschr.
    Beih. p. 24, Anmerkung 1 (1907-08)
4. *P. nanus*, Fairmaire, Ann. Soc. Ent. Fr. p. 172 (1860).   Berberei.
    nanus, Mulsant, Hist. Nat. Col. France, Lamell. p. 370 (1871).   Algier.
    Reitter, Tab. p. 67; Brünn, 30, p. 205.   Marokko, Kleinasien.
    algiricus, Harold, Berl. Ent. Zeitschr. p. 388 (1863).   Algier.
5. *P. nefandus*, Reitter, Deutsche Ent. Zeitschr. p. 408 (1907).   Mandschurei.
6. *P. praeustus*, Ballion, Bull. Soc. Nat. Mosc. 1870, Vol. 43 (2), p. 333 (1871).   Chodschent.
    praeustus, Solsky, Fedtschenko Turkest. Col. p. 343 (1876).   Maracandam.
    Reitter, Tab. p. 67; Brünn, 30, p. 205.   Baku, Kaukasus, Syrien.
7. *P. Reitteri*, Koshantschikow, Hor. Soc. Ent. Ross. 1893-94. Vol. 28,   Westturkestan.
    p. 97 (1894).
8. *P. syriacus*, Harold, Berl. Ent. Zeitschr. p. 389 (1863).   Syrien.
    syriacus, Reitter, Tab. p. 66; Brünn, 30, p. 204.   Araxes, Kaukasus.
9. *P. Theryi*, Clouët, Bull. Soc. Ent. Fr. p. 54 (1896).   Algier.
    sec. d'Orbigny, L'Abeille. Vol, 28, p. 210, Note (1896).

16. Subgenus PHÆAPHODIUS, Reitter

Phæaphodius. Reitter, Best.-Tab. Eur. Col. Coproph. Lamell. Heft 24. p. 67 (1892); Verhandl. Naturf. Ver. Brünn, 1891, Vol. 30, p. 205 (1892).

Charaktere. — Der Körper dieser Arten ist weniger gewölbt, breiter, auf der Oberfläche unbehaart, meistens glänzend, schwarz oder gelbbraun gefärbt, die Flügeldecken der schwarzen Arten sind zuweilen heller, einfarbig oder mit dunkler Makel, die sich von der Seite nach der Mitte und Spitze hinzieht, ohne die letztere zu erreichen.

Der Kopf ist breit, wenig gewölbt, in der Vorderhälfte meistens kräftig und dicht punktirt, hinten ist derselbe mehr glatt, die Stirnnaht ist deutlich, beim Männchen mit drei schwachen Höckerchen, von denen das mittlere mehr rund und entwickelter ist; die Wangen sind klein, rundlich; der Clipeus ist stets deutlich ausgebuchtet und seitlich verrundet, seltener etwas spitz.

Das Halsschild ist quer, an den Seiten und der Basis gerandet, wenig dicht, fein und grob punktiert, die Seiten sind wenig gerundet, hell bewimpert, die Hinterwinkel sind abgeschrägt.

Das Schildchen ist klein, breiter oder schmaler dreieckig, einzeln punktiert.

Die Flügeldecken sind kaum nach hinten verbreitert, deutlich punktiert-gestreift, ihre Zwischenräume sind eben oder schwach gewölbt, meistens nur sehr fein punktiert, höchstens zuweilen vor der Spitze stärker und dichter.

Die Unterseite ist punktiert und behaart.

Die Borstenkränze der Hinterschienen sind ungleich, der obere Enddorn fast so lang als das verlängerte erste Tarsenglied, dieses so lang als die zwei oder drei folgenden Glieder.

Geographische Verbreitung der Arten. — Bosporus, Mittel- und Nordasien, Japan.

1. *P. albociliatus*, Reitter, Tab. p. 68; Brünn, 3o, p. 206; Ent. Nachr. Transkaspien, Turkestan.
   p. 186 (1894).
2. *P. Alleoni*, d'Orbigny, Bull. Soc. Ent. Fr. p. 149 (1896); L'Abeille. 1892- Bosporus.
   1896. Vol. 28, p. 222 (1896).
3. *P. fusculus*, Reitter, Tab. p. 68; Brünn, 3o, p. 206.   Taurus.
      fusculus, d'Orbigny, L'Abeille, Vol. 28, p. 222 (1896).   Taurus.
4. *P. Jouravliowi*, Reitter, Deutsche Ent. Zeitschr. p. 408 (1907).   Uralsk.
      var. *Latonius*. Reitter, ibidem, p. 409 (1907).   Altai.
5. *P. rectus*, Motschulsky, Bull. Soc. Nat. Mosc. Vol. 39 (1). p. 169 (1866).   Japan.
      vitta, Motschulsky, ibidem, p. 170 (1866).   Japan.
      Solskyi, Harold, Berl. Ent. Zeitschr. p. 251 (1871).   Amur.
      diversus, Waterhouse, Trans. Ent. Soc. Lond. p. 82 (1875).   China.
      castaneipennis, Waterhouse, ibidem, p. 83 (1875).   Japan.
         sec. Harold. Col. Hefte, Vol. 15, p. 174 (1876).
         sec. Lewis, Ann. Mag. Nat. Hist (6), Vol. 16, p. 379, 404 (1895).
      var. *biformis*, Reitter, Tab. p. 67; Brünn. 3o, p. 205.   Ostsibirien, Japan.
      var. *semicolor*, Reitter, ibidem, p. 67; ibidem, p. 205.   Ostsibirien, Japan.
6. *P. truncatangalus*, Reitter, Ent. Nachr. p. 186 (1894).   Amasia.
7. *P. Zichyi*, Csiki, Zichy 3. Asiat. Forschungsreise, Vol. 2, p. 107, f. 3 (1901).   Mongolei.

17. SUBGENUS TRICHONOTUS, MULSANT

Trichonotus. Mulsant, Hist. Nat. Col. France, Lamell. p. 259 (1871).

Charaktere. — Diese Untergattung zählt nur zwei kleine Arten. Ihr Körper ist länglich, flach gewölbt, nach hinten nicht verbreitert, schwarz gefärbt, meistens mit helleren Flügeldecken und Beinen, die Oberseite ist mehr oder weniger glänzend und gelblich behaart.

Der flache, nach vorn verschmälerte Kopf ist fein punktiert, ohne deutliche Stirnlinie und Höcker, der Clypeus ist schwach ausgerandet, seine Seiten sind verrundet; die Wangen sind klein und rundlich, mit einem Haarbüschel versehen.

Das Halsschild ist schwachbogig nach hinten erweitert, an den Seiten und der Basis fein gerandet, etwas deutlicher als der Kopf punktiert, die Hinterwinkel sind stumpf abgerundet, die Basis ist schwach zweibuchtig.

Das Schildchen ist klein und schmal, vorn parallel.

Die Flügeldecken haben etwas scharfe Schultern, sie sind mehr oder weniger fein punktiertgestreift, die fast ebenen Zwischenräume sind in Reihen punktiert und behaart.

Die Unterseite ist glänzend, fein punktiert und behaart.

Der Apicalrand der Hintertibien ist mit längeren und kürzeren Borsten besetzt.

Der obere Enddorn ist gleich dem ersten Gliede, dieses gleich den zwei folgenden an Länge.

Geographische Verbreitung der Arten. — Europa, Kaukasus, Turkestan, Mongolei.

1. *T. merdaroides*, Reitter, Wien. Ent. Zeit. p. 288 (1896).   Ostsibirien, Mongolei.

2. *T. scrofa*, Fabricius, Mant. Ins. Vol. 1, p. 11 (1787).   Halle.
    scrofa, Erichson, Naturg. Ins. Deutschl. Vol. 3, p. 857 (1848).   Deutschland.
    Harold. Berl. Ent. Zeitschr. p. 183, 192 (1874).   Europa.
    Reitter. Tab. p. 72; Brünn, 30, p. 210.   Kaukasien, Turkestan.
    sec. Sharp Ent. M. Mag. Vol. 5, p. 100 (1868).   England.
    minutus, Herbst, Natursyst. Ins. Vol. 2, p. 269, t. 18, f. 7 (1789).
    fuscus, Rossi, Fauna Etr. Mant. Vol. 1, p. 8 (1792).   Italien.
    tomentosus, Kugelann, Schneider Mag. Vol. 1 (3). p. 269 (1792).   Preussen.
    cinereus, Mulsant & Rey, Opusc. Ent. Vol. 14, p. 218 (1870).   Sizilien.
    A. Schmidt, Aphodiinen-Zusammenst. Deutsche Ent. Zeitschr.
    Beih. p. 72, Anmerkung (1907-1908).
  var. setiger, Mulsant, Hist. Nat. Col. France, Lamell. p. 295 (1842).   Frankreich.

18. SUBGENUS ESIMAPHODIUS, REITTER

Esimaphodius. Reitter, Best.-Tab. Eur. Col. Coproph. Lamell. Vol. 24, p. 70 (1892); Verhandl. Naturf. Ver. Brünn 1891, Vol. 30, p. 208 (1892).
Meraphodius. Koshantschikow, Hor. Soc. Ent. Ross. 1893-94, Vol. 28, p. 112 (1894).

Charaktere. — Die kleinen Arten dieser Untergattung sind ausgezeichnet durch den gezähnten Clipeus und die hellen Flügeldecken mit der angedunkelten Naht.

Der Körper ist länglich, wenig gewölbt, parallel, seltener nach hinten etwas verbreitert, schwarz oder dunkelbraun gefärbt, die Unterseite ist meistens heller, der Vorderkopf und die Seiten des Halsschildes oder auch nur deren Vorderwinkel sind rötlichgelb, die Flügeldecken sind meistens hellgelbbraun mit angedunkelter Naht, seltener sind die Flügeldecken und die Naht rotbraun.

Der Kopf ist fast immer nur fein punktiert, mit höckerloser Stirnnaht, die Mitte ist beulig erhaben; der Clipeus zeigt neben der Ausbuchtung in der Mitte jederseits je ein Zähnchen oder einen spitzen Winkel; die Wangen sind klein.

Das Halsschild ist quer, fein punktiert, die Seiten, die stumpfen Hinterwinkel und die Basis sind gerandet.

Das Schildchen ist klein, vorn parallel, mit der Farbe der Flügeldecken übereinstimmend oder schwarz.

Die Flügeldecken sind punktiert-gestreift, der Nahtstreif vor der Spitze oft tief eingedrückt, die Zwischenräume meist eben und sehr fein punktiert.

Die Unterseite ist wie die Oberseite glänzend, fein punktiert und behaart, die Metasternalplatte beim Männchen längsgrubig.

Die Hinterschenkel sind stark verbreitert. Der Borstenbesatz am Endrande ihrer Schienen besteht aus ungleichen Borsten.

Der obere Enddorn ist dem ersten Gliede an Länge gleich, dieses so lang als die zwei folgenden zusammen.

Geographische Verbreitung der Arten. — Balearen, Nordafrika, Kleinasien, Syrien, Mesopotamien, Westturkestan, Südrussland.

1. *E. angulosus*, Harold, L'Abeille, Vol. 5, p. 432 (1868-69).   Palästina, Tunis,
    angulosus, d'Orbigny, ibidem, 1892-96. Vol. 28, p. 219 (1896).   Palästina, Tunis.
2. *E. fuscolimbatus*, Harold, Mitt. Münch. Ent. Ver. Vol. 4, p. 155 (1880).   Mesopotamien.
3. *E. kisilkumi*, Solsky, Fedtschenko Turkest. Col. Vol. 2, p. 332 (1876).   Kisil-kum.
    kisilkumi, Koshantschikow, Hor. Soc. Ent. Ross. 1893-94, Vol. 28,
    p. 100, 112 (1894).
4. *E. lepidulus*, Harold, Berl. Ent. Zeitschr. p. 96, 119 (1866).   Kleinasien, Syrien,
    lepidulus, Reitter, Tab. p. 70; Brünn, 30, p. 208.   Mesopotamien.
    sec. Harold, Mitt. Münch. Ent. Ver. Vol. 4 (2), p. 156 (1880).

5. *E. leucopterus*, Klug, Symb. Phys. Vol. 5, N° 3. t. 42. f. 2 (1845).　　　Aegypten.
   leucopterus, Reitter, Tab. p. 71; Brünn, 30, p. 209.　　　Algier, Tripolis.
      d'Orbigny, L'Abeille, Vol. 28, p. 220 (1896).　　　Balearen, Tunis.
   luridipennis, Mulsant, Mém. Acad. Sc. Lyon. Vol. 1, p 138 (1851).　　　Algier.
      sec. Harold, L'Abeille, Vol. 5, p. 433 (1868-69).
   forcipatus, Harold, Col. Hefte, Vol. 3, p. 84 (1868).　　　Algier.
      sec. Clouët, Bull. Soc. Ent. Fr. p. 372 (1896).
      A. Schmidt, Aphodiinen-Zusammenst, Deutsche Ent. Zeitschr.
        Beih. Anmerkung, p. 42 (1907-08).

6. *E. mendidioides*, Reitter, Tab. p. 71; Brünn, 30, p. 209.　　　Ordubad, Baku, Namagan.
   selenocarus, Koshantschikow, Hor. Soc. Ent. Ross. 1893-94, Vol. 28, p. 111　　　Kisil-kum.
     (1894).
      sec. Reitter, Wien. Ent. Zeit. p. 78 (1896).

7. *E. nasalis*, Koshantschikow, Hor. Soc. Ent. Ross. 1893-94, Vol. 28,　　　Turkestan.
   p. 112 (1894).

8. *E. nodulifer*, Koshantschikow, ibidem, p. 110, 112 (1894).　　　Samarkand.

19. SUBGENUS ESYMUS, MULSANT

Esymus. Mulsant, Hist. Nat. Col. France, Lamell. p. 279 (1871).

Charaktere. — Diese Untergattung, die mit der vorigen in Grösse und Färbung grosse Aehnlichkeit besitzt, unterscheidet sich von ihr hauptsächlich in dem Fehlen der Clipealzähnchen.

Der Körper ist länglich, parallel, flach gewölbt, glänzend, schwarz, die Seiten des Halsschildes oder nur deren Vorderwinkel zuweilen rötlich, die Flügeldecken sind immer viel heller gefärbt, entweder hellbraun oder rötlich, zuweilen auch blass weisslichgelb, einfarbig oder mit schwarzer Spitze, seltener mit schwarzer gemeinschaftlicher dreieckiger Makel auf der vordern Hälfte der Flügeldecken, die Naht ist mit einer Ausnahme samt dem ersten Zwischenraum schwarz.

Der Kopf ist wenig gewölbt, in der Mitte schwach aufgetrieben, fein punktiert, mit schwacher, ungehöckerter Stirnlinie, der Clipeus ist schwach ausgerandet, selten stärker, daneben abgerundet, die Wangen sind sehr klein.

Das quere Halsschild ist wenig dicht, nicht sehr stark punktiert, an den Seiten und der Basis gerandet. erstere sind wenig gerundet, die Hinterwinkel sind stumpf.

Das Schildchen ist klein, vorn parallel, schwarz, fein punktiert.

Die Flügeldecken haben meistens nur feine Punktstreifen, seltener sind dieselben etwas kräftiger, die Zwischenräume sind meistens eben und sehr fein punktiert.

Die Unterseite ist glänzend, punktiert und behaart, auch die Schenkel.

Die Beine sind meistens heller gefärbt, die Hinterschienen haben längere und kürzere Borsten am Endrande.

Der obere Enddorn ist kürzer oder so lang als das erste Tarsenglied, dieses den zwei folgenden an Länge gleich. selten länger.

Die Männchen haben das Metasternum in der Mitte vertieft, zuweilen auch die Hintertibien stark verbreitert.

Es sind kleine Arten von 3 bis 4,5 mm Länge.

Geographische Verbreitung der Arten. — Europa, Kaukasus, Kleinasien, Syrien, Turkestan, Nordafrika.

1. *E. alaiensis*, Reitter, Tab. p. 226; Brünn, 31, p. 105　　　Alai-Gebirge.
2. *E. filitarsis*, Reitter, Deutsche Ent. Zeitschr. p. 341 (1898).　　　Akbes.
3. *E. fumigatulus*, Reitter, Tab. p. 70; Brünn, 30, p. 208.　　　Ordubad.
4. *E. merdarius*, Fabricius, Syst. Ent. p. 19 (1775).　　　Europa.

merdarius, Erichson, Naturg. Ins. Deutschl. Vol. 3, p. 869 (1848).   Deutschland.
    Reitter, Tab. p. 69; Brünn, 3o, p. 207.   Kaukasus.
    sec. Bailey, Ent. M. Mag. (2), Vol. 16, p. 90 (1905).   Insel Man.
quisquilius, Schrank, Enum. Ins. Austr. p. 18 (1781).   Oesterreich.
exilis, W. Schmidt, Germar Zeitschr. Ent. Vol. 2, p. 120 (1840).   Sachsen.
var. ictericus, Laicharting, Verz. Tyrol. Ins. Vol. 1, p. 14 (1781).   Tirol.
   foriorum, Panzer, Fauna Germ. p. 58 (9) (1798).
    Sturm, Deutschl. Ins. Vol. 1, p. 146 (1805).   Schlesien.
   gelbinus, Schrank, Fauna Boica, Vol. 1, p. 391 (1798).
var. atricollis, Mulsant. Hist. Nat. Col. France, Lamell. p. 232 (1842).   Frankreich.
   collaris. Dalla Torre, Ber. Ver. Naturk. Oberösterr. Vol. 10, p. 109 (1879).
    sec. Schilsky, Deutsche Ent. Zeitschr. p. 130 (1888).
var. melinopus, Mulsant, Hist. Nat. Col. France, Lamell. p. 232 (1842).   Frankreich.
Biologie : Xambeu, Rev. d'Ent. Caen. Vol. 20, p. 23 (1901). — Ei, Larve
    und Puppe beschrieben.

5. *E. sculpturatus*, Reitter, Tab. p. 70; Brünn, 3o, p. 208.   Ordubad. Syrien, Smyrna.
6. *E. Sicardi*, Reitter, ibidem, p. 226; ibidem, 31, p. 105.   Tunis.
   Sicardi, d'Orbigny, L'Abeille, Vol. 28, p. 219 (1896).   Algier.
7. *E. stereotypus*, Koshantschikow, Hor. Soc. Ent. Ross. 1893-94, Vol. 28,   Samarkand.
   p. 109 (1894).
8. *E. suturalis*. Redtenbacher. Col. Syriæ, Gen. et Spec. Nov. (Russegger   Syrien.
Reise), Vol. 1 (2), p. 986 (1843).
   albidipennis, Reitter, Tab. p. 69; Brünn, 3o, p. 207.   Transkaukasien.
9. *E. terminatus*, Marseul, L'Abeille, Nouv. et Faits (2), Nᵒˢ 14-15, p. 57   Algier.
(1878).
   terminatus, Reitter, Tab. p. 69; Brünn, 3o, p. 207.   Algier.
10. *E. tersus*, Rosenhauer, Tiere Andalus. p. 130 (1856).   Cadiz, Malaga.
   tersus, Erichson, Naturg. Ins. Deutschl. Vol. 3, p. 859, Note (1848).   Portugal, Sizilien.
   Reitter, Tab. p. 69; Brünn, 3o, p. 207.   Spanien, Marokko.
   sec. Heyden, Deutsche Ent. Zeitschr. p. 67 (1890).   Aegypten, Tripolis.
   suturalis || Lucas, Explor. Algér. Ent. p. 263 (1849).   Algier.
11. *E. trochilus*, Reitter, Tab. p. 70; Brünn, 3o, p. 208.   Syrien.

20. SUBGENUS ORODALUS, MULSANT

Orodalus. Mulsant, Hist. Nat. Col. France, Lamell. p. 199 (1871).
Phalacronotus. Motschulsky, Etud. Ent. p. 156 (1859).
Emadus. Mulsant. Hist. Nat. Col. France, Lamell. p. 209 (1871).
Mecynodès. Mulsant, ibidem. p. 225 (1871).
Eudolus. Mulsant, ibidem, p. 277 (1871).

Charaktere. — Der Körper ist länglich, gewölbt, glänzend, auf der Oberseite unbehaart. schwarz, die Flügeldecken zuweilen einfarbig schwarz oder rotbraun, sehr häufig aber mit roten oder gelblichen Makeln, die Naht ist bei den hellen Arten immer angedunkelt, das Halsschild bald schwarz, bald an den Seiten oder Vorderwinkeln rötlich.

Der nach vorn verschmälerte, in der Mitte schwach aufgetriebene Kopf zeigt kleinere oder grössere Wangen und einen ausgerandeten Clipeus, dessen Ecken meistens verrundet sind, seltener bleiben dieselben als solche dem Männchen erhalten, die Oberfläche ist fein, selten grob punktiert, die Stirnlinie ist deutlich, zuweilen schwach gehöckert.

Das Halsschild ist quer, sehr selten an den Seiten stärker gerundet, diese, sowie die Basis, hier jedoch meistens sehr fein, gerandet, die Oberfläche ist deutlich punktiert, die Punktur immer aus grösseren und kleineren Punkten zusammengesetzt, sehr selten ist die Scheibe fast glatt, die Hinterwinkel sind stumpf.

Das Schildchen ist klein, vorn parallel, einzeln punktiert.

Die Flügeldecken sind fast immer parallel, bald stärker, bald feiner punktiert-gestreift, die Zwischenräume sind konvex, zuweilen die neben der Naht gelegenen viel stärker erhaben. Die Unterseite ist glänzend, punktiert und behaart.

Die Beine sind bald hell, bald dunkler, die Borstenkränze an den Hinterschienen sind ungleich, das erste Tarsenglied zuweilen sehr kurz und verdickt, dann ist der obere Enddorn länger als dieses, meistens ist jedoch der Metatarsus schlank und verlängert. länger als die zwei folgenden Glieder, der Enddorn ist dann kürzer.

, Bei dem Männchen ist der Enddorn an den Vordertarsen entweder zugespitzt und stark herabgebogen oder am Ende stumpf erscheinend, weil die Spitze plötzlich umgebogen ist. Die Metasternalplatte ist immer stark vertieft. Die Hintertibien sind nur zuweilen stark verbreitert.

Es sind kleine Arten von 3 bis 6 mm Länge.

Geographische Verbreitung der Arten. — Europa, Algier, Vorder-, Mittel- und Nordasien, Japan.

1. *O. biguttatus*, Germar, Ins. Spec. Nov. p. 111 (1824). Oesterreich.
    biguttatus, W. Schmidt, Germar Zeitschr. Ent. Vol. 2, p. 109 (1840). Oesterreich.
    Erichson, Naturg. Ins. Deutschl. Vol. 3, p. 868 (1848). Oesterreich.
    Reitter, Tab. p. 75; Brünn, Vol. 3o, p. 213. Mitteleuropa, Kaukasus.
    A. Schmidt, Aphodiinen-Zusammenst. Deutsche Ent. Zeitschr.
    Beih. p. 8, Anmerkung (1907-08).
    var. sanguinolentus, Panzer, Fauna Germ p. 43 (4) (1797). Deutschland.
    Erichson, Naturg Ins. Deutschl. Vol. 3, p. 866 (1848). Süd- und Mitteldeutschland.
    biguttatus, Mulsant, Hist. Nat. Col. France, Lamell. p. 215 (1871). Frankreich.
    sec. Harold. Col. Hefte. Vol. 11, p. 120 (1873).
    sanguinolens, Mulsant, Hist. Nat. Col. France, Lamell. p. 206 (1842).
    var. fallax, Schilsky, Deutsche Ent. Zeitschr. p. 315 (1888). Bozen.
    suturalis ‖ Erichson, Naturg. Ins. Deutschl. Vol. 3, p. 867 (1848).
    dubius, Schilsky, Deutsche Ent. Zeitschr. p. 337 (1889)
    var. apicalis, Schilsky, ibidem, p. 315 (1888). Deutschland.
    var. similis, Schilsky, ibidem, p. 315 (1888). Neusohl.
    var. conjunctulus. Reitter, Tab. p. 75; Brünn, 3o, p. 213.
2. *O. Diecki*, Harold, Berl. Ent. Zeitschr. Beih. Heyd. Reise Spanien, Spanien.
    p. 114 (1870).
    Diecki, Reitter, Tab. p. 73; Brünn. 3o, p. 211. Algier.
    var. lunulatus. d'Orbigny, L'Abeille, 1892-96, Vol. 28, p. 214 (1896). Algier.
3. *O. fortimargo*, Reitter, Deutsc e Ent. Zeitschr. p. 409 (1907). Uralsk.
4. *O. hypocrita*, Mulsant & Rey. Hist. Nat. Col. France, Lamell. p. 209 Frankreich.
    (1871).
    hypocrita, Reitter. Tab. p. 72; Brünn, 3o, p. 210. Frankreich.
5. *O. lucifer*, Koshantschikow, Hor. Soc. Ent. Ross. 1893-94. Vol. 28, Samarkand.
    p. 113 (1894).
6. *O. pusillus*, Herbst. Natursyst. Ins. Vol. 2, p. 155, t. 12, f. 12, t. 18, f. 6 Berlin.
    (1789).
    pusillus, Paykull, Fauna Suec. Vol. 1, p. 10 (1798). Schweden.
    Sturm, Deutschl. Ins. Vol. 1, p. 160 (1805). Nürnberg.
    Erichson, Naturg. Ins. Deutschl. Vol. 3, p. 860 (1848). Deutschland.
    Reitter, Tab. p. 74; Brünn, 3o, p. 212. Europa, Kaukasus bis Sibirien
    sec. Bailey, Ent. M. Mag. p. 90 (1905). Insel Man.
    sec. Walker, ibidem (2), Vol. 3o, p. 115 (1894). England.
    granarius, Fabricius, Syst. Ent. p. 16 (1775). Europa.
    granum, Gyllenhal, Ins. Suec. Vol. 1 (1), p. 19 (1808). Schweden.
    haemorrhoidalis, Olivier, Ent. Vol. 1 (3), p. 83, t. 26, f. 223a, b (1789).
    sec. Harold, Col. Hefte. Vol. 8, p. 120 (1871).
    var. coenosus, Ahrens, Neue Schrift. Naturf. Ges. Halle, Vol. 2 (2). p. 36 (1812). Schlesien.
    W. Schmidt, Germar Zeitschr. Ent. Vol. 2, p. 120 (1840). Schlesien.
    *var. phaeopterus**, Stephens, Ill. Brit. Ent. Vol. 3, p. 204 (1830). England.
    var. coecus, Mulsant, Hist. Nat. Col. France, Lamell. p. 213 (1842). Frankreich.
    var. rufulus, Mulsant, ibidem, p. 213 (1842). Frankreich.
    var. macularis, Mulsant, ibidem, p. 213 (1842). Frankreich.

pusillus* ‖ Stephens, Ill. Brit. Ent. Vol. 3, p. 205 (1830).   England.
bicolor, Dalla Torre, Ber. Ver. Naturk. Oberösterr. Vol. 10, p. 109 (1879).   Oberösterreich.
    sec. Schilsky, Deutsche Ent. Zeitschr. p. 320 (1888).
var. rufangulus, Waterhouse, Trans. Ent. Soc. Lond p. 89 (1875).   Japan.
    A. Schmidt, Aphodiinen-Zusammenst. Deutsche Ent. Zeitschr.
    Beih. p. 64, Anmerkung (1907-08).
var. ochripennis, Reitter. Tab. p. 74; Brünn, 30, p. 212.   Ostsibirien.
    Biologie : Rosenhauer, Stett. Ent. Zeit. p. 20 (1882). — Larve und Puppe
    beschrieben.

7. *O. Putoni*, Reitter, Ent. Nachr. p. 187 (1894).   Madrid.
8. *O. quadriguttatus*, Herbst, Fuessly Arch. Ins. Vol. 4, p. 10, t. 19, f. 15 (1783).   Reppen.
    quadriguttatus, Illiger, Verz. Käfer Preuss. p. 35 (1798).   Preussen.
        Erichson. Naturg. Ins. Deutschl. Vol. 3, p. 863 (1848).   Deutschland.
        Reitter, Tab. p. 74, Brünn, 30, p. 212.   Europa, Algier.
        sec. Harold, Verhandl. Naturf. Ver. Brünn, Vol. 16, p. 191   Kaukasus.
        (1877).
    quadrimaculatus, Fabricius, Syst. Ent. p. 19 (1775)   England.
        Paykull, Fauna Suec. Vol. 1, p. 25 (1798).   Schweden.
        Sturm, Deutschl. Ins. Vol. 1, p. 154 (1805).   Nürnberg.
    quadripustulatus, Duftschmid, Fauna Austr. Vol. 1, p. 125 (1805).   Oesterreich.
    macri*, Costa. Ann. Accad. Aspir. Natur. Napoli, Vol. 1. p. 39 (1847).   Italien.
        sec. Reitter, Cat. Eur. Col. p. 721 (1906).
        A. Schmidt, Aphodiinen-Zusammenst. Deutsche Ent. Zeitschr. Beih.
        p. 66, Anmerkung (1907-08).
    var. angularis. Mulsant, Hist. Nat. Col. France, Lamell. p. 261 (1842).   Frankreich.
    var. cruciatus, Mulsant, ibidem, p. 261 (1842).   Frankreich.
    var. astaurus*, Fuente, Ann. Soc. Esp. Hist. Nat. Vol. 26, p 130.   Spanien.
    nigrosuturalis, J. Müller. Verh. Zool.-bot. Ges Wien, Vol. 52, p. 447 (1902).   Dalmatien.
    dilutus, Fiori, Il Natural. Sicil. Vol. 19, p. 115 (1907).   Italien.
9. *O. quadrimaculatus*,. Linné. Fauna Suec. p. 138 (1761).   Schweden.
    quadrimaculatus, Illiger, Verz. Käf. Preuss. p. 35 (1798).   Preussen.
        Erichson, Naturg. Ins. Deutschl. Vol. 3, p. 865 (1848).   Deutschland.
        Reitter, Tab. p. 75; Brünn, 30, p. 213.   Tirol, Sizilien.
        sec. Harold. Brünn, Vol. 16, p. 191 (1877).   Kaukasus.
    quadripustulatus, Fabricius, Ent. Syst. Vol. 1, p. 36 (1792).   Halle.
        Sturm, Deutschl Ins. Vol. 1, p. 156 (1805).   Deutschland.
    var. caudatus. Mulsant, Hist. Nat. Col. France, Lamell. p. 206 (1842).   Frankreich.
    var. prolongatus, Mulsant, ibidem. p. 207 (1842).   Frankreich.
    var. biguttulus, Fiori, Il Natural. Sicil. Vol. 19, p. 115 (1907).   Italien.
10. *O. quadrinaevulus* Reitter. Tab. p. 74; Brünn, 30, p. 212.   Araxes.
11. *O. quadrisignatus*, Brullé, Expéd. Morée, Vol 3, p. 172, t. 38, f. 12 (1836).   Griechenland.
    quadrisignatus, Reitter, Tab. p. 75; Brünn, 30, p. 213.   Türkei, Kleinasien, Syrien, Tur-
    sexpustulatus, Gebler, Bull. Soc. Nat. Mosc. Vol. 14 (4), p. 588 (1841);   Südwest-Sibirien.   [kestan.
        Vol. 20 (4). p. 459 (1847).
        Mulsant, Hist. Nat. Col. France, Lamell. p. 213 (1871).   Griechenland.
12. *O. striatulus*, Waltl, Reise Spanien, Vol. 2, p. 67 (1835).   Andalusien.
    parallelus, Mulsant, Ann. Soc. Agric. Lyon, p. 277 (1843).   Spanien.
        sec. Reitter, Cat. Eur. Col. p. 720 (1906).
        Mulsant, Hist. Nat. Col. France, Lamell. p. 225 (1871).   Südfrankreich.
        Reitter, Tab. p. 73; Brünn, 30, p. 211.   Dalmatien.
        sec. Fairmaire, Ann. Soc. Ent. Fr. p. 171 (1860)   Algier.
        sec. J. Daniel, Münch. Koleopt. Zeitschr. Vol. 1, p. 258 (1903).   Kleinasien.
    tormes*, Graëlls, Mem Conision del Mapa Geol.-Zool. Vol. 4, p. 60, t. 3,   Spanien,
        f. 1 (1858).
        sec. Harold, Berl Ent. Zeitschr. p. 114 (1861).
    var. fenestratus, Reitter, Tab. p. 73; Brünn, 30, p. 211.   Sizilien.
    Biologie : Xambeu, Ann. Soc. Linn. Lyon, 1902. Vol. 49. p. 158 (1903). —
        Larve und Puppe von *parallelus* Mulsant.
        *Xambeu, Le Naturaliste, Vol. 24, p. 145 (1902). — Metamorphose.

13. *O. tirolensis*, Rosenhauer, Beitr. Ins. Faun. Vol. 1, p. 29 (1847).   Tirol.
    tirolensis, Erichson, Naturg. Ins. Deutschl. Vol. 3, p. 862 (1848).   Tirol.
        Reitter, Tab. p. 75; Brünn, 30, p. 213.   Tirol,
14. *O. tristis*, Zenker, Panzer Fauna Ins. Germ. p. 73 (1) (1801).   Dresden.

tristis, Sturm, Deutschl. Ins. Vol. 1, p. 158 (1805).	Nürnberg.
Erichson, Naturg. Ins. Deutschl. Vol. 3, p. 859 (1848).	Deutschland.
Mulsant, Hist. Nat. Col. France, Lamell. p. 206 (1871).	Frankreich.
Reitter, Tab. p. 73; Brünn, 30, p. 211.	Kaukasus, Nord- und Mittel
sec. Beare, Ent. M. Mag. (2), Vol. 5, p. 276 (1894)	England. [europa.
var. coenosus, Panzer. Fauna Ins. Germ. p. 58 (7) (1798).	Schlesien.
mirandus, Mulsant, Hist. Nat. Col. France, Lamell. p. 209 (1842).	Frankreich.
var. vicinus, Mulsant, ibidem, p. 208 (1842).	Frankreich.
var. pellucidus, Mulsant. ibidem, p. 208 (1842).	Frankreich.
var. scapularis, Mulsant, ibidem, p. 209 (1842).	Frankreich.
var. fallax, Mulsant, ibidem. p. 209 (1842).	Frankreich.

21. Subgenus ORODALISCUS, Reitter

Orodaliscus. Reitter, Deutsche Ent. Zeitschr. p. 84 (1900).

Charaktere. — Diese Untergattung stimmt mit der vorigen in der länglichen, gewölbten Gestalt, dem kleinen, schmalen, vorn parallelen Schildchen, der gerandeten Basis des Halsschildes und den ungleichen Borsten am Endrande der Hinterschienen überein, unterscheidet sich aber sofort durch die breit verrundeten Hinterwinkel des Halsschildes, die bei *Orodalus* stumpfwinklig sind.

Der Körper ist schwarz gefärbt, die Flügeldecken sind braunrot, nach hinten schwach verbreitert, die Oberseite ist glänzend und unbehaart.

Der Kopf ist flach, dicht punktiert, besonders vorn, die Stirnnaht ist deutlich, mit schwachen Höckerchen; der Clipeus ist ausgerandet und seitlich verrundet; die Wangen sind sehr klein, die Augen kaum überragend.

Das Halsschild ist quer, an den Seiten und der Basis gerandet, dicht und ziemlich stark punktiert, die Hinterwinkel sind in flachem Bogen mit der Basis verrundet.

Die Flügeldecken zeigen deutliche Punktstreifen, ihre Zwischenräume sind flach gewölbt, fast zweireihig punktiert.

Der obere Enddorn der Hinterschienen ist kürzer als das erste Glied, dieses fast so lang als die drei folgenden Tarsenglieder.

Bei dem Männchen ist der Enddorn an den Vordertibien kurz, an der Spitze hakig umgebogen.

Geographische Verbreitung der Art. — Die einzige bisher bekannte Art bewohnt das südliche Russland.

1. *O. rotundangulus*, Reitter, Deutsche Ent. Zeitschr. p. 84 (1900). Charkow.

22. Subgenus AMIDORUS, Mulsant

Amidorus. Mulsant, Hist. Nat. Col. France. Lamell. p. 249 (1871).
Sigorus. Mulsant, ibidem, p. 255 (1871).
Pubinus. Mulsant. ibidem, p. 257 (1871).
Anomius. Mulsant. ibidem, p. 267 (1871).

Charaktere. — Die Arten dieser Untergattung zeichnen sich durch dichtere Punktierung der Oberfläche aus. Sie sind von länglicher, gewölbter Gestalt, zuweilen matter oder behaarter Oberfläche, von schwarzer oder brauner Farbe, die Flügeldecken sind zuweilen etwas heller, rot oder braungelb.

Der Kopf ist wenig gewölbt, nach vorn verschmälert, sehr dicht und meistens auch kräftig punktiert, die Stirnlinie ist deutlich, gewöhnlich nur schwach gehöckert; die Wangen sind deutlich, stumpfwinklig die Augen überragend, selten sind dieselben vor den Augen nicht erweitert, sie haben gewöhnlich deutliche Borstenbüschel; der Clipeus ist immer deutlich ausgerandet, seine etwas abgerundeten Ecken sind aufgebogen.

Das Halsschild ist quer, an den Seiten mit der Scheibe gleichfarbig oder heller, es ist immer dicht, nicht zu kräftig punktiert, die Punkte sind mit feineren untermischt, die Seiten und Basis sind gerandet, letztere oft sehr fein, zuweilen ist das Halsschild auch vorn gerandet, die Seiten sind schwach gerundet, meistens nach hinten divergierend, die Hinterwinkel sind stumpf oder stumpfwinklig abgerundet, die Seiten sind bewimpert.

Das Schildchen ist klein, dreieckig, vorn nicht parallel, punktiert.

Die Flügeldecken sind, wenn auch manchmal feiner, immer deutlich punktiert-gestreift, die Zwischenräume sind eben und gewölbt, zuweilen matt und chagriniert, feiner oder stärker punktiert, seltener längsgestrichelt.

Die Unterseite ist glänzend, punktiert und behaart, das Metasternum ist in der Mitte meistens deutlich punktiert, beim Männchen längsgrubig.

Die Hinterschienen haben am Endrande ungleiche Borsten, der obere Enddorn ist meistens so lang als das erste Tarsenglied, selten länger, der Metatarsus oft die zwei folgenden Glieder an Länge überragend

Es sind Tiere von 4 bis 8 mm Länge.

Geographische Verbreitung der Arten. — Europa, Nordafrika, Kleinasien, Syrien, Armenien, Kaukasus, Turkestan, Sibirien.

1. *A. baeticus*, Mulsant & Rey, Hist. Nat. Col. France, Lamell. p. 270 (1871).   Spanien.
    badius || Mulsant & Rey, Opuso. Ent. Vol. 14, p. 214 (1870); Ann. Soc.   Spanien.
        Linn. Lyon, 1870-71, Vol. 18, p. 190 (1872).
        Reitter, Tab. p. 76; Brünn, 3o, p. 214.   Spanien.

2. *A. brevithorax*, Sumakow, Wien. Ent. Zeit. p. 47 (1903).   Kaukasus.

3. *A. carinifrons*. Reitter, Tab. p. 76; Brünn, 3o, p. 214.   Tanger.

4. *A. circassicus*. Reitter, ibidem, p. 77; ibidem, p. 215; Wien. Ent. Zeit.   Kaukasus.
    p. 47 (1903).

5. *A. consors*, Reitter, ibidem, p. 225; ibidem, 31, p. 104.   Mongolei.

6. *A. cribrarius*, Brullé, Expéd. Morée, Vol. 3. p. 171, t. 38, f. 11   Griechenland.
    (1836).
        cribrarius, Reiche & Saulcy, Ann. Soc. Ent. Fr. p. 401 (1856).
            Harold, Berl. Ent. Zeitschr. p. 184, 199 (1874).   Syrien, Dalmatien.
        dalmatinus, W. Schmidt, Germars Zeitschr. f. Ent. Vol. 2, p. 130 (1840).   Dalmatien.
        obscurus, var., Kiesenwetter, Berl. Ent. Zeitschr. p. 188 (1859).
        var. *immaturus*, Mulsant, Hist. Nat. Col. France. p. 263 (1842).   Frankreich.
        var. *purpuripennis*, Reitter, Tab. p. 79; Brünn, 3o, p. 217.   Türkei, Kaukasus.

7. *A. cribricollis*, Lucas, Explor. Algér. Ent. Vol. 2, p. 260, t. 23, f. 11 (1849).   Algier.
        cribricollis. Reitter, Tab. p. 78; Brünn, 3o, p. 216.   Marokko.
        var. *barbaroides*, A. Schmidt, nom. nov. 1).
        barbarus, Reitter (non Fairmaire), Tab. p. 78; Brünn, 3o, p. 216.   Südspanien.
            sec. Reitter, Wien. Ent. Zeit. p. 217 (1897).

8. *A. fimicola*, Reiche & Saulcy, Ann. Soc. Ent. Fr. p. 402 (1856).   Naplouse.
        fimicola, Harold, Berl. Ent. Zeitschr. p. 183, 206 (1874).   Kleinasien, Syrien, Palästina.
        Reitter, Tab. p. 79; Brünn, 3o, p. 217.   Griechenland, Türkei.

9. *A. de Fiorei*, Fiori, Il Natural. Sicil. Vol. 19, p. 124 (1907).   Calabrien.

10. *A. flavipennis*, Miller, Verh. Zool.-bot. Ges. Wien, Vol. 33, p. 265 (1883).   Parnass.
        flavipennis, Reitter, Tab. p. 79; Brünn, 3o, p. 217.   Griechenland.

11. *A. fronticornis*, Koshantschikow, Hor. Soc. Ent. Ross. 1893-94, Vol. 28,   Turkestan.
    p. 114 (1894)

12. *A. ibericus*, Harold, Berl. Ent. Zeitschr. p. 184, 203 (1874).   Madrid.
        ibericus, Reitter, Tab. p. 80; Brünn, 3o, p. 218.   Balearen, Morea.
            sec. Clouët, Bull. Soc. Ent. Fr. p. 372 (1896).   Algier.

---

1) *Barba us* Reitte wird wegen *barbarus* Fairmaire in *barbaroides* abgeändert.

13. *A. impolitus*, A. Schmidt, Notes Leyd. Mus. Vol. 31, p. 104 (1909).   Ungarn.

14. *A. obscurus*, Fabricius, Ent. Syst. Vol. 1, p. 25 (1792).   Deutschland.

     obscurus, Erichson, Naturg. Ins. Deutschl. Vol. 3, p. 853 (1848).   Mitteldeutschland, Alpen.
       Harold, Berl. Ent. Zeitschr. p. 184, 198 (1874).   Thüringen. Südeur., Kleinasien,
       Reitter, Tab. p. 79; Brünn, 30, p. 217.   Mitteleur., Kaukasus. [Armen.
     asiaticus, Faldermann, Fauna Transcauc. Vol. 1, p. 252 (1836).   Kaukasus.
       sec. Reiche, Ann. Soc. Ent. Fr. p. 393 (1856).
     sericatus, W. Schmidt, Germars Zeitschr. f. Ent. Vol. 2, p. 128 (1840).   Oesterreich.
       Mulsant, Hist. Nat. Col. France, Lamell. p. 262(1842); p.249(1871).   Frankreich.
     var. *bubulcus*, Faldermann, Fauna Transcauc. Vol. 1, p. 258 (1836).   Kaukasus.
       sec. Reiche, Ann. Soc. Ent. Fr. p. 394 (1856).
     var. *dichrous*, Reitter, Tab. p. 79; Brünn, 30, p. 217.

15. *A. porcus*, Fabricius, Ent. Syst. Vol. 1, p. 26 (1792).   Halle.

     porcus, Illiger, Käf. Preuss. p. 31 (1798).   Preussen.
       W. Schmidt, Germars Zeitschr. f. Ent. Vol. 2, p. 131 (1840).   Oesterreich, Deutschland.
       Erichson, Naturg. Ins. Deutschl. Vol. 3, p. 855 (1848).   Deutschland.
       Harold, Berl. Ent. Zeitschr. p. 184, 202 (1874).   Europa.
       Reitter, Tab. p. 80; Brünn, 30, p. 218.   Mitteleuropa bis Italien.
       sec. Harold, Verh. Naturf. Ver. Brünn, Vol. 16, p. 191 (1877).   Kaukasus.
       sec. Bailey, Ent. M. Mag. p. 90 (1905)   Insel Man.
     anachoreta. Creutzer, Fauna Germ. p 35 (1) (1796).   Neuwaldegg.
     turpis, Marsham. Ent. Brit. Vol. 1, p. 15 (1802).   England.
     var. *ruficrus*, Marsham, ibidem, p. 16 (1802).   England.
       Mulsant, Hist. Nat. Col. France, Lamell. p. 267 (1842).   Frankreich.
     var. *haemorrhoideus*, Mulsant, ibidem, p. 267 (1842).   Frankreich.
     Biologie : Chapman, Ent. M. Mag. Vol. 5, p. 275 (1869); Vol. 6, p. 230 (1870).
     — Ueber Brutablage.

16. *A. Ragusae*, Reitter, Tab. p. 78; Brünn, 30, p. 216.   Sizilien.

17. *A. Sharpi*, Harold, Berl. Ent. Zeitschr. p. 184, 205 (1874).   Algier, Spanien.

     Sharpi, Reitter, Tab p. 78; Brünn, 30, p. 216.   Krim.

18. *A. Solieri*, Mulsant & Rey, Ann. Soc. Ent. Fr. 1870-71, Vol. 18, p. 188   Südfrankreich.
    (1872); Opusc. Ent. Vol. 14, p. 212 (1870).

     Solieri, Reitter, Tab. p. 76; Brünn, 30, p. 214.   Südfrankreich.

19. *A. thermicola*, Sturm, Verzeichn. p 44, t. 2, f. T (1800).   Oesterreich.

     thermicola, Erichson, Naturg. Ins. Deutschl. Vol. 3, p. 854 (1848).   Oesterreich.
       Harold, Berl. Ent. Zeitschr. p. 184, 201 (1874).   Europa, Asien.
       Reitter, Tab. p. 79; Brünn, 30, p. 217.   Frankreich, Bosnien, Russland.
     obscurus, Panzer, Fauna Germ. p. 91 (1) (18).   Niederösterreich.
       Sturm, Deutschl. Ins. Vol. 1, p. 117 (1805).
     var. *meridionalis*, Mulsant, Hist. Nat. Col. France, Lamell. p. 265 (1842).   Frankreich.
     thermicola, var. β, Sturm, Verzeichn. im. Samml. Vol. 1. p. 44 (1800).   Niederösterreich.

20. *A. tomentosus*, Müller, Zool. Dan. Prodr. p. 55 (1776).   Dänemark.

     tomentosus, Harold, Berl. Ent. Zeitschr. p. 183, 191 (1874).   Nordeuropa, Sibirien.
       Reitter, Tab. p. 80; Brünn, 30, p. 218.   Europa.
     lutarius, Fabricius, Ent. Syst. Vol. 1, p. 35 (1792).   Deutschland.
       sec. Harold, Col. Hefte, Vol. 7, p. 115 (1871).
       Paykull, Fauna Suec. Vol. 1, p. 17 (1798).   Schweden.
       Erichson, Naturg. Ins. Deutschl. Vol. 3, p. 856 (1848).   Pommern, Oesterreich.
     immundus, Fabricius, Syst. Eleuth. Vol. 1, p. 77 (1801).   Deutschland.

21. *A. tunicatus*, Reitter, Ent. Nachr. p. 188 (1894).   Russland.

     tunicatus, Reitter, Wien. Ent. Zeit. p. 282 (1896).
     var. *modicus*, Semenow, Bull Soc. Nat. Mosc. 1898, p. 89 (1899).   Russland.
     Biologie : * Semenow, Rev. Russe d'Ent. Vol. 2, p. 135 (1902). — Lebensweise.

22. *A. unicolor*, Olivier, Ent. Vol. 1 (3), p. 183, t. 28, f. 244 (1789).   Spanien.

     unicolor, Reitter, Tab. p. 76; Brünn, 30, p. 214.   Südfrankreich, Sizilien, Algier,
     castaneus, Illiger, Mag. Vol. 2, p. 194 (1803).   Portugal.   [Marokko.
       Mulsant, Hist. Nat. Col. France, Lamell. p. 267 (1871).   Portugal.

23. *A. Zangi*, A. Schmidt, Deutsche Ent. Zeitschr. p. 411 (1906).   Orenburg.

23. Subgenus PSEUDACROSSUS, Reitter

Pseudacrossus. Reitter, Best.-Tab. Coproph. Lamell. Eur. Col. Heft 24, p. 80 (1892); Verhandl. Naturf. Ver. Brünn, 1891, Vol. 3o. p. 219 (1892).

Charaktere. — Hierher gehören grössere, flach gewölbte Arten von schwarzer Grundfarbe, die Flügeldecken sind selten etwas heller, oft nur vor der Spitze, die Oberseite ist glänzend und unbehaart.

Der Kopf hat die Gestalt der vorigen Untergattung, er ist ebenfalls dicht und deutlich punktiert, die Stirnlinie ist schwach gehöckert; die Wangen sind deutlich, sie haben einen Haarbüschel.

Das Halsschild ist dicht, mässig stark punktiert, mit feinen Punkten untermischt, die Seiten und Basis sind gerandet, erstere kaum gerundet, die Hinterwinkel sind stumpf und abgerundet, die Vorderwinkel zeigen oft eine hellere Farbe.

Das Schildchen ist klein, vorn nicht parallel, dreieckig, mit einzelnen Punkten bestreut, die Mitte ist zuweilen schwach gekielt.

Die Flügeldecken sind nach hinten etwas verbreitert, mehr oder weniger fein gestreift, ihre ebenen oder auch zuweilen schwach gewölbten Zwischenräume sind sehr fein und zerstreut punktiert.

Die Unterseite ist wie die Oberseite gefärbt und ebenfalls glänzend, sie ist punktiert und behaart.

Die Borstenkränze an den Hinterschienen bestehen aus längeren und kürzeren Borsten.

Der obere Enddorn ist fast so lang als das erste Tarsenglied, dieses länger als die zwei oder drei nächsten Glieder.

Die Arten haben eine Grösse von 7 bis 8 mm.

Geographische Verbreitung der Arten. — Kleinasien, Turkestan und Sibirien.

1. *P. caminarius*, Reitter, Tab. p. 81; Brünn, 3o, p. 219.   Transbaikalien.
2. *P. Grombczewskyi*, Koshantschikow, Hor. Soc. Ent. Ross. 1890-91,   Altai, Turkestan.
   Vol. 25, p. 439 (1891).
         Grombczewskyi, Reitter, Tab. p. 81; Brünn, 3o, p. 219.   Margelan, Taschkent.
         var. *Daraignizi*, Clermont, L'Echange, Vol. 23, p. 170 (1907).   Turkestan.
3. *P. Zürcheri*, Reitter, Wien. Ent. Zeit. p. 247 (1908); p. 76 (1909).   Adana.

24. Subgenus CHILOTHORAX, Motschulsky

Chilothorax, Motschulsky, Etud. Ent. p. 156 (1859).
Volinus, Mulsant, Hist. Nat. Col France, Lamell. p. 297 (1871).

Charaktere. — Von länglicher, flach gewölbter Gestalt, glänzend, höchstens vor der Flügeldeckenspitze sehr kurz, an den Rändern des Halsschildes und um die Schulterwinkel herum länger behaart. die Arten sind schwarz oder braunrot gefärbt, die Seiten des Halsschildes oft heller, die Flügeldecken sind hellgelbbraun oder rötlichgelb, immer mit dunklen bis schwarzen Flecken, die sich meistens zu zwei Querbinden formieren, selten mit nur wenigen vereinzelten Flecken oder ganz einfarbig, zuweilen sind die Flecken der beiden Binden durch geschwärzte Linien verbunden, überhaupt ist die Anzahl der Flecke, sowie ihre Anordnung wenig constant, sie erweitern sich oft und verbinden sich in mannigfaltiger Weise.

Der Kopf ist wenig gewölbt, einfarbig schwarz oder mit hellerem Rande oder solchen Flecken hinter demselben, die Oberfläche ist feiner oder stärker punktiert, die Stirnlinie ist vorhanden; die Wangen sind bald klein, die Augen nicht überragend, bald grösser und stumpfwinklig; der Clipeus ist mehr oder weniger ausgerandet, seitlich davon verrundet.

Das Halsschild ist quer, zuweilen stark gewölbt, immer ziemlich dicht punktiert, an den Seiten und der Basis gerandet, an letzterer oft sehr fein und schwer sichtbar, die Hinterwinkel sind stumpf, seltener etwas verrundet.

Das Schildchen ist klein, dreieckig. vorn nicht parallel, dichter oder zerstreuter punktiert.

Die Flügeldecken sind fast immer parallel, deutlich punktiert-gestreift, die Zwischenräume sind eben oder wenig konvex, meistens fein und zerstreut, selten dichter und stärker punktiert.

Die Unterseite ist glänzend und behaart.

Die Hinterschienen haben am Endrande längere und kürzere Borsten, der obere Enddorn an denselben ist meist so lang als das erste Glied, dieses gleich den zwei folgenden.

Die Männchen zeichnen sich oft durch ein weniger punktiertes, die Breite der Flügeldecken überragendes Halsschild, deutlich gehöckerte Stirn und vertiefte Metasternalplatte aus.

Geographische Verbreitung der Arten. — Europa, Kanarische Inseln, Nordafrika, Kleinasien, Armenien, Kaukasus, Syrien, Mesopotamien, Transcaspien, Turkestan, Tibet, Sibirien, China, Japan, Vereinigte Staaten von Nordamerika.

1. *C. bistriga*, Reitter, Wien. Ent. Zeit. p. 157, t. 1, f. 3 (1900).	Nanschan.
2. *C. cervorum*, Fairmaire, Ann. Soc. Ent Fr. p. 420 (1871).	Frankreich.
cervorum, Reitter, Tab. p. 84; Brünn, 30, p. 222.	Frankreich.
3. *C. clathratus*, Reitter. ibidem, p. 85; ibidem, p. 223.	Ordubad.
var. deplanatus, Reitter, ibidem, p. 85; ibidem, p. 223.	Kaukasus.
4 *C. comma*, Reitter. ibidem. p. 89; ibidem. p. 227.	Turkmenien. Turkestan, Transbaikalien, Ostsibi-
var. incomma, Reitter, Deutsche Ent. Zeitschr. p. 440 (1906).	Gensin, Mongolei. [rien.
5. *C. conspurcatus*, Linné, Syst. Nat. (ed. 10), Vol. 1, p. 348 (1758).	Europa.
conspurcatus, Marsham, Ent. Brit. Vol. 1, p. 12 (1802).	England
Erichson. Naturg. Ins. Deutschl. Vol. 3, p. 846 (1848).	Norddeutschland.
Mulsant. Hist. Nat. Col. France, Lamell. p. 303 (1871).	Frankreich.
Reitter, Tab p. 84; Brünn, 30, p. 222	Europa.
Biologie : Rosenhauer, Stett. Ent. Zeit. p. 21 (1882). — Lave und Puppe beschrieben.	
6. *C. dilatatus*, Reiche & Saulcy, Ann. Soc. Ent. Fr. p. 399, t. 12, f. 8 (1856).	Peloponnes.
dilatatus, Reitter, Tab. p. 82; Brünn, 30, p. 220.	Griechenland, Türkei.
var. ampliatus, Reitter. ibidem, p. 77, 82; ibidem, p. 215, 220.	Sizilien.
7. *C. discedens*, A. Schmidt, Deutsche Ent. Zeitschr. p. 567 (1907).	Totes Meer.
8. *C. distinctus*, Müller, Zool. Dan. Prodr. p. 53 (1776).	Dänemark.
inquinatus, Herbst, Fuessly Arch. Vol. 4, p. 6, t. 19, f. 5 (1783).	Berlin.
Paykull, Fauna Suec. Vol. 1, p. 19 (1798).	Schweden.
Sturm. Deutschl. Ins. Vol. 1, p. 105 (1805).	Deutschland.
Erichson, Naturg. Ins. Deutschl. Vol. 3, p. 839 (1848).	Nordamerika, Spanien.
Horn, Trans. Amer. Ent Soc. Vol 14, p. 48 (1887).	Vereinigte Staaten ohne Westen.
Reitter, Tab. p. 87; Brünn, 30, p. 225.	Europa, Kaukasus.
vaginosus, Voet, Catal. Syst. Col. Vol. 1, p. 33, t 21, f. 149.	
Voet, Scar. Terric. p. 33 (1769-1804).	
Goeze, Ent. Beitr. Vol. 1, p. 73 (1777).	
Fuessly, Mag. Ins. Vol. 1, p. 44 (1778).	
A. Schmidt. Aphodiinen-Zusammenst. Deutsche Ent. Zeitschr. Beih. p. 38, Anmerkung 1 (1907-08).	
conspurcatus ‖ Schrank. Enum. Ins. Austr. p. 4 (1781).	Oesterreich.
attaminatus, Marsham, Ent. Brit. Vol. 1, p. 13 (1802).	England.
maculipennis, Melsheimer, Proc. Acad. Nat. Sc. Philad. Vol. 2, p. 137 (1844).	Maryland.
inquinatulus. Reitter. Wien. Ent. Zeit. p. 119 (1898).	Olgino
sec. Semenow, Bull. Soc. Nat. Mosc. p. 119 (1899).	
A. Schmidt, Aphodiinen-Zusammenst. Deutsche Ent. Zeitschr. Beih. p. 38, Anmerkung 2 (1907-08).	
var. centrolineatus. Panzer, Fauna Germ. p. 58 (1) (1798).	Schlesien.
var. nubilus, Panzer. ibidem, p. 58 (3) (1798).	Schlesien.
foedatus, Marsham, Ent. Brit. Vol. 1, p. 14 (1802).	England.
var. fumosus, Mulsant, Hist. Nat. Col. France, Lamell. p. 245 (1842).	Frankreich.
var. pauper, Mulsant, ibidem, p. 245 (1842).	Frankreich.
var. baseolus, Mulsant, ibidem, p. 245 (1842).	Frankreich.
var. hemicyclus, Mulsant, ibidem, p. 245 (1842).	Frankreich.

var. *scutellaris*, Mulsant, Hist. Nat. Col. France, Lamell. p. 245 (1842).   Frankreich.
var. *lunatus*, Mulsant, ibidem, p. 245 (1842).   Frankreich.
var. *ophthalmicus*, Mulsant. ibidem, p. 245 (1842).   Frankreich.
var. *auctus*. Mulsant, ibidem, p. 246 (1842).   Frankreich.
var. *subcinctus*, Mulsant, ibidem, p. 246 (1842).   Frankreich.
var. *interruptus*, Mulsant, ibidem, p. 246 (1842).   Frankreich.
var. *anxius*, Mulsant, ibidem, p. 246 (1842).   Frankreich.
var. *confluens*, Schilsky, Deutsche Ent. Zeitschr. p. 311 (1888).   Mark Brandenburg.
Biologie : Mulsant, Hist. Nat. Col. France, Lamell. p. 246, t. 1, f. 9 (1842). —
Abbildung der Larve.
*Lintner, Third Report injur. Ins. New York, p. 102 (1887).
Xambeu, Rev. d'Ent. Caen, Vol. 20. p. 51 (1901). — Lebensweise.

9. *C. exclamationis*, Motschulsky, Bull. Soc. Nat Mosc. Vol. 22 (3), p. 108   Cartagena.
(1849).
exclamationis. Reitter, Tab. p. 90; Brünn, 30, p. 229.   Algier.
d'Orbigny, L'Abeille, Vol. 28, p. 229 (1896).   Tunis, Südspanien

10. *C. figuratus*, A. Schmidt, Deutsche Ent. Zeitschr. p. 410 (1906).   Turkestan.
11. *C. flavimargo*, Reitter, ibidem, p. 75 (1901).   Turkestan.
12. *C. Försteri*, Reitter, Wien. Ent. Zeit. p. 158, t. 1, f. 2 (1900).   Kuku-noor.
13. *C. Grafi*, Reitter. Deutsche Ent. Zeitschr. p. 74 (1901).   Sibirien.
var. *Heinrichi*, Reitter, ibidem, p. 74 (1901).
var *Grafianus*, Reitter, ibidem, p. 74 (1901).
14. *C. Hahni*, Reitter, ibidem, p. 410 (1907).   Uralsk.
15. *C. hieroglyphicus*, Klug. Symb. Phys. Vol. 5, t. 42. f. 5 (1845).   Aegypten.
hieroglyphicus, Reitter, Tab. p. 85; Brünn, 30, p. 223.   Tripolis, Syrien.
maculosus, Wollaston, Cat. Canar. Col. p. 189 (1864).   Kanarische Inseln.
magicus, Fairmaire, Ann. Mus. Stor. Nat. Genova, Vol. 7, p. 507 (1875).   Tunis.
sec. d'Orbigny, L'Abeille, Vol. 28, p. 229 (1896).
*conspurcatus** || Brullé, Webb & Bertholet, Canar. Ent. p. 60 (1838).   Kanarische Inseln.
*sticticus** || Hartig. Geol. Verh. Lanzar. p. 140.   Kanarische Inseln.
var. *castilianus*, J. Daniel, München. Koleopt. Zeitschr. Vol. 1 (2), p. 251 (1903).   Spanien.
16. *C. interstitialis*, Koshantschikow, Hor. Soc. Ent. Ross. 1893-94, Vol. 28,   Turkestan.
p. 115 (1894).

17. *C. lineolatus*, Illiger, Mag. Vol. 2, p. 191 (1803).   Portugal.
lineolatus, Reitter, Tab. p. 83; Brünn, 30, p. 221.   Südeuropa, Nordafrika, Syrien,
Mulsant, Hist. Nat. Col. France, Lamell. p. 298 (1871).   Südfrankreich.   [Transkauk.
lateralis, Brullé, Expéd. Morée, Vol. 3, p. 171 (1836).   Griechenland.
nigrolineatus, Rosenhauer, Beitr. Vol. 1, p. 30 (1847).   Sardinien.
var. *conjunctus*, Mulsant, Hist. Nat. Col. France, Lamell. p. 238 (1842).   Frankreich, Korsika.
var. *deletus*, Mulsant, ibidem, p. 238 (1842).   Frankreich.
var. *fuscicollis*, Mulsant, ibidem, p. 238 (1842).   Frankreich. ·
var. *vittatus*, Mulsant, ibidem, p. 238 (1842).   Frankreich.
18. *C. melanostictus*, W. Schmidt. Germar Zeitschr. Ent. Vol. 2, p. 153 (1840).   Deutschland.
melanostictus, Erichson, Naturg. Ins. Deutschl. Vol. 3, p. 842 (1848).   Mittel-, Süddeutschland, Aegypten, Mesopotamien.
Reitter, Tab. p. 86; Brünn, 30, p. 225.   Europa, Kaukasus, Turkestan.
conspurcatus || Herbst, Natursyst. Ins. Vol. 2, p. 140, t. 12, f. 8 (1789).
Illiger, Verz. Käf. Preuss. p. 25, var α (1798).   Preussen.
Sturm, Deutschl. Ins. Vol. 1, p. 102 (1805).   Deutschland.
*lituratus**, Rey, L'Echange, No 69, p. 164 (1890).   Frankreich.
sec. d'Orbigny, L'Abeille, Vol. 28, p. 228 (1896).
· A. Schmidt, Aphodiinen-Zusammenst. Deutsche Ent. Zeitschr.
Beih. p. 49, Anmerkung (1907-08).
var. *egenus*, Mulsant, Hist. Nat. Col. France, Lamell. p. 241 (1842).   Frankreich.
biguttatus, Dalla Torre, Ber. Ver. Naturk. Oberösterr. Vol. 10, p. 108 (1879).   Oberösterreich.
sec. Schilsky, Deutsche Ent. Zeitschr. p. 320 (1888).
var. *catenatus*, Mulsant, Hist. Nat. Col. France, Lamell. p. 241 (1842).   Frankreich.
var. *sexmaculatus*, Mulsant, ibidem, p. 241 (1842).   Frankreich.
var. *septemmaculatus*, Mulsant, ibidem, p. 241 (1842).   Frankreich.
var. *subannulatus*, Mulsant, ibidem, p. 241 (1842).   Frankreich.
bifasciatus, Dalla Torre, Ber. Ver. Naturk. Oberösterr. Vol. 10, p. 108 (1879).   Oberösterreich.
sec. Schilsky, Deutsche Ent. Zeitschr. p. 320 (1888).

var. graphicus, Kolenati, Melet. Ent. Vol. 5, p. 18 (1846). Südrussland.
    sec. Reitter, Tab. p. 86; Brünn, 3o, p. 225.
  var. lineata, Dalla Torre, Ber. Ver. Naturk. Oberösterr. Vol. 10, p. 108 (1879). Oberösterreich.
19. *C. naevuliger*, Reitter, Ent. Nachr. p. 187 (1894). Tunis.
20. *C. nigrivittis*, Solsky, Fedtschenko, Turkest. Col. p. 327 (1876). Chokand.
  obliquatus, Reitter, Tab. p. 88; Brünn, 3o, p. 226 Taschkent, Turkmenien.
    sec. Semenow, Hor. Soc. Ent. Ross. 1897, Vol. 31, p. 598 (1898).
21. *C. obsoleteguttatus*, Waterhouse, Trans. Ent. Soc. Lond. p. 86 (1875). Japan.
22. *C. pictus*, Sturm, Deutsch. Ins. Vol. 1, p. 100 (1805). Oesterreich-Mähren.
  pictus, Duftschmid, Fauna Austr. Vol. 1, p. 112 (1805). Wien.
  W. Schmidt, Germars Zeitschr. f. Ent. Vol. 2, p. 159 (1840). Pommern.
  Erichson, Naturg. Ins. Deutschl. Vol. 3, p. 847 (1848). Deutschland.
  Reitter, Tab. p. 83; Brünn. 3o, p. 221. Schweden, Finnland.
  inquinatus, var. η, Creutzer, Ent. Vers. p. 24, t. 1, f. 1 (1799).
  var. flavidulus, Mulsant, Hist. Nat. Col. France, Lamell. p. 249 (1842). Frankreich.
  var. brumalis, Mulsant, ibidem. p. 249 (1842). Frankreich.
  var. indigens, Mulsant, ibidem. p. 249 (1842). Frankreich.
23. *C. Plutschewskyi*, Koshantschikow, Hor. Soc. Ent. Ross. 1893-94, Vol. 28, Kirgisen-Steppe.
  p. 123 (1894).
24. *C. pustulifer*, Reitter, Tab. p. 90; Brünn, 3o, p. 228; Deutsche Ent. Sarepta, Beirut, Tanger,
  Zeitschr. p. 75 (1901). Neu-Merw, Transkaspien.
25. *C. scuticollis*, Semenow, Hor. Soc. Ent. Ross. 1897, Vol. 31, p. 598 Issyk-kul.
  (1898); Bull. Soc. Nat. Mosc. 1897, Vol. 11. p. 506, 508 (1898).
  nigrivittis, Reitter (non Solsky), Tab. p. 89; Brünn, 3o, p. 227. Turkestan.
  tescorum, Semenow, Bull. Soc. Nat. Mosc. 1897, Vol. 11, p. 506, 508 (1898). Westsibirien.
  kukunoriensis, Semenow, ibidem, p. 509, (1898). Nordöstliches Tibet.
    sec. A. Schmidt.
26. *C. sesquivittatus*, Fairmaire, C. R. Ann. Soc. Ent. Belg. p. 43 (1883). Batna.
  sesquivittatus, d'Orbigny, L'Abeille, Vol. 28, p. 230 (1896). Südspanien.
27. *C. signifer*, Mulsant & Rey. Ann. Soc. Linn. Lyon, Vol. 28, p. 192 (1870- Syrien.
  71); Opuso. Ent. Vol. 14. p. 216 (1870).
  signifer, Reitter, Tab. p. 83; Brünn, 3o, p. 221. Syrien.
28. *C. sticticus*, Panzer, Fauna Germ. p. 54 (4) (1798). Schlesien.
  sticticus, Creutzer, Ent. Versuche, p. 26 (1799). Wien.
  Sturm, Deutschl. Ins. Vol. 1, p. 106 (1805). Oesterreich, Braunschweig.
  Erichson, Naturg. Ins. Deutschl. Vol. 3, p. 844 (1848). Deutschland.
  Reitter, Tab. p. 83; Brünn, 3o, p. 221. Kaukasus, Nord- und Mitteleu-
  sec. Beare, Ent. M. Mag (2). Vol. 5, p. 276 (1894). England.   [ropa.
  equestris, Panzer, Fauna Germ. p. 58 (2) (1798); Krit. Revis. Vol. 1, p. 21 Schlesien.
  (1805).
  Erichson, Naturg. Ins. Deutschl. Vol. 3, p. 845 (1848).
  nemoralis, Panzer, Fauna Germ. p. 67 (1) (1799). Wien.
  prodromus, Fabricius, Syst. Eleuth. Vol. 1, p. 70 (1810). Deutschland.
  var. clypeolatus, Mulsant, Hist. Nat. Col. France, Lamell. p. 256 (1842). Frankreich.
  var. pallescens, Mulsant, ibidem. p. 256 (1842). Frankreich.
  var. striolatus, Mulsant, ibidem, p. 256 (1842). Frankreich.
  var. prolongatus, Mulsant, ibidem, p. 256 (1842). Frankreich.
  var. ocellatus, Mulsant, ibidem, p. 256 (1842). Frankreich.
  var. confusus, Mulsant, ibidem, p. 256 (1842). Frankreich.
29. *C. tessulatus*, Paykull, Fauna Suec. Vol. 1, p. 20 (1798). Schweden.
  tessulatus, Sturm, Deutschl. Ins. Vol. 1, p. 111 (1805). Oesterreich, Deutschland.
  Erichson, Naturg. Ins. Deutschl. Vol. 3, p. 849 (1848). Deutschland.
  Reitter, Tab. p. 88; Brünn, 3o, p. 226. Europa, Kaukasus.
  inquinatus, Olivier, Ent. Vol. 1 (3), p. 84, t. 26, f. 221 (1789). Frankreich.
  Marsham, Ent. Brit. Vol. 1, p. 13 (1802). England.
  var. irregularis, Mulsant, Hist. Nat. Col. France, Lamell. p. 252 (1842). Frankreich.
  var. connexus, Mulsant, ibidem, p. 252 (1842). Frankreich.
  var. amplificatus, Muslant, ibidem, p. 252 (1842). Frankreich.
  var. appendiculatus, Mulsant, ibidem, p. 252 (1842). Frankreich.
  var. dilatatus, Mulsant, ibidem. p. 252 (1842). Frankreich.
  contaminatus ‖ Panzer, Fauna Germ. p. 47 (7) (1797). Deutschland.

basalis, Schilsky, Deutsche Ent. Zeitschr. p. 313 (1888).	Thüringen.
sec. Schilsky, ibidem, p. 313 (1888).	
var. scutellatus, Mulsant, Hist. Nat. Col. France, Lamell. p. 252 (1842).	Frankreich.
var. intricatus, Mulsant, ibidem, p. 253 (1842).	Frankreich.
var. umbrosus, Mulsant, ibidem, p. 253 (1842).	Frankreich.
var. Gutheili, Schilsky, Deutsche Ent. Zeitschr. p. 313 (1888).	Thüringen, Oesterreich.

30. *C. turkestanicus* 1), Heyden, Deutsche Ent. Zeitschr. p. 323 (1881).   Margljan.

turkestanicus, Reitter, Tab. p. 87; Brünn, 30, p. 225.	Turkestan.

31. *C. variicolor*, Koshantschikow, Hor. Soc. Ent. Ross. 1893-94, Vol. 28,   Kirgisen-Steppe.
p. 124 (1894).

25. Subgenus NIMBUS, Mulsant

Nimbus. Mulsant, Hist. Nat. Col. France, Lamell. p. 338 (1871).

Charaktere. — In den hellbraunen, schwarzgefleckten Flügeldecken mit der vorigen Untergattung übereinstimmend, aber durch den metallisch schwarzgefärbten Kopf und Thorax, durch die vollständig abgerundeten Hinterwinkel des letzteren deutlich verschieden.

Der Körper ist länglich, nicht stark gewölbt, meistens sehr dicht und länger behaart, auch die Ränder des Halsschildes, selten sind die Flügeldecken nur um die Spitze herum fein und kurz, oder Halsschildränder und Flügeldecken vollständig kahl.

Der Kopf ist schwarz, sein Vorderrand zuweilen rötlich durchscheinend, flach gewölbt, meistens stark punktiert, besonders vorn, der Clipeus ist breit, hauptsächlich beim Männchen, wenig ausgerandet, seitlich davon verrundet, die Wangen sind klein, aber deutlich, oft mit Borstenbüschel, die Stirnlinie ist meist deutlich, ohne Höcker, höchstens mit schwachen Ansätzen

Das Halsschild ist quer, wenig gewölbt, seitlich meistens deutlich gerundet und bewimpert, die Seiten, die breit verrundeten Hinterwinkel und die Basis sind gerandet, die Oberfläche ist deutlich und ziemlich dicht punktiert.

Das Schildchen ist klein, dreieckig, schwarz und punktiert.

Die Flügeldecken hinter der Mitte wenig verbreitert, mit deutlichen Streifen, die zuweilen sehr grob punktiert sind, die Zwischenräume sind eben, gewöhnlich nur vor der Spitze gewölbt, seltener in der ganzen Länge, sie sind sehr fein oder auch stärker und dichter, besonders neben den Streifen punktiert.

Die Unterseite ist schwarz, glänzend, punktiert und behaart.

Das Metasternum ist in der Mitte beim Männchen grubig vertieft.

Die Hinterschienen haben am untern Spitzenrande längere und kürzere Borsten.

Die Tarsenglieder sind lang und schlank, das erste derselben ist meistens länger als der obere Enddorn und länger als die zwei folgenden Glieder zusammen.

Die Arten haben eine Grösse von 4 bis 6,5 mm.

Geographische Verbreitung der Arten. — Europa, Algier, Tunis, Syrien, Kaukasus.

1. *N. affinis*, Panzer, Fauna Germ. p. 110 (1).   Oesterreich.

affinis, Erichson. Naturg. Ins. Deutschl. Vol. 3, p. 882 (1848)	Oesterreich.
Reitter. Tab. p. 93; Brünn, 30, p. 231.	Südeuropa.
ciliaris, W. Schmidt, Germar Zeitschr. Ent. Vol. 2, p. 164 (1840)	Süddeutschland.
var. Orbignyi, Clouët, Bull. Soc. Ent. Fr. p. 371 (1896).	Tunis, Algier, Portugal.

2. *N. contamiuatus*, Herbst, Fuessly Arch. Ins. Vol. 4. p. 9. t. 19, f. 13 (1783).   Pommern.

contaminatus, Creutzer, Ent. Versuche, p. 34, t. 1, f. 5 (1799).	Oesterreich.
Panzer, Fauna Germ. p. 110 (2).	Deutschland.
Erichson, Naturg. Ins. Deutschl. Vol. 3, p. 881 (1848).	Deutschland.
Reitter, Tab. p. 94; Brünn, 30, p. 232.	Europa.
sec. Bailey, Ent. M. Mag. p. 90 (1905).	Insel Man.

---

1) Siehe Anmerkung auf Seite 60.

conspurcatus, Olivier, Ent. Vol. 1 (3), p. 81, t. 25, f. 214 (1789).   Europa.
ciliaris, Marsham, Ent. Brit. Vol. 1, p. 14 (1802).   England.
    var. *incoloratus*, Mulsant, Hist. Nat. Col. France, Lamell. p. 292 (1842).   Frankreich.
    var. *miser*, Mulsant, ibidem, p 292 (1842).   Frankreich.
    var. *indistinctus*, Mulsant, ibidem, p. 292 (1842).   Frankreich.

3. *N. harpagonis*, Reitter, Deutsche Ent. Zeitschr. p. 147 (1890); Tab   Syrien.
    p. 93 ; Brünn, 3o, p. 231.

4. *N. Lederi*, Harold, Verh. Naturf. Ver. Brünn, 1877, Vol. 16, p. 189 (1878).   Kaukasus.
    Lederi, Reitter, Tab. p. 93 ; Brünn, 3o, p. 231.

5. *N. obliteratus*, Panzer, Fauna Germ. p. 110 (3).
    obliteratus, W. Schmidt, Germar Zeitschr. Ent. Vol. 2, p. 164 (1840).   Süd- und Mitteldeutschland
    Erichson, Naturg. Ins. Deutschl. Vol. 3, p. 883 (1848).   Sud- und Mitteldeutschland.
    Reitter, Tab. 93; Brünn, 3o, p. 231.   Mittel- und Südeuropa.
    sec. Harold, Verh. Náturf. Ver. Brünn. Vol. 16, p. 192 (1877).   Kaukasus.
    sec. Sharp, Ent. M. Mag. Vol. 1, p. 169 (1864).   England.
    insubidus, Germar, Spec. Ins. Nov. p. 110 (1823).   Halle.
    var. *fulveolus*, Mulsant, Hist. Nat. Col. France, Lamell. p. 289 (1842).   Frankreich.
    Biologie : Xambeu Rev. d'Ent. Caen, Vol. 19, p. 5 (1900). — Kopulation und
    Eiablage.

26. Subgenus MELINOPTERUS, Mulsant

Melinopterus. Mulsant, Hist. Nat. Col. France, Lamell. p. 329 (1871).

Charaktere. — In der länglichen, weniger gewölbten Gestalt, den hellbraunen, oft dicht behaarten Flügeldecken mit *Nimbus* übereinstimmend, unterscheidet sich diese Untergattung von ihr durch das Fehlen der dunklen, strichartigen Makeln und in dem fast immer vorhandenen dunklen Nebelfleck auf den Flügeldecken.

. Der Kopf ist flach, schwarz oder mit rötlichem Rande oder auch jederseits mit einem solchen Flecke hinter demselben, seine Oberfläche ist meistens nur fein punktiert, am Hinterkopf mehr glatt, die Stirnlinie ist bald sichtbar, bald fehlend; der Clipeus ist nur abgestutzt oder schwach ausgerandet, seitlich ist derselbe immer breit verrundet; die Wangen sind klein, aber deutlich, immer einen Haarbüschel tragend.

Das Halsschild ist auf der Scheibe immer schwarz, die Seiten, seltener auch der Hinterrand, gelbrot, erstere sind deutlich gerandet, zuweilen auch der Vorderrand, die Basis ist fast immer sehr fein oder in der Mitte garnicht gerandet, die Hinterwinkel sind stumpf, die Oberfläche ist deutlich, wenn auch nicht sehr dicht punktiert.

Das Schildchen ist klein, dreieckig, vorn nicht verengt, punktiert, schwarz oder braungelb.

Die Flügeldecken sind nach hinten schwach erweitert, gelbbraun oder rotgelb, sehr selten schwarz gefärbt, auf der Scheibe der hellern Arten findet sich sehr häufig ein Nebelfleck, der heller oder dunkler sein kann, sie sind behaart oder glatt, die Streifen der Flügeldecken sind immer deutlich, oft kräftig punktiert, die Zwischenräume sind schwächer oder stärker konvex, meistens feiner, selten stärker punktiert, die Punkte dann mehr neben den Streifen gelegen, so dass die Mitte fast glatt bleibt.

Die Unterseite ist dunkler oder heller, punktiert und behaart.

Die Borsten an den Hinterschienen sind ungleich, der obere Enddorn meistens so lang als das erste Tarsenglied, selten kürzer oder länger, der Metatarsus ist immer reichlich so lang als die zwei folgenden Glieder.

Die Männchen haben oft eine schwach gehöckerte Stirnnaht, einen abgestutzten, an der Spitze umgebogenen Enddorn an den Vordertibien, ein breiteres, auf der Scheibe wenig punktiertes oder glattes Halsschild, eine grubig vertiefte, ganz oder nur am Rande behaarte Metasternalplatte und meistens in der ganzen Länge dicht behaarte Flügeldecken.

Bei den Weibchen ist der Enddorn immer spitz, das Halsschild nie breiter als die Flügeldecken, immer dichter, auch auf der Scheibe punktiert, das Metasternum hat in der Mitte nur eine vertiefte Linie, die Flügeldecken sind höchstens um die Spitze fein und kurz behaart.

Geographische Verbreitung der Arten. — Europa, Nordafrika, Abessinien, Vorder-, Mittel- und Nordasien, Nordamerika, Argentina.

1. *M. Abeillei*, Sietti, Miscell. Ent. Vol. 11, p. 66 (1903).   Algier.
2. *M. Bachofeni*, Reitter, Deutsche Ent. Zeitschr. p. 441 (1906).   Turkestan.
3. *M. Bolassogloi* 1), König, Hor. Soc. Ent. Ross. Vol. 23, p. 304 (1889).   Turkestan.
    Bolassogloi, Reitter, Tab. p. 84; Brünn, 30, p. 235.   Turkestan.
4. *M. Bonnairei*, Reitter, Tab. p. 96; Brünn, 30, p. 234; Deutsche Ent.   Algier, Südfrankreich.
    Zeitschr. p. 440 (1906).
    Bonnairei, d'Orbigny, L'Abeille, Vol. 28, p. 235 (1896).   Algier.
    cuniculorum, Mayet, Bull. Soc. Ent. Fr. p. 131 (1904); Bull. Soc. Nimes,   Nimes.
    Vol. 32, p. 2 (   ).
    sec. Bedel, Bull. Soc. Ent. Fr. p. 92 (1906).
5. *M. consputus*, Creutzer, Ent. Versuche, p. 41, t. 1, f. 6 (1799).   Oesterreich.
    consputus, Erichson, Naturg. Ins. Deutschl. Vol. 3, p. 877 11848).   Deutschland.
    Reitter, Tab. p. 98; Brünn, 30, p. 236; Deutsche Ent. Zeitschr.   Europa, Syrien, Kaukasus, Klein-
    p 439 (1906).   asien.
    sec. d'Orbigny, L'Abeille, Vol. 28, p. 235 (1896).   Algier, Marokko.
    sec. *Fernald, Bull. Brooklyn Soc. Vol. 4, p. 23 (1881).   Maine.
    sec. Walker, Ent. M. Mag. (2), Vol. 5, p 115 (1894).   England.
    prodromus, Duftschmid, Fauna Austr. Vol. 1, p. 109 (1805).   Oesterreich.
    var. *griseus*, W. Schmidt, Germars Zeitschr. f. Ent. Vol. 2, p. 135 (1840).   Pommern.
    mancus, Dalla Torre, Ber. Ver. Naturk. Oberösterr. Vol. 10, p. 109 (1879).   Oberösterreich.
    mendicus, Mulsant, Hist. Nat. Col. France, Lamell. p. 258 (1842).   Frankreich.
    obsoletus, Dalla Torre, Ber. Ver. Naturk. Oberösterr. Vol. 10, p. 109 (1879).   Oberösterreich.
    var. *metallescens*, Mulsant, Hist. Nat. Col. France, Lamell. p. 258 (1842).   Frankreich.
    var. *impunctatus*. Mulsant, ibidem. p. 259 (1842).   Frankreich.
6. *M. costulatus*, Reitter, Deutsche Ent. Zeitschr. p. 33 (1896).   Ostsibirien.
7. *M. eccoptus*, Bates, Ent. M. Mag. Vol. 25, p. 297 (1889).   Japan.
8. *M. Edithae*, Reitter, Deutsche Ent. Zeitschr. p. 437 (1906).   Ordubad.
9. *M. flammulatus*, Harold, Verhandl. Naturf. Ver. Brünn, p. 122 (1876).   Kaukasus.
    flammulatus, Schneider & Lederer, Käf. Kauk. 1877, Vol. 16, p. 190 (1878).   Kaukasus.
    Reitter, Tab p. 96; Brünn, 30, p. 234.   Kaukasus.
10. *M. gregarius*, Harold, Col. Hefte, Vol. 7, p. 112 (1871).   Sarepta.
    gregarius, Reitter, Tab. p. 99; Brünn, 30, p. 237.   Südrussland bis Zentralasien.
    maculicolles || Ballion, Bull. Soc. Nat. Mosc. 1870, Vol. 43 (2), p. 333 (1871).   Südsibirien.
    sec. Harold, Col. Hefte, 09, p. 136 (1872).
11. *M. Gresseri*, ♂, Semenowow, Hor. Soc Ent. Ross. 1898, Vol. 32,   Zentralasien.
    p. 611 (1899); ♀. Bull. Soc. Nat. Mosc. p. 120 (1899).
12. *M. Guillebeaui*, Reitter, Tab. p. 94; Brünn, 30, p 232.   Frankreich.
    Guillebeaui, Reitter, Deutsche Ent. Zeitschr. p. 436 (1906).   Kaukasus.
    pectoralis || Guillebeau, Bull. Soc. Ent. Fr. p. 190 (1888).   Lyon.
13. *M. hastatus*, Reitter, Tab. p. 227; Brünn, 31, p. 106.   Turkestan.
14. *M. inclusus*, Reitter, ibidem, p. 97; ibidem, 30, p. 235; Deutsche Ent.   Araxestal, Transkaspien,
    Zeitschr. p. 441 (1906).   Aulie-Ata.
    Glasunowi, Koshantschinow, Hor. Soc. Ent. Ross. 1893-94, Vol. 28, p. 108   Westturkestan.
    (1894).
    sec. Reitter, Deutsche Ent. Zeitschr. p. 441 (1906).
15. *M. lineimargo*, Reitter, Tab. p. 227; Brünn, 31, p. 106.   Syrien, Kleinasien.
16. *M. Mehelyi*, Csiki, 3. Asiat. Forschungsreise Zichy, Vol. 2, p. 108 (1901).   Mongolei.

---

1) In der *Wien. Ent. Zeit.* 1909, p 110 sagt Reitter : « Ich halte *Bolassogloi* König für das ♂ von *turkestanicus* Heyden » (*Deutsche Ent. Zeitschr.* 1881, p. 323). Da nach der Form dieser Notiz nicht anzunehmen ist, dass Reitter beide Typen vorgelegen, so kann ich seiner Meinung nicht beistimmen; denn beide Arten weichen nach den Beschreibungen in der Zeichnung der Flügeldecken bedeutend voneinander ab, auch erwähnt keiner der Autoren, dass die Anordnung und Zahl der Makeln bei einzelnen Stücken Abweichungen zeigen. Deshalb halte ich beide Tiere für selbständige Arten, bis eine Autopsie Aufklärung bringt.

17. *M. Meuseli*, Reitter, Wien. Ent. Zeit. p. 32 (1906); Deutsche Ent.   Tomsk.
Zeitschr. p. 435 (1906).
18. *M. mossulensis*, Mulsant & Godart, Ann. Soc. Linn. Lyon, Vol. 26,   Mosul.
p. 121 (1879).
19. *M. Mulsanti*, d'Orbigny, L'Abeille. Vol. 28, p. 233 (1896), nom. nov.
    syriacus || Mulsant & Rey. Ann. Soc. Linn. Lyon 1870-71. p. 196 (1872);   Syrien.
    Opuso. Ent. Vol. 14, p. 220 (1870).
20. *M. pallescens**, Walker, Lord List of Coleopt. p. 11 (1871).   Harkeko.
    pallescens, Fairmaire, Ann. Soc. Ent. Fr. p. 443 (1885).   Nordafrika.
    gibbifrons, Fairmaire, Rev. d'Ent. Caen. p. 92 (1892).   Obock
    sec. d'Orbigny. L'Abeille, Vol. 28, p. 261 (1896).   Djibouti.
21. *M. pallididorsis*, Reitter, Hor. Soc. Ent. Ross. Vol. 21, p. 207, 224 (1887);   Chines. - Turkestan, Mon-
Tab. p. 99; Brünn, 30, p. 237.   golei.
22. *M. permodicus*, Reitter, Wien. Ent. Zeit. p. 208 (1895).   Kuku-noor.
23. *M. planus*, Koshantschinow, Hor. Soc. Ent. Ross. 1894-94, Vol. 28,   Orenburg.
p. 125 (1894).
    transvolgensis, Semenow, Hor. Soc. Ent. Ross, 1896-97, Vol. 31, p. 597   Sarepta, Südrussland bis Sibi-
    (1898); Bull. Soc. Nat. Mosc. 1897, Vol. 11. p. 507, 509   rien.
    (1898).
    sec. Reitter, Cat. Col. Eur p. 722 (1906).
    A. Schmidt. Aphodiinen - Zusammenst. Deutsche Ent.
    Zeitschr. Beih. p. 59, Anmerkung (1907-08).
24. *M. prodromus*, Brahm, Insektenkalend. Vol. 1, p. 3 (1790)
    prodromus, Illiger, Mag. Ins. Vol. 1, p. 26 (1802).   Preussen.
    Sturm, Deutschl. Ins. Vol. 1, p. 147 (1805).   Deutschland.
    Erichson, Naturg. Ins. Deutschl. Vol. 3. p. 871 (1848).   Deutschland.
    Reitter, Tab. p. 94; Brünn, 30, p. 232.   Europa, Nordasien.
    Horn, Trans Amer. Ent. Soc. Vol. 14, p. 60 (1887).   Maine, Montreal, Kanada.
    sec. Bailey, Ent. M. Mag. p. 90 (1905).   Insel Man.
    contaminatus, ♂, Paykull. Fauna Suec. Vol. 1, p. 21 (1798).   Schweden.
    contaminatus, var. β, Illiger, Verz. Käf. Preuss. p. 26 (1798).   Preussen.
    contaminatus, ♀, var. γ, Illiger, ibidem, p. 26 (1798).   Preussen.
    sphacelatus, ♀, Panzer, Fauna Germ. p. 58 (5) (1798).   Schlesien.
    Gyllenhal, Ins. Suec. Vol. 1 (1), p. 37 (1808).   Schweden.
    consputus. Fabricius, Syst. Eleuth. Vol. 1, p. 77 (1801).
    Duftschmid, Fauna Austr. Vol. 1, p. 119 (1805).   Oesterreich.
    rapax, Faldermann, Fauna Transcauc. Vol. 1. p. 256 (1836).   Transkaukasien.
    sec. Harold, L'Abeille, Vol. 5, p. 435 (1869).
    var. *restrictus*, Mulsant, Hist. Nat. Col. France, Lamell. p. 284 (1842).   Frankreich.
    var. *flavogriseus*, Mulsant, ibidem, p. 284 (1842).   Frankreich.
    griseus, Dalla Torre, Ber. Ver. Naturk. Oberösterr. Vol. 10, p. 109 (1879).   Oberösterreich.
    var. *angustatus*, Mulsant, ibidem, p. 284 (1842).   Frankreich.
    var. *semilunus*, Mulsant, ibidem, p. 284 (1842).   Frankreich.
    var. *obliquus*, Mulsant. ibidem, p. 285 (1842).   Frankreich.
    var. *semipellitus*, Solsky, Fedtschenko Turkest. Col. p. 335 (1876).   Taschkent.
    Reitter, Tab. p. 98; Brünn, 30, p. 236; Deutsche Ent. Zeitschr.   Tirol, Kaukasus, Turkestan,
    p. 436 (1906).   Zentralasien, Syrien, Griechen-
    circumductus, Solsky, Fedtschenko Turkest. Col. p. 338 (1876).   Kisilkum. [land, Mitteleuropa.
    sec. Reitter, Deutsche Ent. Zeitschr. p. 436 (1906).
    var. *Weberi*, Reitter, ibidem, p. 436 (1906).   Griechenland, Kurdistan.
25. *M. pubescens*, Sturm, Ent. Handb. Vol. 1, p. 40, t. 2, f. S (1800);   Würzburg.
Deutsch. Inst. Vol. 1, p. 150 (1805).
    pubescens, Erichson, Naturg. Ins. Deutschl. Vol. 3, p. 874 (1848).   Mittel- und Süddeutschland.
    Reitter, Tab. p 98, Brünn, 30, p. 236; Deutsche Ent. Zeitschr.   Deutschland, Oesterreich, Kau-
    p. 437 (1906).   kasus, Südfrankreich. Griechen-
    tabidus, Erichson, Naturg. Ins. Deutschl. Vol. 3, p. 876 (1848).   Dalmatien. [land, Kleinasien.
    sec. Reitter, Deutsche Ent. Zeitschr. p. 437 (1906).
    var. *nebulosus*, Schilsky, ibidem, p. 316 (1888).   Bayern, Sachsen.
26. *M. punctatosulcatus*, Sturm. Deutschl. Ins. Vol. 1, p. 113, t. 13, f. A (1805).   Oesterreich.
    punctatosulcatus, Erichson. Naturg Ins. Deutschl. Vol. 3, p. 872 (1848).   Deutschland
    Thomson, Skand. Col. Vol. 10 (1), p. 15 (1868).   Skandinavien.

Reitter, Tab. p. 95: Brünn, 3o, p. 233; Deutsche Ent Zeit.   Europa, Nordasien, Kaukasus.
p. 438 (1906).
    sec. Bailey, Ent. M. Mag. p. 90 (1905).   Insel Man.
fimicola, Gebler, Bull. Soc. Nat. Moscou. Vol. 6, p. 284 (1833).   Westsibirien.
hirtellus, Castelnau, Hist. Nat. Ins. Vol. 2, p. 95 (1840).   Oesterreich.
sabulicola. Thomson, Skand. Col. Vol. 10 (1), p. 16 (1868).   Schweden.
    sec. Harold, Col. Hefte, Vol. 6, p. 117 (1870).
sphacelatus, Marsham, Ent. Brit. Vol. 1, p. 15 (1802).
prodromus, var. *b*, Gyllenhal, Ins. Suec. Vol. 1 (1), p. 36 (1808).   Schweden.
laeviceps*, Rey, L'Echange. p. 164 (1890).   Frankreich.
convexifrons, Rey, ibidem, p. 164 (1890).   Frankreich
    sec. Walker, Ent. M. Mag. (2), Vol. 5 (3o), p. 115 (1894).   England.
var. *marginalis**, Stephens. Ill. Brit. Ent. Vol. 3, p. 203 (1830).   England
var. *extensus*, Mulsant, Hist. Nat. Col. France, Lamell. p. 285 (1842).   Frankreich
punctatosulcatus, var. B., Sturm, Deutschl. Ins. Vol. 1, p. 114 (1805)
prodromus. var. *c*, Gyllenhal, Ins. Suec. Vol. 1 (1), p. 36 (1808).
var. *obscurellus*, Schilsky, Deutsche Ent. Zeitschr. p. 315 (1888).   Mark Brandenburg.
    Reitter, Tab. p. 95; Brünn, 3o, p. 233.   Deutschland. Kaukasien.
funebris, Reitter, ibidem, p. 95; ibidem, p. 233.   Ostsibirien.
    sec. Reitter, Deutsche Ent. Zeitschr. p. 438 (1906).

27. *M. Reyi*, Reitter, Tab. p. 95; Brünn, 3o. p. 233; Deutsche Ent. Zeitschr.   Südfrankreich.
p. 436, Note (1906).
    Reyi, A. Schmidt, Aphodiinen-Zusammenste Deutsche Ent. Zeitschr Beih.
p. 67, Anmerkung (1907-08).

28. *M. Roschlapili*, Csiki, 3. Asiat. Reise, Zichy, Vol. 2, p. 108 (1901).   Mongolei.

29 *M. semiluteus*, Reitter, Hor Soc. Ent. Ross. Vol. 21, p. 225 (1887);   Zaïdam, Chinesisch-Tur-
Tab. p. 96; Brünn, 3o, p. 234.   kestan.
    acutangulus, Reitter, Tab. p. 68; Brünn., 3o, p. 206.   Transkaspien.
    sec. Reitter, Deutsche Ent. Zeitschr. p. 439, Note. (1906).

3o. *M. serotinus*, Panzer, Fauna Germ. p. 67 (2).   Oesterreich.
    serotinus, Creutzer, Ent. Versuche, p. 61, t. 1, f. 11 (1799).   Wien.
    W. Schmidt, Germar Zeitschr. Ent. Vol. 2, p. 106 (1840).   Wien.
    Erichson, Naturg. Ins. Deutschl. Vol. 3, p. 878 (1848).   Triest.
    Reitter, Tab. p. 97; Brünn, 3o. p. 235; Deutsche Ent. Zeitschr.   Europa, Sibirien.
p. 441 (1906).
    sec. Müller, München. Koleopt. Zeitschr. Vol. 2, p. 317 (1904).   Monfalcone (Görzischen).

31. *M. similis*, Koshantschikow, Hor. Soc. Ent. Ross. Vol. 28, p 116 (1894).   Turkestan.
    similis, Reitter, Deutsche Ent. Zeitschr. p. 441. Note (1906).

32. *M. Stolzi*, Reitter, Deutsche Ent. Zeitschr. p. 439 (1906).   Korfu.

33. *M. strigimargo*, Reitter, Tab. p. 100; Brünn, 3o, p. 238; Deutsche Ent.   Turkestan, Taschkent.
Zeitschr. p. 442 (1906)

34. *M. tingens* (var. *olim*), Reitter, Tab. p. 95; Brünn, 3o, p. 233.   Marokko.
    tingens (var. *olim*), Abeille de Perrin, Bull. Soc. Ent. Fr. p. 210 (1895).   Algier. Korsika.
    Reitter, Deutsche Ent. Zeitschr. p. 438 (1906).   Südfrankreich, Spanien.

35. *M. x-signum*, Reitter, Tab. p. 97; Brünn, 3o. p. 235; Deutsche Ent.   Irkutsk, Ostsibirien.
Zeit. p. 441 (1906).

27. SUBGENUS MELAPHODIUS, REITTER

Melaphodius. Reitter, Best.-Tab. Coproph. Lamell. Eur. Col. Heft 24, p. 100 (1892); Verh. Nat. Ver. Brünn, 1891, Vol. 3o, p. 238 (1892).

    Charaktere. — Zwischen dieser und der vorigen Untergattung besteht grosse Aehnlichkeit in der Gestalt und Farbe, beide unterscheiden sich aber in der Randung des Halsschildes. Dasselbe ist am Vorderrande nie, an den Seiten und der Basis deutlicher und stärker als bei *Melinopterus* gerandet, wo die Randung oft schwer sichtbar ist oder in der Mitte ganz fehlt.

    Der Körper ist länglich, wenig gewölbt, schwarz. das Halsschild an den Seiten manchmal heller, die Flügeldecken sind gelbbraun, mit angedunkelter Naht, die Scheibe ist entweder einfarbig oder mit grossem dunklen Längsfleck, seltener sind auch die Seiten dunkel.

Der Kopf ist flach, in der Mitte beulig aufgetrieben, die Stirnnaht zeigt zuweilen drei kleine Höckerchen; der Clipeus ist meistens nur schwach ausgebuchtet, bei einer Art tiefer und beim männlichen Geschlecht derselben sehr tief, die Ecken sind in lange, gekielte Zipfel umgebildet; die Wangen sind nur klein, sie tragen schwache Haarbüschel: die Oberfläche des Kopfes ist deutlich punktiert.

Das Halsschild ist etwas quergewölbt, meistens nicht sehr dicht und ziemlich gleichmässig punktiert, die Hinterwinkel sind stumpf, die Seiten wenig dicht bewimpert.

Die Flügeldecken verbreitern sich wenig nach hinten, ihre Schultern sind mit einzelnen langen Haaren besetzt, die Streifen sind mehr oder weniger stark und ebenso punktiert, die meist etwas konvexen Zwischenräume zeigen nur zuweilen eine stärkere und dichtere Punktierung, um die Spitze herum sind sie öfter fein behaart.

Die Unterseite ist schwärzlich, punktiert und ziemlich lang behaart.

Die Borsten am Endrande der Hinterschienen sind ungleich.

Der obere Enddorn dieser Schienen ist länger oder kürzer als das erste Tarsenglied, dieses fast immer deutlich länger als die zwei folgenden Glieder zusammen.

Die Männchen haben immer in der Mitte grubig vertieftes Metasternum, zuweilen auch noch eine gehöckerte Stirn oder zweizipfligen Clipeus und in der Mitte der Vordertibien befestigten Enddorn, auch ist die Punktierung des Halsschildes gewöhnlich zerstreuter und feiner.

Geographische Verbreitung der Arten. — Spanien, Oesterreich, Algier, Südrussland, Kaukasus, Transcaspien, Turkestan.

1. *M. barbarus*, Fairmaire, Ann. Soc. Ent. Fr. p. 171 (1860).   Algier, Spanien.
   irritans, Reitter, Tab. p. 101; Brünn, 30, p. 239; Ent. Nachr. p. 188 (1894).   Algier.
   sec. Clouët, Bull. Ent. Soc. Fr p. 15 (1897).
2. *M. caspius*, Ménétriés, Cat. Rais, p. 181 (1832).   Derbent.
   caspius, Faldermann, Fauna Transcauc. Vol. 1, p. 255 (1836).   Transkaukasien.
   Reitter, Tab. p. 101; Brünn, 30, p. 239.   Krim, Kaukasus.
3. *M. limbatus*, Germar, Inst. Spec. Nov. p. 112 (1824).   Oesterreich.
   limbatus, Erichson, Naturg. Ins. Deutschl. Vol. 3, p. 876 (1848)   Oesterreich.
   Mulsant, Hist. Nat. Col. France, Lamell. p 337 (1871).   Südrussland.
   Reitter, Tab. p. 101; Brünn, 30, p. 239.   Kirgisen-Steppe.
   circumcinctus, W. Schmidt, Germar Zeitschr. Ent. Vol. 2, p. 143 (1840).   Oesterreich.
4. *M. lunifer*, Solsky, Fedtschenko Turkest. Col. Vol. 1, p. 336, t. 1, f. 18   Taschkent.
   (1876). — **Taf. I, Fig. 3.**
   lunifer, Reitter, Tab. p. 100; Brünn, 30, p. 238   Taschkent.

28. SUBGENUS LIMARUS, MULSANT

Limarus. Mulsant, Hist. Nat. Col. France, Lamell. p. 264 (1871).

Charaktere. — In diese Untergattung gehören nur wenige Arten. Ihr Körper ist kürzer, etwas breiter, gewölbt, schwarz gefärbt, der Vorderkopf und die Seiten des Halsschildes sind etwas heller, die rotbraunen Flügeldecken sind einfarbig oder mit kleinen Flecken, kahl oder dicht abstehend behaart.

Der Kopf ist flach, deutlich punktiert, die Stirnnaht ist gehöckert, der mittelste Höcker nach vorn beulig verlängert, der Seitenrand ist deutlich verflacht; der Clipeus ist ausgerandet, seitlich davon mit winkliger und aufgebogener Ecke; die Wangen sind zwar klein aber deutlich.

Das Halsschild ist quergewölbt, ziemlich dicht mit gröberen und feinen Punkten besetzt, die Seiten sind bewimpert, wenig gerundet und bis um die stumpf abgerundeten Hinterwinkel gerandet, die Basis selbst ist ohne Rand.

Das Schildchen ist schwarz, punktiert, dreieckig, vorn nicht verengt.

Die an der Schulter bewimperten Flügeldecken sind hinten verbreitert und haben deutliche

Punktstreifen, die Zwischenräume sind entweder schwach gewölbt oder haben stumpfe Rippen, sie sind immer deutlich punktiert, die Punkte aber mehr neben den Streifen liegend.

Die Unterseite ist schwärzlich oder mehr braun, glänzend, punktiert und behaart.

Die Hinterschienen haben am untern Spitzenrande längere und kürzere Borsten, ihr oberer Enddorn ist nicht ganz so lang als das erste Glied, dieses fast so lang als die drei folgenden Glieder zusammen.

Geographische Verbreitung der Arten. — Nord- und Mitteleuropa, Norditalien, Algier, Kaukasus.

1. *L. hirtipennis*, Lucas, Explor. Algér. Ent.Vol. 2, p. 263, t. 23, f. 13 (1849).	Algier.
hirtipennis, Harold. Berl. Ent. Zeitschr. p. 184, 195 (1874).	Algier.
Reitter, Tab. p. 102; Brünn, 30, p. 240.	Algier.
2. *L. maculatus*, Sturm, Ent. Handb. Vol. 1, p. 42 (1800).	Neuwaldegg (Oesterreich).
maculatus, Sturm, Deutschl Ins. Vol. 1, p. 109 (1805).	Neuwaldegg (Oesterreich).
Erichson, Naturg. Ins. Deutschl Vol. 3, p. 851 (1848).	Süd- und Mitteldeutschland.
Harold, Berl. Ent. Ent. Zeitschr. p. 184, 193 (1874).	Nord- und Mitteleuropa.
Reitter, Tab. p. 101; Brünn, 30, p. 239.	Kaukasus.
tessellatus, var. α, Creutzer, Ent. versuche, p. 29, t. 1, f. 2 (1799).	Neuwaldegg.
styriacus, Grimmer, Steierm. Col. p. 40 (1841).	Steiermark.
var. *obsoletus*, Dalla Torre, Ber. Ver. Naturk. Oberösterr. Vol. 10, p. 108 (1879).	Oberösterreich.
immaculatus, Schilsky, Deutsche Ent. Zeitschr. p. 313 (1888).	Oesterreich.
sec. Schilsky, ibidem, p. 320 (1888).	
var. *fasciatus*, Dalla Torre, Ber. Ver. Naturk. Oberösterr. Vol. 10, p. 108 (1879).	Oberösterreich.
3. *L. Zenkeri*, Germar, Mag. Ent. Vol. 1, p. 118 (1813).	Halle, Leipzig.
Zenkeri, Erichson, Naturg. Ins. Deutschl. Vol. 3, p. 852 (1848).	Harz.
Mulsant, Hist. Nat. Col. France, Lamell. p. 264 (1871).	Frankreich.
Harold, Berl. Ent. Zeitschr. p. 184, 194 (1874).	Mitteleuropa.
Reitter, Tab. p. 101; Brünn. 30, p. 239.	Deutschland, Norditalien.
sec. Beare. Ent. M. Mag. (2), Vol. 5, p 276 (1894).	England.

29. SUBGENUS PHARAPHODIUS, REITTER

Pharaphodius. Reitter, Best.-Tab. Coproph. Lamell. Eur. Col. Vol. 24, p. 34 (1892); Verhandl. Natur. Ver. Brünn, 1891, Vol. 30, p. 172 (1892).

Charaktere. — Die Untergattung unterscheidet sich von allen andern durch die Streifung der Flügeldecken, die alle unverbunden bis zur Spitze reichen.

Der Körper ist schwarz oder auch rotbraun, stark gewölbt, glänzend, unbehaart, vor der Spitze kaum verbreitert.

Der Kopf ist wenig gewölbt, bogig nach vorn verschmälert, fein punktiert, die Stirnlinie trägt in der Mitte einen Tuberkel. die seitlichen fehlen; die Wangen sind stumpfwinklig; der Clipeus ist deutlich ausgerandet, seitlich mehr stumpfwinklig und aufgebogen.

Das Halsschild ist quer, stark herabgewölbt, aber wenig gerundet, der Seitenrand setzt sich nur bis um die stumpfen Hinterwinkel fort und erlischt dann, die Oberfläche ist zerstreut und grob punktiert.

Das Schildchen ist vorn parallel, länglich und glatt.

Die Streifen der Flügeldecken sind kräftig und stark punktiert, sie werden nach hinten zu breiter, die Zwischenräume dagegen schmaler, diese sind hier stark konvex, auf dem Rücken und an den Seiten jedoch nur schwach gewölbt, alle bleiben bis zur Spitze unverbunden und sind nur mikroskopisch fein aber sehr zerstreut punktiert.

Die Unterseite, besonders die Beine, ist heller, punktiert und behaart, das Metasternum hat in der Mitte eine vertiefte Linie.

Die Borsten am untern Endrande der Hinterschienen sind kurz, nach oben hin mit einigen längeren dazwischen.

Das erste Glied an den Hinterfüssen ist kürzer als der obere Enddorn, es ist so lang als die zwei folgenden Glieder.

Hierher gehört nur eine Art von 5,5 bis 6 mm Länge.

Geographische Verbreitung der Art. — China.

1. *P. putearius*, Reitter, Wien. Ent. Zeit. p. 208 (1895).
   puterrius, Clouët, Ann. Soc. Ent. Fr. p. 240 (1898).

China.

30. SUBGENUS MENDIDAPHODIUS, REITTER

Mendidaphodius, Reitter, Deutsche Ent. Zeitschr. p. 73 (1901).

Charaktere. — Der Körper ist länglich, parallel, glänzend, unbehaart, braunschwarz, der Vorderkopf und die Seiten des Halsschildes sind heller, die Flügeldecken haben eine schmutzig braungelbe Farbe.

Der Kopf ist wenig gewölbt, in der Mitte etwas aufgetrieben, er ist runzlig punktiert, mit gerader, ungehöckerter Stirnnaht; die rundlichen Wangen überragen die Augen; der Clipeus ist ausgerandet und zeigt jederseits zwei kleine Zähnchen.

Das Halsschild ist quer und gewölbt, stärker und fein, aber nicht dicht punktiert, seine Seiten sind wenig gerundet, die Hinterwinkel stumpf, die Basis ist ungerandet.

Das Schildchen ist klein, dreieckig, vorn nicht parallel, einzeln punktiert.

Die Flügeldecken sind nach hinten wenig verbreitert, fast parallel, mit dunkler Naht und deutlichen Punktstreifen, die fast ebenen Zwischenräume sind fein und zerstreut punktiert und haben auf der Scheibe zwei dunkle Längsstreifen.

Die Vorderschienen sind am Aussenrande mit drei langen und starken Zähnen versehen, darüber haben sie noch mehrere Kerbzähnchen.

Die Borsten am Endrande der Hinterschienen sind ungleich, das erste Glied an den letzteren ist so lang als der obere Enddorn, aber kürzer als die zwei folgenden Glieder.

Durch den grobpunktierten Kopf, den gezähnten Clipeus ähnelt diese Untergattung *Mendidius* Harold, entfernt sich aber von ihr durch die ungerandete Basis des Halsschildes und die ungleichen Borsten an den Hinterschienen.

Hierher gehört eine Art von 4,5 mm Länge.

Geographische Verbreitung der Art :

1. *M. spinifrontis*, Reitter, Deutsche Ent. Zeitschr. p. 73 (1901).

Indersk.

31. SUBGENUS GONAPHODIUS, REITTER

Gonaphodius. Reitter. Best.-Tab. Coproph. Lamell. Eur. Col. Heft 24, p. 102 (1892); Verhandl. Naturf. Ver. Brünn, 1891, Vol. 30, p. 241 (1892).

Charaktere. — Die zwei Arten dieser Untergattung haben in Farbe und Gestalt grosse Aehnlichkeit mit der Untergattung *Pseudacrossus* Reitter, sie unterscheiden sich aber von letzterer durch die gerandete Basis.

Der Körper ist länglich, hinten schwach verbreitert, gewölbt, glänzend, unbehaart, schwarz gefärbt, die Flügeldecken zeigen manchmal eine dunkelrote Farbe.

Der Kopf ist kurz und breit, nach vorn stark verschmälert, wenig gewölbt, deutlich punktiert, die Stirnnaht ist undeutlich, ohne Höckerchen; der Clipeus ist breit ausgebuchtet und dann verrundet; die Wangen sind stumpfwinklig und haben schwache Borstenbüschel.

Das Halsschild ist quer, wenig herabgewölbt, die Seiten sind schwach gerundet und bewimpert,

der Seitenrand reicht entweder bis an die Hinterwinkel oder um dieselben herum, die Basis ist zweibuchtig, ohne Randung, die Hinterwinkel sind rundlich oder abgeschrägt und schwach ausgerandet, die
Oberfläche ist feiner und stärker punktiert, bald dichter, bald zerstreuter.

Das Schildchen ist dreieckig, glatt oder punktiert.

Die Flügeldecken sind punktiert-gestreift, die Zwischenräume flach und sehr fein punktiert.

Die Unterseite ist glänzend, punktiert und behaart.

Der Enddorn an den Vordertibien ist lang und kräftig, zuweilen an der Spitze umgebogen.

Die Endborsten am untern Spitzenrande der Hinterschienen sind lang und kurz, der obere Enddorn ist dem ersten Gliede an Länge gleich, dieses ist länger als die zwei folgenden, aber nicht so lang als
die drei nächsten Glieder.

Die Arten sind 7 bis 8 mm lang.

Geographische Verbreitung der Arten. — Chinesisch-Turkestan.

1. *G. postangulus*, Reitter, Hor. Soc. Ent. Ross. Vol. 21, p. 225 (1887);   Chinesisch-Turkestan.
  Tab. p. 102; Brünn, 30, p. 240.
2. *G. Przewalskyi*, Reitter, Hor. Soc. Ent. Ross. Vol. 21, p. 226 (1887);   Tibet, Chinesisch-Turke-
  Tab p. 102; Brünn, 30, p. 241.   stan.

32. Subgenus CALAPHODIUS, Reitter

Calaphodius. Reitter, Best.-Tab. Coproph. Lamell. Eur. Col. Heft 24, p. 90 (1892; Verh. Nat. Ver.
Brünn, 1891, Vol. 30, p. 228 (1892).

Charaktere. — Wegen der schwarzgefleckten Flügeldecken könnten diese Arten leicht zu der
Untergattung *Volinus* Mulsant gezählt werden, doch die vollständig ungerandete Basis des Halsschildes
und die höckerlose Stirn unterscheiden sie.

Die Arten sind flach gewölbt, länglich, glänzend, schwarz; der Kopf ist selten rot gesäumt, die
Seiten des Halsschildes sind schmaler oder breiter rotgelb, die Flügeldecken hellbraun oder rötlichgelb,
immer mit mehreren dunklen Flecken oder solchen und Längsstrichen, vor der Spitze und an den
Seiten sind die Flügeldecken meistens hell behaart.

Der Kopf ist flach, nach vorn verengt, der Clipeus ist abgerundet oder abgestutzt, nur selten
schwach ausgebogt, die Oberfläche ist punktiert, die Stirnnaht ist undeutlich und ohne Höcker; die
Wangen sind deutlich, mit Haarbüscheln.

Das Halsschild ist quer, wenig gewölbt und seitlich nur schwach gerundet, selten breiter als die
Flügeldecken, der Seitenrand ist sparsam bewimpert und reicht bis an die Basis, diese ist ohne Rand,
die Hinterwinkel sind stumpf, die Oberfläche ist deutlich punktiert.

Das Schildchen ist schwarz oder braun, dreieckig und meistens glatt.

Die Flügeldecken haben deutliche, oft tiefe Punktstreifen, die Zwischenräume sind meistens nur
flach gewölbt, zuweilen vor der Spitze stärker, sie sind fast immer nur fein und zerstreut punktiert, vor
der Spitze und an den Seiten manchmal dichter und gröber.

Die Unterseite ist schwarz, die Seiten der Hinterbrust, die Schenkel und das Abdomen sind
punktiert und behaart.

Der untere Spitzenrand der Hintertibien zeigt kurze und längere Borsten. Der obere Enddorn
dieser Tibien ist gewöhnlich so lang als das erste Glied, dieses nicht ganz so lang als die drei folgenden
Glieder zusammen.

Die Männchen sind kenntlich an dem weniger punktierten Halsschilde und der vertieften, an
den Seiten behaarten Metasternalplatte, die beim Weibchen nur vertiefte Mittellinie zeigt.

Hierher gehören mittelgrosse Tiere von 5 bis 9 mm Länge.

Geographische Verbreitung der Arten. — Spanien, Zentralasien, Ostsibirien.

1. *C. Bonvouloiri*, Harold, Ann. Soc. Ent. Fr. p. 615 (1860); Berl. Ent.   Spanien.
Zeitschr. p. 380, 387 (1862).

Bonvouloiri, Reitter, Tab. p 91; Brünn, 30, p. 229.   Spanien.

2. *C. fundator*, Reitter, ibidem, p. 92; ibidem, p. 230.   Chinesisch-Turkestan.

ignobilis, Heyden (non Reitter).
sec. Heyden, Catal. Sib. 1. Nachtr. p. 72 (1895).

3. *C. ignobilis*, Reitter, Hor. Soc. Ent. Ross. Vol. 21, p. 223 (1887); Tab.   Zentralasien, Burchan-Bu-
p. 92; Brünn, 30, p. 230.   da-Gebirge.

4. *C. Koltzei*, Reitter, Tab. p. 91; Brünn, 30. p. 229.   Ostsibirien.

5. *C. Makowskyi*, Koshantschikow, Hor. Soc. Ent. Ross. 1890-91, Vol. 25,   Turkestan.
p. 438 (1891).

Makowskyi, Reitter, Tab. p. 92; Brünn, 30, p. 230.   Taschkent.

6. *C. nigrotessellatus*, Motschulsky, Bull. Soc. Nat. Mosc. Vol. 39 (1), p. 170   Japan.
(1866).

variabilis, Waterhouse, Trans. Ent. Soc. Lond. p. 90 (1875).   Japan.
sec. Lewis, Ann. Mag. Nat. Hist. (6), Vol. 16, p. 381 (1895).

33. Subgenus AGOLIUS, Mulsant

Agolius. Mulsant, Hist. Nat. Col. France, Lamell. p. 232 (1871); J. Daniel, München. Koleopt. Zeitschr. Vol. 1 (1), p. 73 (1902).

Charaktere. — Der Körper ist meistens hinten nur wenig breiter, gewölbt, glänzend, seltener etwas matt auf den Flügeldecken, unbehaart, schwarz oder braun gefärbt, der Vorderrand des Kopfes und Seiten des Halsschildes ist bei den dunklen Arten gewöhnlich etwas heller; die Flügeldecken sind einfarbig schwarz oder mit hellerem Scheibenfleck, aber auch rotbraun oder gelbbraun mit helleren oder dunkleren Flecken, auch zuweilen einfarbig braun, überhaupt ändert die Farbe bei diesen Arten sehr ab.

Der Kopf ist klein, flach, ohne Höckerchen, immer deutlich punktiert, die Stirnnaht ist zuweilen leicht wahrnehmbar; der Clipeus ist mehr oder weniger breit verflacht, rundlich oder abgestutzt und dann schwächer oder stärker ausgerandet und seitlich stark verrundet; die Wangen sind klein, aber deutlich.

Das Halsschild ist bedeutend breiter als der Kopf, meistens stark gewölbt und dicht, ungleich gross punktiert, die Seitenrandung setzt sich mehr oder weniger weit um die gerundeten Hinterwinkel fort, die Mitte der Basis bleibt ungerandet, nur bei *picturatus* J. Daniel ist manchmal die Basis ganz gerandet.

Das Schildchen ist klein, dreieckig, entweder nur an der Basis einzeln oder in der ganzen Ausdehnung dichter punktiert

Die Flügeldecken haben deutliche Punktstreifen, die Zwischenräume sind meistens eben, deutlich punktiert, seltener chagriniert und dann sehr fein punktiert.

Die Unterseite ist glänzend, punktiert und behaart, auch die Schenkel, aber nur mehr vereinzelt.

Die Borstenkränze an den Hinterschienen sind ungleich, der obere Enddorn ist fast immer dem ersten Gliede gleich, dieses gewöhnlich etwas länger als die zwei folgenden Glieder.

Der Enddorn an den Vordertibien zeigt bei dem Männchen der einzelnen Arten die grösste Abweichung und wird mit zu ihrer Unterscheidung verwendet; er ist entweder spitz und kurz oder verlängert, schmaler oder stark verbreitert, zugespitzt, abgestutzt oder mit hakig umgebogener Spitze, er liegt entweder in derselben Ebene mit den Tibien oder ist weniger oder stärker herabgebogen.

Die Weibchen weichen von den Männchen ab in der Form des Enddorns, in der mehr verbreiterten, mehr konvexen Gestalt, der mehr glänzenden, oft anders gefärbten Oberseite, auch in der Form des Halsschildes.

Hierher gehören nur kleine Tiere von 4 bis 6,5 mm Länge, die ausschliesslich die Gebirge bewohnen.

Geographische Verbreitung der Arten. — Pyrenäen, Apenninen, Bosnien, Herzegowina, Karpathen, Sudeten, Alpen.

1. *A. abchasicus*, Reitter. Tab. p. 103; Brünn, 3o, p. 241.　　　　Kaukasus.
   abchasicus, J. Daniel, München. Koleopt. Zeitschr Vol. 1, p. 75, 78 (1902).　Circassien, Abhasien.
2. *A. amblyodon*, K. Daniel, Soc. Ent. Zürich, Vol. 15, p. 139 (1900);　Westalpen.
   München. Koleopt. Zeitschr. Vol. 1, p. 76, 85 (1902).
3. *A. consobrinus*, K. Daniel, Soc. Ent. Zürich, Vol. 15, p. 139 (1900);　Tirol, Südtirol.
   München. Koleopt. Zeitschr. Vol. 1, p. 76, 82 (1902).
   var. samniticus, J. Daniel, München, Koleopt. Zeitschr. Vol. 1, p. 83 (1902).　Abruzzen.
   Bilimecki, Seidlitz, Fauna Transsylv. p. 149 (1891) (ex parte).
4. *A. Danielorum*, Semenow, Rev. Russe d'Ent. Vol. 2, p. 294 (1902).
   Bilimecki, Seidlitz. Fauna Transsylv. p. 149 (1891) (pars).　Schweiz, Abruzzen.
   Reitter. Tab. p. 104; Brünn, 3o, p. 242.　Schweiz, Abruzzen.
   J. Daniel, München. Koleopt. Zeitschr. Vol. 1, p. 79 (1902).　Schweiz.
   var. picturatus, J. Daniel, ibidem, p. 80 (1902).
5. *A. Haroldi*, Koshantschikow, Hor. Soc. Ent. Ross. 1893-94, Vol. 28, p. 98　Turkestan.
   (1894).
   Haroldi, J. Daniel, München. Koleopt. Zeitschr. Vol. 1, p. 93 (1902).
6. *A. Heydeni*, Harold, Col. Hefte, Vol. 7, p. 112 (1871).　Asturien.
   Heydeni, Reitter, Tab. p. 104; Brünn, 3o, p. 243.　Nordspanien.
   J. Daniel, München. Koleopt. Zeitschr. Vol. 1, p. 76, 79 (1902).　Nordspanien.
7. *A. limbolarius*, Reitter. Tab. p. 104; Brünn, 3o, p. 242.　Bosnien, Herzegowina.
   limbolarius, J. Daniel, München. Koleopt. Zeitschr. Vol. 1, p. 76, 80 (1902).　Sudeten.
   Bernhaueri, ♀, Reitter, Wien. Ent. Zeit. p. 269 (1896).　Altvatergebirge.
8. *A. mixtus*. Villa, Col. Eur. Dupl. p. 34 (1833); *Col. Diagn. Repet.　Alpen.
   p. 11 (1868).
   mixtus, Reitter, Tab. p. 103; Brünn, 3o, p. 241.　Apenninen, Karpathen.
   J. Daniel, München. Koleopt. Zeitschr. Vol. 1, p. 75, 77 (1902).　Pyrenäen.
   *abdominalis**, Bonelli, Spec. Fauna Subalp. No 1 (1812).　Piemont
   Ghilian, Berl. Ent. Zeitschr. p. 87 (1859).
   var. discus, W. Schmidt, Germar Zeitschr. Ent. Vol. 2, p. 127 (1840).　Triest.
   Erichson, Naturg. Ins. Deutschl. Vol. 3, p. 885 (1848).　Alpen.
   Dejean, Cat. (ed. 3), p. 160 (1837).　Spanien.
   var. cyclocephalus, Mulsant, Hist. Nat. Col. France, Lamell. p. 270 (1842).　Frankreich.
   var. unicolor, Schilsky, Deutsche Ent. Zeitschr. p. 316 (1888)　Triest.
   var. conjunctus, Schilsky, ibidem. p. 316 (1888).　Schweiz.
   Biologie : Xambeu, L'Echange Lyon, p. 53 (1893). — Larve und Puppe beschrieben.
9. *A. montanus*, Erichson, Naturg. Ins. Deutschl. Vol. 3, p. 887 (1848).　Monte Baldo.
   montanus, Reitter, Tab. p. 105; Brünn, 3o, p. 243.　Monte Baldo.
   J. Daniel, München, Koleopt. Zeitschr. Vol. 1, p. 77, 91 (1902).　Lessiner Alpen, Mont Thabor,
   Rosenhauer, Beitr. Insektenf. Vol. 1, p. 115 (1847).　[Bosnien, Herzegowina.
   Denheli, ♀. Reitter, Deutsche Ent. Zeitschr. p. 76 (1897).　Siebenbürgen.
   sec. Harold, Verh. Naturg. Ver. Brünn, Vol. 16, p. 192 (1877).　Kaukasus.
10. *A. montivagus*, Erichson. Naturg. Ins. Deutschl. Vol. 3, p. 889 (1848).　Steirische Alpen.
    montivagus, Mulsant, Hist. Nat. Col. France, Lamell. p. 235 (1871).　Steirische Alpen.
    Reitter, Tab. p. 105; Brünn, 3o, p. 243.　Kärnthen.
    var. brunnens, Schilsky, Deutsche Ent. Zeitschr. p. 316 (1888).　Steiermark.
    var. cenisius, J. Daniel, München. Koleopt. Zeitschr. Vol. 1, p. 85 (1902).　Mont Cenis.
11. *A. pollicatus*, Erichson. Naturg. Ins. Deutschl. Vol. 3, p. 888 (1848).　Krain, Illyrien.
    pollicatus, Reitter, Tab. p. 104; Brünn, 3o, p. 242.　Oesterreich, Steirische, Kärn-
    J. Daniel, München. Koleopt. Zeitschr. Vol. 1, p. 76, 78 (1902).　Karawanken. [thner Alpen.
12. *A. praecox*, Erichson, Naturg. Ins. Deutschl. Vol. 3, p. 889 (1848).　Steiermark.
    praecox, J. Daniel München Koleopt. Zeitschr. Vol. 1, p. 77, 78 (1902).　Kärnthen, Koralpe. Zirbitzkogl.
    picimanus, Erichson, Naturg. Ins. Deutschl. Vol. 3, p. 890 (1848).　Steiermark.
    Schmidti, Rosenhauer, Beitr. Insektenf. Vol. 1, p. 115 (1847).　Tirol.
    var. penninus, J. Daniel, München. Koleopt. Zeitschr. Vol. 1, p. 89 (1902).　Penninische Alpen.
    ? *var. liguricus*, J. Daniel, ibidem, p. 90 (1902).　Ligurische Alpenninen.
13. *A. Schlumbergeri*, Seidlitz, Fauna Transsylv. p. 150 (1891).　Pyrenäen.
    Schlumbergeri, Reitter, Tab. p. 104; Brünn, 3o, p. 242.　Pyrenäen.
    J. Daniel. München. Koleopt. Zeitschr. Vol. 1, p. 76, 83 (1902).　Pyrenäen.

34. Subgenus BIRALUS, Mulsant

Biralus, Mulsant, Hist. Nat. Col. France, Lamell. p. 227 (1871).

Charaktere. — Diese Untergattung umfasst sehr flach gewölbte, breite, stark glänzende Arten von schwarzer Grundfarbe, deren Flügeldecken zuweilen rot mit schwarzen Makeln oder schwarz mit rotem Schulterfleck und manchmal an der Spitze behaart sind.

Der Kopf ist flach, nur mit schwacher Beule und ebensolcher Stirnnaht, ohne Höcker und fein punktierter Oberfläche, seine Seiten nähern sich nach vorn bogig; der Clipeus ist meistens nur schwach ausgebuchtet und seitlich stark verrundet; die Wangen sind stark abgerundet, sie überragen kaum die Augen.

Das Halsschild ist quer, wenig gewölbt, meistens auf der Scheibe sehr fein, an den Seiten stärker punktiert, seltener mehr gleichmässig und fein, der Seitenrand reicht entweder nur bis zu den abgerundeten Hinterwinkeln oder um diese herum, nur bei *Edgardi* Solsky ist die ganze Basis gerandet, dieselbe ist meistens sehr deutlich zweibuchtig.

Das Schildchen ist breit dreieckig, zum grössten Teil punktiert und schwarz.

Die Flügeldecken sind hinter der Mitte wenig verbreitert, sie haben deutliche Punktstreifen und meist äusserst fein und zerstreut punktierte flache Zwischenräume, die vor der Spitze und an den Seiten eine feine und kurze Behaarung zuweilen aufweisen.

Die Unterseite ist schwärzlich, nur die Beine sind heller, sie ist punktiert und behaart.

Die Hinterschienen haben ungleiche Borsten am untern Spitzenrande.

Der obere Enddorn hat die Länge des ersten Gliedes, selten ist er kürzer, dieses ist länger als die zwei folgenden Glieder.

Es sind mittelgrosse Arten von 5 bis 8 mm Länge.

Die Männchen haben nur an den Seiten des Halsschildes grössere Punkte, eine grubig vertiefte und behaarte Metasternalplatte, selten ist dieselbe kahl, dann ist aber der Enddorn an den Vordertibien weit oben, dem ersten äussern Zahne gegenüber eingelenkt.

Die Weibchen haben auch auf der Scheibe des Halsschildes vor der Basis grössere Punkte und in der Mitte des Metasternums nur eine vertiefte Linie.

Geographische Verbreitung der Arten. — Mittel- und Südeuropa, Syrien, Turkestan.

1. *B. Edgardi,* Solsky, Fedtschenko Reise Turkest. p. 340 (1876).   Turkestan.
     Edgardi, Reitter, Tab. p. 106; Brünn, 30, p. 244.   Turkestan.
2. *B. equinus,* Faldermann, Fauna Transcauc. Col. Vol. 1, p. 257 (1836).   Kaukasus.
     equinus, Reitter, Tab. p. 106; Brünn, 30, p. 244.   Syrien, Turkmenien.
3. *B. Menetriesi,* Ménétriés, Mém. Acad. St-Pétersb. (6), Vol. 6, p. 59, t. 2,   Buchara.
     f. 10 (1849).
     Menetriesi, Reitter, Tab. p. 106; Brünn, 30, p. 244.   Kaukasus, Turkmenien, Syrien.
     Dejean, Cat. (ed 3), p. 161 (1837).   Südrussland.
4. *B. satellitius,* Herbst, Natursyst. Ins. Vol. 2, p. 281, t. 19, f. 1 (1789).   Hannover.   [reich.
     satellitius, Reitter, Tab. p. 106; Brünn, 30. p. 244.   Deutschland,Oesterreich,Frank-
     d'Orbigny, L'Abeille, Vol. 28, p. 239 (1896).   Südeuropa, Syrien, Kaukasus.
     pecari, Fabricius, Ent. Syst. Vol. 1, p. 38 (1792).   Ungarn.
     sec. Harold, Col. Hefte, Vol. 5, p. 114 (1869).
     Illiger, Verz. Käf. Preuss. p. 29 (1798).
     Erichson, Naturg. Ins. Deutschl. Vol. 3, p. 898 (1848).   Deutschland.
     affinis, Brahm, Ins. Kalend. Vol. 1, p. 66 (1790).   Deutschland.
     decipiens, Schrank, Fauna Boica, Vol. 1, p. 382 (1798).   Bayern.
     var. *planus,* W. Schmidt, Germar Zeitschr. Ent. Vol. 2, p. 170 (1840).   Deutschland, Oesterreich.
     var. *invisibilis,* Dalla Torre, Ber. Ver. Naturk. Oberösterr. Vol. 10, p. 109 (1879).   Oberösterreich.
     Biologie : Mulsant, Hist. Nat. Col. France, Lamell. t. 1, f. 7 (1842); Ann. Soc. Agric. Lyon (4), Vol. 3, t. 1, f. 7 (1870). — Abbildung der Larve.

35. Subgenus ACROSSUS, Mulsant

Acrossus, Mulsant, Hist. Nat. Col. France, Lamell. p. 236 (1871).

Charaktere. — Durch den grossen, halbkreisförmigen Kopf mit den spitzen Wangen und das verlängerte erste Tarsenglied der Vordertibien ist diese Untergattung kenntlich.

Der Körper ist bald breit und schwach gewölbt, bald schmaler, parallel und stärker gewölbt, fast immer glänzend, schwarz oder rotbraun gefärbt, das Halsschild ist selten am Rande rotgelb, die Flügeldecken oft heller, einfarbig rot oder mit runder schwarzer Makel, zuweilen auch schwarz mit rotgelber Querbinde oder gelbbraun mit kürzeren oder längeren Strichmakeln, die sich teilweise miteinander verbinden.

Der Kopf ist gross, halbkreisförmig, selten vorn etwas abgestutzt und dann sehr schwach ausgerandet, die Wangen sind meistens gross und spitz, die Oberfläche ist sparsam punktiert, hinten fast glatt, die Stirnlinie ist deutlich, aber immer ungehöckert.

Das Halsschild ist quer, wenig gewölbt, an den Seiten zuweilen sehr dick gerandet, die Basis ist stets ohne Rand, sie ist manchmal schwach zweibuchtig oder mit kurzem Eindruck neben der Mitte, die Oberfläche ist sehr fein, seitlich gewöhnlich mit eingestreuten grösseren Punkten, selten dichter und mehr gleichmässig punktiert.

Das Schildchen ist klein, dreieckig, einzeln punktiert oder auch glatt.

Die Flügeldecken sind selten vor der Spitze behaart, meist nur fein punktiert-gestreift, die ebenen oder schwach gewölbten Zwischenräume sind bald fein, bald stärker, seltener runzlig punktiert.

Die Unterseite stimmt gewöhnlich mit der Oberseite in der Farbe überein, bei *bimaculatus* Laxmann ist der grösste Teil des Abdomens rot, sie ist punktiert und behaart.

Das erste Glied an den Vordertarsen ist länger als das zweite.

Die Endborsten an den Hinterschienen sind ungleich; der obere Enddorn ist meistens nur so lang als das erste Glied, dieses so lang als die drei folgenden Glieder.

Die sexuellen Unterschiede dieser Untergattung sind mancherlei Art. Die Männchen zeichnen sich aus entweder durch dickwulstig gerandeten Kopf, kräftiger punktierte oder matte Flügeldecken, abgestutzten oder stumpf zugerundeten Enddorn an den Vordertibien oder auch durch das vertiefte Metasternum in der Mitte.

Hierher gehören meist grössere Arten.

Geographische Verbreitung der Arten. — Europa, Marokko, Armenien, Persien, Mittel- und Nordasien, Antillen.

1. *A. bimaculatus,* Laxmann, Nov. Comment. Acad. Petrop. Vol. 14 (1),   Südrussland.
   p. 593, t. 24, f. 1 (1770). — **Taf. I, Fig. 4.**
       bimaculatus, Reitter, Tab. p. 170; Brünn, 30, p. 245; Cat. p. 723 (1906).   Norddeutschland, Frankreich.
       bipunctatus, Lepechin, Tageb. Vol. 2, p. 201, t. 10, f. 7 (1775).   Ural.
           Goeze, Ent. Beytr. Vol. 1, p. 96 (1777).
           Fabricius, Mant. Ins. Vol. 1, p. 10 (1787).   Russland.
           Herbst, Natursys. Ins. Vol. 2. p. 294, t. 16, f. 10 (1789).
           Erichson, Naturg. Ins. Deutschl. Vol. 3, p. 893 (1848).   Hinterpommern.
       coccinelloides, Pallas, Icon. Vol. 1, p. 12. t. A, f. 12 (1781).   Südrussland.
           Harold, Berl. Ent. Zeitschr. p. 380, 386 (1862).   Sibirien.
2. *A. binaevulus,* Heyden, Deutsche Ent. Zeitschr. p. 303 (1887).   Wladiwostok.
       binaevulus, Reitter, Tab. p. 109; Brünn, 30, p. 247.   Ostsibirien.
       var. *diaphanomaculatus,* Heyden, Deutsche Ent. Zeitschr. p. 303 (1887).   Ostsibirien.
3. *A. carpetanus,* Graëlls, Ann. Soc. Ent. Fr. (2), Vol. 5, p. 306, t. 4, f. 3   Spanien.
   (1847).
       carpetanus, Harold, Berl. Ent. Zeitschr. p. 381, 391 (1862).   Spanien.

Mulsant, Hist. Nat. Col. France, Lamell. p. 246 (1871).   Spanien.
Reitter, Tab. p. 108; Brünn. 3o, p. 246.   Sizilien.
  var. siculus, Harold, Berl. Ent. Zeitschr. p. 380, 395 (1862).   Sizilien.
4. *A. depressus*, Kugelann, Schneiders Mag. Vol. 1 (3), p. 262 (1792).   Osterode.
  depressus, Paykull, Fauna Suec. Vol. 1, p. 15 (1798).   Schweden.
  Illiger, Verz. Käf. Preuss. p. 28 (1798).   Preussen.
  Erichson, Naturg. Ins Deutschl. Vol. 3, p. 896 (1848).   Deutschland.
  Harold, Ann. Soc. Ent. Fr. p. 301 (1862); Berl. Ent. Zeitschr.   Nord- und Mitteleuropa, Westsi-
   p. 381, 389 (1862).   birien, Kaukasus.
  Reitter, Tab. p. 109; Brünn, 3o, p. 247.   Europa, Nord- und Mittelasien.
  nigripes, var. ε, Duftschmid, Fauna Austr. Vol. 1, p. 117 (1805).   Oesterreich.
  var. rufus, Dalla Torre, Ber. Ver. Naturk. Oberösterr. Vol. 10, p. 109 (1879).   Oberösterreich.
   sec. Schilsky, Deutsche Ent. Zeitschr. p. 321 (1888).
  *var. nigripes**, Stephens, Ill. Brit. Ent. Vol. 3, p 201 (1830).   England.
   Kriechbaumer, Stett. Ent. Zeit. p 21 (1847).   Bayern.
  var. caminarius, Faldermann, Fauna Transcauc. Vol. 1, p. 251 (1836). Transkaukasien.
   sec. Reiche & Saulcy, Ann. Soc. Ent. Fr. p. 393 (1856).
  var. atramentarius, Erichson, Naturg. Ins. Deutschl. Vol. 3, p. 897 (1848).   Mittel- und Süddeutschland.
  var. biceps, Dalla Torre, Ber. Ver. Naturk. Oberösterr. p. 109 (1879). Oberösterreich.
  var. marginatus, Dalla Torre, ibidem, p. 109 (1879).   Oberösterreich.
  Biologie : Rosenhauer. Stett. Ent. Zeit. p. 19 (1882). — Larve und Puppe
   beschrieben.
   Kambeu, Ann. Soc. Linn. Lyon, Vol. 39, p. 162 (1892). — Larve
  und Lebensweise.
5. *A. gagatinus*, Ménétriés. Cat. Rais. p. 182 (1832).   Kaspisches Meer, Trans-
  gagatinus, Faldermann, Fauna, Transcauc. Vol. 1, p. 250 (1836).   kaukasien.
  Reitter, Deutsche Ent. Zeitschr. p. 390 (1890); Tab. p. 107;   Lenkoran, Daghestan, Nordper-
   Brünn, 3o, p. 245.   sien.
6. *A. impressiusculus*, Fairmaire, Bull. Soc. Ent. Fr. p. 201 (1888).   Peking.
7. *A. laticollis*, Baudi, Berl. Ent. Zeitschr. p. 68 (1870).   Meeralpen.
  laticollis, Reitter, Tab. p. 107; Brünn, 3o, p. 245.   Apenninen.
8. *A. luridus*, Fabricius, Syst. Ent. p. 19 (1775).   England.
  luridus, Olivier, Ent. Vol. 1 (3), p. 90, t. 18, f. 168; t. 26, f. 168 (1789). Europa.
  Paykull, Fauna Suec. Vol. 1, p. 13 (1798).   Schweden.
  Erichson, Naturg. Ins. Deutschl. Vol. 3. p. 894 (1848).   Deutschland.
  Harold, Berl. Ent. Zeit. p. 381, 392 (1862).   Sibirien, Kaukasus, Kleinasien,
  Reitter, Tab. p. 109; Brünn, 3o, p. 247.   Zentralasien.   [Marokko.
  Arrow, Trans. Ent. Soc. Lond. p. 511 (1903).   Antillen.
  rufipes, var. γ, Illiger, Verz. Käf Preuss. p. 28 (1798).   Preussen.
  nigripes, Schönherr, Syn. Ins. Vol. 1, p. 80 (1806).
   Heer, Fauna Helv. Vol. 1, p. 529 (1841).   Schweiz.
  rufitarsis, Latreille, Gen. Crust. Ins. Vol. 2, p. 88 (1807).   Europa.
  var. gagates, Müller, Zool. Dan. Prodr. p. 55 (1776).   Dänemark.
  Olivier, Ent. Vol 1 (3), p. 87, t. 24, f. 213 (1789).   Paris.
  Marsham. Ent. Brit. Vol. 1, p. 26 (1802).   England.
  arator, Herbst, Fuessly Arch. Vol 4. p. 9 (1783).   Berlin.
  gagatinus, Fourcroy, Ent. Par. Vol. 1, p. 10 (1785).
   Mulsant, Hist. Nat. Col. France, Lamell. p. 276 (1842); p. 242   Frankreich.
   (1871).
  nigripes, Fabricius, Ent. Syst. Vol. 1, p. 35 (1792).   Europa.
  Panzer, Fauna Germ. p. 47 (9) (1797).   Deutschland.
  Sturm, Ins. Deutschl. Vol. 1, p. 134 (1805).   Deutschland.
  Gyllenhall, Ins. Suec. Vol. 1. p. 32 (1808).
  var. interpunctatus, Herbst, Fuessly Arch. Vol. 4, p. 8, t. 19, f. 11 (1783).
  lutarius, Fabricius, Syst Eleuth. Vol. 1, p. 77 (1801).   Deutschland.
  informis, Mulsant, Hist. Nat. Col. France, Lamell. p. 275 (1842).   Frankreich.
   sec. Mulsant. ibidem, p. 241 (1871).
  var. varigatus, Herst, Fuessly Arch. Vol. 4, p. 9, t. 19, f. 12 (1783).   Berlin.
  Marsham, Ent. Brit. Vol. 1, p. 26 (1802).   England.
  varius, Linné, Syst. Nat. ed. Gmelin, Vol. 1 (4), p. 1553 (1788).   Berlin.
  rufipes, var. β, Illiger, Verz. Käf. Preuss. p. 28 (1798).
  deplanatus, Ménétriés, Catal. Rais. p. 181 (1832).   Armenien, Kaspisches Meer.
  Faldermann, Fauna Transcauc. Vol. 1, p. 253 (1836).   Transkaukasien.
   sec. Reiche & Saulcy, Ann. Soc. Ent. Fr. p. 393 (1856).

var. nigrosulcatus, Marsham, Ent. Brit. Vol. 1, p. 27 (1802).   England.
lividus, Walckenaer, Fauna Paris. Vol. 1, p. 12 (1802).   Frankreich.
var. intricarius, Mulsant, Hist. Nat. Col. France, Lamell. p. 275 (1842).   Frankreich.
var. connexus, Mulsant, ibidem, p. 275 (1842).   Frankreich.
var. apicalis, Mulsant, ibidem, p. 276 (1842).   Frankreich.
var. lateralis, Mulsant, ibidem, p. 276 (1842).   Frankreich.
var. bipaginatus, Mulsant, ibidem, p. 277 (1842).
var. humeralis, Dalla Torre, Ber. Ver. Naturk. Oberösterr. Vol. 10, p. 110 (1879).   Oberösterreich.
   Hilleri, Schilsky, Deutsche Ent. Zeitschr. p. 317 (1888).
     sec. Schilsky, ibidem, p. 321 (1888).
var. strigosus, Dalla Torre, Ber. Ver. Naturk. Oberösterr. Vol. 10, p. 110 (1879).   Oberösterreich.
var. rufonotatus, Dalla Torre, ibidem, p. 110 (1876).   Oberösterreich.
var. lividibasis, Reitter, Deutsche Ent. Zeitschr. p. 342 (1898).   Morea.
Biologie : De Haan, Nouv. Ann. Mus. Hist. Natur. Vol. 4, p. 146, t. 12, f. 4;
   t. 14, f. 8; t. 15, f. 7 (1835).—Larve beschrieben und abgebildet.
Erichson, Naturg. Ins. Deutschl. Vol. 3, p. 896 (1848). — Larve
beschrieben.

9. *A. planicollis,* Reitter, Deutsche Ent. Zeitschr. p. 390 (1890); Tab. p. 108;   Kaukasus.
  Brünn, 30, p. 246.
    gagatinus, Harold, Berl. Ent. Zeitschr. p. 381, 393 (1862).   Kaukasus.
     sec. Reitter, Tab. p. 108.

10. *A. rufipes,* Linné, Syst. Nat. Vol. 1, p. 353 (1758).   Europa.
    rufipes, Paykull, Fauna Suec. Vol. 1, p. 15 (1798).   Schweden.
    Erichson, Naturg. Ins. Deutschl. Vol. 3, p. 892 (1848).   Deutschland.   [asien, Persien
    Harold, Berl. Ent. Zeitschr. p. 381, 390 (1862).   Nord- und Mitteleuropa, West-
    Reitter, Tab. p. 107; Brünn, 30, p. 245.   Europa, Nordasien.
    Horn, Trans. Amer. Ent. Soc. Vol. 14. p. 53 (1887).   Maryland, Pennsylvanien.
     sec. Bailey, Ent M. Mag. p. 90 (1905).   Insel Man.
    capitatus, De Geer, Mém. Ins. Vol. 4, p. 263, t. 10, f. 6 (1774).
    muticus*, Stephens, Ill. Brit. Ent. Vol. 3, p. 20 (1830).   England.
    capicola, Harold, Berl. Ent. Zeitschr. p. 381, 390 (1862).   Kap der guten Hoffnung.
     sec. Harold, ibidem, p. 251 (1871).
     sec, Harold, Col. Hefte, Vol. 14, p. 195 (1875).   Kap der guten Hoffnung.
  var. oblongus, Scopoli, Ent. Carn. p. 8 (1763).
    Herbst, Natursys. Ins. Vol. 2, p. 261, t. 18, f. 2 (1789).
    juvenilis, Mulsant, Hist. Nat. Col. France, Lamell. p. 272 (1842).   Frankreich.
    rufo-testaceus, Dalla Torre, Ber. Ver. Naturk. Oberösterr. Vol. 10, p. 109 (1879).   Oberösterreich.
     sec. Schilsky, Deutsche Ent. Zeitschr. p. 321 (1888).
  Biologie : *Schioedte, Nat. Tidsskr. Vol. 9, p. 324, t. 14, f. 10-16, t. 19, f. 10
   (1874). — Larve beschrieben und abgebildet.
  *Xambeu, Ann. Soc. Linn. Lyon, 1895 (sec. Wiegmann, Arch. f.
  Naturg., Bericht 1895, p. 485 [1898]).

11. *A. scoparius,* Harold, Mitt. München. Ent. Ver. Vol. 1, p. 112 (1877).   Kiachta.
12. *A. semiopacus,* Reitter, Hor. Soc Ent. Ross. Vol. 21, p. 227 (1887);   Tibet, Chinesisch-Turkes-
  Tab. p. 108; Brünn, 30. p. 247.   tan.
    var. luteoirroratus, Heyden, Hor. Soc. Ent. Ross. Vol. 23, p. 657 (1889).   Kan-ssu.
13. *A. tingitanus,* Fairmaire, in litt?
    tingitanus, Reitter, Tab. p. 108; Brünn, 30, p. 246.   Tanger.
    d'Orbigny, L'Abeille, Vol. 28, p. 245 (1896).   Fes.
14. *A. Viturati,* Reitter. Deutsche Ent. Zeitschr. p. 411 (1907).   Nanschan.

36. Subgenus AGANOCROSSUS, Reitter

Aganocrossus. Reitter, Wien. Ent. Zeit. p. 208 (1895).

Charaktere. — In der etwas flachen Gestalt, den gerandeten Vorderwinkeln und der ungeran-deten Basis des Halsschildes, sowie in dem verlängerten ersten Gliede der Vorderbeine und zum Teil auch in der Punktierung des Halsschildes kommt diese Untergattung der vorigen nahe.

Von länglicher, flacher Gestalt, glänzend, schwarz gefärbt, der Vorderkopf, die Seiten des Hals-schildes oftmals heller, die Flügeldecken sind einfarbig oder bräunlich mit hellem Fleck an der Basis und vor der Spitze, zuweilen sind auch die Flügeldecken abwechselnd heller oder dunkler braun.

Der Kopf ist klein, nicht halbkreisförmig, flachbogig verengt, der Vorderrand ist abgestutzt, schwach gebuchtet, die Stirnlinie ist deutlich vertieft, ohne Höcker, die Oberfläche ist fein und grösser punktiert; die Wangen sind rundlich und undeutlich.

Das Halsschild ist quer, nach hinten wenig gerundet erweitert, bis zu den stumpf abgerundeten Hinterwinkeln gerandet, die schwach zweibuchtige Basis ist ohne Rand, die Oberfläche ist sehr zerstreut und sehr fein, an den Seiten stärker, aber auch sehr vereinzelt punktiert.

Das Schildchen ist klein, vorn parallel, unpunktiert.

Die Flügeldecken sind parallel, um die Schultern herum behaart, die Punktstreifen sind deutlich, die Zwischenräume vorn fast flach, vor der Spitze deutlich gewölbt, sie sind äusserst fein und zerstreut punktiert, vor der Spitze und längs der Seiten mit grösseren, je ein längeres Haar tragenden Punkten.

Die Unterseite ist glänzend, punktiert und behaart, die Bauchspitze besonders lang.

Die Füsse sind viel heller, sie sind unpunktiert und unbehaart.

Die Hinterschienen haben ungleiche Borsten, der obere Enddorn ist wenig kürzer als das erste Glied, dieses fast so lang als die drei folgenden.

Hierher gehört nur eine Art von 4 bis 5 mm Länge.

Geographische Verbreitung der Art. — China.

1. *A. postpilosus*, Reitter = *urostigma*, Harold.

Aphoiden des paläarktischen Gebietes die einer der vorstehenden Untergattungen nicht zugewiesen werden konnten

1. *Aphodius arabicus*, Harold, Col. Hefte, Vol. 13, p. 89 (1875). — Aegypten, Arabien.
2. *A. atratus*, Waterhouse, Trans. Ent. Soc. Lond. p. 91 (1875). — Japan.
3. *A. Beloni*, Mulsant & Godart, Ann. Soc. Linn. Lyon. Vol. 26, p. 123 (1879). — Mosul.
4. *A. breviusculus*, Motschulsky, Bull. Soc. Nat. Mosc. Vol. (39) 1, p. 170 (1866). — Japan.
    breviusculus, Lewis, Ann. Mag. Nat. Hist. (6), Vol. 16, p. 380 (1895). — Japan.
5. *A. capitulatus*, Clouët, Bull. Soc Ent. Fr. p. 186 (1898). — Algier.
6. *A. clypeatus*, Fischer von Waldheim, Lettre à Pander, p. 11 (1821). — Bokhara.
7. *A. costalis*, Gebler, Bull. Soc. Nat. Mosc. Vol. 21 (3), p. 83 (1848). — Südwestsibirien.
    sibiricus, Harold, Berl. Ent. Zeitschr. p. 332, 341 (1863). — Westsibirien.
8. *A. dauricus*, Harold, ibidem, p. 332, 337 (1863). — Sibirien.
9. *A. desertus*, Klug, Symb. Phys. Vol. 5, t. 42, f. 4 (1845). — Arabien.
    desertus, Harold, Berl. Ent. Zeitschr. p. 142, 150 (1862). — Aegypten, Senegal.
    d'Orbigny, L'Abeille, Vol. 28, p. 261 (1896). — Djibouti, Obock, Angola, Abes-
    var. perplexus, Harold, Berl. Ent. Zeitschr. p. 151 (1862). — Senegal.   [sinien.
10. *A. digitatus*, Harold, ibidem, p. 258, 278 (1871). — Aegypten.
11. *A. dubius*, A. Schmidt, Deutsche Ent. Zeitschr. p. 201 (1907), nom. nov.
    fimbriolatus ‖ Reiche, Ann. Soc. Ent. Fr. p. 397 (1856). — Jerusalem.
    Harold, Berl. Ent. Zeitschr. p. 120, 125 (1866).
12. *A. elongatulus*, Fabricius, Syst. Eleuth. Vol. 1, p. 68 (1801). — China.
    elongatulus, Harold, Berl. Ent. Zeitschr p. 141, 149 (1862). — Ostindien.
    Clouët, Ann Soc. Ent. Fr. p. 240 (1898).
    testaceus, Germar, Mag. Ent. Vol. 1, p. 118 (1813). — Amerika.
    cornutus, Wiedemann, Zool. Mag. Vol 2 (1), p. 26 (1823). — Bengulen.
    robustus, Walker, Ann. Mag. Nat. Hist. (3). Vol. 2, p. 207 (1858). — Ceylon.
13. *A. ephippiger*, Mulsant & Rey, Ann. Soc. Linn. Lyon, Vol. 18, p. 186 (178) (1871); Opusc. Ent. Vol. 14, p. 210 (1870). — Arabien.
14. *A. globulus*, Harold, Berl. Ent. Zeitschr. p 207 (1859); p. 331, 335 (1863). — China, Ostasien.
    var. bisectus, Waterhouse, Trans. Ent. Soc. Lond. p. 80 (1875). — Japan
    sec. Heyden, Hor. Soc. Ent. Ross. Vol. 23, p. 657 (1889). — Kan-ssu
15. *A. hilaris*, Harold, L'Abeille, Vol. 5, p. 433 (1869). — Persien.
    hilaris, Marseul, L'Abeille, Nouv. et Faits (2), Vol. 14-15, p. 56 (1878). — Palästina.
16. *A. hirtipes*, Fischer, Bull. Soc. Nat. Mosc. Vol. 17 (1), p. 45 (1844). — Südrussland.

17. *A. humeridens*, Reitter, Deutsche Ent. Zeitschr. p. 341 (1898). Sivas.
18. *A. impunctatus*, Waterhouse, Trans. Ent. Soc. Lond. p. 85 (1875). Japan.
19. *A. laevigatus*, Harold, Deutsche Ent. Zeitschr. p. 290 (1886). Peking.
20. *A. Lewisi*, Waterhouse, Trans. Ent. Soc. Lond. p. 92 (1875). Japan.
21. *A. lividipennis*, Waterhouse, ibidem, p. 81 (1875). Japan.
22. *A. marginatus*, Fischer von Waldheim, Cat. Col. Sib. orient. coll. Sibirien.
    p. 11 (1842).
23. *A. maurus*, Gebler, Bull. Soc. Nat. Mosc. Vol. 6, p. 285 (1833); Vol. 14 (4), Saisan-nor.
    p. 587 (1841).
        maurus, Harold, Berl. Ent. Zeitschr. p. 334, 376 (1863). Mittelasien, Songorei
24. *A. micros**, Walker, Lord List of Coleopt. p. 12 (1871). Nordafrika.
25. *A. mongolicus*, Mannerheim, Bull. Soc. Nat. Mosc. Vol. 25 (4), p. 300 (1852). Mongolei.
26. *A. orientalis*, Harold, Berl. Ent. Zeitschr. p. 147 (1862); Ann. Mus. China, Celebes.
    Stor. Nat. Genova, Vol. 10; p 85 (1877).
27. *A. ornatulus*, Harold, Berl. Berl. Ent. Zeitschr. p. 121 (1866). Kleinasien.
        sec. Harold, Mitt. München, Ver. Vol 4 (2), p. 156 (1880).
28. *A. ovalis*, Waterhouse, Trans. Ent. Soc. Lond. p. 89 (1875). Japan.
29. *A. Paivanus*, Wollaston, Col. Hesperid. p. 90 (1867). Kapverdische Inseln.
30. *A. pallidiligonis*, Waterhouse, Trans. Ent. Soc. Lond. p. 87 (1875). Japan.
31. *A. palmetincolus*, Karsch, Berl. Ent. Zeitschr. p. 45 (1881). Sockna.
32. *A. Pedrosi*, Wollaston, Ins. Maderens. p. 226 (1854). Madeira.
33. *A. punctatus*, Waterhouse, Trans. Ent. Soc. Lond. p. 87 (1875). Japan.
34. *A. Rendalli*, Wollaston, Col. Hesperid. p. 91 (1867). St. Vicente.
35. *A. rugosostriatus*, Waterhouse, Trans. Ent. Soc. Lond. p. 92 (1875). Japan, Korea.
        rugostriatus, Reitter, Tab. p. 109; Brünn, 30, p. 247. Japan, Korea.
36. *A. Segonzaci*, Bedel, Segonzac Voy. Maroc, p. 368; L'Abeille, 1900-1906, Marokko.
    Vol. 30, p. 255 (1905).
37. *A. signatipennis*, Mulsant & Wachanru, Mém Acad. Sc. Lyon, Vol. 2, Caramanien.
    p. 6 (1852); Opusc. Ent. Vol. 1, p. 166 (1852).
38. *A. Smithi*, Shipp, in Smith, Through. unk. Afr. Coleopt., App. p. 451 (1897). Afrika.
39. *A. sobrinus*, Harold, Berl. Ent. Zeitschr. p. 334, 384 (1863). Sibirien.
40. *A. stercorarius*, Mulsant & Rey, Opusc. Ent. Vol. 14, p. 208 (1870); Ann. Mesopotamien.
    Soc. Linn. Lyon, 1870-71, Vol, 18, p. 176 (1872).
        stercorarius, d'Orbigny, L'Abeille, Vol 28, p. 261 (1896). Mesopotamien.
41. *A. subcostatus*, Kolbe, Wiegmann Arch. f. Naturg. Vol. 1, p. 189 (1886). Korea.
42. *A. sublimbatus*, Motschulsky, Schrencks Reise, Col. Vol. 2, p. 132, t. 9, Ochotsk.
    f. 2 (1860).
43. *A. subpolitus*, Motschulsky, ibidem, p. 132 (1860). Irkutsk.
44. *A. subsericeus*, Ballion, Bull. Soc. Nat. Mosc. Vol. 53 (1), p. 283 (1878). Kuldsha.
45. *A. thoracicus*, Fischer von Waldheim, Cat. Col. Sib. orient Coll p. 23 (1842). Songoria.
46. *A. trituberculatus*, A. Schmidt, Deutsche Ent. Zeitschr. p. 201 (1907),
    nom. nov.
        nitidulus ‖ Waterhouse, Trans. Ent. Soc. Lond. p. 93 (1875). Japan.
47. *A. turbatus*, Baudi, Berl. Ent. Zeitschr. p. 66 (1870). Cypern.
48. *A. uniformis*, Waterhouse, Trans. Ent. Soc. Lond. p. 84 (1875). Japan.
49. *A. uniplagiatus*, Waterhouse, ibidem, p. 84 (1875). Japan.
50. *A. variegatus*, Motschulsky, Schrencks Reise, Vol. 2, p. 132 (1860). Ostsibirien.

B. — Aphodien des afrikanischen Gebietes

1. *Aphodius abessinicus*, Harold, Berl. Ent. Zeitschr. p. 94, 102 (1861). Abessinien.
2. *A. adustus*, Klug, Monatsb. Berl. Akad. Wiss. p. 656 (1855); Peters Tette, Sesse-Inseln.
    Reise Mossamb. p. 244 (1862).
        adustus, Péringuey, Trans. S. Afric. Philos. Soc. 1901-03, Vol. 12, Cat. Kapkolonie, Mozambique.
        p. 407 (1901).

3. *A. amabilis*, Boheman, Ins. Caffr. Vol. 2, p. 333 (1857).　　　Limpopo.
　　amabilis, Harold, Berl. Ent. Zeitschr. p. 177 (1874).
　　　Péringuey, Trans. S. Afric. Philos. Soc. 1901-03, Vol. 12, Cat.　　Natal, Transvaal, Südrhodesia.
　　　p. 404 (1901).
4. *A. ambiguus*, Boheman, Preg. Eug. Resa, Vol. 2 (1), p. 51 (1858).　　Kap der guten Hoffnung.
　　ambiguus, A. Schmidt, Aphodiinen-Zusammenst. Deutsche Ent. Zeitschr.
　　　Beih. p. 4. Anmerkung 1 (1907-08).
　　tarsalis, A. Schmidt, Deutsche Ent. Zeitschr. p. 201 (1907), nom. nov.
　　brevitarsis ‖ Péringuey, Trans. S. Afric. Philos. Soc. 1901-03, Vol. 12, Cat.　　Kapkolonie.
　　　p. 388 (1901).
　　　　sec. A. Schmidt, Deutsche Ent. Zeitschr. p. 201 (1907).
　　　　sec. A. Schmidt, Notes Leyd. Mus. Vol. 31, p. 123 (1909).
　　Frenchi 1), Blackburn, Trans. Roy. Soc. S. Austral. Vol. 15, p. 35 (1892).　　Südaustralien.
　　var. accola, Kolbe, Jenaische Denkschr. Vol. 13, p. 127 (1908).　　Klein-Namaland.
5. *A. amoenus*, Boheman, Ins. Caffr. Vol. 2, p. 354 (1857). — **Taf. I,**　　Orange.
　　Fig. 10.
　　amoenus, Péringuey, Trans. S. Afric. Philos. Soc. 1901-03, Vol. 12, Cat.　　Kapkolonie, Natal, Transvaal,
　　　p. 384 (1901).　　Südrhodesia.
　　centralis 2), Harold, Col. Hefte, Vol. 3, p. 84 (1868).　　Südafrika.
　　var. vestitus 2), Boheman, Ins. Caffr. Vol. 2, p. 359 (1857).　　Orange.
　　　　sec. Péringuey, Trans. S. Afric. Philos. Soc. 1901-03, Vol. 12,　　Sesse-Inseln.
　　　　Cat. p. 384 (1901).
　　var. pallidicornis 2), Walker, Ann. Mag. Nat. Hist. (3), Vol. 2, p. 207 (1858).　　Ceylon, Malabar.
　　　Harold, Ann. Mus. Stor. Nat. Genova, Vol. 10, p. 86 (1877);　　Java, China, Japan.
　　　Mitteil. München. Ver. p. 156 (1880).
　　var. impugnans, A. Schmidt, Aphodiinen-Zusammenst. Deutsche Ent. Zeitschr.　　Transvaal.
　　　Beih. p. 4. Anmerkung (1907-08).
6. *A. anceps*, A. Schmidt, Stett. Ent. Zeit. p. 3 (1911).　　Bolama (Portug.-Guinea).
7. *A. anomalipus*, Péringuey, Trans. S. Afric. Philos. Soc. 1901-03,　　Kapkolonie.
　　Vol. 12, Cat. p. 393 (1901).
8. *A. anthrax*, Gerstäcker, Wiegmann Arch. f. Naturg. Vol. 1, p. 47 (1871).　　Sansibar.
　　anthrax, v. Decken, Reise Ostafr. Vol. 3 (2), p. 120 (1873).　　Uru, Sesse-Inseln.
9. *A. apertus*, A. Schmidt, Notes Leyd. Mus. Vol. 31, p. 102 (1909).　　Caffrarien.
10. *A. ardens*, Harold, Berl. Ent. Zeitschr. p. 96, 103 (1866).　　Kap der guten Hoffnung.
11. *A. argutus*, A. Schmidt, Stett. Ent. Zeit. p. 4 (1911).　　Sesse-Inseln.
12. *A. armaticeps*, Péringuey, Trans. S. Afric. Philos. Soc. 1901-03,　　Kapkolonie.
　　Vol. 12, Cat. p. 410 (1901) (*Ammoecius*).
13. *A. armatulus*, Fairmaire, Ann. Soc. Ent. Belg. Vol. 37, p. 148 (1893).　　Somaliland.
14. *A. atomus*, Fairmaire, ibidem, p. 370 (1897).　　Madagaskar.
15. *A. atroscutellatus*, A. Schmidt, Soc. Ent. Zürich. Vol. 23, p. 188 (1909).　　Südafrika.
16. *A. auriculatus*, A. Schmidt, ibidem, p. 53 (1908).　　Usambara.
　　var. bimaculatopennis, A. Schmidt, Stett. Ent. Zeit. p. 30 (1911).　　Estcourt (Natal).
17. *A. badius*, Boheman, Ins. Caffr. Vol. 2, p. 357 (1857).　　Limpopo.
　　badius, A. Schmidt, Aphodiinen-Zusammenst. Deutsche Ent. Zeitschr.
　　　Beih. p. 24. Anmerkung 2 (1907-08).
18. *A. Ballioni*, A. Schmidt, Deutsche Ent. Zeitschr. p. 411 (1906), nom.
　　nov. — **Taf. I, Fig. 12.**
　　thoracicus ‖ Roth, Wiegmann Arch. f. Naturg. Vol. 1, p. 131 (1851).　　Tigré, Choa.
　　　Boheman, Ins. Caffr. Vol. 2, p. 326 (1857).　　Abessinien, Orange.
　　　Harold, Berl. Ent. Zeitschr. p. 94, 101 (1861).
　　senegalensis, Reiche, Ann. Soc. Ent. Fr. p. 99 (1852).　　Abessinien, Orange.
19. *A. basalis*, A. Schmidt, Deutsche Ent. Zeitschr. p. 411 (1906), nom. nov.
　　plagiatus ‖ Raffray, Rev. Mag. Zool. (3), Vol. 5, p. 326 (1877).　　Abessinien.
20. *A. beninensis*, Harold, Berl. Ent. Zeitschr. p. 141, 143 (1862).　　Alt-Calabar.
21. *A. biangulatus*, Fairmaire, Ann. Soc. Ent. Belg. p. 18 (1893) (*Mendidius*).　　Choa.

---

1) Die Arten, die ich mehrfach als *Frenchi* Blackburn von Australien erhielt, erwiesen sich stets als *ambiguus* Boheman. Da die Beschreibung von *Frenchi* genau auf *ambiguus* passt, so müssen beiden Arten vereinigt werden.
　2) A. Schmidt, « Aphodiinen-Zusammenst. », *Deutsche Ent. Zeitschr.* Beih. p. 4. Anmerkung 2-4 (1907-08).

22. *A. bicoloratus*, A. Schmidt, Ann. Soc. Ent. Belg. Vol. 52, p. 38 (1908).   Sumbu (Kongo).
23. *A. bidentulus*, Harold, Col. Hefte, Vol. 7, p. 4, 19 (1871) (*Ammoecius*).   Kap der guten Hoffnung.
24. *A. binodulus*, Harold, Berl. Ent. Zeitschr. p. 97, 116 (1866).   Kap der guten Hoffnung.
25. *A. binominatus*, A. Schmidt. Deutsche Ent. Zeitschr. p. 202 (1906),
    nom. nov.
        tuberifrons ‖ Fairmaire, Ann. Soc. Ent. Fr. p. 187 (1903).   Madagaskar.
26. *A. binotatus**, Thunberg, Mem. Acad. Petr. Vol. 6, p. 401 (1818).   Kap der guten Hoffnung.
27. *A. brunneus**, Thunberg, ibidem, p. 401 (1818).   Kap der guten Hoffnung.
28. *A. buxeipennis*, Harold. Berl. Ent. Zeitschr. p. 255 (1871).   Kap der guten Hoffnung.
29. *A. calcaratus*, Boheman, Ins. Caffr. Vol. 2, p. 353 (1857).   Orange.
        calcaratus, Péringuey, Trans. S. Afric. Philos. Soc. 1901-03, Vol. 12, Cat.   Ovampoland, Usambara.
        p. 399 (1901).
        Schaumi, Harold, Berl. Ent. Zeitschr. p. 205 (1859).   Abessinien.
        sec. Clouët, Bull. Soc. Ent. Fr. p. 188 (1898).   Transvaal, Choa.
30. *A. calidus*, Harold, Berl. Ent. Zeitschr. p. 258, 277 (1871).   Senegal.
31. *A. calvus*. A. Schmidt. Soc. Ent. Zürich, Vol. 24, p. 19 (1909).   Südafrika.
32. *A. capensis*, Harold, Berl. Ent. Zeitschr. p. 96, 110 (1866).   Kap der guten Hoffnung.
33. *A. cinerascens*, Klug, Monatsb. Berl. Akad.Wiss. p. 656 (1855); Peters   Tette.
    Reise Mossamb. Vol. 5, p. 246 (1862).
        cinerascens, Péringuey, Trans. S. Afric. Philos. Soc. 1901-03, Vol. 12, Cat.   Tette
        p. 386 (1901).
34. *A. circumdatus*, Klug, Monatsb. Berl. Akad. Wiss. p. 656 (1855);   Sena, Sesse-Inseln, Angola.
    Peters Reise Mossamb. Vol. 5, p. 246, t. 14, f. 11 (1862).
        circumdatus, Péringuey, Trans. S. Afric. Philos. Soc. 1901-03, Vol. 12,   Mozambique.
        Cat. p. 415 (1901).
        sec. Quedenfeldt, Berl. Ent. Zeitschr. p. 380 (1884).   Malange.
35. *A. comptus*, A. Schmidt, Stett. Ent. Zeit. p. 6 (1911).   Sesse-Inseln.
36. *A. concolor*, Harold, Berl. Ent. Zeitschr. p. 215 (1859).   Kap der guten Hoffnung.
37. *A. confinis*, A. Schmidt, Sett. Ent. Zeit. p. 7 (1911).   Sansibar, Dar-es-Salâm.
38. *A. connexus*, Klug, Monatsb. Berl. Akad. Wiss. p. 656 (1855); Peters   Tette.
    Reise Mossamb. Vol. 5, p. 245, t. 14, f. 9 (1862).
        connexus, Péringuey, Trans. S. Afric. Philos. Soc. 1901-03, Vol. 12, Cat.   Mozambique.
        p. 384 (1901).   [Hoffnung.
39. *A. consimilis*, Boheman, Ins. Caffr. Vol. 2, p. 341 (1857).   Caffraria, Kap der guten
        consimilis, Péringuey, Trans. S. Afric. Philos. Soc. 1901-03, Vol. 12,   Kapkolonie, Mozambique.
        Cat. p. 391 (1901).
        dolosus, Harold, Berl. Ent. Zeitschr. p. 258, 280 (1871).   Südafrika.
        Péringuey, Trans. S. Afric. Philos. Soc. 1901-03, Vol. 12, Cat.   Kapkolonie.
        p. 399 (1901).
        sec. A. Schmidt, Notes Leyd. Mus. Vol. 31, p. 123 (1909).
40. *A. cruentus*, Klug, Monatsb. Berl. Akad. Wiss. p. 656 (1855); Peters   Tette.
    Reise Mossamb. Vol. 5, p. 245, t. 14, f. 10 (1862).
        sec. Péringuey, Trans. S. Afric. Philos. Soc. 1901-03. Vol. 12, Cat.   Mozambique.
        p. 415 (1901)
41. *A. crux*, Wiedemann, Zool. Mag. Vol. 2 (1), p. 26 (1823).   Kap der guten Hoffnung.
42. *A. curvodilatatus*, A. Schmidt, Soc. Ent. Zürich, Vol. 23, p. 177 (1909).   Kap der guten Hoffnung.
    — Taf. I, Fig. 9, 9a.
43. *A. damarinus*, Kolbe, Jenaische Denkschr. Vol. 13, p. 127 (1908).   Damaraland.
44. *A. Dejeani*, Harold. Berl. Ent. Zeitschr. p. 155, 165 (1862).   Kap der guten Hoffnung.
45. *A. dentellus*, A. Schmidt. Soc. Ent. Zürich, Vol. 23, p. 54 (1908).   Kap der guten Hoffnung.
46. *A. dentinus*, Péringuey, Trans. S. Afric. Philos. Soc. 1901-02, Vol. 12,   Transvaal.
    Cat. p. 410 (1901).
47. *A. detruncatus*, A. Schmidt, Ann. Soc. Ent. Belg. Vol. 52, p. 37   Boma (Kongo).
    (1908).
48. *A. dimidiatus*, Roth, Wiegmann, Arch. f. Naturg. Vol. 1, p. 133   Tigré.
    (1851).
        dimidiatus, Harold, Berl. Ent. Zeitschr. p. 155, 162 (1862).   Abessinien, Senegal.

49. *A. discoidalis*, Boheman, Ins. Caffr. Vol. 2, p. 346 (1857) — **Taf. I, Fig. 13.** Limpopo.
　　discoidalis, Harold, Berl. Ent. Zeitschr. p. 178 (1874).
　　Péringuey, Trans. S. Afric. Philos. Soc. 1901-03, Vol. 12, Kapkolonie.
　　　Cat. 400 (1901).
50. *A. discolor*, Erichson, Doubl. Verz. Seneg. Ins. p. 7 (1842); Stett. Senegal.
　Ent. Zeit. p. 84 (1859).
　　discolor, Harold, Berl. Ent. Zeitschr. p. 141, 144 (1862).
　　Clouët, Ann. Soc. Ent. Fr. p. 240 (1898).
51. *A. ditus*, Péringuey, Trans. S. Afric. Philos. Soc. 1901-03. Vol. 12, Natal.
　Cat. p. 388 (1901).
52. *A. divisus*, A. Schmidt, Soc. Ent. Zürich, 1808-09, Vol. 23, p. 41 (1908). [Sansibar. Transvaal.
53. *A. Doriae*, Harold, Col. Hefte, Vol. 8, p. 18 (1871). Bagamoyo, Dar-es-Salaam, Abessinien.
54. *A. dorsalis*, Klug, Monatsb. Berl. Akad. Wiss. p. 656 (1855); Peters Tette.
　Reise Mossamb. p. 245, t. 14. f. 8 (1862).
　　dorsalis, Boheman, Ins. Caffr. Vol. 2, p. 344 (1857). Orange.
　　Péringuey, Trans. S. Afric. Philos. Soc. 1901-03, Vol. 12, Cat. Natal.
　　　p. 406 (1901).
　　rufolaterus, Motschulsky, Bull. Soc. Nat. Mosc. Vol. 36 (2), p. 462 (1863). Kolombo.
　　— Abbildung, ibidem, Vol. 34 (1), t. 9, f. 23 (1861).
　　tranquebarius, Harold. Berl. Ent. Zeitschr. p. 208 (1874). Vorderindien.
　　sec. A. Schmidt, Notes Leyd. Mus. Vol. 31, p. 123 (1909).
55. *A. dubiosus*, Péringuey, Trans. S. Afric. Philos. Soc. 1901-03. Vol. 12, Kapkolonie, Transvaal.
　Cat. p. 398 (1901).
56. *A. duplicatus*, A. Schmidt, Deutsche Ent. Zeitschr. p. 201 (1907),
　nom. nov.
　　decipiens ‖ Péringuey, Trans. S. Afric. Philos. Soc. 1901-03. Vol. 12, Cat. Transvaal.
　　　p. 390 (1901).
57. *A. effetus*, Kolbe, Jenaische Denkschr. Vol. 13, p. 126 (1908). Gross-Namaland.
58. *A. emeritus*, Péringuey, Trans. S. Afric. Philos. Soc. 1901-03. Vol. 12, Südrhodesia.
　Cat. p. 382 (1901).
59. *A. erugatus*, Harold, Col. Hefte, Vol. 8, p. 20 (1871). Abessinien.
60. *A. evanescens*, Boheman, Ins. Caffr. Vol. 2, p. 358 (1887). Limpopo.
　　evanescens, Péringuey, Trans. S. Afric. Philos. Soc. 1901-03, Vol. 12. Cat. Kapkolonie. Natal, Transvaal.
　　　p. 412 (1901)
　　A. Schmidt, Aphodiinen Zusammenst. Deutsche Ent. Zeitschr.
　　Beih. p. 24, Anmerkung 2 (1907-08).
61. *A. excultus*, Péringuey, Trans. S. Afric. Philos. Soc. 1904-08, Vol. 13, Südrhodesia.
　p. 632 (1908).
62. *A. fallax*, Harold, Berl. Ent. Zeitschr. p. 258, 281 (1871). Kap der guten Hoffnung.
63. *A. fastigatus*, A. Schmidt, Soc. Ent. Zürich, 1908-09, Vol. 23. p. 41, Transvaal, Senegal.
　(1908); Notes Leyd. Mus. Vol. 31, p. 122 (1909).
64. *A. feculentus*, Fairmaire, Rev. d'Ent. Caen, Vol. 11, p. 93 (1892) Obock.
　(*Mendidius*).
65. *A. flagrans*, Erichson, Wiegmann Arch. f. Naturg. Vol. 1, p. 234 (1843). Angola.
66. *A. foveiventris*, Raffray, Rev. Mag. Zool. (3), Vol. 5, p. 326 (1877). Abessinien, Keren, Choa.
67. *A. fugitivus*, Péringuey, Trans. S. Afric. Philos. Soc. 1901-03, Vol. 12, Natal, Transvaal, Südrho-
　Cat. p. 405 (1901). desia, Kapkolonie.
68. *A. fulvescens*, Harold, Berl. Ent. Zeitschr. p. 183, 189 (1874). Senegal.
69. *A. genialis*, Péringuey, Trans. S. Afric. Philos. Soc. 1901-03, Vol. 12, Kapkolonie.
　Cat. p. 390 (1901).
70. *A. Gilleti*, A. Schmidt, Soc. Ent. Zürich, 1909-10, Vol. 24, p. 11 (1909). Kongo.
71. *A. goniocephalus*, Roth, Wiegmann Arch. f. Naturg. Vol. 1, p. 132 (1851). Tigré.
　　goniocephalus, Harold, Berl. Ent. Zeitschr. p. 331, 334 (1863). Abessinien, Sumbu, Matadi.
72. *A. gracilis*, Boheman, Ins. Caffr. Vol. 2, p. 343 (1857). Limpopo.
　　gracilis, Péringuey, Trans. S. Afric. Philos. Soc. 1901-03, Vol. 12, Cat. Limpopo.
　　　p. 387 (1901).

73. *A. granulatus*, Boheman, Ins. Caffr. Vol. 2. p. 342 (1857).   Caffrarien.
    granulatus, Harold, Berl. Ent. Zeitschr. p. 184, 197 (1874).   Südafrika.
    Péringuey, Trans. S. Afric. Philos. Soc. 1901-03, Vol. 12, Cat.   Kapkolonie.
    p. 391 (1901).

74. *A. guineensis*, Klug. Erman Reise. Atlas, p. 34 (1835).   Guinea.
    guineensis, Clouët, Ann. Soc. Ent. Fr. p. 240 (1898).
    ferrugineus || Boheman, Ins. Caffr. Vol. 2, p. 331 (1857).   Orange.
    Bohemani, Harold, Berl. Ent. Zeitschr. p. 148 (1862), nom. nov.
        sec. Harold, Mitt. München. Ent. Ver. Vol. 4 (2), p. 156 (1880).
    Péringuey, Trans. S. Afric. Philos. Soc. 1901-03, Vol. 12, Cat.   Südrhodesia, Mozambique.
    p. 396 (1901)
        sec. Quedenfeldt, Berl. Ent. Zeitschr. p. 280 (1884).   Malange.
        sec. A. Schmidt, Aphodiinen-Zusammenst. Deutsche Ent.   Abessinien, Kamerun, Togo, Se-
    Zeitschr. Beih. p. 33, Anmerkung 1 (1907-08).   negal, Angola, Asmara (Ery-

75. *A. haematicus*, Boheman, Ins. Caffr. Vol. 2, p. 349 (1857).   Caffrarien.   [threa).
    haematicus, Péringuey, Trans. S. Afric. Philos. Soc. 1901-03, Vol. 12, Cat.   Caffrarien.
    p. 389 (1901).

76. *A. harpalinus*, Gerstäcker, Jahrb. Wiss. Anstalt. Hamburg, 1883.   Massai.
    Vol. 1, p. 49 (1884).

77. *A. hepaticolor*, Quedenfeldt, Berl. Ent. Zeitschr. p. 281 (1884).   Malange.

78. *A. hepaticus*, Roth, Wiegmann. Arch. f. Naturg. Vol. 1, p. 132 (1851).   Tigré.
    hepaticus, Harold, Berl. Ent. Zeitschr. p. 94 (1866).   Abessinien, Kap der guten Hoff-
    peregrinus, Boheman, Ins. Caffr. Vol. 2, p. 352 (1857)   Limpopo.   [nung.
    Fauveli, Harold, Col. Hefte, Vol. 5, p. 100 (1869).   Südafrika.
        sec. Harold, ibidem, Vol. 10, p. 206 (1872).
    timidus, Boheman, Ins. Caffr. Vol. 2, p. 345 (1857).   Caffrarien.
    Péringuey, Trans. S. Afric. Philos. Soc. 1901-03, Vol. 12, Cat.   Kapkolonie, Natal.
    p. 400 (1901).
        sec. Clouët, Bull. Soc. Ent. Fr. p. 188 (1898).

79. *A. hirticeps*, Péringuey, Trans. S. Afric. Philos. Soc. 1901-03. Vol. 12,   Kapkolonie.
    Cat. p. 408 (1901).

80. *A. humilis*, Roth, Wiegmann. Arch. f. Naturg. Vol. 1, p. 132 (1851).   Tigré.
    humilis, Harold, Col. Hefte, Vol. 8, p. 21 (1871).   Abessinien.
        sec. Quedenfeldt. Berl. Ent. Zeitschr. p. 280 (1884).   Malange, Natal.

81. *A. imperiosus*, A. Schmidt, Stett. Ent. Zeit. p 8 (1911).   Senegal.

82. *A. impressipennis*, A. Schmidt, Soc. Ent. Zürich, 1908-09. Vol. 23,   Kubub (Deutsch-Südwest-
    p. 52 (1908).   afrika).

83. *A. impurus*, Roth, Wiegmann, Arch. f. Naturg. Vol. 1, p. 131 (1851).   Tigré.
    impurus, Boheman, Ins. Caffr. Vol. 2, p. 332 (1857).   Orange.   [kar.
    Harold, Berl. Ent. Zeitschr. p. 142, 152 (1862)   Ost- und Westafrika, Madagas-
    Péringuey, Trans. S. Afric. Philos. Soc. 1901-03, Vol. 12, Cat.   Kapkolonie, Natal, Südrhodesia.
    p. 397 (1901).
    Clouët, Ann. Soc. Ent. Fr. p. 240 (1898).
    picipes, Klug. Monatsb. Berl. Akad. Wiss. p. 656 (1855); Peters Reise   Mozambique.
    Mossamb. p. 244 (1862).
    Boheman, Ins. Caffr. Vol. 2, p. 337 (1857).   Orange.

84. *A. innocens*. A. Schmidt. Stett. Ent. Zeit. p 9(1911).   Galla-Land.

85. *A. inornatus*, A. Schmidt, Soc. Ent. Zürich, 1908-09.Vol. 23, p. 52 (1908). Transvaal.

86. *A. insignis*, A. Schmidt, Stett. Ent. Zeit. p. 10 (1911).   Bolama (Portug.-Guinea).

87. *A. intercalaris*, Péringuey, Trans. S. Afric. Philos. Soc. 1901-03,   Kapkolonie.
    Vol. 12, Cat. p. 392 (1901).

88. *A. iridescens*, Péringuey, ibidem, p. 383 (1901).   Natal.

89. *A. kububanus*, Kolbe. Jenaische Denkschr. Vol. 13, p. 127 (1908).   Gross-Namaland.

90. *A. lacunosus*, A. Schmidt, Stett. Ent. Zeit. p. 12 (1911).   Galla-Land.

91. *A. laetus*, Wiedemann, Zool. Mag. Vol. 2 (1), p. 26 (1823).   Kap der guten Hoffnung.
    laetus, Harold, Berl. Ent. Zeitschr. p. 96, 109 (1866).   Senegal.
    productus, Boheman, Ins. Caffr. Vol. 2, p. 329 (1857).   Caffrarien.
    Péringuey, Trans. S. Afric. Philos. Soc. 1901-03, Vol. 12, Cat.   Kapkolonie. Natal.
    p. 404 (1901).
        sec. Harold, Col. Hefte, Vol. 10, p. 206 (1872).

92. *A. lanuginosus*, Péringuey, Trans. S. Afric. Philos. Soc. 1901-02,   Natal, Südrhodesia.
      Vol. 12, Cat. p. 385 (1901).
93. *A. latecinctus*, Fairmaire, Ann. Soc. Ent. Fr. p. 186 (1903).   Madagaskar.
94. *A. lateritius,* Roth, Wiegmann Arch. f. Naturg. Vol. 1, p. 130 (1851).   Tigré.
95. *A. latus*, A. Schmidt, Stett. Ent. Zeit. p. 29 (1911).   Choa.
96. *A. leoninus*, A. Schmidt, ibidem, p. 13 (1911).   Salisbury (Mashonaland).
97. *A. levis*, A. Schmidt, Ann. Soc. Ent. Belg. Vol. 52, p. 37 (1908).   Loango (Kongo).
98. *A. lineatosulcatus,* Harold, Berl. Ent. Zeitschr. p. 216 (1859).   • Kap der guten Hoffnung.
99. *A. longepilosus*, A. Schmidt, Stett. Ent. Zeit. p. 14 (1911).   Angola, Abessinien, Sene-
100. *A. lucidulus*, Boheman, Ins. Caffr. Vol. 2, p. 340 (1857).   Caffrarien.   [gal.
        lucidulus, Péringuey, Trans. S. Afric. Philos. Soc. 1901-03, Vol. 12, Cat.   Transvaal.
          p 387 (1901).
        splendidulus, Harold, Berl. Ent. Zeitschr. p. 96, 100 (1866).   Kap der guten Hoffnung.
          sec. Harold, Col. Hefte, Vol. 10, p. 207 (1872).
101. *A. lugubris*, Boheman, Ins. Caffr. Vol. 2 p. 364 (1857) (*Ammoecius*).   Caffrarien.
        lugubris, Harold, Col. Hefte, Vol. 7, p. 4, 18 (1871).   Kap der guten Hoffnung.
        terminatus, Harold, ibidem, Vol. 5, p. 100 (1869).   Südafrika.
          sec. Harold, ibidem, Vol. 7, p. 19 (1871).
102. *A. luridipes*, Harold, Berl. Ent. Zeitschr. p. 106 (1861).   Senegal.
103. *A. maculicollis*, Reiche, Voy. Abyss. Ferret et Galin. Vol. 3, p. 341,   Abessinien.
      t. 20, f. 9 (1847).
        maculicollis, Boheman, Ins. Caffr. Vol. 2, p. 327 (1857).   Caffrarien.
          Harold, Berl. Ent. Zeitschr. p. 205 (1859); p. 104 (1861); Col.   Kap der guten Hoffnung, Mozam-
          Hefte, Vol. 8, p. 17 (1871).   bique.
        macropterus, Roth, Wiegmann Arch. f. Naturg. Vol. 1, p. 131 (1851).   Tigré.
        marginicollis 1), Harold, Berl. Ent. Zeitschr. p. 204 (1859); p. 94; 104   Kap der guten Hoffnung.
          (1861) (*Colobopterus*).
          Klug, Peters Reise Mossamb. p. 244 (1862).   Senegal, Port Natal, Tette.
          Péringuey, Trans. S. Afric. Philos. Soc. 1901-03, Vol. 12,   Südafrika, Deutsch-Ostafrika.
          Cat. p. 380 (1901).
          sec. Harold, Col. Hefte, Vol. 8, p. 17 (1872).   Abessinien, Mozambique.
          sec. Quedenfeldt, Berl. Ent. Zeitschr. p. 280 (1884).   Angola.
          sec. A. Schmidt, Notes Leyd. Mus. Vol. 31, p. 123 (1909).
104. *A. magnificus*, A. Schmidt, ibidem, p. 108 (1909). — **Taf. I, Fig. 8.**   Abessinien.
105. *A. manifestus*, A. Schmidt, Stett. Ent. Zeit. p. 15 (1911).   Estcourt (Natal).
106. *A. marchicus*, Raffray, Rev. Mag. Zool. (3), Vol. 5, p. 325 (1877).   Abessinien.
107. *A. mashunensis*, Péringuey, Trans. S. Afric. Philos. Soc. 1901-03,   Südrhodesia.
      Vol. 12, Cat. p. 406 (1901).
108. *A. massaicus*. Gerstäcker, Jahrb. Wiss. Anstalt Hamburg, p. 49 (1884).   Massai.
109. *A mimus*, Péringuey, Trans. S. Afric. Philos. Soc. 1901-03, Vol. 12,   Kapkolonie.
      Cat. p. 409 (1901) (*Ammoecius*).
110. *A. minatorius*, Péringuey, ibidem, 1904-08, Vol. 13, p 631 (1908).   Südrhodesia.
111. *A. minusculus*, Fairmaire, Ann. Soc. Ent. Belg. p. 148 (1893).   Somali-Land.
112. *A. montuosus*, A. Schmidt, Stett. Ent. Zeit. p. 16 (1911).   Britisch-Ostafrika.
113. *A. mutilus*, A. Schmidt, ibidem. p. 17 (1911).   Ulundi (Natal), Transvaal.
114. *A. nigrita* 2), Fabricius, Syst. Eleuth. Vol. 1, p. 73 (1801).   Insel Mauritius.
        nigrita, *Klug, Abhandl. Berl. Akad. Wiss. Vol. 1, p. 164 (1832).   Madagaskar.
          Harold, Berl. Ent. Zeitschr. p. 250 (1871).   Südafrika.
        nigritulus, Boheman, Ins. Caffr. Vol. 2, p. 338 (1857).   Limpopo.
        expertus, Harold, Col. Hefte, Vol. 8, p. 19 (1871).   Abessinien.
          sec. Clouët, Bull. Soc. Ent. Fr. p. 188 (1898).
115. *A. nobilis*, Harold, Berl. Ent Zeitschr. p. 176 (1874).   Abessinien, Südafrika.
116. *A. novus*. A. Schmidt, Stett. Ent. Zeit. p. 18 (1911).   Salisbury (Mashonaland).
117. *A. parvulus*, Harold, Col. Hefte, Vol. 8, p. 17 (1871).   Abessinien.
        parvulus, sec. Sharp, Second Yarkand Miss. Col. p. 44 (1890).   Ostindien.

---

1) Vom Kilima-Ndjaro von Port Natal, Angola, Sierra Leona und Guinea erhalten.
2) Von Erythrea, Mexiko und Columbien erhalten.

118. *A. penetrans*, A. Schmidt, Stett. Ent. Zeit. p. 19 (1911).   Somali-Land.
119. *A. Peringueyi*, A. Schmidt, Notes Leyd. Mus. Vol. 31, p. 106 (1909).   Senegal, Transvaal.
120 *A. picescens*, Fairmaire, Ann. Soc. Ent. Fr. p. 187 (1903).   Madagaskar.
121. *A. pilosellus*, A. Schmidt, Deutsche Ent. Zeitschr. p. 201 (1907), nom.
   nov. (*Esimaphodius*).
        bidentulus, Fairmaire, Rev. d'Ent. Caen, Vol. 11, p. 92 (1892).   Obock.
               Reitter, Tab. p. 71; Brünn, 3o, p. 209, Anmerkung.
122. *A. planatus*, A. Schmidt, Notes Leyd. Mus. Vol. 31, p. 110 (1909).   Deutsch-Ostafrika.
123. *A. principalis*, Harold, Berl. Ent. Zeitschr. p 94, 100 (1859)   Kap der gutten Hoffnung.
124. *A. probes*, Péringuey, Trans. S. Afric. Philos. Soc. 1901-03, Vol. 12,   Natal.
   Cat. p. 401 (1901).
125. *A. procerus*, Harold, Berl. Ent. Zeitschr. p. 169(1862); p. 96, 97 (1866). Kap der gutten Hoffnung.
        procerus, Péringuey. Trans. S. Afric. Philos. Soc. 1901-03, Vol. 12, Cat.   Kapkolonie.
               p. 403 (1901).
126. *A. pulcherrimus*, Reiche. Voy. Abyss. Ferret et Galin. Vol. 3, p. 345,   Abessinien.
   t. 21, f. 2 (1847) (*Acrossus*). — **Taf. I, Fig. 6.**
        pulcherrimus, Harold, Berl. Ent. Zeitschr. p. 176 (1874).
        coloratus, Roth, Wiegmann Arch. f. Naturg. Vol. 1, p. 130 (1851).   Tigré.
        var. aequabilis, A. Schmidt, Aphodiinen-Zusammenst. Berl. Ent. Zeitschr.   Asmara.
               Beih. p. 62. Anmerkung (1907-08).
127. *A. pumilus*, Quedenfeldt. Berl. Ent. Zeitschr. p. 284 (1884).   Malange.
128. *A. pygmaeus*, Boheman, Ins. Caffr. Vol. 2, p. 357 (1857).   Orange.
        pygmaeus, Péringuey, Trans. S. Afric. Philos. Soc. 1901-03, Vol. 12, Cat.   Natal.
               p. 412 (1901).
129. *A. quadridentulus*, Fairmaire, Ann. Soc. Ent. Belg. p. 652 (1894)   Senegal.
   (*Mendidius*).
130. *A. quisquilius*, Roth, Wiegmann Arch. f. Naturg. Vol. 1, p. 133 (1851).   Tigré.
131. *A. rhinocerus*, Reiche, Voy. Abyss. Ferret et Galin. Vol. 3, p. 343,   Abessinien.
   t. 21, f. 1 (1847). — **Taf. I, Fig. 7, 7a.**
        rhinocerus, Boheman, Ins. Caffr. Vol 2, p. 334 (1857).   Caffrarien.
               Péringuey, Trans. S. Afric. Philos. Soc. 1901-03, Vol. 12, Cat.   Kapkolonie, Natal, Südrhodesia.
               p. 402 (1901).
        armatus, Roth, Wiegmann Arch. f. Naturg. Vol. 1, p. 130 (1851).   Tigré, Togo.
132. *A. rubricosus*, Boheman, Ins. Caffr. Vol. 2, p. 335 (1857).   Caffrarien.
        rubricosus, Harold, Berl. Ent. Zeitschr. p. 142, 153 (1862).   Kap der guten Hoffnung.
133. *A. rugulicollis*, Fairmaire, Ann. Soc. Ent. Belg. p. 17 (1893).   Choa.
134. *A. russatus*, Erichson, Doubl. Verz. Seneg. Ins. p. 7 (1842); Stett.   Senegal
   Ent. Zeit. p. 84 (1859).
        russatus, Harold, Berl. Ent. Zeitschr. p. 142, 151 (1862).   Kap der guten Hoffnung.
               Péringuey. Trans. S. Afric. Philos. Soc. 1901-03, Vol. 12, Cat.   Kapkolonie.
               p. 394 (1901).
        posticus, Boheman, Ins. Caffr. Vol. 2, p. 347 (1857).   Caffrarien.
135. *A. salebrosus*, A. Schmidt, Stett. Ent. Zeit. p. 22 (1911).   Chirinda (Mashonaland).
136. *A. seminitidus*, Quedenfeldt. Berl. Ent. Zeitschr. p. 282 (1884).   Malanga.
137. *A. senegalensis*, Klug. Ermans Reise, Atlas, p. 34 (1835). — **Taf. I,**   Senegal.
   Fig. 11.
        senegalensis, Castelnau, Hist. Nat. Vol. 2, p. 96 (1840).
               Reiche, Voy. Abyss. Ferret et Galin., Atlas, t. 20, f. 8 (1847).   [Guinea.
               Harold, Berl. Ent. Zeitschr. p. 94, 98 (1861).   Alt-Calabar. Abessinien, Kap,
138. *A. septemmaculatus*, Fabricius, Spec. Ins. Vol. 1, p. 20 (1781).   Mittelafrika.
139. *A. serenus*, Péringuey, Trans. S. Afric. Philos. Soc. 1901-03, Vol. 12,   Kapkolonie.
   Cat. p. 393 (1901).
140. *A. sericeus*, A. Schmidt, Notes Leyd. Mus. Vol. 31, p. 107 (1909).   Senegal.
141. *A. serrulatus*, Quedenfeldt, Berl. Ent. Zeitschr. p. 283 (1884).   Malanga.
142. *A. sexmaculosus*, A. Schmidt, Stett. Ent. Zeit. p. 23 (1911).   Senegal.
143. *A. spectabilis*, Péringuey. Trans. S. Afric. Philos. Soc. 1901-03, Vol. 12, Kapkolonie.
   Cat. p. 410 (1901) (*Ammoecius*).

144. *A. strigilatus*, Roth, Wiegmann Arch. f. Naturg. Vol. 1, p. 132 (1851). Tigré, Choa.
  lineellus, Harold, Berl. Ent. Zeitschr. p. 66, 106 (1866). Südafrika, Abessinien.
    sec. Harold, ibidem, p. 256 (1871).
145. *A. tenuitarsis*, Fairmaire, Ann. Soc. Ent. Belg. p. 98 (1897). Madagaskar.
146. *A. teter*, Roth, Wiegmann Arch. f. Naturg. Vol. 1, p. 132 (1851). Tigré.
147. *A. tetricus*, Harold, Berl. Ent. Zeitschr. p. 257, 263 (1871). Abessinien.
148. *A. tibialis*, A. Schmidt. Sjöstedts Kilima-Ndjaro-Meru Exped. 1905-06, Meru-Niederung.
  p. 55 (1908).
149. *A. triangularis*, A. Schmidt, Deutsche Ent. Zeitschr. p. 568 (1907). Caffrarien.
150. *A. tricarinulatus*, A. Schmidt, ibidem, p. 201 (1907), nom. nov.
  carinulatus ‖ Péringuey, Trans. S. Afric. Philos. Soc. 1901-03, Vol. 12, Cat. Transvaal.
    p. 411 (1901).
151. *A. trimaculatus*, A. Schmidt. Notes Leyd. Mus. Vol. 31, p. 103 (1909). Weyns (Kongo).
152. *A. tumulosus*, A. Schmidt, Stett. Ent. Zeit. p. 24 (1911). Abessinien, Bogos.
153. *A. turbidus*, Erichson, Wiegmann, Arch. f. Naturg. Vol. 1, p. 234 Angola.
  (1843); Naturg. Ins. Deutschl. Vol. 3, p. 880. Note (1848).
154. *A. unicornutus*, A. Schmidt, Notes Leyd. Mus. Vol. 31, p. 111 (1909). Rhodesia.
155. *A. valens*, Péringuey, Trans. S. Afric. Philos. Soc. 1901-03, Vol. 12, Südafrika.
  Cat. p. 382 (1901).
156. *A. venalis*, A. Schmidt, Stett. Ent. Zeit. p. 25 (1911). Ghinda, Massaua.
157. *A. vernilis*, A. Schmidt, ibidem, p. 26 (1911). Sokotra.
158. *A. Vethi*, Lansberge, Notes Leyd. Mus. Vol. 8, p. 91 (1886). Humpata.
159. *A. Wahlbergi*, Boheman, Ins. Caffr. Vol. 2, p. 350 (1857). — **Taf. I,** Caffrarien.
  Fig. 5.
  Wahlbergi, Péringuey, Trans. S. Afric. Philos. Soc. 1901-03, Vol. 12, Cat. Natal, Transvaal.
    p. 381 (1901).
  var. Holubi, Dohrn, Stett. Ent. Zeit. p. 107 (1883). Südafrika
    sec. Clouët, Bull. Soc. Ent. Fr. p. 188 (1898).
  nigrosignatus, Péringuey, Trans. S. Afric. Philos. Soc. 1883-85, Vol. 3 (2), Sambesi, Delagoa-Busen.
    p. 91 (1885).
    sec. Péringuey, ibidem, Vol. 12, Cat. p. 381.

C. — Aphodien aus dem amerikanischen Gebiete

1. — NORDAMERIKA UND MEXIKO

1. *Aphodius abusus*, Fall, Trans. Amer. Ent. Soc. Vol. 33, p. 242 (1907). Texas.
2. *A. acerbus*, Horn, ibidem, Vol. 14, p. 56 (1887). Texas.
3. *A. aegrotus*, Horn, ibidem, Vol. 3, p. 127 (1870-71); Vol. 14, p. 43 (1887). Nordcarolina, Florida.
4. *A. aemulus*, Horn, ibidem, Vol. 14. p. 38 (1887). Arizona.
5. *A. alternatus*, Horn, ibidem, Vol. 3, p. 129 (1870); Vol. 14, p. 22 (1887). Westen der Vereinigten
6. *A. anthracinus**, Le Conte, U. S. Geol. Survey, Bull. Vol. 4 (2), Utha. [Staaten Nordam.
  p. 455 (1878).
  anthracinus, Horn, Trans. Amer. Ent. Soc. Vol. 14, p. 15 (1887). Utah.
7. *A. arizonensis*, Schaeffer, Journ. New York Ent. Soc. Vol. 15, p. 61 Arizona.
  (1907).
8. *A. asellus*, A. Schmidt, Deutsche Ent. Zeitschr. p. 201 (1907), nom. nov.
  nanus, Horn, Trans. Amer. Ent. Soc. Vol. 14, p. 55 (1887). Texas.
9. *A. azteca*, Harold, Berl. Ent. Zeitschr. p. 334, 381 (1863); p. 252 (1871). Mexiko.
  azteca, Bates, Biol. Centr. Amer. Col. Vol. 2 (2), t. 6, f. 11 (1887). Mexiko. [deau.
10. *A. bicolor*, Say, Journ. Acad. Nat. Sc. Philad. Vol. 3. p. 212 (1823). Pennsylvanien, Kap Gerar-
  bicolor, Horn, Trans. Amer. Ent. Soc. Vol. 3, p. 130 (1870); Vol. 14, Kanada bis Texas, Massachusetts
    p. 46 (1887).
11. *A. bidentatus*, A. Schmidt. Deutsche Ent. Zeitschr. p. 201 (1906).
  nom. nov.
  bidens* ‖ Le Conte, U. S. Geol. Survey, Bull. Vol. 4 (2), p. 453 (1878). Colorado.
  Horn, Trans. Amer. Ent. Soc. Vol 14 p. 11 (1887). Colorado.

12. *A. bimaculosus*, A. Schmidt, Soc. Ent. Zürich, 1909-10, Vol. 24, p. 19   Mexiko.
    (1909).
13. *A. brevicollis**, Le Conte, U. S. Geol. Survey, Bull. Vol. 4 (2),   Nebraska.
    p. 455 (1878).
        brevicollis, Horn, Trans. Amer. Ent. Soc. Vol. 14, p. 32 (1887).   Nebraska.
14. *A. cadaverinus*, Mannerheim, Bull. Soc. Nat. Mosc. Vol. 16 (2), p. 261   Kalifornien.
    (1843).
15. *A. charmionus*, Bates, Biol. Centr. Amer. Col. Vol. 2 (2), p. 89 t. 6,   Mexiko.
    f. 18 (1887).
16. *A. coloradensis*, Horn, Trans. Amer. Ent. Soc. Vol. 3, p. 130 (1870);   Colorado.
    p. 45 (1887).
17. *A. concavus*, Say, Journ. Acad. Nat. Sc. Philad. Vol. 3 (1), p. 214 (1823).   Rocky Mountains.
        concavus, Horn, Trans. Amer. Ent. Soc. p. 128 (1870); p. 37 (1887).   Georgia bis Missouri, Kansas,
                                                                                    Nebraska, Colorado.

        laevigatus, Haldeman, Journ. Acad. Nat. Sc. Philad.(2),Vol. 1 p. 103 (1848).   Mittel- und Südstaaten.
18. *A. congregatus*, Mannerheim, Bull. Soc. Nat. Mosc. Vol. 26 (3), p. 219   Halbinsel Kenai.
    (1853).
        congregatus, Harold, Berl. Ent. Zeitschr. p. 333, 362 (1863).   Alaska.
                       Horn, Trans. Amer. Ent. Soc. Vol. 3, p. 119 (1870); Vol. 14,   Russisch, Amerika, Nordkali-
                       p. 12 (1887).   fornien bis Alaska.
        var. arcticus, Harold, Berl. Ent. Zeitschr. p. 333, 361 (1863).   Alaska.
                       sec. Horn, Trans. Amer. Ent. Soc. Vol. 5, p. 141 (1875).
19. *A. consentaneus*, Le Conte, Agass. Lake Sup. p. 225 (1850).   Nordamerika.
        consentaneus, Horn, Trans. Amer. Ent. Soc. Vol. 3, p. 128 (1870); Vol. 14,   Kanada, Missouri, Kansas, Neu-
                       p. 40 (1887).   Mexiko.
20. *A. consociatus*, Horn, ibidem, Vol. 14, p. 21 (1887).   Kalifornien.
21. *A. conspersus*, Horn, ibidem, p. 9 (1887).   Kalifornien.
22. *A. constricticollis*, Bates, Biol. Centr. Amer. Suppl. 1889, p. 392, t. 24,   Mexiko.
    f. 11 (1890).
23. *A. Coquilletti*, Linell, Proc. U. S. Nat. Mus. Vol. 18, p. 722 (1896).   Kalifornien.
24. *A. crassuloides*, Fall, Trans. Amer. Ent. Soc. Vol. 33, p. 243 (1907).   New-Mexiko.
25. *A. crassulus*, Horn, ibidem, Vol. 3, p. 118 (1870); Vol. 14, p. 10 (1887).   Georgia, Florida bis Texas.
26. *A. cribratus**, Le Conte, U. S. Geol. Survey, Bull. Vol. 4, p. 455 (1878).   Oregon.
        cribratus, Horn, Trans. Amer. Ent. Soc. Vol. 14, p. 24 (1887).   Kalifornien.
27. *A. cruentatus**, Le Conte, U. S. Geol. Survey, Bull. Vol. 4 (2), p. 456 (1878).   Neu-Mexiko.
        cruentatus, Horn, Trans. Amer. Ent. Soc. Vol. 14, p. 52 (1887).   Arizona.
                      Bates, Biol. Centr. Amer. Col. Vol. 2 (2), p. 86 (1887).   Nordamerika.
28. *A. decipiens*, Horn, Trans. Amer. Ent. Soc. Vol. 14, p. 28 (1887).   Nevada.
29. *A. denticulatus*, Haldeman, Journ. Acad. Nat. Sc. Philad. (2), Vol. 1,   Rocky Mountains.
    p. 104 (1848).
        denticulatus, Horn, Trans. Amer. Ent. Soc. Vol. 3, p. 116 (1870); Vol. 14,   Wyoming bis Neu-Mexiko.
                       p. 9 (1887).
30. *A. dentiger*, Le Conte, Proc. Acad. Nat. Sc. Philad. 1858, p. 65 (1859).   Kalifornien.
        dentiger, Horn, Trans. Amer. Ent. Soc. Vol. 3, p. 130 (1870); Vol. 14, p. 45   Arizona, Texas.
31. *A. depressiusculus*, A. Schmidt, Deutsche Ent. Zeitschr. p. 201 (1907),
    nom. nov.
        marginatus* || Le Conte, U. S. Geol. Survey, Bull. Vol. 4 (2), p. 456 (1878).   Nevada.
                       Horn, Trans. Amer. Ent. Soc. Vol. 14, p. 32 (1887).   Nevada.
32. *A. dialytoides*, Fall, ibidem, Vol. 33, p. 247 (1907).   Massachusetts.
33. *A. Dugesi*, Bates, Biol. Centr. Amer. Col. Vol. 2 (2 , p. 83, t. 6, f. 9 (1887).   Mexiko.
34. *A. duplex**, Le Conte, U.S. Geol. Survey, Bull. Vol. 4 (2), p. 454 (1878).   Colorado.
        duplex, Horn, Trans. Amer. Ent. Soc Vol. 14, p. 14 (1887).   Colorado.
                  Bates, Biol. Centr. Amer. Col. Vol 2 (2), Ins. p. 87 (1887).   Mexiko, Costa Rica.
35. *A. explanatus**, Le Conte, U.S. Geol. Survey, Bull. Vol. 4 (2), p. 457 (1878).   Colorado.
        explanatus, Horn, Trans. Amer. Ent. Soc. Vol. 14, p. 30 (1887).   Colorado.
36. *A. femoralis*, Say, Journ. Acad. Nat. Sc. Philad. Vol. 3, p. 215 (1823).   Missouri.
        femoralis, Horn, Trans. Amer. Ent. Soc. Vol. 3, p. 131 (1870); Vol. 14,   Pennsylvanien bis Kansas, Te-
                    p. 59 (1887).   xas, Massachusetts.

37. *A. Flohri*, Bates, Biol. Centr. Amer. Col. Vol. 2 (2), p. 86 (1887).   Mexiko.
38. *A. fuliginosus*, Harold, Berl. Enf. Zeitschr. p. 327, 330 (1863).   Mexiko.
    fuliginosus, Bates, Biol. Centr. Amer. Col. Vol. 2 (2), p. 90, t. 6, f. 21 (1887).   Mexiko.
39. *A. gentilis*, Horn, Trans. Amer. Eht. Soc. Vol. 14, p. 24 (1887).   San Francisco.
40. *A. glyptus*, Bates, Biol. Centr. Amer. Col. Vol. 2 (2), p. 86, t. 6, f. 12   Mexiko.
    (1887).
41. *A. gravidus*, Harold. Berl. Ent. Zeitschr. p. 329, 330 (1863).   Mexiko.
42. *A. guttatus**, Eschscholtz, Mém. Soc. Nat. Mose. p. 97 (1823); Bull.   Unalaschka.
    Soc Nat. Mose. Vol. 2, p. 261 (1843).
    guttatus, Harold, Berl. Ent. Zeitschr. p. 332, 352 (1863).   Unalaschka.
    Horn, Trans. Amer. Ent. Soc. Vol. 14, p. 17 (1887).   Alaska.
43. *A. Haldemani*, Horn, Trans. Amer. Ent. Soc. Vol. 14, p. 33 (1887).   Texas, Kansas.
    politus ‖ Horn, ibidem, Vol. 3, p. 128 (1870).
44. *A. hamatus**, Say, Long's Expēd. Vol. 2, p. 277, ed. Le C. Vol. 1, p. 183   Nordamerika.
    (*Diapterna*). — **Taf. I, Fig. 14.**
    hamatus, Horn, Trans. Amer. Ent. Soc. Vol. 3, p. 113 (1870).   Lake Superior, Illinois, Dakota.
    Harold, Berl. Ent. Zeitschr. p. 181 (1874).   [Staaten, Neu-Mexiko.
    Horn, Trans. Amer. Ent. Soc. Vol. 14, p. 5 (1887).   Hudson-Bai, Norden der Ver.
    concavus, Haldeman, Journ. Acad. Nat. Sc. Philad. (2), Vol. 1, p. 103 (1848).   Rocky Mountains, Lake Super.
    pinguis, Haldeman, ibidem, p. 103 (1848).   Lake Superior.
    Horn, Trans. Amer. Ent. Soc. Vol. 3, p. 112 (1870).   Lake Superior.
    angularis, Le Conte, Agass. Lake Super. p. 225 (1850).   Lake Superior.
    omissus, Le Conte, ibidem, p. 225 (1850).   Lake Superior.
    hyperboreus, Le Conte, ibidem, p. 225 (1850).   Lake Superior.
    Horn, Trans. Amer. Ent. Soc. Vol. 3, p. 113 (1870).   Lake Superior bis Oregon.
    sagittarius, Harold, Ann. Soc. Ent. Fr. p. 615 (1860); Berl. Ent. Zeitschr.   Nordamerika, Michigan, Oregon
    p. 155, 163 (1862).
    torpidus, Horn, Trans. Amer. Ent. Soc. Vol. 3, p. 114 (1870).   Lake Superior, Oregon.
    var. occidentalis, Horn. ibidem, p. 114 (1870).   Montana bis Oregon.
    sec. Horn, ibidem, p. 106 (1887).
45. *A. Högei*, Bates, Biol. Centr. Amer. Col. Vol. 2 (2), p. 90 (1887).   Mexiko.
    var. durangoensis, Bates, ibidem, p. 90 (1887).   Mexiko.
46. *A. humeralis**, Le Conte, U. S. Geol. Survey, Bull. Vol. 4 (2),   Michigan.
    p. 459 (1878).
    humeralis, Horn, Trans. Amer. Ent. Soc. Vol. 14. p. 63 (1887).   Maryland.
47. *A. indutilis*, Harold, Berl. Ent. Zeitschr. p. 178 (1874).   Mexiko.
    sec. Bates, Biol. Centr. Amer. Col. Vol. 2 (2), p. 84 (1887).   Guatemala.
48. *A. innexus**, Say, Journ. Boston, Vol. 1, p. 177 (1837).   Mexiko.
    innexus, Harold. Berl. Ent. Zeitschr. p. 257, 270 (1871).   Mexiko.
    flavocinctus, Harold, Ann. Soc. Ent. Fr. p. 614 (1860).   Kalifornien.
49. *A. inutilis*, Horn, Trans. Amer. Ent. Soc. Vol. 14, p. 50 (1887).   Kalifornien, Oregon.
50. *A. Knausi*, Fall, Ent. News Philad. Vol. 16, p. 130 (1905).   Kansas.
    kansanus*, Wickham, The Canad. Entom. p. 169 (1905).
51. *A. Lansbergei*, Harold, Berl. Ent. Zeitschr. p. 179 (1874).   Mexiko.
    Lansbergei, Bates, Biol. Centr. Amer. Col. Vol. 2 (2), p. 84 (1887).   Mexiko.
52. *A. larreae*, Horn, Trans. Amer. Ent. Soc. Vol. 14, p. 41 (1887).   Texas.
    bifrons, Bates, Biol. Centr. Amer. Col. Vol. 2 (2), p. 90, t. 6, f. 20 (1887).   Mexiko.
    Suppl. p. 392.
53. *A. lentus*, Horn, Trans. Amer. Ent. Soc. Vol. 3, p. 125 (1870); Vol. 14,   Pennsylvanien, Georgia,
    p. 27 (1887).   Illinois, Massachusetts.
    lentus, Wickham, The Canad. Entom. Vol. 26, p. 205 (1894).   Kansas.
54. *A. leopardus*, Horn, Trans. Amer. Ent. Soc. Vol. 3, p. 124 (1870);   Maine, Ostkanada.
    Vol. 14, p. 49 (1887).
55. *A. levatus*, A. Schmidt, Deutsche Ent. Zeitschr. p. 568 (1907).   Mexiko.
56. *A. longitarsis*, Fall, Trans. Amer. Ent. Soc Vol. 33, p. 246 (1907).   El Paso, Aweme, Manitoba.
57. *A. luridiventris*, Harold, Berl. Ent. Zeitschr. p. 380, 385 (1862);   Mexiko.
    p. 330 (1863).
    luridiventris, Bates, Biol. Centr. Amer. Col Vol. 2 (2), p. 92 (1887).   Mexiko.
58. *A. luteolus*, Horn, Trans. Amer. Ent Soc. Vol. 14, p. 40 (1887).   Neu-Mexiko.

59. *A. lutulentus,* Haldeman, Proc. Acad. Nat. Sc. Philad. Vol. 1, p. 304 (1843); Journ. Acad. Nat. Sc. Philad. (2), Vol. 1, p. 104 (1848).
  lutulentus, Horn, Trans. Amer. Ent. Soc. Vol. 3, p. 124 (1870); p. 26 (1887).
  Harold, Berl. Ent. Zeitschr. p. 184, 196 (1874.
Nordamerika, Pennsylvanien, Carolina.
Mittel- und Südstaaten.
Mittel- und Südstaaten.

60. *A. luxatus,* Horn, Trans. Amer. Ent. Soc. Vol. 14, p. 46 (1887).
Südkalifornien, Arizona.

61. *A. mexicanus,* Harold. Berl.Ent.Zeitschr.p.380,382(1862); p.330(1863).
  mexicanus, Bates, Biol. Centr. Amer. Col. Vol. 2 (2), p. 91 (1887).
Mexiko.
Guatemala.

62. *A. militaris,* Le Conte, Proc. Acad. Nat. Sc Philad. p. 65 (1858).
  militaris, Horn, Trans. Amer. Ent. Soc. Vol. 3, p. 127 (1870); Vol. 14, p. 38 (1887).
Kalifornien.
San Diego, Nevada.

63. *A. moquinus,* Fall, Trans. Amer. Ent. Soc. Vol. 33, p. 242 (1907).
Arizona.

64. *A. neotomae,* Fall, ibidem, p. 243 (1907).
Kalifornien.

65. *A. nevadensis.* Horn,Trans.Amer.Ent.Soc.Vol.3,p.121(1870);Vol.14. p. 23 (1887).
Nevada, Nordkalifornien.

66. *A. nigricans (Euparia),* Westwood, Proc. Ent. Soc. Lond. p. 93 (1843).
  nigricans, Westwood, Trans. Ent. Soc. Lond. Vol. 4, p. 240, t. 17, f. 4 (1847).
  sec. Clouët, Ann. Soc. Ent. Fr. p. 240 (1898).
Amerika.
                                  [vanien.

67. *A. oblongus,* Say, Journ. Acad. Nat. Sc. Philad. Vol. 3, p. 215 (1823).
  oblongus, Haldeman, ibidem (2), Vol. 1, p. 103 (1848).
  Horn, Trans. Amer. Ent. Soc. Vol. 3, p. 132 (1870); Vol. 14, p. 61 (1887).
  Wickham, The Canad. Entom. Vol. 26, p. 204 (1894).
  badipes, Melsheimer, Proc. Acad. Nat.Sc. Philad. 1844,Vol.2, p. 135 (1846).
Rocky-Mountains, Pennsyl-
Mittel- und Südstaaten.
Pennsylvanien bis Colorado,Arizona.
Kanada.
Pennsylvanien.

68. *A. obtusus*,* Le Conte, U. S. Geol. Survey,Bull.Vol.4 (2),p.454 (1878).
  obtusus, Horn, Trans. Amer. Ent. Soc. Vol. 14, p. 20 (1887)
Colorado.
Wyoming.

69. *A. ochreipennis,* Horn, ibidem,Vol.3, p. 295 (1871); Vol. 14, p. 33 (1887).
Kalifornien.

70. *A. oleosus,* Harold, Berl. Ent. Zeitschr. p. 257, 260 (1871).
Mexiko.

71. *A. omiltemius,* Bates, Biol. Centr. Amer. Col. Vol. 2 (2), Suppl. p. 392 (1889).
Mexiko.

72. *A. opacus,* Le Conte, Col. Hefte, Vol. 10, p. 193 (1872).
  opacus, Horn, Trans. Amer. Ent. Soc. Vol. 14, p. 25 (1887).
Vancouver-Insel.
Kalifornien.

73. *A. opisthius,* Bates, Biol. Centr. Amer. Col. Vol. 2 (2), p. 92, Note (1887), Suppl. p. 392 (1889):
  duplex || Bates, ibidem, p. 87, t. 6. f. 15 (1887).
Mexiko, Costarica.

74. *A. ovipennis,* Horn, Trans. Amer. Ent. Soc. Vol. 3, p. 133 (1870); Vol. 14. p. 63 (1887).
Kalifornien.

75. *A. parcus,* Horn, ibidem, p. 42 (1887).
Florida.

76. *A. pardalis*,* Le Conte, Pacific R. R. Rep, App. 1, p. 41 (1857).
  pardalis, Horn, Trans. Amer. Ent. Soc. Vol 3, p. 123 (1870); Vol. 14, p 49 (1887).
Kalifornien.
San Francisco bis Vancouver-
Insel. Nebraska.

77. *A. pectoralis*,* Le Conte, Pacific R. R. Report, App. 1, p. 41 (1857).
  pectoralis, Horn, Trans. Amer. Ent. Soc. Vol. 3, p. 120 (1870); Vol. 14, p. 14 (1887).
Kalifornien.
San Francisco bis Alaska, Washington Territoire.

78. *A. phaeopterus*,* Le Conte, U. S. Geol. Survey. Bull. Vol. 4 (2), p. 456 (1878).
  phaeopterus, Horn, Trans. Amer. Ent. Soc. Vol. 14, p. 31 (1887).
Idaho.

79. *A. phalerioides,* Horn, ibidem,Vol.3, p.131(1870);Vol.14,p.41(1887).
Washington, Montana.

80. *A. plutonicus,* Fall, ibidem, Vol. 33, p. 245 (1907).
Mittelstaaten, New York,
Townsend.   [New Jersey.

81. *A. pumilio,* A. Schmidt, Deutsche Ent.Zeitschr.p. 201(1907),nom.nov.
  pumilus || Horn, Trans. Amer. Ent. Scc. Vol. 14, p. 50 (1887).
Neu-Mexiko.

82. *A. punticeps,* Harold, Berl. Ent. Zeitschr. p. 380(1862); p. 330 (1863).
Mexiko.

83. *A. rotundiceps,* Fall, Trans. Amer. Ent. Soc. Vol. 33, p. 244 (1907).
Nordcarolina.

84. *A. rubeolus,* Beauvois, Ins. Afric. et Amer. p. 90, t. 2, f. 4 (1805).
  rubeolus, Horn, Trans. Amer. Ent. Soc. Vol. 3, p. 126 (1870); Vol. 14, p. 34 (1887).
  copronymus, Melsheimer, Proc. Acad. Nat. Sc. Philad. 1844, p. 136 (1846).
Südcarolina.
Mittelstaaten bis Texas, Massachusetts.
Pennsylvanien.

85. *A. rubidus*,* Le Conte, Pacific R. R. Report, App. 1, p. 41 (1857).
  rubidus, Horn, Trans. Amer. Ent. Soc. Vol. 14, p. 37 (1887).
Kalifornien.
Arizona.

86. *A. rubiginosus*, Horn, Trans. Amer. Ent. Soc. Vol. 3, p. 127 (1870);   Arizona.
Vol. 14, p. 39 (1887).
87. *A. rubripennis*, Horn, ibidem, p. 132 (1870); ibidem, p. 57 (1887).   Kanada,   Pennsylvanien,
88. *A. rudis**, Le Conte. U. S. Geol. Survey, Bull. Vol. 4 (2); p. 458 (1878).   Colorado.   [Maryland.
    rudis, Horn, Trans. Amer. Ent. Soc. Vol. 14, p. 31 (1887).   Colorado.
89. *A. rugatus*, A. Schmidt, Deutsche Ent. Zeitschr. p. 202 (1907), nom. nov.
    rugifrons ‖ Horn. Trans. Amer. Ent. Soc. p. 295 (1871); p. 19 (1887).   Kalifornien.
90. *A. ruricola*, Melsheimer, Proc. Acad. Nat. Sc. Philad. Vol. 2, p. 136 (1844).   Pennsylvanien.
    ruricola, Harold, Berl. Ent. Zeitschr p 333, 373 (1863).   Nordamerika.
    Horn, Trans. Amer. Ent. Soc. Vol. 3, p. 118 (1870); Vol. 14,   Kanada bis Texas, Nordost-Staa-
      p. 15 (1887).   ten bis Texas und Colorado.
    curtus, Haldeman. Journ. Acad. Nat. Sc. Philad. (2), Vol. 1, p. 105 (1848).   Rocky Mountains.
    aurelianus, Harold, Berl. Ent. Zeitschr. p. 334, 375 (1863).   Neu-Orleans.
      sec. Harold, Col. Hefte, Vol. 6, p. 106 (1870).
91. *A. Sallei*, Harold, Berl. Ent. Zeitschr. p. 331, 336 (1863).   Mexiko.
    Sallaei, Bates, Biol. Centr. Amer. Col. Vol. 2 (2), p. 84, t. 6, f. 10 (1887).   Mittelamerika.
92. *A. scabriceps**, Le Conte. U. S. Geol. Survey, Bull. Vol. 4 (2), p. 457   Colorado.
(1878).
    scabriceps, Horn, Trans. Amer. Ent. Soc. Vol. 14, p. 55 (1887).   Colorado.
93. *A. serval**, Say, Bost. Journ. p. 177 (1837).   Indiana.
    serval, Horn, Trans. Amer. Ent. Soc. p. 122 (1870); p. 47 (1887).   Pennsylvanien, Mittelstaaten bis
    Steinheili, Harold, Col. Hefte, Vol. 5, p. 100 (1869).   Illinois ?   [Texas.
      sec. Horn, Trans. Amer. Ent. Soc. Vol. 5, p. 141 (1875).
94. *A. sparsus**, Le Conte. U. S. Geol. Survey. Hayden, Bull. Vol. 4 (2),   Kalifornien.
p. 458 (1878).
    sparsus, Horn, Trans. Amer. Ent. Soc. Vol. 14, p. 62 (1887).   Kalifornien.
    Blaisdelli, Fall, Ent. News, Philad. Vol. 16, p. 129 (1905).   Kalifornien.
      sec. Fall, ibidem, Vol. 18, p. 177 (1907).
95. *A. stercorosus*, Melsheimer, Proc. Acad. Nat. Sc. Philad. Vol. 2, p. 136   Pennsylvanien.
(1844).
    stercorosus, Horn, Trans. Amer. Ent. Soc. Vol. 3, p. 127 (1870); Vol. 14,   Osten der Vereinigten Staaten
      p. 35 (1887).
96. *A. stupidus*, Horn. ibidem, Vol. 3, p. 125 (1870).   Georgia.
    stupidus, Harold, Berl. Ent. Zeitschr. p. 184, 204 (1874).   Oestliches Nordamerika.
    Horn, Trans. Amer. Ent. Soc. Vol. 14, p. 27 (1887).   Nordcarolina.
97. *A. subaeneus**, Le Conte, Pacific R. R. Report. App. 1, p. 41 (1857).   Kalifornien.
    subaeneus, Horn, Trans. Amer. Ent. Soc. Vol. 3, p. 129 (1870); Vol. 14,   Kalifornien.
      p. 21 (1887).
98. *A. subtruncatus**, Le Conte, U. S. Geol. Survey, Bull. Vol. 4, (2),   Colorado.
p. 457 (1878).
    subtrunctatus, Horn, Trans. Amer. Ent. Soc. Vol. 14, p. 57 (1887).   Nebraska.
99. *A. tenuistriatus*, Horn, ibidem, p. 60 (1887).   Texas.
100. *A. terminalis*, Say, Journ. Acad. Nat. Sc. Philad. Vol. 3 (1), p. 213 (1823).   Vereinigte Staaten.
    terminalis, Horn, Trans. Amer. Ent. Soc. Vol. 3, p. 129 (1870); Vol. 14,   Pennsylvanien bis Illinois, Mit-
      p. 51 (1887).   telstaaten bis Kansas und
      sec. Wickham, The Canad. Entom. Vol. 26, p. 204 (1894).   Kanada.   [Texas.
101. *A. troglodytes**, Hubbard, Insect Life, Vol. 6, p. 312 (1894).   Florida.
102. *A. umbricollis*, Fall. Trans. Amer. Ent. Soc. Vol. 33, p. 245 (1907).   El Paso (Texas).
103. *A. ungulatus**, Fall. Occas. Pap. Calif. Acad. Vol. 8, p. 254 (1902).   Südkalifornien.
104. *A. validus*, Horn, Trans. Amer. Ent. Soc. Vol. 3, p. 112 (1870); p. 5   Hudsón-Bai.
(1887) (*Diapterna*).
    validus. Harold, Berl. Ent. Zeitschr. p. 181 (1874).
105. *A. venustus*, A. Schmidt, Stett. Ent. Zeit. p. 28 (1911).   Mexiko.
106. *A. vestiarius*, Horn, Trans. Amer. Ent. Soc. Vol. 3, p. 121 (1870);   Florida.
Vol. 14, p. 18 (1887).
107. *A. villosipes*, Harold, Berl. Ent. Zeitschr. p. 380, 384 (1862); p. 330 (1863).   Mexiko.
108. *A. Walshi*, Horn, Trans. Amer. Ent. Soc. Vol. 3, p. 132 (1870);   Illinois, Kansas.
Vol. 14. p. 58 (1887).

2. — MITTELAMERIKA UND WESTINDIEN

1. *A. cuniculus*, Chevrolat, Ann. Soc. Ent. Fr. p. 411 (1864).   Cuba.
    cuniculus, Harold, Berl. Ent. Zeitschr. p. 257, 271 (1871).   St. Domingo.
        sec. Bates, Biol. Centr. Amer. Col. Vol 2 (2), p. 85 (1887).   Mittelamerika.
        sec. Arrow, Trans. Ent. Soc. Lond. p. 511 (1903).   Kleine Antillen.
2. *A. diminutus*, Bates, Biol. Centr. Amer Col. Vol. 2 (2), p. 89 (1887).   Guatemala.
3. *A. erythrinus*, Bates, ibidem. p. 89 (1887).   Panama.
4. *A. euprosopus*, Bates, ibidem, p. 87, t. 6. f. 14 (1887).   Guatemala.
5. *A. guatemalensis*, Bates, ibidem, p. 88, t. 6, f. 17 (1887).   Guatemala.
    var. scotinus, Bates, ibidem, p. 89 (1887).   Mexiko.
    var. chiriquinus, Bates, ibidem, p. 89 (1887).   Panama.
6. *A. latecrenatus*, Bates, ibidem, p. 86, t. 6, f. 13 (1887).   Guatemala.
7 *A. quadridentatus*, Harold. Berl. Ent. Zeitschr. p. 107 (1861); p. 331 (1863).   Kuba.
    quadridentatus, Chevrolat, Ann. Soc. Ent. Fr. (4), Vol. 4, p. 412 (1864).   Kuba.
8. *A. xanthus*, Bates, Biol. Centr. Amer. Col. Vol. 2 (2), p. 90, t. 6, f. 19   Panama.
    (1887).

3. — SÜDAMERIKA

1. *A. anomalus*, Harold, Berl. Ent. Zeitschr. p. 183, 185 (1874).   Chile.
2. *A. argentinensis*, A. Schmidt, Notes Leyd Mus. Vol. 31, p. 101 (1909).   Argentina,
3. *A. biimpressus*, A. Schmidt, Soc. Ent. Zürich, 1908-09, Vol. 23, p. 177   Paraguay.
    (1909).
4. *A. brasiliensis*, Castelnau. Nat. Hist. Ins. Vol. 2. p. 95 (1840).   Brasilien.
    brasiliensis, Harold, Berl. Ent. Zeitschr. p. 257, 274 (1871).   Brasilien.
        sec. Erichson, Wiegmann Arch. f. Naturg. Vol. 1, p. 110 (1847).   Peru.
        sec. A. Schmidt, Aphodiinen-Zusammenst. Deutsche Ent.   Mexiko.
        Zeitschr. Beih. Anmerkung. p. 10 (1907-08).
5. *A. columbicus*, Harold, Stett. Ent. Zeit. p. 36 (1880).   Bogotá.
6. *A. Erichsoni*, Harold, Berl. Ent. Zeitschr. p. 104 (1861); p. 155 (1862). Brasilien.
7. *A. fulviventris*, Fairmaire, Rev. Mag. Zool. (2), Vol. 12. p. 268 (1860).   Chile.
    fulviventris, Harold, Berl. Ent. Zeitschr. p. 279 (1867); p. 183, 186 (1874).   Chile.
8. *A. furcatus*, A. Schmidt, Soc. Ent. Zürich 1909-10, Vol. 24. p. 10 (1909).   Matto Grosso.
9. *A. gracilipes*, Harold. Berl. Ent. Zeitschr. p. 279 (1867); p. 183, 188   Chile.
    (1874).
10. *A. pacatus*, Harold, Stett. Ent. Zeit. p. 37 (1880).   Columbien.
11. *A. peruanus**, Erichson, Nov. Act. Acad. Carol. Halle, Vol. 16, p. 237   Peru.
    (1833). — Pl. I, Fig. 15.
    peruanus, Harold, Berl. Ent. Zeitschr. p. 183, 187 (1874).   Bolivien.
    longitarsis. Harold, Ann. Soc. Ent. Fr. p. 615 (1860).   Bolivien.
        sec. Harold, ibidem, p. 187 (1874).
12. *A. Richteri*, A. Schmidt. Stett. Ent. Zeit. p. 21 (1911).   Argentina.
13. *A. rugosiceps*, Harold, Berl. Ent. Zeitschr. p. 213 (1859); p. 96, 97   Chile, Peru.
    (1866); p. 279 (1867).
14. *A. Volxemi*, Harold, C. R. Ann. Soc. Ent. Belg. p. 93 (1876).   Barbacena.

D. — Indisches Gebiet

1. *A. acutus*, A. Schmidt, Ent. Wochenbl. p. 47 (1908).   Karachi.
2. *A. aeger**, Sharp, Journ. Asiat. Soc. Bengal, Vol. 47 (2), p. 170 (1878); Yangihissar.
    Scient. Results second Yarkand Miss. Col. p. 43 (1890).
3. *A. Andrewesi*, A. Schmidt, Ent. Wochenbl. p. 46 (1908).   Belgaum, Nilgiri Hills.
4. *A. atricapillus*, Fabricius, Ent. Syst. Suppl. p. 24 (1798); Syst. Eleuth.   Ostindien.
    Vol. 1, p. 80 (1801).
5. *A. biseriatus*, A. Schmidt, Ent. Wochenbl. p. 46 (1908).   Belgaum, Nilgiri Hills.

6. *A. bostrichoides,* Harold, Ann. Soc. Ent. Fr. p. 615 (1860); Berl. Ent.   Nordindien.
    Zeitschr. p. 160 (1862).
        bostrichoides, Reitter. Tab. p. 42 ; Brünn, 3o, p. 180.
7. *A. brahminus,* Harold, Col. Hefte, Vol. 16, p. 227 (1879).   Birma.
8. *A. cancelliventris,* Motschulsky, Etud. Ent. p. 55 (1858).   Birma.
9. *A. carinipennis,* Motschulsky, ibidem, p. 56 (1858).   Birma.
10. *A. carinulatus,* Motschulsky, Bull. Soc. Nat. Mosc. Vol. 36(2), p.461(1863).   Ceylon.
        carinulatus, Harold, Berl. Ent. Zeitschr. p. 184. 207 (1874).   Vorderindien.
11. *A. castanicolor,* Motschulsky, Etud. Ent. p. 54 (1858).   Birma.
12. *A. compacticollis* 1), Motschulsky, ibidem, p. 55 (1858).   Birma.
13. *A. costatulus,* A. Schmidt, Ent. Wochenbl. p. 47 (1908).   Belgaum, Kulu, Rajmahal.
14. *A. crenatus,* Harold, Berl. Ent. Zeitschr. p. 141, 142 (1862).   Luzon.
        crenatus, Clouët, Ann. Soc. Ent. Fr. p. 240 (1898).
        Dejean, Cat. (ed. 3), p. 162 (1837).   Ostindien.
15. *A. deplorandus,* A. Schmidt, Deutsche Ent. Zeitschr. p.202(1907), nom. nov.
        mixtus || Motschulsky, Etud. Ent. p. 56 (1858).   Birma.
16. *A. fasciger,* Harold, Mitt. München. Ent. Ver. Vol. 5, p. 89 (1881).   Darjeeling.
17. *A. immarginatus,* A. Schmidt, Deutsche Ent. Zeitschr. p. 201 (1907),
    nom. nov.
        crassulus || Fairmaire, Ann. Soc. Ent. Belg. p. 305 (1893).   Nördliches Tonking.
18. *A. impudicus,* Fabricius, Syst. Eleuth. Vol. 1, p. 81 (1801).   Ostindien, Sumatra.
19. *A. irregularis,* Westwood, Royle Himalaya, Vol. 1,p. 55, t. 9, f 8 (1839).   Himalaya.
        irregularis, Harold, Berl. Ent. Zeitschr. p. 332, 345 (1863).   Nördliches Ostindien.
20. *A. javanus,* A. Schmidt, Notes Leyd. Mus. Vol. 31, p. 114 (1909).   Batavia.
21. *A. kashmirensis**, Sharp, Journ. Asiat. Soc. Bengal, Vol. 47 (2), p. 171   Ladak, Kashmir.
    (1878); Scient. Res. second Yarkand Mission, Col. p. 44 (1890).
22. *A. lepidus,* A. Schmidt, Ent. Wochenbl. p. 47 (1908).   Belgaum, Madura, Madras.
23. *A. marginellus,* Fabricius, Spec. Ins. Vol. 1, p. 21 (1781).   Koromandel.
        marginellus, Olivier, Ent. Vol. 1 (3), p. 91, t. 13, f. 116 (1789).   Koromandel.
        Harold, Berl. Ent. Zeitschr. p. 141, 146 (1862).   Ostindien, Bengalen, Polyne-
        diadema, Wiedemann, Zool. Mag. Vol. 2 (1), p. 27 (1823).   Java.   sien.
        var. priscus, Motschulsky, Etud. Ent. p. 56 (1858).   Birma.
        sec. Harold, Ann. Mus. Stor. Nat. Genova, Vol. 10, p. 84 (1877).   Borneo, Celebes, Neu-Guinea.
24. *A. miliaris,* A. Schmidt, Soc. Ent. Zürich, 1908-09, Vol. 23, p. 53 (1908).   Hinterindien.
25. *A. minutissimus,* A. Schmidt, Ent. Wochenbl. p. 47 (1908).   Nilgiri Hills.
26. *A. moestus,* Fabricius, Syst. Eleuth. Vol. 1, p. 78 (1801).   Ostindien.
        moestus, Boheman, Ins. Caffr. Vol. 2, p. 351 (1857).   Caffrarien.
        Péringuey, Trans. S. Afric. Philos. Soc. 1901-1903, Vol. 12, Cat.   Transvaal, Ostküste Afrikas, Ma-
        p. 395 (1901).   dagaskar, Ceylon.
        mutans, Walker, Ann. Mag. Nat. Hist. (3), Vol. 2, p. 207 (1858).   Ceylon.
        sec. Harold, Berl. Ent. Zeitschr. p. 403 (1862).
        madagascariensis, Harold, ibidem, p. 208 (1859).   Madagaskar.
        sec. Harold, ibidem, p. 114 (1861).
        subvittatus, Fairmaire, Ann. Soc. Ent. Belg. p. 452 (1896).   Diego-Suarez.
        sec. A. Schmidt. Notes Leyd. Mus. Vol. 31, p. 123 (1909).
27. *A. nigellus,* A. Schmidt, ibidem, p. 114 (1909).   Java.
28. *A. nigrovirgatus,* A. Schmidt, Stett. Ent. Zeit. p. 49 (1911), nom. nov.
        nigrosulcatus, A. Schmidt, Soc Ent. Zürich, 1908-09, Vol. 23, p. 189 (1909).   Yünnan.
29. *A. ovatulus,* Harold, Berl. Ent. Zeitschr. p. 108 (1861).   Ostindien, Ceylon.
        ovatulus, sec. Gemminger & Harold, Cat. Col. Vol. 4, p. 1055.   Java.
30. *A. perfidus,* A. Schmidt, Ent. Wochenbl. p. 46 (1908).   Belgaum.
31. *A. piceoniger,* Motschulsky, Bull. Soc. Nat. Mosc. Vol. 36(2), p.461(1863).   Ceylon.
32. *A. pilosus,* Harold, Berl. Ent. Zeitschr. p. 183. 190 (1874).   Hindostan.
33. *A. Reichei,* Harold, ibidem, p. 210 (1859); Ann. Mus. Stor. Nat. Genova,   Java.
    Vol. 10, p. 85 (1877).
        Reichei, sec. Baer, Ann. Soc. Ent. Fr. p. 114 (1886).   Luzon.

---

1) Ob die Art zur Gattung *Aphodius* gehört, ist zweifelhaft.

34. *A. Ritsemai*, A. Schmidt, Notes Leyd. Mus. Vol. 31, p. 112 (1909).   Sikkim.
35. *A. rufopustulatus*, Wiedemann, Zool. Mag. Vol. 2 (1), p. 27 (1823).   Bengalen.
36. *A. Schenklingi*, A. Schmidt, Deutsche Ent. Zeitschr. p. 202 (1907).   Khasis.
    var. infestus, A. Schmidt, ibidem, p. 570 (1907).   Assam.
    var sexsignatus, A. Schmidt, ibidem, p. 570 (1907).   Sikkim.
37. *A. segmentarius*, Harold, Col. Hefte, Vol. 16, p. 227 (1879).   Birma.
38. *A. segmentaroides*. A. Schmidt, Soc. Ent Zürich, 1909-1910, Vol. 24,   Vorderindien.
    p. 11 (1909).
39. *A. sinuatus*, Harold, Ann. Soc. Ent. Fr. p. 614 (1860); Berl. Ent.   Philippinen.
    Zeitschr. p. 93, 95 (1861).
40. *A. tectoformibus*. A. Schmidt, Notes Leyd. Mus. Vol. 31, p. 115 (1909).   Manila.
41. *A. tenuimanus**, Sharp, Journ. Asiat. Soc. Bengal. Vol. 47 (2), p. 171   Zentralasien.
    (1878); Scient. Results second Yarkand Miss. p. 45 (1890).
42. *A. tuberifrons*, Fairmaire, Ann. Soc. Ent. Fr. p. 13 (1889).   Jünnan.
43. *A. urostigma*, Harold, Berl. Ent. Zeitschr. p. 170 (1862).   Java, Ceylon.
    urostigma, Waterhouse, Trans. Ent. Soc. Lond. p. 90 (1875).   China, Japan.
    Harold, Mitt. München. Ent. Ver. p. 156 (1880).
    postpilosus. Reitter. Wien. Ent. Zeit. p. 209 (1895).   Shanghai.
    sec. Clouët, Bull. Soc. Ent. Fr. p. 187 (1898).
44. *A. ustulatus*, Harold. Berl. Ent. Zeitschr. p. 380, 386 (1862).   Ostindien.
    sec. A. Schmidt, Aphodiinen-Zusammenst. Deutsche Ent. Zeitschr. Beih.   Natal, Transvaal, Usambara
    Anmerkung 2, p. 85 (1907-08).   Kongo.

E. — Australisches Gebiet

1. *A. Albertisi*, Harold, Ann. Mus. Stor. Nat. Genova, Vol. 10, p. 86 (1877).   Somerset.
    Albertisi, Blackburn, Proc. Roy. Soc. Victoria, Vol. 17, p. 151 (1904).
2. *A. Andersoni*, Blackburn, ibidem, p. 152, 154 (1904).   Südaustralien.
3. *A. australasiae*, Boheman, Res. Eugen. p. 50 (1858).   Sidney.
    australasiae, Blackburn, Proc. Roy. Soc. Victoria, Vol. 17. p. 152 (1904).
    Gestroi, Harold, Ann. Mus. Stor. Nat Genova, Vol. 10, p. 87 (1877).   Celebes.
4. *A. baldiensis*, Blackburn, Proc. Roy. Soc. Victoria, Vol. 17, p. 153, 156   Victoria.
    (1904).
5. *A. callabonensis*, Blackburn, Trans. Roy. Soc. S. Austral. Vol. 19, p. 32   Südaustralien.
    (1895); Proc. Roy. Soc. Victoria, Vol. 17, p. 153 (1904).
6. *A. Candezei*, Harold, Col. Hefte, Vol. 4, p. 85 (1868).   Adelaide.
    Candezei, Blackburn, Proc. Roy. Soc. Victoria, Vol. 17, p. 152 (1904).
7. *A. erosus*, Erichson, Wiegmann Arch. f. Naturg. Vol. 1, p. 157 (1842);   Tasmanien.
    Naturg. Ins. Deutschl. Vol. 3, p. 880, Anmerkung (1848).
    erosus, Blackburn, Proc. Roy. Soc. Victoria, Vol. 17, p. 152 (1904).   Tasmanien.
8. *A. fortipes*, Broun, Man. New Zeal. Col. p. 954 (1886).   Neu-Seeland.
9. *A. insignior*, Blackburn, Proc. Roy. Soc. Victoria, Vol. 17. p. 153, 156   Westaustralien.
    (1904).
10. *A. Lindensis*, Blackburn, Trans. Roy. Soc. S. Austral. Vol. 15, p. 35   Südaustralien.
    (1892); Proc. Roy. Soc. Victoria, Vol. 17, p. 153 (1904).
11. *A. pacificus* 1). Sharp, Trans. Ent. Soc. Lond. p. 90 (1879).   Sandwich-Inseln.
12. *A. suberosus*, Blackburn, Proc. Roy. Soc. Victoria, Vol. 17, p. 153, 155   Victoria.
    (1904).
13. *A. tasmaniae*, Hope, Proc. Ent. Soc. Lond. p. 147 (1846); Trans. Ent.   Tasmanien.
    Soc. Lond. Vol. 4, p. 285 (1847).
    tasmaniae, Harold, Berl. Ent. Zeitschr. p. 217 (1859); p. 94 (1861); p. 381   Tasmanien.
    (1862).
    Howitti. Hope, Proc. Ent. Soc. Lond. p. 147 (1846).   Australien.
    sec. Harold, Berl. Ent. Zeitschr. p. 250 (1871).

---

1) Die Zugehörigkeit zur Gattung *Aphodius* scheint mir zweifelhaft.

australasiae, Blanchard, Voy. Pôle Sud, Vol. 4. p. 101, t. 7, f. 14 (1853).   Tasmanien.
longitarsus, Redtenbacher, Reise Novara, Col. Vol. 2, p. 58 (1867).   Sydney.

14. *A. Victoriae*, Blackburn, Trans. Roy. Soc. S. Austral. Vol. 21, p. 88   Victoria.
(1897); Proc. Roy. Soc. Victoria. Vol. 17, p. 153 (1904).

15. *A. yorkensis*, Blackburn, ibidem. Vol. 15, p. 209 (1892); ibidem, Vol. 17,   Südaustralien.
p. 152 (1904).

8. Genus OXYOMUS, Castelnau

Oxyomus. Castelnau. Hist. Nat. Ins. Col. Vol. 2, p. 98 (1840).

Charaktere. — In der Körperform, den dreizähnigen Vordertibien und den mit Querleisten versehenen Mittel- und Hintertibien mit der Gattung *Aphodius* übereinstimmend, aber durch die Mittelfurche des Halsschildes und die gerippten Flügeldecken deutlich verschieden. Es sind meistens dunkel gefärbte Arten mit wenig Glanz und meistens auch unbehaarter Oberfläche.

Der Kopf ist schwach gewölbt, herabgeneigt, deutlich punktiert, mit sehr undeutlicher oder auch fehlender Stirnlinie, dieselbe ist nie mit Höckerchen versehen; der Clipeus ist nur schwach ausgerandet, die Ecken sind abgerundet, nie spitz oder zu Zähnchen umgestaltet; die Wangen überragen sehr deutlich die Augen, welche zum grössten Teile vom Vorderrande des Halsschildes bedeckt sind.

Das Halsschild ist stets deutlich quergewölbt, an den Seiten immer, an der Basis nur zuweilen gerandet, stets ohne Bewimperung, die Hinterwinkel sind stumpf, abgerundet oder auch ausgerandet, die Scheibe ist immer mehr oder weniger deutlich punktiert und meistens mit nach vorn verkürzter, deutlicher Längsfurche vor dem Schildchen versehen.

Das Schildchen ist schmal-dreieckig.

Die Flügeldecken sind von der Breite des Halsschildes, gewöhnlich nach hinten etwas verbreitert, ihre Schultern sind deutlich, sogar zuweilen mit kleinem Dörnchen versehen, sie haben keine punktierten Streifen, sondern statt dieser zehn scharfe Rippen, die alle bis zur Basis reichen, auch die seitlichen, der Raum zwischen zweien derselben ist fast immer mit Querpunkten ausgefüllt.

Die Unterseite ist wie bei *Aphodius*.

Die Vordertibien zeigen einen Enddorn und drei Aussenzähne. Die Mittel- und Hintertibien sind an der Aussenseite mit zwei Querleisten versehen, ihr unterer Endrand zeigt einen Borstenbesatz und zwei Enddorne.

Die Tarsen sind fünfgliedrig, das erste Glied ist länger als eins der vier folgenden.

Die Klauen sind normal.

Die Männchen sind an der tiefgrubigen Metasternalplatte erkennbar.

Zu dieser Gattung gehören fast nur kleine Arten.

Geographische Verbreitung der Arten. — Die Gattung ist in allen Erdteilen zu finden.

1. *O. aciculatus*, A. Schmidt, Soc. Ent. Zürich, 1909-10, Vol. 24, p. 55   Carin Cheba.
(1909).
2. *O. cameratus*, A. Schmidt, Ent. Wochenbl. p. 47 (1908).   Nilgiri Hills.
3. *O. costipennis*, Boheman, Ins. Caffr. Vol. 2, p. 362 (1857). — **Taf. I,**   Caffrarien, Kap der guten
Fig. 17.   Hoffnung.
costipennis, Péringuey, Trans. S. Afric. Philos. Soc. 1901-03, Vol. 12, Cat.   Kapkolonie, Natal.
p. 414 (1901).
4. *O. costulatus*, Fairmaire, Rev. Mag. Zool. (2), Vol. 1, p. 413 (1849).   Taïti.
5. *O. curvus*, A. Schmidt, Soc. Ent. Zürich, 1909-10, Vol. 24, p. 54   Kamerun.
(1909).
6. *O inaequalis*, Lansberge, Notes Leyd. Mus. Vol 8, p. 92 (1886).   Humpata.
7. *O. interstitialis*, Fairmaire, Ann. Soc. Ent. Belg. p. 5 (1883).   Insel Mioko.

8. *O. jucundulus*. Péringuey, Trans. S. Afric. Philos. Soc. 1901-03, Vol. 12,   Natal.
   Cat. p. 412 (1901).
9. *O. jugalis*, Péringuey, ibidem, p. 413 (1901).   Natal.
10. *O. jugosus*, Lewis, Ann. Mag. Nat. Hist. (6), Vol. 16, p. 383, f. 6 (1895).   Japan.
11. *O. medioximus*, Péringuey, Trans. S. Afric. Philos. Soc. 1901-03, Vol. 12,   Kapkolonie, Natal.
   Cat. p. 414 (1901).
12. *O. morosus*. Harold, Col. Hefte, Vol. 5, p. 100 (1869).   Chile.
13. *O. pusio*, Kolbe, Jenaische Denkschr. Vol. 13, p. 125 (1908).   Kalahari.
14. *O. simillimus*, A. Schmidt. Ent. Wochenbl. p. 48 (1908). — **Taf. I,**   Nilgiri Hills.
   Fig. 16.
15. *O. striatocrenatus*, Fairmaire, Ann. Soc. Ent. Fr. p. 14 (1889).   Moupin.
16. *O. sulcipennis*, Boheman, Ins. Caffr. Vol. 2, p. 362 (1857).   Caffrarien, Kap der guten
   sulcipennis. Péringuey, Trans. S. Afric. Philos. Soc. 1901-03, Vol. 12, Cat.   Transvaal.   [Hoffnung.
   p. 412 (1901).
17. *O. sylvestris*, Scopoli, Ent. Carn. p. 5 (1763).
         sylvestris, Reitter, Tab. p. 32; Brünn, 30, p. 170.   Europa, Westasien.
         d'Orbigny, L'Abeille, Vol. 28, p. 248 (1896).   Europa, Westasien.
      porcatus, Fabricius, Syst. Ent. p. 20 (1775).   Leipzig.
         Olivier, Ent. Vol. 1 (3), p. 96, t. 19, f. 178 (1789).   Europa.
         Paykull, Fauna Suec. Vol. 1, p. 29 (1798).
         Sturm, Deutschl. Ins. Vol. 1, p. 164 (1805).   Deutschland.
         Erichson, Naturg. Ins. Deutschl. Vol. 3, p. 906 (1848).   Deutschland.
         Horn, Trans. Amer. Ent. Soc. Vol. 14, p. 64 (1887).   New York, Philadelphia.
      fenestralis, Schrank, Enum. Ins. Austr. p. 17 (1781).   Linz.
      foveolatus, Moll, Fuessly Neu. Ent. Mag. Vol. 2, p. 170 (1784).   Zillertal.
      platycephalus, Marsham, Ent. Brit. Vol. 1, p. 56 (1802).   England.
         sec. Harold. Col. Hefte, Vol. 12, p. 94 (1874).
      opacifrons, Horn, Trans. Amer. Ent. Soc. Vol. 3, p. 284 (1871).   Mittelstaaten.
         sec. Horn. ibidem, Vol. 14, p. 109 (1887).
      var. foveolatus, Mulsant, Hist. Nat. Col. France. Lamell. p. 309 (1842).   Frankreich.
         Biologie : Rey, Ann. Soc. Linn. Lyon, 1886, Vol. 33, p. 196 (1887). — Larve
            beschrieben. Fühler abgebildet.
         Xambeu, ibidem, 1898, Vol. 45, p. 165 (1899). — Puppe beschrieben.
         Chapman, Ent. M. Mag. p. 273 (1869). — Brutablage.
18. *O. tricostatus*, Harold. Col. Hefte, Vol. 5, p. 101 (1869).   Columbien.

9. Genus HEPTAULACUS, Mulsant

Heptaulacus. Mulsant. Hist. Nat. Col. France, Lamell. p. 296 (1842).

Charaktere. — Diese Gattung wird durch die fünf bis neun, meist zweistreifig punktierten, nicht durch vertiefte Streifen, sondern durch Rippen getrennte Zwischenräume charakterisiert. Diese letztere Eigenschaft bringt sie der Gattung *Oxyomus* nahe, doch die meist längere Behaarung auf Halsschild und Flügeldecken, die Bewimperung der Halsschildbasis, das Fehlen einer Längsfurche auf dem Thorax und die geringere Anzahl von Rippen auf den Flügeldecken unterscheiden sie vollständig von derselben.

Der Körper ist von länglicher, wenig gewölbter Gestalt.

Der Kopf ist flach, vorn mehr oder weniger breit abgerundet, abgestutzt oder auch ausgerandet, eine Stirnlinie ist fast immer vorhanden, sie ist aber stets ohne Höcker; die Wangen sind immer deutlich.

Das Halsschild und der Kopf sind immer deutlich punktiert und behaart, die Hinterwinkel des ersteren sind deutlich, aber auch mehr oder weniger abgerundet, die Seiten sind gerandet, kurz oder länger bewimpert, ebenso auch die stets ungerandete Basis.

Das Schildchen ist meistens schmal-dreieckig, klein.

Die Rippen der Flügeldecken sind gewöhnlich nicht so scharf wie bei *Oxyomus*, sondern mehr flach, der Raum zwischen zwei derselben ist ein- oder zweireihig punktiert.

Alles andere stimmt mit *Aphodius* überein.

Die Arten sind meistens gelbbraun gefärbt, einfarbig oder mit dunklem Kopf, Halsschild und ebensolchen Flecken auf den Flügeldecken, seltener sind sie einfarbig schwarzbraun.

Die sexuellen Unterschiede sind in dieser Gattung verschiedener Art. Bei den Männchen ist gewöhnlich der Clipeus etwas breiter, mehr abgestutzt, der Enddorn der Vordertibien ist zugespitzt und nach innen gebogen, zuweilen ist der Enddorn stumpf, stark nach unten gebogen und die Vordertibien sind an der Innenkante in der vordern Hälfte stumpfwinklig verbreitert, manchmal sind die Vordertibien sehr schlank und einwärts gebogen, der äussere Enddorn der Mitteltibien ist stark verbreitert und sichelförmig gebogen, die Metasternalplatte ist gewöhnlich etwas tiefer in der Mitte, doch lässt sich in diesem Merkmal keine scharfe Grenze ziehen.

Die Grösse der Arten schwankt zwischen 3 und 7 mm.

Geographische Verbreitung der Arten. — Die Gattung ist in allen Gebieten, ausser in Amerika vertreten.

1. *H. alpinus**, Drapiez, Ann. Gén. Sc. Phys. Brux. Vol. 1, p. 49, t. 4, f. 3   Europa.
(1819). — **Taf. 2, Fig. 18.**
    alpinus, Mulsant, Hist. Nat. Col. France, Lamell. p. 349 (1871).   Frankreich.
        Reitter, Tab. p. 110; Brünn, 30, p. 248.   Mittel- und Südeuropa, Kauka-
    carinatus, Germar, Ins. Spec. Nov. p. 111 (1824).   Sibirien. [sus bis Ostsibirien.
        sec. Reiche, Berl. Ent. Zeitschr. p. 88 (1859).
        Erichson, Naturg. Ins. Deutschl. Vol. 3, p. 902 (1848).   Oesterreich.
    nivalis, Mulsant, Hist. Nat. Col. France, Lamell. p. 298 (1842).   Frankreich.
2. *H. delibis*, Harold, Ann. Mus. Stor. Nat. Genova. Vol. 10, p. 88   Celebes.
(1877).
3. *H. iniquus*, A. Schmidt. Soc. Ent. Zürich, 1909-10,Vol. 24, p. 20 (1909).   Yünnan.
— **Taf. 2, Fig. 19.**
4. *H. palustris*, Montrouzier, Ann. Soc. Ent. Fr. p. 268 (1860).   Insel Art.
    sec. Panvel, Rev. d'Ent. Caen, Vol. 22, p. 365 (1903).
5. *H. Pirazzolii*, Fairmaire. Bull. Soc. Ent. Fr. p. 145 (1881).   Tunis.
    Pirazzollii. Reitter, Tab. p. 111; Brünn, 30, p. 249.   Tripolis.
        A. Schmidt, Aphodiinen-Zusammenst. Deutsche Ent.
        Zeitschr., Beih. p. 101, Anmerkung 2 (1907-08).
6. *H. porcellus**, Frivaldszky, Term. Füzet. Vol. 3. p. 5 (1879).   Ungarn.
    porcellus, Reitter, Tab. p. 110; Brünn, 30, p. 248.   Oesterreich.
7. *H. puberulus*, Boheman, Ins. Caffr. Vol. 2, p. 360 (1857).   Caffrarien.
    puberulus, Péringuey. Trans. S. Afric. Philos. Soc. 1901-03, Vol. 12,   Mozambique.
        Cat. p. 413 (1901).
8. *H. sus*, Herbst. Fuessly Arch. Vol. 4. p. 9 (1783), t. 9, f. 14.
    sus, Fabricius, Maut. Ins. Vol 1, p. 11 (1787).   Deutschland.
        Erichson, Naturg. Ins. Deutschl. Vol. 3, p. 901 (1848).   Deutschland.
        Reitter, Tab. p. 110; Brünn, 30, p. 248.   Europa, Kaukasus.
    pubescens, Olivier, Ent. Vol. 1 (3), p. 91, t. 24, f. 205 (1789).   Paris.
    quisquilus, Schrank, Fauna Boica, Vol. 1, p. 391 (1798).   Bayern.
9. *H. syrticola*, Fairmaire. Bull. Soc. Ent. Fr. p. 177 (1882).   Tripolis.
    syrticola, d'Orbigny, L'Abeille, Vol. 28, p. 247 (1896).   Algier.
10. *H. testudinarius*, Fabricius, Syst. Ent. p. 19 (1775).   England.
    testudinarius, Olivier, Ent. Vol. 1 (3), p. 93, t. 20, f. 186 (1789).   Frankreich.
        Herbst, Natursyst. Ins. Vol. 2, p. 277, t. 18, f. 13 (1789).
        Marsham, Ent. Brit. Vol. 1, p. 28 (1802).   England.
        Erichson, Naturg. Ins. Deutschl. Vol. 3, p. 904 (1848).   Deutschland.
        Mulsant, Hist. Nat. Col. France, Lamell. p. 351 (1871).   Frankreich.
        Reiter, Tab. p. 111; Brünn, 30, p. 249.   Nord- und Mitteleuropa.
    Biologie : Sopp, Ent. M. Mag. p. 114 (1898). — Lebensgewohnheiten.

11. *H. villosus*, Gyllenhal in Schönherr, Syn. Ins. Vol. 1, p. 83 (1806).

    villosus*, Stephens, Illust. Brit. Vol. 3, p. 208 (1830).   England.
        Erichson, Naturg. Ins. Deutschl. Vol. 3, p. 904 (1848)   Oesterreich, Sachsen, Hessen.
        Mulsant, Hist. Nat. Col. France, Lamell. p. 353 (1871).   Frankreich.
        Reitter, Tab. p. 110; Brünn, 30, p. 248.   Nord- und Mitteleuropa.
  Biologie : Rosenhauer, Stett. Ent. Zeit. p, 24 (1882). — Larve, Puppe
    und Lebensweise beschrieben.

10. Genus LORDITOMÆUS, Péringuey

Lorditomæus. Péringuey, Trans. S. Afric. Philos. Soc. 1901-03, Vol. 12, Cat. p. 370, 436 (1901).

Charaktere. — In der länglichen, flachen Gestalt, in den weniger als zehn Zwischenräumen auf den Flügeldecken stimmt diese Gattung mit der·vorigen überein, sie unterscheidet sich aber von derselben dadurch, dass die Zwischenräume durch vertiefte Punktstreifen, nicht durch Rippen getrennt sind. Durch diese letztere Eigenschaft nähert sie sich wieder der Gattung *Aphodius*, der auch die typische Form von Roth zugerechnet wurde, doch der meistens ganz flach ausgebreitete Rand der Flügeldecken, sowie die sehr breiten Epipleuren trennen sie leicht von *Aphodius* wie auch von allen andern Gattungen.

    Die Oberfläche ist meistens behaart, mit stärkeren aufstehenden und feineren liegenden Haaren.

    Der Kopf ist wenig gewölbt, am Rande mehr oder weniger breit verflacht, der Vorderrand ist gerundet oder abgestutzt, nie gezahnt, die Mitte ist gewöhnlich schwach erhöht, zwischen den Augen befindet sich eine deutliche, ungehöckerte Stirnlinie, die Oberfläche ist punktiert, meistens aber sehr ungleich gross ; die Wangen sind klein, oft nicht die Augen überragend.

    Das Halsschild ist schwach quergewölbt, mit grösseren und kleineren Punkten, bald dichter, bald zerstreuter besetzt, die Seiten sind fein gerandet, die Basis ist stets ohne Rand, die Hinterwinkel sind deutlich oder verrundet.

    Das Schildchen ist gewöhnlich klein, dreieckig.

    Die Flügeldecken haben Punktstreifen, ihre Zwischenräume, deren Anzahl acht oder neun beträgt, sind eben, konvex oder auch selbst scharf gerippt, der Flügeldeckenrand ist oft sehr breit und liegt dann fast wagerecht.

    Die Mittelhüften sind weiter voneinander entfernt als bei *Aphodius*, das Mesosternum ist infolgedessen zwischen ihnen breiter

    Die Vordertibien haben drei Aussenzähne und einen Enddorn neben den Tarsen, die Mittel- und Hintertibien zwei Querleisten am Aussenrande, ungleiche Borsten und zwei Enddorne am untern Spitzenrande; die Füsse sind fünfgliedrig; die Klauen sind normal.

    Alle Arten sind einfarbig heller oder dunkler braun gefärbt, einige zeigen vor der Spitze eine hellere, dunkelumgrenzte Makel.

    Die sexuellen Unterschiede bestehen in dem abgestutzten, einwärts oder mehr abwärts gebogenen Enddorn der Vordertibien beim Männchen.

    Es sind kleine und mittelgrosse Arten.

    Geographische Verbreitung der Arten. — Die Gattung ist bisher nur aus dem afrikanischen Gebiet bekannt.

    1. *L. aequus*, A. Schmidt, Stett. Ent. Zeit. p. 237 (1908).   Zentralafrika.
    2. *L. bifidus*, A. Schmidt. ibidem, p. 236 (1908).   Deutsch-Ostafrika.
    3. *L. deplanatus*, Roth, Wiegmann Arch. f. Naturg. Vol. 1, p. 131 (1851).   Nordabessinien.
    — **Taf. 2, Fig. 20.**
        deplanatus, Harold, Berl. Ent. Zeitschr. p. 183, 188 (1874).   Mozambique, Senegal.

Péringuey, Trans. S. Afric. Philos. Soc. 1901-03, Vol. 12, Cat.
p. 437 (1901). . ..

opatroides, Klug. Monatsb. Berl. Akad. Wiss. p. 656 (1855) : Peters Reise
Mossamb. p. 246, t. 14, f. 12 (1862).
sec. Quedenfeldt, Berl. Ent. Zeitschr. p. 200 (1884).

4. *L. fornicatus*, A. Schmidt, Stett. Ent. Zeit. p. 234 (1908).
5. *L. infuscatus*, A. Schmidt, ibidem. p. 235 (1908).
6. *L. invenustus*, A. Schmidt, ibidem. p. 233 (1908).
7. *L. lunatulus*, A. Schmidt, Kiliman-djaro. Meru Exp. Sjöstedt, 1905-06,
p. 56 (1908).
8. *L. proditor*, Gestro, Ann. Mus. Stor. Nat. Genova (2), Vol. 15 (35),
p. 326 (1895).
9. *L. setulosus*, A. Schmidt, Stett. Ent. Zeit. p. 232 (1908).
10. *L. tenuis*, A. Schmidt, ibidem, p. 239 (1908).

Südrhodesia, Erythrea, Arussi-
Galla.
Sena.

Angola.
Kongo.
Manow(Deutsch-Ostafrika),
Senegambien. [Choa.
Usambaru, Kiliman-djaro.

Galla-Land.

Luitpoldkette, Ikutha.
Dakar (Senegal).

11. Genus HARMODACTYLUS, Péringuey

Harmodactylus. Péringuey, Trans. S. Afric. Philos. Soc. 1901-03, Vol. 12, Cat. p. 369 (1901).

Charaktere. — Diese Gattung ist bisher durch eine einzige Art vertreten. Sie gewährt ganz den Anblick eines *Aphodius*, unterscheidet sich von letzterem nur in der Form der Vordertibien und ihrer Bezahnung beim Männchen.

Die Oberfläche ist glatt und glänzend, unbehaart.

Der Kopf ist am Vorderrande abgestutzt und wenig ausgerandet, die Oberfläche ist dicht und deutlich punktiert, ohne Höcker, die Wangen sind gross, vom Seitenrande abgesetzt, deshalb gewährt der Kopf einen ziemlich breiten Anblick.

Das Halsschild ist wenig konvex, quer, dicht und tief punktiert an den Seiten und vor der Basis, letztere ist gerandet und seitlich von der Mitte ausgebuchtet, die gerandeten Seiten sind fast parallel, die Hinterwinkel abgeschrägt.

Die Flügeldecken verbreitern sich nach der Spitze, sie sind punktiert-gestreift, die fein punktierten Zwischenräume sind vor der Spitze und an den Seiten mehr konvex als auf dem Rücken.

Die Unterseite ist fast unpunktiert, zeigt sonst nichts Abweichendes von *Aphodius*.

Vordertibien sind nach der Spitze nicht verbreitert, sehr schlank, gebogen, am Aussenrande mit nur zwei Aussenzähnen, einem obern kleinen und einem zweiteiligen an der Spitze, die Tarsen und der Enddorn sind nicht wie gewöhnlich am inneren Spitzenwinkel, sondern weiter oben, ungefähr in der Mitte der Tibien, eingefügt.

Das Weibchen dieser Art ist bisher nicht bekannt.

Die einzige Art ist rotbraun gefärbt mit dunkleren Flügeldecken; sie ist mittelgross.

Geographische Verbreitung der Art. — Südafrika.

1. *H. oscitans*, Péringuey, Trans. S. Afric. Philos. Soc. 1901-03, Vol. 12, Kapkolonie.
Cat. p. 371 (1901).

12. Genus SYBAX, Boheman

Sybax. Boheman, Ins. Caffr. Vol. 2, p. 365 (1857).
Hypoplatys. Harold, Berl. Ent. Zeitschr. p. 221, t. 5, f. 3 (1859).

Charaktere. — Diese von Boheman gegründete Gattung wurde noch einmal von Harold als *Hypoplatys* beschrieben.

Die Arten haben eine dunkle Farbe, die aber von einem gelblichen, glänzenden Ueberzuge vollständig bedeckt wird und höchstens auf der Unterseite teilweise sichtbar bleibt.

Von *Aphodius* unterscheidet sich diese Gattung durch die Bildung der Vorderschenkel und Tibien, sowie durch die Skulptur des Halsschildes und der Flügeldecken.

Der Körper ist von länglicher, nach der Spitze etwas verbreiterter, dann zugespitzter, wenig gewölbter Gestalt, der Hinterleib ist fast ganz eben.

Der Kopf ist kurz und breit, herabgewölbt, am Vorderrande in der Mitte ausgerandet und jederseits verrundet, die Mitte ist längsbeulig, zwischen den Augen befindet sich eine Querfurche, die vorn wulstig begrenzt ist; Höckerchen fehlen, die Oberfläche ist punktiert; die Wangen sind deutlich; die Augen werden fast ganz vom Vorderrande des Halsschildes bedeckt.

Das Halsschild ist quer, geradlinig oder etwas gerundet nach der Basis verbreitert, an den Seiten verflacht und dick gerandet, die Hinterwinkel sind stumpf oder abgerundet, die Basis ist bewimpert, die Oberfläche ist punktiert, vor dem Schildchen befindet sich ein Längseindruck und zuweilen jederseits noch je ein schräg nach vorn gerichteter.

Das Schildchen ist länglich und sehr schmal.

Die Flügeldecken haben je fünf stumpfe Rippen, die durch eine Punktreihe jederseits begrenzt werden.

Die Unterseite ist punktiert und behaart. Das breit verflachte Metasternum hat in der Mitte eine vertiefte Längslinie.

Die Mittelschenkel sind wenig entfernt voneinander, sie sind wie die Hinterschenkel an ihrem Vorder- und Hinterrande bewimpert, ebenso die Tibien am Innenrande.

Mittel- und Hintertibien haben am Aussenrande zwei Querleisten und am Endrande einen Borstenbesatz und zwei kurze Enddorne.

Die Vordertibien sind aussen dreizähnig, diese drei Zähne sind entweder getrennt oder die zwei unteren miteinander verbunden; neben der Einlenkung der Tarsen befindet sich ein kurzer, kräftiger Enddorn und an der Innenseite ein nach vorn sich verbreiternder, gelblich durchscheinender Ansatz, der bei angezogenen Tibien in eine rinnenförmige, am Vorderrande der Schenkel liegende Vertiefung passt.

Die Tarsen sind fünfgliedrig, das erste Glied der Vordertarsen ist sehr kurz, das der mittlern und hintern verlängert, das letzte Glied hat zwei normale Klauen.

Hierher gehören zwei Arten von 7 bis 9 mm Länge.

Geographische Verbreitung der Arten. — Südliches und nördliches Afrika.

1 · S. *impressicollis*, Boheman, Ins. Caffr. Vol. 2, p. 367, t. 1, f. D6 (1857)   Orange.
    impressicollis, Péringuey, Trans. S. Afric. Philos. Soc. 1901-03, Vol. 12,   Abessinien, Somaliland.
      Cat. p. 440 (1901).
    helophoroides, Harold, Berl. Ent. Zeitschr. p. 221, t. 5, f. 3 (1859).   Fassogl.
      sec. Harold, ibidem. p. 115 (1861).
2. S. *sulcico'lis*, Boheman, Ins. Caffr. Vol. 2, p. 366, t. 1, f. D1-5 (1857).   Orange.
    sulcicollis, Péringuey, Trans. S. Afric. Philos. Soc. 1901-03, Vol. 12, Cat.   Südrhodesia.
      p. 439 (1901).

13. GENUS PROCTOPHANES, HAROLD

Proctophanes. Harold, Berl. Ent. Zeitschr. p. 111 (1861).

Proctammodes. Blackburn, Trans. Roy. Soc. S. Austral. Vol. 15, p. 37 (1892).

Charaktere. — Diese und die folgenden Gattungen unterscheiden sich von den vorhergehenden durch das freie Pygidium, dessen Grösse aber, wie schon vorher angegeben, sehr abändert. Durch die gerippten Flügeldecken und die Längsfurche auf dem Thorax erinnert diese Gattung an *Oxyomus*, von der sie sich aber durch das freistehende Pygidium entfernt.

Der Körper ist robust, stark gewölbt. schwarz gefärbt, glänzend, unbehaart.

Der Kopf ist kurz und breit, vorn in der Mitte sehr deutlich ausgerandet und daneben verrundet, eine Stirnlinie ist vorhanden, sie zeigt drei kleine, quere Höcker, zwischen ihr und dem Vorderrande befindet sich eine kurze, scharfe Querleiste; die Wangen sind deutlich, vom Kopfrande abgesetzt; die Augen sind von oben sichtbar.

Das Halsschild ist stark herabgewölbt, deutlich punktiert, um die Seiten und Hinterwinkel gerandet, an der Mitte der Basis fehlt eine Randung, vor dem Schildchen befindet sich eine deutliche, nach vorn verkürzte Längsfurche.

Das Schildchen ist breit-dreieckig.

Die Flügeldecken sind parallel, an der Spitze breit gerundet, tief und breit gefurcht, in den Furchen mit queren Punkten, die rippenförmigen Żwischenräume sind schmaler als die Furchen.

Die Unterseite ist glänzend und punktiert. Die Bauchsegmente sind untereinander verwachsen, das Pygidium ist von den Flügeldecken unbedeckt, es ist gross, wenig nach unten gebogen, in der Mitte mit einem Längskiel versehen. Die Mittelhüften stehen weit auseinander.

Die Vordertibien sind nach der Spitze etwas verbreitert, an der Aussenseite mit drei Zähnchen, neben den Tarsen mit einem Enddorn versehen, das erste Glied der Vordertarsen ist länger als das zweite.

Die Mittel- und Hintertibien haben aussen zwei deutliche Querleisten, die Hintertibien am Endrande kurze, starre Borsten und zwei Enddorne.

Die Tarsen sind fünfgliedrig, das letzte trägt zwei normale Klauen.

Hierher gehören zwei kleine Arten von 4 mm Länge.

Geographische Verbreitung der Arten. — Australien.

1. *P. minor*, Blackburn, Trans. Roy. Soc. S. Austral. Vol. 21, p. 89 (1897).   Victoria.
2. *P. sculptus*, Hope, Proc. Ent. Soc. Lond. p. 147 (1846); Trans. Ent.   Australien.
   Soc. Lond. Vol. 4, p. 285 (1847). — **Pl. 2, Fig. 21.**
   sculptus, Harold, Berl. Ent. Zeitschr p. 111 (1861).   Südaustralien.

14. Genus MACRORETRUS, Péringuey

Macroretrus. Péringuey, Trans. S. Afric. Philos. Soc. 1904-08, Vol. 13, p. 632 (1908).

Charaktere. — Diese interessante Gattung ist bisher durch eine Art vertreten, sie unterscheidet sich von allen Aphodiinen durch die nach oben gerückten Epipleuren, die bei dem Weibchen besonders stark hervortreten; dadurch wird, von oben gesehen, eine plötzliche Erweiterung der Flügeldeckenseiten hinter der Mitte bewirkt. Mit der vorhergehenden Gattung stimmt dieselbe in dem breiten Mesosternum zwischen den Mittelhüften und dem sehr deutlichen, freien Pygidium überein, unterscheidet sich aber von ihr in der Bildung der Mitteltarsen und Klauen beim Männchen; eine ähnliche Bildung der Mitteltarsen findet sich z. B. auch bei *Aph. calcaratus* Boheman.

Der Körper ist kurz und gedrungen, nach hinten verbreitert, wenig gewölbt, glänzend, unbehaart, dunkel gefärbt, das Halsschild in den Vorderwinkeln, die Flügeldecken an der Basis und vor der Spitze heller.

Der Kopf ist ziemlich flach, ringsum gerandet, fein punktiert, ohne sichtbare Stirnlinie und Höcker; der Clipeus ist vorn abgestutzt; die Wangen sind sehr klein, die Augen nicht überragend.

Das Halsschild ist deutlich breiter als der Kopf, besonders beim Männchen, es ist flach gewölbt, quer, nach hinten verschmälert, an den Seiten gerandet, die etwas vorgezogene Mitte der Basis ist ohne Rand, die Hinterwinkel sind abgeschrägt und ausgerandet, die Oberfläche zeigt grössere und kleinere Punkte, die die Mitte mehr frei lassen.

Das Schildchen ist gross, dreieckig.

Die Flügeldecken sind an der Spitze einzeln abgerundet, punktiert-gestreift, ihre Zwischenräume sind konvex, der zehnte ist nur hinten sichtbar, da er in der vordern Hälfte durch die nach oben gerückten Epipleuren verdrängt wird, die Schultern sind deutlich, aber weder gezahnt noch gedornt.

Die Mittelhüften sind weit voneinander entfernt.

Das Metasternum hat eine schmale, längsvertiefte Platte.

Das Pygidium ist nach unten gerichtet, einzeln punktiert.

Die Form der Schenkel und Tibien weicht von den Arten der Gattung *Aphodius* nicht ab.

Die Vordertibien sind aussen dreizähnig, die beiden obern Zähne sind klein, der untere ist lang und spitz, das erste Tarsenglied ist länger als das zweite.

Mittel- und Hintertibien haben zwei schwache Querleisten, ihr Endrand ist beborstet und mit zwei Enddornen versehen.

Die Tarsen sind fünfgliedrig, das erste Glied der Hintertarsen ist stark verlängert.

Die Klauen sind normal.

Die sexuellen Unterschiede :

Bei dem Männchen ist der Enddorn an den Vordertibien sehr lang, fast die Länge der drei ersten Glieder erreichend, stark verbreitert und zugespitzt, die Tarsenglieder der Mittelfüsse sind stark verdickt, sehr verkürzt, das fünfte ist so lang als die vorhergehenden, die äussere Klaue ist lappenförmig verbreitert, seitlich zusammengedrückt, wenig länger als breit, an der Spitze breit abgerundet, die innere ist mehr rundlich und stark gebogen.

Beim Weibchen treten die Epipleuren breiter hervor, der Enddorn der Vordertibien ist schlanker, nur so lang als zwei Tarsenglieder, die Fussglieder der Mitteltibien sind normal.

Hierher gehört eine kleine Art von kaum 4 mm Grösse.

Geographische Verbreitung der Art. — Südrhodesia und Angola.

1. *M. singularis*. Péringuey, Trans. S. Afric. Philos. Soc. 1904-1908, Südrhodesia, Angola. Vol. 13, p. 633 (1908). — **Taf. 2, Fig. 22.**

15. Genus DIDACTYLIA, d'Orbigny

Didactylia. d'Orbigny, Synopsis des Aphodiens d'Europe et du Bassin de la Méditerranée, L'Abeille, Vol. 28, p. 247 (1896).

Charaktere. — d'Orbigny gründete diese Gattung auf *pallicolor* Fairmaire, welche als *Aphodius* beschrieben wurde, daraus geht hervor, dass *Didactylia* dieser Gattung sehr nahe stehen muss, sie gleicht derselben in der Körperform, den kleinen Wangen, den nahe zusammenstehenden Mittelhüften, unterscheidet sich aber von ihr hauptsächlich in der Bezahnung der Vordertibien beim Männchen, in der Form der Mittel- und Hintertibien, den mehr oder weniger verwachsenen Hinterleibsringen, sowie in dem freien Pygidium.

Der Körper ist sehr langgestreckt, parallel, mehr oder weniger glänzend, schwach konvex, meist hell gefärbt, einfarbig oder mit dunklen Flecken oder dunkler Scheibe; die Seiten der Flügeldecken sind wenig dicht behaart.

Der Kopf ist flach, mit schwacher Erhöhung in der Mitte, ohne sichtbare Stirnlinie und ohne Höcker, nur sehr fein punktiert; der Clipeus ist abgestutzt oder schwach ausgerandet, meist breit abgesetzt; die Augen sind gross, von den Wangen seitlich wenig überragt.

Der Thorax ist quer, an den Seiten meist deutlich gerundet und lang bewimpert, die Basis ist entweder ungerandet oder sehr fein wie die Seiten gerandet, die Hinterwinkel sind verrundet, abgestutzt oder ausgebuchtet, die Oberfläche ist mehr oder weniger stark punktiert.

Das Schildchen ist klein, lang und schmal oder mehr kurz-dreieckig.

Die Flügeldecken sind von der Breite des Halsschildes, ohne Dorn an der Schulter, meistens tief gestreift, die seitlichen Streifen sind vorn abgekürzt, zuweilen aber auch bis zur Basis verlängert, die Zwischenräume sind verhältnismässig schmal, flach oder wenig konvex.

Die Mittelhüften stehen nahe beieinander.

Das Metasternum ist meistens in der Mitte nur schwach ausgehöhlt.

Die Abdominalsegmente sind untereinander verwachsen, diese Vereinigung ist zuweilen eine so vollständige, dass die Ränder der Bauchringe fast vollständig unsichtbar sind.

Das Pygidium ist nur klein, unbedeckt und lang behaart.

Die Mittel- und Hintertibien sind stark dreieckig erweitert, seitlich zusammengedrückt, aussen ohne Querleisten, höchstens an den Mitteltibien mit solchen versehen, der Endrand hat einen Borstenbesatz und zwei Enddorne, die meistens etwas gebogen sind.

Die Tarsen sind fünfgliedrig, die Klauen normal.

Die Männchen zeichnen sich aus durch lange und schmale Vordertibien, die an der Aussenseite meistens nur mit zwei grösseren Zähnen besetzt sind, seltener ist ein dritter kleiner Zahn bemerkbar, zuweilen sind aber auch die Vordertibien an der innern Kante in der Vorderhälfte flach ausgerandet oder das Abdomen ist in der Mitte längseingedrückt wie bei den Männchen mancher Cetoniden. der Enddorn ist gewöhnlich stumpf und herabgebogen, gewöhnlich sind die Tarsen schlanker und länger.

Die Weibchen haben normale, an der Aussenkante mit drei Zähnen versehene Vordertibien, der Enddorn an ihnen ist immer spitz, das Halsschild ist dichter punktiert.

Geographische Verbreitung der Arten. — Die Arten dieser Gattung sind bisher aus Afrika und Südamerika bekannt.

1. *D. cicatricosa*, A. Schmidt, Ann. Soc. Ent. Belg. Vol. 52, p. 39 (1908). Kinchassa (Kongo).
   — **Taf. 2, Fig. 24.**
2. *D. exsecta*, A. Schmidt, Stett. Ent. Zeit. p. 35 (1911). Madagaskar.
3. *D. flaveolus*, Harold, Berl. Ent. Zeitschr. p. 280 (1867). Chile.
   flaveolus, Burmeister, Stett. Ent. Zeit. p. 406 (1877). Argentinien.
4. *D. infuscatopennis*, A. Schmidt, Soc. Ent. Zürich, 1909-10, Vol. 24, p. 12 Argentina, Uruguay.
   (1909); Notes Leyd. Mus. Vol. 31, p. 122 (1909).
5. *D. Kolbei*, A. Schmidt, Stett. Ent. Zeit. p. 36 (1911). Bolivia.
6. *D. notata*, Harold, Berl. Ent. Zeitschr. p. 211, t. 5, f. 2 (1859). Columbien.
7. *D. pallicolor*, Fairmaire, Ann. Soc. Ent. Fr. p. 442 (1885). Obock.
   pallicolor, d'Orbigny, L'Abeille, Vol. 28, p. 248 (1896).
   A. Schmidt, Aphodiinen-Zusammenst. Deutsche Ent. Zeitschr.
   Beih. p. 99, Note 2 (1907-08).
8. *D. panamensis*, Harold, Berl. Ent. Zeitschr. p. 212 (1859). Panama.
   panamensis, Bates, Biol. Centr. Amer. Vol. 2 (2), p. 88, t. 6, f. 16 (1887). Panama.
9. *D. pictipennis*, Fairmaire, Ann. Soc. Ent. Belg. p. 99 (1897). Madagaskar.
   pictipennis, sec. A. Schmidt, Notes Leyd. Mus. Vol. 31, p. 123 (1909).
10. *D. varia*, A. Schmidt, Ann. Soc. Ent. Belg. Vol. 52, p. 40 (1908). — Kinchassa (Kongo).
    Taf. 2, Fig. 23.

16. Genus CÆLIUS, Lewis

Cælius. Lewis, Ann. Mag. Nat Hist. (6), Vol. 16, p. 381 (1895).

 Charaktere. — Die einzige Art dieser Gattung ist von länglicher, paralleler Gestalt, glänzend, unbehaart, sie stimmt in der Form des Körpers mit *Saprosites* überein, unterscheidet sich aber von allen Gattungen durch die eigentümliche Randung des Halsschildes.

 Der Kopf ist breit, vorn eingedrückt, nicht ausgerandet, mit deutlicher Stirnlinie, die aber keine Höckerchen trägt, die Oberfläche ist punktiert; die Augen sind sichtbar.

 Das Halsschild ist vorn so breit wie der Kopf, nach der Basis gerundet verschmälert, der Seitenrand ist vorn gekerbt, nach den Hinterwinkeln zu werden die Kerben grösser und zahnartig, die Oberfläche ist deutlich punktiert, vorn feiner.

 Das Schildchen ist dreieckig, schwach punktiert.

 Die Flügeldecken sind vorn breiter als die Basis des Halsschildes, die Schultern sind scharf, zahnartig, die Oberfläche ist punktiert-gestreift, die Streifenpunkte greifen die Ränder der Zwischenräume an.

 Die Unterseite ist glänzend und punktiert.

 Das Metasternum zeigt eine Mittelfurche.

 Die Mittelschenkel stehen weniger dicht beieinander als die übrigen.

 Die Vordertibien sind nach der Spitze verbreitert, ihr Aussenrand hat drei deutliche Zähne, der Enddorn ist nach innen gebogen.

 Die Mittel- und Hintertibien haben am Aussenrande zwei Querleisten, am Ende einen Borstenbesatz und zwei Enddorne.

 Die Tarsen sind fünfgliedrig, das erste Glied ist verlängert, das letzte trägt zwei normale Klauen.

 Das Pygidium ist frei.

 Hierher gehört eine kleine, rotbraune Art von 4 mm Länge.

 Geographische Verbreitung der Art. — Japan.

 1. *C. denticollis*, Lewis. Ann. Mag. Nat. Hist. (6), Vol. 16, p. 382 (1895). Japan.

17. Genus COPTOCHIRUS, Harold

Coptochirus. Harold, Berl. Ent. Zeitschr. p. 202 (1859).

 Charaktere. — Ausgezeichnet von allen Gattungen durch den eigentümlichen Bau der Vordertibien beim Männchen, stimmen die Arten dieser Gattung sonst im allgemeinen mit *Aphodius* überein.

 Der Körper ist von länglicher, gleichbreiter, flacher Gestalt, glänzend, glatt oder behaart und meistens nur fein punktiert.

 Ihre Farbe ist meistens ein helleres oder dunkleres Braun, nur einzelne Arten sind schwarz.

 Der Kopf ist flach gewölbt, ringsum mit Rand, meistens ohne Stirnlinie, aber immer fehlen die Höcker; der Clipeus ist mehr oder weniger tief ausgerandet, darüber in der Mitte immer schwach quervertieft; die Augen sind zum Teil frei; die Wangen fast immer nur klein.

 Das Halsschild ist wenig breiter als der Kopf, quer gewölbt, an den Seiten gerundet und gewöhnlich nach hinten verschmälert, die Seiten sind stets gerandet, zuweilen hier sowie an der Basis bewimpert, letztere mit oder ohne Randung, die Hinterwinkel sind ausgeschweift, abgestutzt oder auch nur abgerundet, vor dem Schildchen befindet sich bei manchen Arten eine verkürzte, schwache Längsfurche.

Das Schildchen ist klein, schmal-dreieckig.

Die Flügeldecken haben die Breite des Halsschildes und deutliche, aber nicht scharfe Schultern, sie sind punktiert-gestreift, die seitlichen Streifen sind vor der Basis abgekürzt, die Zwischenräume sind konvex oder auch nur die abwechselnden, gewöhnlich sind es deren zehn, nur C *haemonius* Reitter hat fünfzehn Zwischenräume.

Die Unterseite zeigt nichts Abweichendes von *Aphodius,* nur dass das Pygidium frei-ist, dasselbe ist aber nur klein, jedoch lang behaart.

Die Mittel- und Hintertibien haben am Aussenrande zwei deutliche Querleisten, am Endrande Borstenbesatz und zwei Enddorne.

Die Füsse haben fünf Glieder und zwei normale Klauen.

Die sexuellen Unterschiede in dieser Gattung beruhen in der Form der Vordertibien und zuweilen in der Form des ersten Gliedes der Hinterfüsse.

Beim Männchen sind die Vordertibien immer ohne Enddorn neben der Einlenkung der Tarsen, am Aussenrande befinden sich meistens nur zwei Zähne, der letzte derselben ist sehr verlängert, nicht zugespitzt, sondern breit abgestutzt, seltener zeigt sich ein drittes, sehr kleines Aussenzähnchen, dann sind aber die Tibien innen hinter der Einlenkung der Tarsenglieder stumpf-dreieckig erweitert, das erste Glied der Hinterfüsse ist entweder einfach, oder etwas gekrümmt, seltener zu einer breiten, dünnen, senkrecht stehenden, länglich-runden Platte erweitert, an deren innern Seite das eigentliche Tarsenglied als erhabene Leiste sichtbar bleibt (*C. pteropus* Harold).

Beim Weibchen sind die Vordertibien aussen dreizähnig und neben den Tarsen mit einem Enddorn versehen, das erste Glied der Hinterfüsse ist normal.

Geographische Verbreitung der Arten. — Thessalien, Kleinasien, Südafrika.

1. *C. brachypterus,* Harold, Col. Hefte, Vol. 3, p. 85 (1868). Südafrika.
      brachypterus, Péringuey, Trans. S. Afric. Philos. Soc. 1901-03, Vol. 12, Kapkolonie.
      Cat. p. 430 (1901).
2. *C. cognatus,* Péringuey, ibidem, p. 428 (1901). Kapkolonie.
3. *C. emarginatus,* Germar, Ins. Spec. Nov. p. 112 (1824). Kap der guten Hoffnung.
      emarginatus, Péringuey, Trans. S. Afric. Philos. Soc. 1901-03, Vol. 12, Kapkolonie.
      Cat. p. 428 (1901).
      variegatus, Wiedemann, Zool. Mag. Vol. 2 (1), p. 29 (1823). Kap der guten Hoffnung.
4. *C. excisus,* Harold, Col. Hefte, Vol. 3, p. 85 (1868). Kap der guten Hoffnung.
      excisus, Péringuey, Trans. S. Afric. Philos. Soc. 1901-03, Vol. 12, Cat. Südafrika.
      p. 430 (1901).
5. *C. haemonius,* Reitter, Wien. Ent. Zeit. p. 176 (1903). Thessalien.
6. *C. pallidipennis,* Harold, Col. Hefte, Vol. 4, p. 84 (1868). Kap der guten Hoffnung.
      pallidipennis, Péringuey, Trans. S. Afric. Philos. Soc. 1901-03, Vol. 12, Kapkolonie.
      Cat. p. 429 (1901).
7. *C. pteropus,* Harold, Berl. Ent. Zeitschr. p. 202, t. 5, f. 1 (1859). — Kap der guten Hoffnung.
   Taf. 2, Fig. 25.
      pteropus, Péringuey, Trans. S. Afric. Philos. Soc. 1901-03, Vol. 12, Cat. Kapkolonie.
      p. 427 (1901).
8. *C. singularis,* Harold, Berl. Ent. Zeitschr. p. 396 (1868). Kleinasien.
9. *C. vulgatus,* Harold, Col. Hefte, Vol. 3, p.84 (1868). — **Taf. 2, Fig. 26.** Südafrika.
      vulgatus, Péringuey, Trans. S. Afric. Philos. Soc: 1901-03, Vol. 12, Cat. Kapkolonie.
      p. 429 (1901).

18. Genus DREPANOCANTHUS, Péringuey

Drepanocanthus. Péringuey, Trans. S. Afr. Philos. Soc. 1901-03, Vol. 12, Cat. p. 370, 431 (1901).

Charaktere. — Diese Gattung ähnelt durch das mit einer Längsfurche versehene Halsschild und die gerippten Flügeldecken der Gattung *Oxyomus,* unterscheidet sich aber von ihr sowie allen anderen durch die Form der Vordertibien und das bedornte erste Glied der Hintertarsen beim Männchen.

Die Arten haben einen länglichen, nach hinten schwach verbreiterten, wenig konvexen Körper, sie sind meistens nicht vollglänzend, glatt oder kurz behaart, ihre Farbe ist ein helleres oder dunkleres Braun, einzelne Arten sind aber auch schwärzlich.

Der Kopf ist geneigt, wenig gewölbt, ohne Höcker, nur mit schwacher, oft kaum sichtbarer Stirnlinie, der Vorderrand zuweilen sehr tief ausgerandet und jederseits zipfelartig aufgebogen; die Wangen sind deutlich, kaum vom Seitenrande abgesetzt.

Das Halsschild ist breiter als der Kopf, seitlich mehr oder weniger gerundet und meistens nach hinten deutlich verbreitert, vor dem Schildchen mit schwacher, kurzer Längsfurche, die Seiten und Basis sind gerandet und selten ohne Haarbewimperung, die Hinterwinkel sind fast immer breit verrundet, seltener nur abgestutzt, die Oberfläche ist punktiert.

Das Schildchen ist klein, dreieckig, in der Mitte mit schwacher Erhöhung.

Die Flügeldecken sind von der Breite des Halsschildes, an der Schulter ohne Dorn, nach hinten schwach verbreitert, sie haben statt der vertieften Punktstreifen fünf oder zehn Längsrippen (die Naht mitgezählt), von denen die seitlichen vor der Basis verkürzt sind und dadurch unter der Schulter ein glatter Raum gebildet wird, die Fläche zwischen zwei Rippen ist entweder mit queren oder runden Punkten ausgefüllt.

Die Unterseite ist wie bei *Aphodius* gebildet, nur das Pygidium ragt als kleine, lang behaarte Spitze hervor.

Die Mittel- und Hintertibien besitzen an der Aussenseite zwei schwache Querleisten, ihr Endrand hat einen Borstenbesatz und zwei Enddorne.

Die Füsse haben fünf Glieder und zwei normale Klauen.

Bei dem Männchen sind die Vordertibien in der vordern Hälfte oder dem untern Drittel plötzlich erweitert und dann mit der Aussenkante parallel verlaufend, sie sind hier noch einmal so breit als in dem basalen Teile, der Enddorn ist nach innen gebogen, er ist kurz und erreicht nicht die Spitze des zweiten Gliedes, das erste Glied an den Mittel- und Hintertibien ist, besonders bei den letzten, stark gebogen und in einen längeren oder kürzeren Dorn an der Spitze ausgezogen.

Die Weibchen haben normale, also nach der Spitze allmählich verbreiterte Vordertibien, am Aussenrande wie die Männchen drei grössere Zähne und einen zugespitzten und nach vorn gerichteten Enddorn, das erste Glied an den Mittel- und Hintertarsen ist gerade und ohne Dorn.

Es sind kleine Arten.

Geographische Verbreitung der Arten. — Südafrika.

1. *D. connexus*, Péringuey, Trans. S. Afric. Philos. Soc. 1901-03, Vol. 12,   Kapkolonie.
   Cat. p. 434 (1901).
2. *D. eximius*, Péringuey, ibidem, p. 433 (1901).   Kapkolonie.
3. *D. intrusus*, Péringuey, ibidem, p. 434 (1901).   Kapkolonie, Natal.
4. *D. lineatus*, Wiedemann, Zool. Mag. Vol. 2 (1), p. 28 (1823). —   Kap der guten Hoffnung.
   Taf. 2, Fig. 27.
        acanthotarsis, Péringuey, Trans. S. Afric. Philos. Soc. 1901-03, Vol. 12,   Kapkolonie, Südrhodesia.
               Cat. p. 432 (1901).
5. *D. nasutus*, Harold. Col. Hefte, Vol. 5, p. 101 (1869).   Südafrika.
6. *D. spinitarsis*, Péringuey, Trans. S. Afric. Philos. Soč. 1901-03, Vol. 12,   Natal.
   Cat. p. 433 (1901).

19. Genus HARMOGASTER, Harold

Harmogaster, Harold, Berl. Ent. Zeitschr. p. 112 (1861).

Odontaphodius, A. Schmidt, Deutsche Ent. Zeitschr. p. 249 (1907); sec. A. Schmidt, Stett. Ent. Zeit. p. 49 (1911).

Charaktere. — Durch die mit mehr als zehn Punktstreifen versehenen Flügeldecken wird diese Gattung charakterisiert.

Der Körper ist konvex, glänzend, zuweilen äusserst fein behaart, schwarz gefärbt.

Der Kopf ist breit, stark herabgewölbt, ringsum gerandet, mehr oder weniger dicht und deutlich punktiert, die Mitte ist gewöhnlich stumpfbeulig, zwischen den Augen befindet sich meistens eine schwach erhabene, höckerlose Querlinie und zuweilen eine zweite zwischen ihr und dem Vorderrande; der Clipeus ist ausgerandet und daneben verrundet oder gezahnt; die Wangen sind gross; die Augen sind bei angezogenem Kopfe kaum sichtbar.

Das Halsschild ist quer, in der Mitte am breitesten, nach hinten verschmälert, die Seiten und Basis sind gerandet und manchmal mit Haaren bewimpert, die Hinterwinkel können abgestutzt oder verrundet sein, vor dem Schildchen liegt eine flache Längsvertiefung.

Das Schildchen ist klein und dreieckig, mit erhabener, glänzender Mitte.

Die Flügeldecken sind ungefähr von der Breite der Halsschildbasis, nach hinten etwas verbreitert, an der Schulter scharfeckig, ohne eigentlich gezahnt zu sein, sie haben zwölf oder zwanzig punktierte Streifen, die Zwischenräume sind schmal, entweder alle konvex oder nur die abwechselnden, die Mitte derselben ist entweder bei allen Zwischenräumen glatt oder nur bei den ungeraden, die geraden sind dann in einzelne Tuberkeln aufgelöst, seltener sind auch die ungeraden Zwischenräume weitläufig und fein gekerbt.

Die Unterseite ist punktiert; die Bauchsegmente sind verwachsen, das Pygidium ist unbedeckt, klein, zugespitzt und einzeln lang behaart.

Die Mittelhüften stehen bald weiter, bald näher zusammen.

Die Vordertibien sind aussen dreizähnig und neben den Tarsen mit kürzerem Enddorn versehen.

Die Mittel- und Hintertibien haben an der Aussenseite zwei Querleisten, am untern Spitzenrande einen Borstenbesatz und zwei Enddorne.

Die Füsse sind fünfgliedrig, das erste Glied ist verlängert, alle sind an der Spitze etwas verdickt. Die Klauen sind normal.

Die sexuellen Unterschiede : Bei den Männchen sind die Vordertibien zuweilen innen schwach verbreitert, der Enddorn ist nach innen gebogen, bei andern Arten sind sie innen nicht erweitert, sondern sie haben auf der Unterseite zwei kräftige Zähne, der Enddorn ist auch bei diesen Arten nach innen gebogen.

Die Weibchen haben normale Vordertibien, ihr Enddorn ist nach vorn gerichtet, die Unterseite ist nicht gezahnt.

In diese Gattung gehören mittelgrosse Arten von 4 bis 7 mm Länge, von rot- oder schwarzbrauner Färbung.

Geographische Verbreitung der Arten. — Bisher nur aus Südafrika nachgewiesen.

1. *H. exarata*, Harold, Berl. Ent. Zeitschr. p. 113 (1861).   Kap der guten Hoffnung.
     exarata, Péringuey, Trans. S. Afric. Philos. Soc. 1901-03, Vol. 12, Cat.   Kapkolonie.
       p. 422 (1901). — **Taf. 2, Fig. 28.**
     tenebrioides, A. Schmidt, Deutsche Ent. Zeitschr. p. 249 (1907).   Kap der guten Hoffnung.
       sec A. Schmidt, Stett. Ent. Zeit. p. 49 (1911).
2. *H. geminata*, A. Schmidt, Stett. Ent. Zeit. p. 46 (1911).   Transvaal, Natal, Kap der
                                                                                guten Hoffnung.
3. *H. opacula*, Harold, Col. Hefte, Vol. 5, p. 101 (1869).   Kapkolonie.
4. *H. quadridentella*, A. Schmidt, Stett. Ent. Zeit. p. 47 (1911).   Kap der guten Hoffnung.
5. *H. sulcatula*, A. Schmidt, ibidem, p. 48 (1911).   Natal.
6. *H. transitoria*, Péringuey, Trans. S. Afric. Philos. Soc. 1901-03, Vol. 12, Kapkolonie, Natal.
     Cat. p. 423 (1901).

2. GRUPPE EUPARIINA

Charaktere. — In dieser Gruppe sind sechs Gattungen vereint, deren Zusammengehörigkeit in dem grossen, stark herabgewölbten, glatten und ungekörnten Kopfe mit den sehr entwickelten Wangen, sowie in den leistenlosen Hintertibien beruht. Das schliesst natürlich nicht aus, dass einzelne Arten dieser Gruppe zum Teil abweichende Bildung zeigen.

Der Kopf ist mit geringen Ausnahmen fast immer glatt, nur fein punktiert, stets ohne Hocker und meistens auch ohne deutliche Stirnlinie; die Wangen sind viel grösser als bei *Aphodius*; die Augen werden zum grössten Teile von dem Vorderrande des Halsschildes bedeckt.

Der Thorax ist fast immer quer, stärker gewölbt, seine Seiten sind entweder flach ausgebreitet (*Euparia*) oder nicht, auch zuweilen stumpf gezahnt, meistens aber glatt gerandet, mit oder ohne Haarwimpern daselbst, die Basis ist oft ungerandet, die Hinterwinkel sind von oben sichtbar, nur bei *Dialytus* nach unten umgeschlagen, die Scheibe ist meistens punktiert, stets ohne mehrere Querwülste, höchstens mit schwächerem Quereindruck bei *Odontoderus*, zuweilen befindet sich vor dem Schildchen eine mehr oder weniger deutliche Längsfurche.

Ein sichtbares Schildchen ist immer vorhanden, aber sehr klein, dreieckig.

Die Flügeldecken haben meistens eine gleichbreite Gestalt, seltener sind dieselben mehr oval, oft mit kleinem Schulterdorn, sie sind fast immer punktiert-gestreift, glatt oder beborstet, die Zwischenräume sind bald eben, bald konvex, seltener gerippt (*Dialytes*).

Die Mittelhüften sind mehr oder weniger weit voneinander entfernt, das Mesosternum zwischen ihnen meistens abschüssig, nur bei *Saprosites* liegt es meistens in gleicher Höhe mit dem Metasternum, die Platte des letzteren ist bald schmal, bald breiter, nur mit Mittellinie oder schmaler oder breiter vertieft.

Die Abdominalsegmente sind unverbunden, alle von gleicher Breite, immer punktiert, auch wohl am Vorderrande oder in der ganzen Länge gerieft (*Odontoderus*).

Die Vordertibien sind am Aussenrande mit drei deutlichen grösseren oder mehren kleinen Zähnchen versehen, ihr Vorderrand verläuft entweder schräg oder er ist quer abgestutzt, der abgestutzte Vorderrand trägt entweder auch einen Zahn (*Dialytes*) oder derselbe fehlt (*Simogoneus*), neben der Einlenkung der Füsse, am innern Spitzenwinkel also, ist stets ein Enddorn vorhanden.

Die Mittel- und Hintertibien sind gerade oder stark gebogen (*Euparia*) und haben am Endrande einen Borstenbesatz und zwei Enddorne.

Nur eine Art gehört aus dieser Gruppe dem palæarktischen Gebiet an.

BESTIMMUNGS-TABELLE DER GATTUNGEN

1. *Vorderrand des Clipeus von oben sichtbar, Halsschild am Seitenrande ungezahnt, Abdominalsegmente höchstens am Vorderrande mit kurzen Längsleistchen.*

2. *Halsschild an den Seiten breit verflacht und dicht bewimpert, Mittel- und Hintertibien nach der Spitze stark verbreitert und deutlich gebogen . . . .* 1. Genus EUPARIA, Serville.

2'. *Halsschild seitlich nicht verflacht, zuweilen bewimpert, dann aber nicht dicht, Mittel- und Hintertibien nach der Spitze nicht stark verbreitert und gebogen.*

3 *Wangen gross, Vordertibien am Vorderrande nicht abgestutzt, nie mit Zahn daselbst, wohl aber am innern Spitzenwinkel mit Enddorn und an der Aussenseite mit drei deutlichen Zähnen.*

4. *Körper meist stark konvex, nach hinten verbreitert, Kopf gross, stark
herabgewölbt, ohne Höcker, Flügeldecken an der Basis deutlich
gerandet, Mesosternum zwischen den Mittelhüften meistens vertieft,
Mitteltibien an der Aussenseite ohne Spur von Querleisten, am Endrande nie gezahnt, Füsse sind lang und schlank, Metatarsus sehr
lang, oft gleich dem übrigen Fuss* . . . . 2. Genus Atænius, Harold.

4'. *Körper weniger konvex, gleichbreit. Kopf gross, stark herabgewölbt,
glatt, ohne Höcker, so breit als Thorax, Flügeldecken stets ohne
deutliche Randung an der Basis, Mesosternum meistens wagerecht,
Mittelschienen aussen gewöhnlich mit schwachen Querleistchen, am
Endrande gezahnt, Füsse kurz, Metatarsus nicht besonders lang,
höchstens den zwei folgenden Gliedern an Länge gleich, selten länger* . 3. Genus Saprosites, Redtenbacher.

3'. *Wangen weniger gross, Vordertibien vorn abgestutzt, daselbst mit oder
ohne Zahn, stets mit Enddorn am innern Spitzenwinkel.*

5. *Hinterwinkel des Halsschildes nach unten dreieckig umgeschlagen, der
obere Rand dieser Umbiegung scharfkantig, Vordertibien am abge-
stutzten Vorderrande ohne Zahn, an der Aussenseite mit drei Zähnen.* 4. Genus Simogonius, Harold.

5'. *Hinterwinkel nicht umgeschlagen, normal, von oben sichtbar, Vorderrand der Vordertibien mit einem Zahn, Aussenseite mit vielen
kleinen Kerbzähnchen, von denen zwei oder drei etwas grösser sind.* 5. Genus Dialytes, Harold.

1'. *Vorderrand des Clipeus von oben nicht sichtbar, nach unten umgeschlagen und nach oben von einer scharfen Querleiste begrenzt, Halsschild
seitlich mit ein oder zwei Zähnen, Abdominalsegmente in der ganzen
Länge mit Leistchen* . . . . 6. Genus Odontoderus, Clouët.

I. Genus EUPARIA, Serville

Euparia. Serville, Encycl. Méthod. Vol. 10, p. 357 (1825).

Charaktere. — Diese Gattung ist kenntlich an dem breiten, verhältnismässig kurzen Kopfe, dem seitlich verflachten und bewimperten Thorax, den an der Spitze stark verbreiterten, gekrümmten Mittel- und Hintertibien.

Die Arten sind dunkelrotbraun oder schwarz gefärbt, ihre Oberfläche ist glänzend, zuweilen behaart.

Der Kopf ist stark herabgewölbt, nach vorn bogig verschmälert, daher ziemlich breit erscheinend; der Clipeus ist ausgerandet und seitlich davon verrundet, sehr selten mit einem Zähnchen jederseits; die Oberfläche ist entweder deutlich punktiert oder längsgestrichelt, stets ohne Tuberkeln, höchstens mit schwacher Stirnlinie, die Mitte ist beulig aufgetrieben, nur bei einer Art befindet sich vor derselben eine Querleiste; die Wangen sind gross und stumpfwinklig, meistens sehr wenig vom Seitenrande abgesetzt.

Das Halsschild ist quer, stark gewölbt, wenig breiter als der Kopf. der Seitenrand ist fast immer deutlich verflacht, die Breite dieser Verflachung ist aber bei Exemplaren derselben Art nicht immer dieselbe, die Basis ist wohl meistenteils, wenigstens in der Mitte, gerandet; diese, sowie die Seiten, tragen gewöhnlich einen dichten Haarbesatz, die Hinterwinkel sind meistens stumpf verrundet, die Oberfläche ist stärker oder schwächer, aber immer sehr deutlich punktiert.

Ein Schildchen ist immer vorhanden, es ist klein, schmal-dreieckig.

Die Flügeldecken sind an der Basis gewöhnlich schmaler als das Halsschild, schwächer oder stärker nach hinten verbreitert, ihre Basis ist flach ausgerandet, die Schultern sind scharf, mit oder ohne Zahn, ihre Punktstreifen sind tief und kräftig, getrennt durch ebene oder konvexe Zwischenräume.

Die Unterseite ist glänzend, deutlich punktiert, die Abdominalsegmente ausserdem gewöhnlich am Vorderrande gerieft.

Die Mittelhüften sind gewöhnlich weiter entfernt stehend als bei *Aphodius*.

Die Metasternalplatte ist breit verflacht.

Die Schenkel, mit Ausnahme der vorderen, sind schlank.

Die nach der Spitze allmählich verbreiterten Vordertibien sind aussen dreizähnig und haben neben den Tarsen einen Enddorn, Mittel- und Hintertibien sind nach der Spitze stark verbreitert und gekrümmt, am Spitzenrande beborstet und mit zwei Enddornen versehen.

Die Tarsen sind immer fünfgliedrig, die Klauen normal.

Die sexuellen Unterschiede sind bei keiner Beschreibung zugefügt, es hat dies vielleicht darin seinen Grund, dass so wenig Material vorhanden ist. Vielleicht sind die äussern Geschlechtsunterschiede denen von *Euparia excavaticollis* Blanchard analog, bei der das Männchen einen scharf zugespitzten, nach innen gebogenen Enddorn an den Vordertibien besitzt.

Es sind mittelgrosse Arten.

Geographische Verbreitung der Arten. — Afrika, Australien, Amerika.

1. *E. africana*, A. Schmidt, Soc. Ent. Zürich, 1909-10, Vol. 24, p. 54 (1909).   Malinde.
2. *E. argentina*, Harold, Col. Hefte, Vol. 2, p. 99 (1867); Vol. 6, p. 23, 26 (1870).   San Luis, Mendoza.
3. *E. attenuata*, Harold, Col. Hefte, Vol. 6, p. 28 (1870).   Brasilien.
4. *E. bitubericollis*, A. Schmidt. Soc. Ent. Zürich. 1909-10. Vol. 24, p. 44 (1909). — **Taf. 2, Fig. 30.**   Argentina.
5. *E. castanea*, Serville, Encycl. Méthod. Vol. 10, p. 357 (1825).
   castanea. Westwood, Trans Ent. Soc. Lond. Vol. 4, p. 239, t. 17, f. 3 (1847).   Nordamerika.
   Harold, Col. Hefte, Vol. 6, p. 23 (1870).   Georgia.
   Bates, Biol. Centr. Amer. Col. Suppl. p. 393 (1889).   Mexiko.
   Horn, Trans. Amer. Ent. Soc. Vol. 3, p. 289 (1871); Vol. 14, p. 87 (1887).   Golfstaaten, Florida, Alabama, Louisiana.
6. *E. costulata*, Harold, Col. Hefte, Vol. 1, p. 82 (1867); Vol. 6, p. 23, 25 (1870).   Brasilien.
7. *E. excavaticollis*, Blanchard, Voy. d'Orbigny, Col. Vol. 6 (2), p. 184 (1837-43). — **Taf. 2, Fig. 29.**   Corrientes.
   excavaticollis, Harold, Col. Hefte, Vol. 6, p. 23, 29 (1870).   Itaty.
8. *E. Friedenreichi*, Harold, ibidem, p. 23, 27 (1870).   Brasilien.
9. *E. Olliffi*, Blackburn, Proc. Roy. Soc. Victoria, Vol. 17, p. 171 (1904).   Neu-Südwales.
10. *E. ovalipennis*, Harold, Col. Hefte, Vol. 8, p. 116 (1871).   Argentina.
11. *E. rauca*, A. Schmidt, Soc. Ent. Zürich, 1908-09. Vol. 23, p. 57 (1908).   Madagaskar.
12. *E. separata*, A. Schmidt, ibidem, 1909-10, Vol. 24, p. 44 (1909).   Paraguay.
13. *E. tuberculata*, Bates, Biol. Centr. Amer. Col. Vol. 2 (2), p. 94, t. 6, f. 23 (1887).   Panama.

2. GENUS ATÆNIUS, HAROLD

Atænius. Harold, Col. Hefte, Vol. 2, p. 100 (1867).

Euparia. Erichson, Wiegmann Arch. f. Naturg. Vol. 1, p. 110 (1847); Burmeister, Stett. Ent. Zeit. p. 401 (1877).

Oxyomus. Blanchard, Voy. d'Orbigny, Col. Ins. Vol. 6 (2), p. 184 (1837-1843).

Hexalus. Mulsant & Rey, Opusc. Ent. Vol. 14. p. 200 (1870).

Charaktere. — Diese ziemlich umfangreiche Gattung ist eine der schwierigsten, weil in ihr die Punktierung des Kopfes, Halsschildes und die Skulptur der Flügeldecken ausschliesslich die unterscheidenden Merkmale bilden, also Kriterien, die oft sehr schwer in der richtigen Weise zu deuten sind, die auch selbst bei mehreren Exemplaren derselben Art merkliche Unterschiede aufweisen. Das Verhältnis des ersten Tarsengliedes zu den folgenden, die Verbindung der Flügeldeckenstreifen, die Skulptur des Kopfes und andere Merkmale, die bei *Aphodius* als gute Unterscheidungsmerkmale gelten, sind in dieser Gattung nicht zu verwenden, weil in dieser Beziehung die Arten eine grosse Uebereinstimmung zeigen.

Der Körper ist meistens stark gewölbt, nach hinten verbreitert, behaart oder glatt, fast immer glänzend.

Der Kopf ist gross, herabgewölbt, nicht so breit als der Thorax, stärker oder schwächer punktiert, manchmal auch fast glatt, zuweilen mit undeutlicher Stirnlinie, aufgetriebener Mitte, stets aber ohne Höcker; der Clipeus ist ausgebuchtet, seitlich gezähnt oder abgerandet; die Wangen sind gross; die Augen werden zum grössten Teil vom Halsschilde bedeckt.

Das Halsschild ist etwas breiter als der Kopf, es ist an den Seiten entweder parallel, gerundet oder nach hinten verschmälert, an den Seiten fast immer, zuweilen auch an der Basis gerandet, die Oberfläche zeigt meistens eine dichte, feinere oder stärkere Punktierung, die Hinterwinkel können gerundet, stumpf oder ausgerandet sein.

Das Schildchen ist immer sichtbar, es ist aber klein, meistens dreieckig gestaltet.

Die Flügeldecken sind an der Basis ausgebuchtet und deutlich gerandet, nach hinten meistens verbreitert, die Schultern sind oft gezahnt, die Oberfläche ist fast immer sehr deutlich punktiert-gestreift, die Streifenpunkte sind feiner oder stärker, sie greifen sehr oft die Ränder der Zwischenräume an, entweder gleichmässig oder die innere Seite derselben bevorzugend; die Zwischenräume sind eben, konvex oder gerippt, gewöhnlich nur fein punktiert oder auch ganz glatt.

Die Unterseite ist meistens auch nur fein punktiert.

Die Bauchsegmente sind frei, ihr Vorderrand ist manchmal kurz gerieft.

Die Mittelhüften sind mehr oder weniger voneinander entfernt.

Die Vordertibien haben neben den Tarsen einen Enddorn und am Aussenrande drei deutliche, grössere Zähne, die Mittel- und Hintertibien sind ohne Querleisten, an ihrem Spitzenrande nach aussen in einen Dorn ausgezogen, an der untern Kante des Endrandes haben sie einen Borstenbesatz und zwei Enddorne.

Die Füsse sind lang, fünfgliedrig, das erste Glied ist meistens so lang als der übrige Fuss, das letzte Glied trägt zwei normale Klauen.

Aeussere Geschlechtsunterschiede scheinen zu fehlen, ich habe bisher keine finden können.

Es sind kleine und mittelgrosse Tiere von rotbrauner oder schwarzer Farbe, selten sind bei den dunklen Arten die Ränder heller.

Geographische Verbreitung der Arten. — Die Gattung ist in allen Gebieten vertreten, am zahlreichsten in Amerika.

1. *A. abditus*, Haldeman, Journ. Acad. Nat. Sc. Philad. (2), Vol. 1, p. 106 (1848).	Nordamerika (Mittelstaaten).
abditus, Horn, Trans. Amer. Ent. Soc. Vol. 3, p. 289 (1871); Vol. 14, p. 72 (1887).	Vereinigte Staaten, Mexiko, Sudamerika.
attenuator, Harold, Col. Hefte, Vol. 12, p 22 (1874).	Columbien, Neu-Granada.
sec. Horn, Trans. Amer. Ent. Soc. Vol. 5, p. 142 (1874-76).	
var. *texanus*, Harold, Col. Hefte, Vol. 12, p. 23 (1874).	Texas.
sec. Bates Biol. Centr. Amer. Col. Vol. 2 (2), p. 101 (1887).	Nordamerika, Texas.
A. Schmidt, Aphodiinen-Zusammenst. Deutsche Ent. Zeitschr. Beih. p. 88 Note. (1907-08).	
2. *A. aequalis*, Harold, Stett. Ent. Zeit. p. 40 (1880).	Columbien.

3. *A. alternatus*, Melsheimer, Proc. Acad. Nat. Sc. Philad. Vol. 2, p. 137   Pennsylvanien.
(1844).
    alternatus, Horn, Trans. Amer. Ent. Soc. Vol. 3, p. 285 (1871); Vol. 14,   Pennsylvanien bis Florida und
      p. 75 (1887).   Texas.
4. *A. angusticollis*, A. Schmidt, Soc. Ent. Zürich. 1909-10, Vol. 24, p. 20   Bolivia.
(1909). — **Taf. 2, Fig. 31**.
5. *A. arator*, Harold, Col. Hefte, Vol. 5, p. 102 (1869).   Brasilien.
6. *A. arenosus*, Harold, ibidem, Vol. 3. p. 86 (1868); Vol. 12, p. 21 (1874).   Brasilien.
7. *A. atramentarius*, Erichson, Wiegmann Arch. f. Naturg. Vol. 1, p. 110   Peru.
(1847).
    atramentarius, Harold, Col. Hefte, Vol. 6, p. 22 (1870).
8. *A. australis*, Harold, Col. Hefte,. Vol. 13, p. 89 (1875).   Südaustralien.
    australis, Blackburn, Proc. Roy. Soc. Victoria, Vol. 17, p. 159 (1904).
9. *A, brevicollis*, Wollaston, Ins. Madar. p. 229 (1854).   Madeira.
    sec. Wollaston, Cat. Canar. Col. p. 191 (1864).   Kanarische Inseln.
10. *A. californicus*, Horn, Trans. Amer, Soc. Vol. 14, p. 84 (1887).   Kalifornien.
11. *A. capitosus*, Harold, Col. Hefte, Vol. 1. p. 83 (1867).   Columbien, Mexiko.
    capitosus, Bates, Biol. Centr. Amer. Col. Vol. 2 (2), p 98 (1887).   Antillen, Zentral- u. Südamerika.
12. *A. carinator*, Harold, Col. Hefte, Vol. 12, p. 20 (1874).   Venezuela.
    carinator, Bates, Biol. Centr. Amer. Col. Vol. 2 (2), p. 101 (1887).   Panama, Mexiko.
13. *A. catenulatus*, Erichson, Wiegmann Arch. f Naturg. Vol. 1, p. 110 (1847).   Peru.
    catenulatus, Harold, Col. Hefte, Vol. 6, p. 22 (1870).
14. *A. cognatus*, Le Conte, Proc. Acad. Nat. Soc. Philad. p. 65 (1858).   Texas, Sonora.
    cognatus, Horn, Trans. Amer. Ent. Soc. Vol. 14, p. 83 (1887).   Neu-England bis Rocky Mount.
    A. Schmidt,. Aphodiinen-Zusammenst. Deutsche Ent. Zeitschr.
    Beih. p. 89, Anmerkung (1907-08).
15. *A. coloratus*, Blackburn, Proc. Roy. Soc. Victoria, Vol. 17, p. 161, 169   Westaustralien.
(1904).
16. *A. columbicus*, Harold, Stett. Ent. Zeit. p. 39 (1880).   Columbien, Venezuela.
17. *A. complicatus*, Harold. Col. Hefte, Vol. 5, p. 102 (1869).   Brasilien.
    complicatus, Harold, C. R. Ann. Soc. Ent. Belg. p. 96 (1876); (2), N° 32,   San João del Rey, Bahia.
      p. 12 (1876).
    Bates. Biol. Centr. Amer. Col. Vol. 2 (2), p. 97 (1887).   Mexiko, Guatemala.
18. *A. consors*, Blackburn. Proc. Roy. Soc. Victoria, Vol. 17, p. 161, 168   Queensland.
(1904).
19. *A. crenatipennis*, Mac Leay, Trans. Ent. Soc. N. S. Wales, Vol. 2,   Australien.
p. 184 (1871).
    crenatipennis, Blackburn, Proc. Roy. Soc. Victoria, Vol. 17, p. 158 (1904).   Gaindah.
20. *A. crenator*, Harold, C. R. Ann. Soc. Ent. Belg. Vol. 19, p. 97 (1876);   San João del Rey.
(2), N° 32, p. 14 (1876).
21. *A. crenatostriatus*. Blanchard. Voy. d'Orbigny, Col. 6 (2), p. 184   Santa Cruz.
(1837-43).
22. *A. cribricollis*. Burmeister, Stett. Ent. Zeit. p. 411 (1877).   Buenos Aires.
    cribricollis, Harold, Col. Hefte, Vol. 6, p. 20 (1870).
    crenatulus, Fairmaire, Ann. Soc. Ent. Fr. p. 489 (1883).   Punta-Arena.
    sec. Berg. Bull. Soc. Ent. Fr. p. 98 (1884).   [ragua, Panama.
23. *A. cribrithorax*, Bates, Biol. Centr. Amer. Col. Vol. 2 (2), p. 95 (1887).   Mexiko, Guatemala, Nica-
24. *A. cylindricus*, Horn, Trans. Amer. Ent. Soc. Vol. 3, p. 289 (1871);   Südcarolina, Georgia, Flo-
Vol. 14. p. 71 (1887).   rida.
    Horni, Harold, Col. Hefte, Vol. 12, p. 19 (1874).   Südcarolina
    sec. Horn, Trans. Amer. Ent. Soc. Vol, 14, p. 109 (1887).
25. *A. Derbesis*, Solier, Gay Hist. Nat. fis. Chile, Vol. 5, p. 72 (1851).   Chile.
    Derbesis, Harold, Berl. Ent. Zeitschr. p. 280 (1867); C. R. Soc. Ent. Belg.   Chile, Buenos Aires.
      p. 94 (1876); ibidem (2), No. 32, p. 10 (1876).
    Burmeister, Stett. Ent. Zeit. p. 412 (1877).
26. *A. deserti*, Blackburn, Proc. Linn. Soc. N. S. Wales (2), Vol. 9,   Australien.
p. 95 (1894).
    deserti, Blackburn, Proc. Roy. Soc. Victoria, Vol. 17, p. 159 (1904).

27. *A. desertus*, Horn, Trans. Amer. Ent. Soc. Vol. 3, p. 289 (1871);   Kalifornien, Arizona, Süd-
Vol. 14, p. 72 (1887).   utah.
28. *A. elegans*, Harold, Col. Hefte, Vol. 3, p. 85 (1868).   Brasilien.
29. *A. elongatus*, Beauvois, Ins. Afr. et Amér. p. 104, t. 3c, f. 8 (1805).   St Domingo.
      sec. Fleutiaux & Sallé, Ann. Soc. Ent. Fr. p. 397 (1889).   Guadeloupe.
30. *A. euglyptus*, Bates, Biol. Centr. Amer. Col. Vol. 2 (2), p. 97 (1887).   Mexiko.
31. *A. exaratus*, Fleutiaux & Sallé, Ann. Soc. Ent. Fr. (6), Vol. 9, p. 397   Guadeloupe.
(1889).
32. *A. figurator*, Harold, Col. Hefte, Vol. 12, p. 24 (1874).   Louisiana.
      figurator, Bates, Biol. Centr. Amer. Col. Vol. 2 (2), p. 99 (1887).   Nordamerika, Mexiko.
      Horn, Trans. Amer. Ent. Soc. Vol. 14, p. 79 (1887).   Georgia, Texas.
33. *A. frater*, Arrow, Trans. Ent. Soc. Lond. p. 512 (1903).   Westindien.
34. *A. gibbus*, Blackburn, Proc. Roy. Soc. Victoria, Vol. 17, p. 160, 166 (1904).   Neu-Südwales.
35. *A. goyderensis*, Blackburn, Horn's Exped. Centr. Austral. Vol. 2, p. 264   Australien.
(1896); Proc. Roy. Soc. Victoria, Vol. 17, p. 160 (1904).
36. *A. gracilis*, Melsheimer. Proc. Acad. Nat. Sc. Philad. Vol. 2, p. 137   Pennsylvanien.
(1844).
      gracilis, Jacquelin Du Val, Ramon Hist. Cuba, Vol. 7, p. 119 (1856).   Kuba.
      Chevrolat, Ann. Soc. Ent. Fr. p. 414 (1864).   Porto Rico, Guadeloupe. [Chile.
      Harold, Berl. Ent. Zeitschr. p. 281 (1867).   Westindien, Columbien, Peru,
      Horn, Trans. Amer. Ent. Soc. Vol. 3, p. 286 (1871); Vol. 14, p. 79   VereinigteStaaten Nordamerika.
      (1887).
      chilensis, Solier, Gays Hist. Nat. fis. Chile, Vol. 5, p. 72, t. 16, f. 1 (1851).   Chile.
37. *A. granulator*, Harold, Ann. Mus. Stor. Nat. Génova, Vol 10, p. 95 (1877).   Neu-Guinea.
38. *A. Haroldi*, Steinheil, Atti Soc. Ital. Sc. Nat. Vol. 15, p. 556 (1872).   San Luis.
      Haroldi, Harold, Col. Hefte, Vol. 12, p. 17 (1874).   San Luis.
39. *A. hirsutus*. Horn, Trans. Amer. Ent. Soc. Vol. 3, p. 288 (1871); Vol. 14,   Arizona.
p. 86 (1887).
      sec. Bates, Biol. Centr. Amer. Col. Vol. 2 (2), p. 98 (1887).   Mexiko.
40. *A. hispidus*, Harold, Col. Hefte, Vol. 1, p. 83 (1867).   Venezuela.
41. *A. horticola*, Harold, L'Abeille, Vol. 5, p, 429 (1869).   Konstantinopel.
      horticola, Reitter, Tab. p. 31; Brünn, 30, p. 169.   Griechenland, Türkei, Syrien,
      cyprius, Baudi, Berl. Ent. Zeitschr. p. 68 (1870).   Cypern. [Armenien,Transkauk.
      sec. Harold, Col. Hefte, Vol. 6, p. 119 (1870).
      Alleoni, Fairmaire, Bull. Soc. Ent. Fr. p. 193 (1875).   Konstantinopel.
      sec. d'Orbigny, L'Abeille, Vol. 28, p. 248 (1896).
42. *A. imbricatoides*, A. Schmidt, Soc. Ent. Zürich, 1909-10, Vol. 24, p. 36   Argentina.
(1909).
43. *A. imbricatus*, Melsheimer, Proc. Acad. Nat. Sc. Philad. Vol. 2, p. 136   Pennsylvanien.
(1844).
      imbricatus, Horn, Trans. Amer. Ent. Soc. Vol. 3, p. 285 (1871); Vol. 14,   Massachusetts bis Texas,Mexiko,
      p. 74 (1887).   Kuba.
      sordidus, Harold, Col. Hefte, Vol. 5, p. 103 (1869).   Mittelamerika.
      sec. Horn, Trans. Amer. Ent. Soc. Vol. 14, p. 75 (1887).
44. *A. imparilis*, Blackburn, Proc. Roy. Soc. Victoria, Vol. 17, p. 159, 163   Neu-Südwales.
(1904).
45. *A. inops*, Horn, Trans. Amer. Ent. Soc. Vol. 14, p. 73 (1887).   Arizona, Texas.
      inops, Bates, Biol. Centr. Amer. Col. Vol. 2 (2), p. 101 (1887).   Mexiko.
46. *A. inquisitus*, Horn, Trans. Amer. Ent Soc. Vol. 14, p. 81 (1887).   Texas.
47. *A. insculptus*, Horn. ibidem, p. 70 (1887).   Florida.
      sculptilis*, Le Conte, Proc. Amer. Philos. Soc. p. 402 (1878).
48. *A. insolitus*, A. Schmidt, Notes Leyd. Mus. Vol. 31. p. 116 (1909).   Senegal.
49. *A. Koebelei*, Blackburn, Proc. Roy. Soc. Victoria, Vol. 17. p. 159, 162   Queensland.
(1904).
50. *A. laborator*, Harold, Col. Hefte, Vol. 5, p. 102 (1869).   Brasilien.
51. *A. laeviventris*, Horn, Trans. Amer. Enr. Soc. Vol. 14, p. 74 (1887).   Südarizona.
52. *A. languidus*, A. Schmidt, Stett. Ent. Zeit. p. 31 (1911).   Mexiko.

53. *A. Lecontei*, Harold, Col. Hefte, Vol. 12, p. 20 (1874).   Carolina.
    Lecontei, Horn, Trans. Amer. Ent. Soc. Vol. 14, p. 73 (1887).   Columbia bis Louisiana.
54. *A, limbatus*, Bates, Biol. Centr. Amer. Col. Vol. 2 (2), p. 98 (1887).   Mexiko:
55. *A. liogaster*, Bates, ibidem, p. 94 (1887).   Mittelamerika.
    var. castaniellus, Bates, ibidem, p. 95 (1887)   Guatemala.
56. *A. lobatus*, Horn, Trans. Amer. Ent. Soc. Vol. 3, p. 287 (1871);   Kalifornien, Kap San Lucas.
    Vol. 14. p. 85 (1887).
57. *A. lucanus*, Horn, ibidem, Vol. 3, p. 288 (1871); Vol. 14, p. 70   Kalifornien, Kap San Lucas.
    (1887).
58. *A. luctuosus*. Burmeister, Stett. Ent. Zeit. p. 411 (1877).   Buenos Aires.
    luctuosus, Harold, Col. Hefte. Vol. 6, p. 20 (1870).
59. *A. macilentus*, Blackburn, Proc. Roy. Soc. Victoria, Vol. 17, p. 160, 167   Neu-Südwales.
    (1904).
60. *A. mariarum*, Bates, Biol. Centr. Amer. Col. Vol. 2 (2), p 102 (1887).   Mexiko.
61. *A. moniliatus*, Blackburn. Proc. Roy. Soc. Victoria. Vol. 17, p. 159,   Nordwestaustralien.
    161 (1904).
62. *A. montanus*, A. Schmidt, Stett Ent. Zeit. p. 32 (1911).   Loja (Ostcordilleren).
63. *A. morator*, Harold. Col. Hefte. Vol. 5, p. 103 (1869).   Bahia.
64. *A. nanus*, De Geer, Mém. Ins. Vol. 4, p. 318, t. 9, f. 3 (1774).   Surinam.
    nanus, Harold, Stett. Ent. Zeit. p. 42 (1880).
65. *A. nudus*, Blackburn, Proc. Roy. Soc. Victoria, Vol. 17, p. 160, 166   Westaustralien.
    (1904).
66. *A. nugator*, Harold, Stett. Ent. Zeit. p. 41 (1880).   Columbien.
67. *A. oblongus*, Horn, Trans, Amer. Ent. Soc. Vol. 3, p. 286 (1871);   Kalifornien.
    Vol. 14, p. 81 (1887).
68. *A. obscurus*, Mac Leay, Trans. Ent. Soc. N. S. Wales, Vol. 2, p. 184   Australien.
    (1871).
    obscurus, Harold, Col. Hefte. Vol 11, p. 147 (1873).
            Blackburn, Proc. Roy. Soc. Victoria, Vol. 17, p. 162 (1904).
69. *A. opacus*, Harold, Col. Hefte. Vol. 2, p. 100 (1867); C. R. Ann. Soc.   Brasilien, Montevideo.
    Ent. Belg. p. 97 (1876); (2), N° 32, p. 13 (1876).
70. *A. opatrinus*, Harold, ibidem, Vol. 1. p. 82 (1867); ibidem, p. 96 (1876);   Bahia, San Joâo del Rey.
    ibidem, p. 12 (1876).
71. *A. opatroides*, Blanchard, Voy. d'Orbigny, Vol. 6 (2), p. 185 (1837-43).   Montevideo.
    — Taf. 2, Fig. 33.
            opatroides, Harold, C. R. Ann. Ent. Belg. p. 97 (1876); (2), N° 32, p. 13   Uruguay.
            (1876).
            sec. Burmeister, Stett. Ent. Zeit. p. 411 (1877).   Buenos Aires.
72. *A. orbicularis*, A. Schmidt, Denkschr. Akad. Wiss. Wien, Math. Nat.   Samoa.
    Cl. 1910.
73. *A. ovatulus*, Horn, Trans. Amer. Ent. Soc. Vol. 3, p. 286 (1871);   Pennsylvanien bis Loui-
    Vol. 14; p 78 (1887).   siana.
74. *A. Palmerstoni*, Blackburn, Trans. Roy. Soc. S. Austral. Vol. 14.   Südaustralien.
    p. 135 (1891); Proc. Roy. Soc. Victoria, Vol. 17, p. 159 (1904).
75. *A. perbrevitarsis*, A. Schmidt, Soc. Ent. Zürich, 1909-10, Vol. 24,   Kamerun.
    p. 43 (1909).
76. *A. peregrinator*, Harold, Ann. Mus. Stor. Nat. Genova, Vol. 10, p. 96   Celebes, Borneo.
    (1877).
77. *A. perforatus*. Harold, Col Hefte, Vol. 1, p. 83 (1867).   Columbien.
    perforatus, Bates, Biol. Centr. Amer. Col. Vol. 2 (2), p. 97 (1887).   Mittelamerika.
78. *A. picinus*, Harold, Berl. Ent. Zeitschr. p. 281 (1867); Col. Heft.   Mendoza, Montevideo, La
    Vol. 13, p. 71 (1875); C. R. Ann. Soc. Ent. Belg. p. 95; (2) No. 2,   Plata, Buenos Aires, San
    p. 11 (1876).   Joâo del Rey.
79. *A. picipes*. Fleutiaux & Sallé, Ann. Soc. Ent. Fr. (6), Vol. 9, p. 397   Guadeloupe.
    (1889).

80. *A. platensis*, Blanchard, Voy. d'Orbigny, Vol. 6 (2), p. 185 (1837-43).   Argentinien.
    — **Taf. 3, Fig. 34.**
> *integer*, Harold, Col. Hefte, Vol. 3, p. 86 (1868).   Brasilien.
> sec. Harold, C. R. Ann. Soc. Ent. Belg. p. 95 (1876); (2) No. 32,   Buenos Aires, Montevideo.
>   p. 11 (1876).
> A. Schmidt, Aphodiinen-Zusammenst. Deutsche Ent. Zeitschr.
>   Beih. p. 94. Anmerkung (1907-08).

81. *A. polyglyptus*, Bates, Biol. Centr. Amer. Col. Vol. 2 (2), p. 99 (1887).   Guatemala.
> *polyglyptus*, Arrow. Trans. Ent. Soc. Lond. p. 513 (1903).   Grenada, St. Vincent.
> *var. intermedius*, Bates, Biol. Centr. Amer. Col. Vol. 2 (2), p. 100 (1887).   Panama.
> *var. jalapensis*, Bates, ibidem, p. 100 (1887).   Mexiko.
> *var. Hieronymi*, Bates, ibidem, p. 100 (1887).   Guatemala.

82. *A. punctatohirsutus*, A. Schmidt. Soc. Ent. Zürich. 1909-10, Vol 24,   Argentina.
    p. 36 (1909).

83. *A. puncticollis**, Le Conte, Prọc. Ácad. Nat. Sc. Philad. p. 66 (1858).   Texas.
> *puncticollis*, Horn, Trans. Amer. Ent. Soc Vol. 3, p. 288 (1871); Vol. 14,   El Paso.
>   p. 77 (1887).

84. *A. punctipennis*, Harold, Col. Hefte, Vol. 3, p. 86 (1868).   Columbien.

85. *A. purator*, Harold, ibidem, Vol. 4, p. 85 (1868).   Pará.

86. *A. pusillus*, Burmeister, Stett. Ent. Zeit. p. 410 (1877).   Argentinien.
> *pusillus*, Harold, Col. Hefte, Vol. 6, p. 20 (1870).

87. *A. rhyticephalus*, Chevrolat, Ann. Soc. Ent. Fr. p. 413 (1864).   Kuba.

88. *A. robustus*, Horn, Trans. Amer. Ent. Soc. Vol. 3. p. 285 (1871); Vol. 14,   Missouri, Wisconsin, Kan-
    p. 80 (1887).   sas.

89. *A. rubripes*, Boheman. Fregatt. Eugen. Resa, Vol. 2 (1), p. 51 (1858).   Buenos Aires.

90. *A. rubrotessellatus*, Blanchard, Voy. d'Orbigny, Vol. 6 (2), p. 185 (1837-43).   Santa Cruz.

91. *A. scabrellus*, A. Schmidt, Notes Leyd. Mus. Vol. 31, p. 118 (1909).   La Guayra (Venezuela).

92. *A. scalptifrons*, Bates, Biol. Centr. Amer. Col. Vol. 2 (2), p. 100, t. 6,   Mexiko, Guatemala.
    f. 25 (1887).

93. *A. sculptilis*, Harold, Col. Hefte, Vol. 3, p. 86; Vol. 12, p. 16 (1874).   Venezuela.

94. *A. sculptor*, Harold, ibidem, Vol. 4, p. 85 (1868). — **Taf. 2, Fig. 32.**   Columbien.

95. *A. scutellaris*, Harold, Col. Hefte, Vol. 1, p. 82 (1867); C. R. Ann.   Columbien, Antillen, Bra-
    Soc. Ent. Belg. p. 96; (2) No. 32, p. 12 (1876).   silien.
> *scutellaris*, Bates, Biol. Centr. Amer. Col. Vol. 2 (2), p. 96 (1887).   Mittelamerika.

96. *A. semicoecus*, Mac Leay, Proc. Linn. Soc. N. S. Wales (2). Vol. 3,   King-Sund.
    p. 904 (1888).
> *semicoecus*, Blackburn, Proc. Roy. Soc. Victoria. Vol. 17, p. 161, 169 (1904).

97. *A. semicornutus*, Mac Leay, Trans. Ent. Soc. N. S. Wales, Vol. 2,   Gayndah.
    p. 184 (1871).
> *semicornutus*. Blackburn, Proc. Roy. Soc. Victoria, Vol. 17, p. 159, 164 (1904).   Gayndah.

98. *A. setiger*, Bates, Biol. Centr. Amer. Col. Vol. 2 (2), p. 98 (1887).   Mexiko.

99. *A. setosus*, A. Schmidt, Notes Leyd. Mus. Vol. 31, p. 119 (1909).   Kisantu (Kongo).

100. *A. simplicipes*, Mulsant & Rey, Opusc. Ent. Vol. 14, p. 200 (1870);   Loudun.
    Hist. Nat. Col. France, Lamell. p. 366 (1871).
> *simplicipes*, Reitter, Tab. p. 31; Brünn, 30, p. 169.

101. *A. simulator*, Harold, Col. Hefte, Vol. 3, p. 85 (1868).   Mendoza.
> *simulator*, sec. Burmeister, Stett. Ent. Zeit. p. 412 (1877).

102. *A. socialis*, Horn, Trans. Amer. Ent. Soc. Vol. 3, p. 287 (1871); Vol. 14,   Georgia, Louisiana, Texas.
    p. 76 (1887).
> *socialis*, Harold, Berl. Ent. Zeitschr. p. 174 (1874).   Nordamerika.

103. *A. sparsicollis*, Blackburn, Proc. Roy. Soc. Victoria, Vol. 17, p. 159,   Zentralaustralien.
    164 (1904).

104. *A. speculator*, Blackburn, Trans. Roy. Soc. S. Austral. Vol. 14, p. 135   Victoria.
    (1891); Proc. Roy. Soc. Victoria. Vol. 17, p. 159 (1904).

105. *A. spinator*, Harold, Ann. Mus. Stor. Nat. Genova, Vol. 10. p. 94 (1877).   Neu-Guinea.

106. *A. spissus*, Blackburn, Proc. Roy. Soc. Victoria, Vol. 17, p. 160,   Queensland.
    167 (1904).

107. *A. Steinheili*, Harold, Col. Hefte, Vol. 12, p. 18 (1874).   Neu-Granada.
 Steinheili, Bates, Biol. Centr Amer. Col. Suppl. p. 393 (1889).   Mexiko, Yucatan.
108. *A. stercorator*. Fabricius, Syst. Ent. p. 20 (1775).   Brasilien.
 stercorator, Olivier, Ent. Vol. 1 (3), p. 89, t. 17, f. 155 (1789).   Brasilien.
 Harold, Col. Hefte, Vol. 13, p. 70 (1875).   Nord- und Südamerika, Antillen.
 bonariensis*, Klug, Preisverz. p. 4 (1829).
  sec. Harold, Col. Hefte, Vol. 13, p. 70 (1875).
 Heinekeni, Wollaston, Ins. Mader. p. 228 (1854); Ann. Mag. Nat. Hist.   Madeira, Ascension.
  p. 302 (1861).
 ?denominatus, Chevrolat, Ann. Soc. Ent. Fr. p. 413 (1864).   Kuba.
109. *A. strigatus**, Say, Journ. Acad. Nat. Sc. Philad. Vol. 3, p. 212 (1823);   Vereinigte Staaten Nord-
 *Say's Works, ed. Le Conte. Vol. 2, p. 137 (   ).   amerika.
 spretulus, Haldeman, Journ. Acad. Nat. Sc. Philad. (2), Vol. 1, p. 106(1848).   Rocky Mountains.
 stercorator, Horn (non Fabricius), Trans. Amer. Ent. Soc. Vol. 3, p. 286   Nord- und Südamerika.
  (1871) (pars).
  sec. Harold, Col. Hefte, Vol. 13, p. 71 (1875).
  sec. Bates, Biol. Centr. Amer. Col. Vol. 2 (2), p. 94 (1887).   Mexiko.
110. *A. strigicauda*, Bates, Biol. Centr. Amer. Col. Vol. 2 (2), p. 96, t. 6,   Mexiko, Mittelamerika,
 f. 24 (1887).   Brasilien.
 strigicauda, Arrow, Trans. Ent. Soc. Lond. p. 511 (1903).   Antillen.
111. *A. sulcatulus*, Chevrolat, Ann. Soc. Ent. Fr. p. 413 (1864).   Kuba.
 sulcatulus, sec. Fleutiaux & Sallé, ibidem, p. 397 (1889).   Guadeloupe.
112. *A. tenebrosus*, Arrow Trans. Ent. Soc. Lond. p. 512 (1903).   Grenada, Trinidad, Marajo,
113. *A. terminalis*, Chevrolat, Ann. Soc. Ent. Fr. p. 414 (1864).   Kuba. [Brasili.
 terminalis, sec. Fleutiaux & Sallé, ibidem, p. 396 (1889).   Guadeloupe.
 Arrow, Trans. Ent. Soc Lond. p. 512 (1903).   Antillen.
114. *A. torridus*, Blackburn, Trans. Roy. Soc. S. Austral Vol. 15, p. 36   Südaustralien.
 (1892); Proc. Roy. Soc. Victoria, Vol. 17, p. 161 (1904).
115. *A. transversarius*, A. Schmidt, Soc. Ent. Zürich, 1909-10, Vol. 24,   Bolivia.
 p. 43 (1909).
116. *A. Tremolerasi*, A. Schmidt, Stett. Ent. Zeit. p. 33 (1911).   Montevideo.
117. *A. tweedensis*, Blackburn, Proc. Roy. Soc. Victoria, Vol. 17, p. 160,   Neu-Südwales.
 165 (1904).
118. *A. vethianus*, A. Schmidt. Notes Leyd. Mus. Vol. 31, p. 120 (1909).   Manna (Sumatra).
119. *A. vexator*, Harold, Col. Hefte, Vol. 5, p. 103 (1869).   Brasilien, St. Thomas.
120. *A. vincentiae*, Arrow, Trans. Ent. Soc. Lond. p. 513 (1903).   St. Vincent.
121. *A. Walkeri*, Blackburn, Proc. Roy. Soc. Victoria, Vol. 17, p. 161,   Südaustralien.
 170 (1904).   [lorado.
122. *A. Wenzeli*, Horn, Trans. Amer. Ent. Soc. Vol. 14, p. 77 (1887).   Atlantic City, Florida, Co-

3. GENUS SAPROSITES, REDTENBACHER

Saprosites. Redtenbacher, Fauna Austr. p. 436 (1858).

Charaktere. — In der dunklen Färbung, dem herabgewölbten glatten Kopfe mit den grossen Wangen, dem kleinen Schildchen stimmt diese Gattung mit der vorigen überein, doch durch die flache, gleichbreite Gestalt, den breiteren Kopf, die an der Basis ungerandeten oder sehr undeutlich gerandeten Flügeldecken, die viel kürzeren Füsse und anderen Merkmale vollständig unterschieden.

Der Kopf ist sehr breit, nicht schmaler als der Thorax, er ist meistens nur fein punktiert, seltener stärker oder gar gekörnt, in der Mitte schwach beulig, ohne Höcker, höchstens mit schwacher Stirnlinie; die Wangen sind gross, undeutlich vom Seitenrande abgesetzt; der Clipeus ist meistens ausgerandet, darüber eingedrückt und seitlich gerundet.

Das Halsschild ist parallel, an den Seiten immer, an der Basis nur zuweilen gerandet, die Hinterwinkel sind rundlich, abgestutzt, bei manchen Arten auch ausgerandet, die Oberfläche ist fast immer deutlich punktiert, oft nach vorn schwächer.

Das Schildchen ist klein, dreieckig, meistens sehr schmal.

Die Flügeldecken haben die Breite des Halsschildes, sie sind parallel — nur bei *marchionalis* und *convexus* Harold haben sie gewölbtere, nach hinten verbreiterte Gestalt —, an der Basis fast immer ohne deutliche Randung und abgestutzt, immer unbehaart, stärker oder feiner punktiert-gestreift, die Zwischenräume sind meistens sehr schmal, eben oder konvex, höchstens sehr fein punktiert, die Schultern zeigen meistens ein kleines Zähnchen.

Die Unterseite ist glänzend, wenig punktiert; das Mesosternum zwischen den Mittelhüften liegt gewöhnlich in gleicher Höhe mit dem Metasternum; die Abdominalsegmente, besonders die letzten, sind oft stark nach vorn gebogen, am Vorderrande gerieft; die Metasternalplatte ist in der Mitte mit tiefer Mittellinie versehen.

Die Vordertibien haben drei kleine, spitze Aussenzähne und neben den Tarsen einen Enddorn.

Die Mitteltibien sind fast immer sehr kurz, stark dreieckig erweitert, der Aussenrand zeigt gewöhnlich zwei schwache Querleisten, und der Endrand ist gewöhnlich gezähnelt.

Die Hintertibien sind meistens ohne deutliche Querleistchen, sie haben am Endrande einen Borstenbesatz und zwei Enddorne.

Die Tarsen sind fünfgliedrig, sehr kurz, das erste Glied ist kürzer als der obere Enddorn, meistens nur so lang als die zwei folgenden Glieder.

Auch in dieser Gattung scheinen äussere Geschlechtsmerkmale zu fehlen.

Geographische Verbreitung der Arten. — Die Gattung kommt in allen Gebieten vor.

1. *S. aspericeps,* Harold, C. R. Ann. Soc. Ent. Belg. Vol. 19, p. 98   Botafogo.
   (1876); (2) No. 32, p. 15 (1876).
   sec. Harold, Stett. Ent. Zeit. p. 38 (1880).   Columbien.
2. *S. breviusculus,* Harold, Col. Hefte, Vol. 1, p. 81 (1867); C. R.   Brasilien, Argentinien.
   Ann. Soc. Ent. Belg. p. 98 (1876); (2) No. 32, p. 15 (1876).
3. *S. Brouni,* Sharp, Ent. M. Mag. Vol. 13, p. 71 (1876).   Neu-Seeland.
   Brouni, Broun, Man. New. Zeal. Col. p. 260 (1880).   Neu-Seeland.
   sec. Harold, Ann. Mus. Stor. Nat. Genova, Vol. 10, p. 92 (1877).
4. *S. calvus,* A. Schmidt, Stett. Ent. Zeit. p. 39 (1911).   Fernando Poò.
5. *S. cancellatus,* Bates, Biol. Centr. Amer. Col. Vol. 2 (2), p. 92 (1887).   Brasilien : Ega.
6. *S. candens,* Broun, Man. New Zeal. Col. p. 258 (1880).   Neu-Seeland.
7. *S. capitalis,* Fairmaire, Le Naturaliste. p. 238 (1883).   Neu-Britannia.   [bar.
8. *S. cavus,* A. Schmidt, Ann. Soc. Ent. Belg. Vol. 52, p. 41 (1908).   Kinchassa (Kongo), Sansi-
9. *S. communis* 1), Broun, Man. New Zeal. Col. p. 260 (1880).   Neu-Seeland.
10. *S. consonus,* A. Schmidt, Stett. Ent. Zeit. p. 40 (1911).   Kamerun, Insel S. Thomé.
11. *S. convexus,* Harold, Stett. Ent. Zeit. p. 38 (1880).   Columbien.
12. *S. corticalis,* Bates, Biol. Centr. Amer. Col. Vol. 2 (2), p. 93 (1887).   Brasilien : Ega.
13. *S. cossonoides,* Bates, ibidem, p. 93, t. 6, f. 22 (1887).   Mexiko, Guatemala, Pana-
14. *S. declivis.* A. Schmidt, Stett. Ent. Zeit. p. 41 (1911).   Fernando Poo.   [ma.
15. *S. dentipes,* Harold, Col. Hefte, Vol. 1. p. 80 (1867).   Brasilien.
16. *S. difficilis,* Harold, Ann. Mus. Stor. Nat. Genova, Vol. 10, p. 91 (1877).   Borneo.
17. *S. dilutus,* Fairmaire, Rev. Mag. Zool. (2), Vol. 1, p. 413 (1849).   Taïti.
18. *S. dynastoides,* Walker, Ann. Mag. Nat. Hist. (3), Vol. 2, p. 207 (1858).   Ceylon.
    — Taf. 3, Fig. 35.
    dynastoides, Harold, Ann. Mus. Stor. Nat. Genova, Vol. 10, p. 90 (1877).   Ceylon.
    pleurophoroides, Motschulsky, Bull. Soc. Nat. Mosc. Vol. 2, p. 464 (1863).   Ceylon.
19. *S. elongatulus,* Mac Leay, Proc. Linn. S. N. S. Wales (2), Vol. 3, p. 905   King-Sund.
    (1888).
    elongatulus, Blackburn, Proc. Roy. Soc. Victoria, Vol. 17, p. 158 (1904).
20. *S. eugastricus,* Harold, Col. Hefte, Vol. 5, p. 101 (1869).   Brasilien.

---

1) Die Zugehörigkeit zu dieser Gattung vielleicht zweifelhaft.

21. *S. exsculptus*, White, Voy. Ereb. et Terr. Col. p. 9 (1846).　　　　　　Neu-Seeland.
　　　exsculptus, Broun, Man. New Zeal. Col. p 258 (1880).
　　　　　　sec. Harold, Ann. Mus. Stor. Nat. Genova, Vol. 10, p. 92 (1877).
　　　distans, Sharp, Ent. M. Mag. Vol. 13, p. 70 (1876).　　　　　　Tairua.
　　　　　　sec. Broun, Man. New Zeal. Col. p. 258 (1880).
22. *S. falcatus*, A. Schmidt, Soc. Ent. Zürich, 1908-09, Vol. 23, p. 57 (1908).　Madagaskar.
23. *S. Gestroi*, A. Schmidt, Stett. Ent. Zeit. p. 42 (1911).　　　　　　Fernando Poo.
24. *S. grenadensis*, Arrow, Trans. Ent Soc. Lond. p. 514 (1903).　　　　Grenada.
25. *S. japonicus*, Waterhouse, ibidem, p. 93 (1875).　　　　　　　　Japan.
26. *S. laeviceps*, Harold, Ann. Mus. Stor. Nat Genova, Vol. 10, p. 90 (1877).　Borneo.
27. *S. madagascariensis*, A. Schmidt, Stett. Ent. Zeit. p. 43 (1911).　　　Madagaskar.
28. *S. mansuetus*, Blackburn, Proc. Roy. Soc. Victoria, Vol. 17, p. 175, 177　Westaustralien.
　　　(1904).
29. *S. marchionalis*, Harold, Ann. Mus. Stor. Nat. Genova, Vol. 10, p. 89 (1877).　Borneo.
30. *S. medilans*, Harold, Col. Hefte, Vol. 1, p. 81 (1867).　　　　　　Columbien.
31. *S. mendax*, Blackburn, Trans. Roy. Soc. S. Austral. Vol. 15, p. 36 (1892);　Victoria. Neu - Südwales,
　　　Proc. Roy. Soc. Victoria, Vol. 17, p. 176, 178 (1904).　　　　　Tasmanien.
32. *S. narae*, Lewis, Ann. Mag. Nat. Hist. (6), Vol. 16. p. 382 (1895).　　Japan.
33. *S. nitidicollis*, Mac Leay, Trans. Ent Soc. N. S. Wales, Vol. 2, p. 185　Australien.
　　　(1871).
　　　nitidicollis, Blackburn, Proc. Roy. Soc. Victoria, Vol. 17, p. 177 (1904).　Australien.
34. *S. occidentalis*, Mac Leay, Proc. Linn. Soc. N. S. Wales (2), Vol. 3,　King-Sund.
　　　p. 905 (1888).
　　　occidentalis, sec. Blackburn, Proc. Roy. Soc. Victoria, Vol. 17, p. 158 (1904).
35. *S. Ohausi*, A. Schmidt, Stett. Ent. Zeit. p. 45 (1911).　　　　　Joinville (S. Catharina).
36. *S. parallelus*, Harold, Col. Hefte, Vol. 1, p. 81 (1867). — **Taf. 3, Fig. 36.**　Columbien.
　　　parallelus, Bates, Biol. Centr. Amer. Col. Vol. 2 (2), p. 93 (1887).　Panama, Guatemala.
37. *S. Pascoei*, Sharp, Ent. M. Mag. Vol 13, p. 71 (1876).　　　　Neu-Seeland.
　　　Pascoei, Broun, Man. New Zeal. Col. p. 259 (1880).　　　　　Neu-Seeland.
38. *S. peregrinus*, Redtenbacher, Fauna Austr. p. 437 (1859).　　　　Amerika.
　　　peregrinus, Reitter, Tab. 3; Brünn, 30, p. 169.　　　　　　　Schönbrunn, Columbien.
39. *S. puncticollis*, Harold, Col. Hefte, Vol. 1, p. 81 (1867); C. R. Ann.　Brasilien, Botafogo.
　　　Soc. Ent. Belg. p. 98 (1876); ibidem (2), N° 32, p. 14 (1876).
40. *S. pygmaeus*, Harold, Ann. Mus. Stor. Nat. Genova, Vol. 10, p. 91 (1877).　Insel Key.
41. *S. rugicollis* 1), Mac Leay, Proc. Linn. Soc. N. S. Wales (2), Vol. 3,　King-Sund.
　　　p. 905 (1888).
42. *S. sternalis*, Blackburn, Proc. Roy. Soc. Victoria, Vol. 17, p. 176, 178　Neu-Südwales.
　　　(1904).
43. *S. sulcatus*, Harold, Col. Hefte, Vol. 5, p. 102 (1869).　　　　　Brasilien : Ega.
44. *S. suspectus*, Sharp, Ent. M. Mag. Vol. 13, p. 70 (1876).　　　　Neu-Seeland.
　　　suspectus, Broun, Man. New Zeal. Col. p. 259 (1880).　　　　　Neu-Seeland.
　　　　　　sec. Harold, Ann. Mus. Stor. Nat. Genova, Vol. 10, p. 92 (1877).
45. *S. verecundus*, A. Schmidt, Notes Leyd. Mus. Vol. 31, p. 121 (1909).　Mentawei.

4. Genus SIMOGONIUS, Harold

Simogonius. Harold, Col. Hefte, Vol. 8, p. 22 (1871).
Liparochirus. Péringuey, Trans. S. Afric. Philos. Soc. 1901-03, Vol. 12, Cat. p. 370, 435 (1901).

　　　Charaktere. -- Die Gattung ist an den umgeschlagenen Hinterwinkeln des Halsschildes leicht
kenntlich und dadurch von allen Gattungen abgesondert.

———————
1) Ob *Saprosites* zugehörig ?

Der Körper ist länglich-oval, gewölbt, schwarz gefärbt, glänzend, behaart, von mittlerer Grösse. Der Kopf ist gross, fast senkrecht herabgewölbt, dicht punktiert, ohne Höcker; der Clipeus ist vorn eingedrückt, deshalb erscheint er von oben gesehen gebuchtet, seitlich ist derselbe verrundet; die Wangen sind klein, winklig und vertieft.

Das Halsschild ist vorn kaum breiter als der Kopf, nach hinten bogig erweitert, an den Seiten gerandet, die Basis ist ohne Rand, die Oberfläche ist ziemlich dicht punktiert, die glatten Hinterwinkel sind nach unten umgeschlagen und liegen deshalb wagerecht, sie werden nach oben ziemlich scharfrandig begrenzt.

Das Schildchen ist klein, schmal-dreieckig.

Die Flügeldecken sind breiter als das Halsschild, sie haben eine scharfe, flachbogige Basis und scharfwinklige Schultern, nach hinten werden dieselben breiter, sie sind punktiert-gestreift, die Ränder werden deutlich von den Streifenpunkten angegriffen, besonders die seitlichen, die Zwischenräume sind gewölbt, vor der Spitze und an den Seiten deutlicher, sie sind punktiert und behaart.

Die Unterseite ist glänzend und sehr deutlich, mit Ausnahme der Schenkel, punktiert, letztere sind mehr vereinzelt und feiner, auch auf der hintern Hälfte der Metasternalplatte fehlen die Punkte, dieselbe ist mit feiner, tiefer Mittellinie versehen.

Die Hinterleibsringe sind unverbunden und behaart.

Die Vordertibien verbreitern sich nach vorn stark, am Vorderrande sind sie gerade abgeschnitten und haben neben der Einlenkung der Tarsen einen kurzen, kräftigen Enddorn, der Aussenrand ist dreizähnig.

Die Mittel- und Hintertibien lassen am Aussenrande Spuren schwacher Querleistchen erkennen, sie haben am Spitzenrande einen Borstenbesatz und zwei Enddorne.

Die Füsse sind fünfgliedrig, der Metatarsus ist verlängert.

Die Klauen sind normal.

Bei den Männchen ist das Metasternum in seiner ganzen Länge grubig vertieft, die Vertiefung ist ziemlich scharfrandig, besonders hinten, begrenzt.

Die Weibchen haben nur eine vertiefte Mittellinie.

Geographische Verbreitung der Art. — Erythrea, Abessinien, Sesse-Inseln, Südafrika.

1. *S. Beccarii*, Harold, Col. Hefte, Vol. 8, p. 22 (1871). — **Taf. 3, Fig. 37.**   Abessinien.
    simplex, Péringuey, Trans. S. Afric. Philos. Soc. 1901-03, Vol. 12, Cat.   Südrhodesia.
    p. 435 (1901).
    sec. A. Schmidt, Stett. Ent. Zeit. p. 49 (1911).

5. Genus DIALYTES, Harold

Dialytes. Harold, Col. Hefte, Vol. 5, p. 101 (1869).

Charaktere. — In diese Gattung sind einige Arten aufgenommen, die von der typischen Form bedeutend abweichen, aber trotz dieser Heterogenität der Arten stimmen alle im Bau der Vordertibien überein.

Der Körper ist länglich, stark konvex.

Der Kopf ist gross und breit, herabgebogen, mehr oder weniger gewölbt, punktiert, mit schwacher Stirnlinie, ohne Höcker; der Clipeus ist ausgerandet, daneben verrundet, stumpfwinklig oder mit Zähnchen; die Wangen sind deutlich; die Augen werden bei angezogenem Kopfe vollständig vom Vorderrande des Halsschildes bedeckt.

Der Thorax ist kaum breiter als der Kopf, er ist an den Seiten stark herabgebogen, breiter als lang, seitlich und an der Basis gerandet, die Hinterwinkel sind meistens abgestutzt und ausgerandet, die Oberfläche ist entweder mit Längsfurche vor dem Schildchen oder zwei schwächeren und kurzen Quereindrücken an den Seiten versehen oder auch ganz ohne Vertiefungen, ausserdem ist dieselbe meist deutlich punktiert.

Das Schildchen ist immer sichtbar, es ist klein, schmal-dreieckig.

Die Flügeldecken haben scharfe oder gedornte Schultern, sie sind an der Basis wenig ausgebuchtet, mehr gerade und wenig nach hinten verbreitert, immer deutlich punktiert-gestreift, die Zwischenräume sind eben, konvex oder auch gerippt.

Die Unterseite ist glänzend, immer deutlich punktiert, besonders die Mittelbrust.

Die Mittel- und Hintertibien sind mehr oder weniger zur Spitze verbreitert, sie zeigen zuweilen Spuren von Querleistchen, am Spitzenrande sind sie beborstet und haben daselbst zwei Enddorne.

Von den fünfgliedrigen Tarsen ist das erste Glied verlängert.

De Klauen sind normal.

Die Arten dieser Gattung sind immer mehr oder weniger glänzend, nie behaart.

Es sind mittelgrosse Tiere von schwarzer Farbe.

Geographische Verbreitung der Arten. — Japan, Nordamerika, Australien, Sumatra.

1. *D. foveatus*, A. Schmidt, Soc. Ent. Zürich, 1909-10, Vol. 24, p. 61 (1909).   Japan.
2. *D. granifer*, A. Schmidt, ibidem, p. 66 (1909).   Australien.
3. *D. monstrosus*, Harold, Ann. Mus. Stor. Nat. Genova, Vol. 10, p. 92 (1877);   Borneo.
   Notes Leyd. Mus. Vol. 2. p. 198 (1880). — **Taf 3, Fig. 38.**
   javanus, A. Schmidt, Deutsche Ent. Zeitschr. p. 569 (1907).   Java.
   sec. A. Schmidt, Soc. Ent. Zürich, 1909-10, Vol. 24, p. 61 (1909).
4. *D. striatulus*, Say, Journ. Acad. Nat. Sc. Philad. Vol. 5 (1). p. 192 (1825);   Vereinigte Staaten Nord-
   *Edit. Lec. Vol. 2. p. 295. — **Taf. 3, Fig. 39.**   amerika.
   striatulus, Horn, Trans. Amer. Ent. Soc. Vol. 3, p. 134 (1870); Vol. 14,   Mittelstaaten bis Kanada, Nord-
   p. 66 (1887).   osten der Vereinigte Staaten.
   cribrosus, Le Conte, Agass. Lake Super. p. 225 (1850).   Oberer-See.
5. *D. truncatus*, Melsheimer, Proc. Acad. Nat. Sc. Philad. 1844-45, Vol. 2,   Pennsylvanien.
   p 135 (1846).
   truncatus, Horn, Trans. Amer. Ent. Soc. Vol. 3. p. 133 (1870); Vol. 14,   Mittelstaaten, Kanada, Mary-
   p. 65 (1887).   land, Massachusetts.
   corvinus, Haldeman, Journ. Acad. Nat. Sc. Philad. (2), Vol. 1, p. 104 (1848).   Pennsylvanien.
   A. Schmidt, Aphodiinen-Zusammenst. Deutsche Ent. Zeitschr.
   Beih. p. 99, Anmerkung 1 (1907-08).
6. *D. Ulkei*, Horn, Trans. Amer. Ent. Soc. Vol. 5, p. 141 (1875); Vol 14,   Maryland.
   p. 66 (1887).
   sec. Wickham, The Canad. Entom. Vol. 26, p. 203 (1894).   Kanada.

6. Genus ODONTODERUS, Clouët

Odontoderus. Clouët, Ann. Soc. Ent. Belg. Vol. 44, p. 247 (1900).

Charaktere. — Der nach unten umgeschlagene Clipeus und die stumpfzähnigen Seiten des Halsschildes lassen diese Gattung leicht erkennen und scheiden sie von den andern Gattungen. In dem gezähnten Thorax nähert sich *Odontoderus* der Gattung *Odochilus* Harold, aber die Querleisten auf Kopf und Halsschild trennen beiden Gattungen genügend.

Der Körper ist länglich, mehr oder weniger konvex, gleichbreit, manchmal nach hinten verbreitert.

Der Kopf ist gross, breit, in der Mitte beulig aufgetrieben, zwischen den Augen mit deutlicher Stirnlinie, aber ohne Höcker; die Wangen sind deutlich; obwohl die Augen ziemlich gross sind, werden

sie doch bei angezogenem Kopfe vollständig von dem Vorderrande des Halsschildes bedeckt; der
Clipeus ist nach unten umgebogen, er ist glatt und glänzend und wird nach oben von einer scharfen
Leiste begrenzt, die sich bis zum Seitenrande verlängert und vor den Augen in denselben übergeht,
der übrige Teil des Kopfes ist sehr deutlich punktiert.

Das Halsschild ist so breit als der Kopf, nach hinten verschmälert, in der Vorderhälfte seitlich
schwach gebuchtet, dadurch bildet sich hinter der Mitte ein spitzes Zähnchen ; die Basis ist an der
Seite auch in ein spitzes, seitwärts stehendes Zähnchen ausgezogen ; hinter den Vorderwinkeln befindet
sich ein flacher Eindruck, der sich erst schräg nach hinten hinzieht und dann nach der Mitte wendet und
diese auch erreicht, dadurch erscheint die Vorderhälfte wulstig aufgetrieben, seitlich gesehen ist auch
vor dem Schildchen ein flacher Längseindruck bemerkbar, Seiten und Basis sind gerandet.

Das Schildchen fehlt bei keiner Art, es bildet ein sehr schmales und längliches Dreieck.

Die Flügeldecken sind meistens etwas breiter als der Hinterrand des Halsschildes, sie haben an
der Schulter einem kurzen Dorn, ihre Basis ist wenig ausgerandet, sie sind parallel oder hinten verbreitert, ihre Oberfläche ist punktiert-gestreift, die Zwischenräume sind entweder abwechselnd oder
gleichmässig rippenförmig.

Die Unterseite ist wie die Oberseite gefärbt und deutlich punktiert; die Hinterleibsringe sind
längsgerieft; das Pygidium ist frei, aber klein, mit oder ohne Längskiel.

Die Mittelhüften stehen weit auseinander, das Mesosternum zwischen ihnen ist stumpf gekielt;
das Metasternum ist in der Mitte breit grubig vertieft und mit Mittellinie.

Die Vorderschenkel sind breiter als die hinteren.

Die Vordertibien haben drei Aussenzähne und einen Enddorn neben der Tarseneinfügung;
Mittel- und Hintertibien sind an der Aussenseite ohne Querleisten, sie haben am Endrande einen
Borstenbesatz und zwei Enddorne.

Der Fuss ist fünfgliedrig, das erste Glied ist verlängert, das Klauenglied ist verhältnismässig kurz
und hat zwei hornige Klauen.

Es sind kleine Arten von 3 bis 4 mm Länge und mehr oder weniger dunkler, rotbrauner Farbe.

Geographische Verbreitung der Arten :

1. *O. Gestroi*, Clouët, Ann. Soc. Ent. Belg. p. 249 (1900).   Freetown.
2. *O. Oberthüri*, Clouët, ibidem, p. 250 (1900).   Freetown.
3. *O. spinicollis*, Harold, Col. Hefte, Vol. 8, p. 23 (1871).   Abessinien.
      spinicollis, Clouët, Ann. Soc. Ent. Belg. p. 249 (1900).

3. GRUPPE PSAMMOBIINA

Charaktere. — Hierher gehören zehn Gattungen, die in der Körperform sehr voneinander
abweichen.

Der Körper ist bald hochgewölbt, nach hinten stark verbreitert, bald mehr flach und parallel, die
Oberfläche desselben ist entweder glatt oder rauh punktiert, nackt oder beborstet.

Der Kopf ist im grössten Teile gekörnt; der Clipeus ausgerandet, seitlich mit Zähnchen versehen
oder abgerundet.

Das Halsschild ist breiter als der Kopf, es ist quer und seitlich stark herabgewölbt, Seiten- und
Basalrand sind meistens mit kurzen Borsten besetzt, die Oberfläche zeigt gewöhnlich mehrere Querwülste, die durch Furchen getrennt werden, seltener nur mit zwei schwachen seitlichen Eindrücken
oder nur einem wenig bemerkbaren quer vor dem Schildchen, eine Längsfurche fehlt selten.

Das sichbare Schildchen ist immer vorhanden.

Die Flügeldecken sind fast immer sehr deutlich punktiert-gestreift, die Zwischenräume können eben, konvex oder rippenförmig sein.

Die Unterseite ist mehr oder weniger deutlich punktiert und behaart.

Die Mittelhüften sind wenig voneinander enfernt.

Die Bauchsegmente sind unverbunden, das letzte ist klein, von den Flügeldecken nicht bedeckt.

Die Vorderschenkel sind bald stärker, bald schwächer als die übrigen.

Die Vordertibien haben an der Aussenseite drei deutliche Zähne, ihre Vorderkante verläuft immer schräg, neben den Tarsen ist ein Enddorn; die Mittel- und Hintertibien sind fast immer ohne Querleisten, ihr oberer Rand an der Aussenseite ist glatt oder gezähnt, der Apikalrand immer mit Borsten bekleidet, die beiden Enddorne sind spitz und schlank, häufiger aber breit, blattartig, mit stumpfer Spitze.

Die Füsse sind immer fünfgliedrig, die einzelnen Glieder schlank, oder nach der Spitze, wenigstens das erste, stark dreieckig erweitert.

Die Klauen sind meistens klein und unscheinbar, hornig oder haarförmig.

BESTIMMUNGS-TABELLE DER GATTUNGEN

1. *Fühler achtgliedrig, Kopf granuliert, Körper nach hinten stark verbreitert, Tarsen kurz, dreieckig erweitert* . . . . 1. Genus Phycochus, Broun.

1'. *Fühler neungliedrig.*

2. *Thorax seitlich verflacht mit dreizähnigem Aussenrande, Kopf mit Quer- und Längsleistchen, Halsschild mit kurzer Längsfurche und Querrippen, Flügeldecken mit Längsrippen* . . . . . 2. Genus Odochilus, Harold..

2'. *Thorax seitlich nicht verflacht, mit glattem Aussenrande, Kopf gekörnt, Halsschild mit Querfurchen oder kurzen Quereindrücken und einer Längsfurche, die zuweilen auch fehlt, es ist mehr oder weniger stark punktiert, Flügeldecken nie scharf gerippt.*

3. *Körper gedrungen, hoch gewölbt und meistens nach hinten verbreitert, Flügeldecken punktiert-gestreift, das erste Glied der Hintertarsen dreieckig verbreitert nach der Spitze, Enddorne der Hintertibien blattartig, abgestutzt, seltener schlanker und zugespitzt.*

4. *Klauen zwar klein, jedoch hornig, der achte Flügeldeckenstreifen meistens nicht oder wenig vorn verkürzt, Oberfläche meist wenig glänzend.*

5. *Halsschild mit mehreren Querfurchen und einer Längsfurche, zuweilen statt der ersteren nur zwei kurze seitliche Eindrücke, Thorax zerstreut und grob punktiert, erstes Glied der Hintertarsen vor der Spitze meist stark dreieckig erweitert, Enddorne stark verbreitert, blattartig, seltener schlank und zugespitzt* . . . . 3. Genus Psammobius, Heer.

5'. *Halsschild nur mit einer Längsfurche und zwei schwachen seitlichen Quereindrücken, ziemlich dicht punktiert, erstes Glied der Hinterfüsse und Enddorne schlank und spitz* . . . . 4. Genus Diastictus, Mulsant.

4'. *Klauen haarförmig, Halsschild ohne Längsfurche, hinter den Vorderwinkeln und vor der Basis eine schwache Quervertiefung, Hintertibien sehr kurz, Metatarsus dreieckig, Enddorne kurz und breit, abgestutzt, Oberfläche sehr glänzend, der achte Streifen vorn und hinten stark verkürzt.* . . . . 5. Genus Sicardia, Reitter.

3'. *Körper länglicher, parallel. Halsschild mit oder ohne Querfurchen, meist an den Seiten und der Basis bewimpert, erstes Glied der Hintertarsen länglich, nie stark dreieckig verbreitert, Enddorne schlank und spitz.*

6. *Kopf granuliert, Halsschild mit Querfurchen und abgekürzter Längsfurche, die Furchen fast immer dicht granuliert oder runzlig.*

7. *Oberfläche nicht behaart.*

8. *Letztes Abdominalsegment durch eine Furche von dem vorhergehenden getrennt.*

9. *Metatarsus parallel, fast den drei folgenden Gliedern an Länge gleich, so lang als das erste Glied der Mitteltarsen* . . . . 6. Genus RHYSSEMUS, Mulsant.

9'. *Metatarsus nicht parallel, kürzer als drei folgende Glieder, kürzer als der erste Glied der Mittelfüsse* . . . . 7. Genus RHYSSEMODES, Reitter.

8'. *Letztes Abdominalsegment nicht durch eine Furche getrennt.* . . 8. Genus RHYSSEMORPHUS, Clouët.

7'. *Oberfläche behaart.* . . . . 9. Genus TRICHIORHYSSEMUS, Clouët.

6' *Kopf granuliert, Thorax ohne Querfurchen, nur mit zwei seitlichen, schwachen Eindrücken und schwacher Längsfurche, vereinzelt grob punktiert* . . . . 10. Genus PLEUROPHORUS, Mulsant.

I. GENUS PHYCOCHUS, BROUN

Phycochus. Broun, Man. New Zeal. Col. Vol. 3, p. 770 (1886).

Charaktere. — Diese Gattung ist bisher nur durch wenige Arten vertreten, sie nimmt unter den Aphodiinen durch ihre achtgliedrigen Fühler eine gesonderte Stellung ein.

In der stark erhabenen, nach hinten verbreiterten Gestalt, der Form der Enddorne und Tarsen an den Hinterfüssen haben die Arten dieser Gattung die grösste Aehnlichkeit mit der typischen Form von *Psammobius.*

Die Oberfläche ist glänzend, unbehaart, schwarzbraun gefärbt.

Der Kopf ist breit, stark gewölbt, zum grössten Teil gekörnt, nur hinter der Stirnlinie glatt und glänzend, am Vorderrande ausgebuchtet und daneben gerundet; die Augen sind vollständig vom Vorderrande des Halsschildes bedeckt.

Das Halsschild ist quer, die Seiten sind deutlich gerandet, gewöhnlich mit Längseindruck vor dem Schildchen versehen, zuweilen aber auch mit schwachen, stark punktierten Quereindrücken geschmückt.

Das Schildchen ist klein, entweder von dreieckiger oder mehr rundlicher Gestalt.

Die Flügeldecken sind an der Basis so breit als das Halsschild, nach hinten erweitert und stark konvex, sie sind mehr oder weniger fein gestreift, zuweilen nur noch der Nahtstreif allein sichtbar, die Zwischenräume sind schmaler oder breiter, immer höchst fein punktiert.

Die Hinterschenkel sind stark verbreitert, sie stehen wie die Vorderschenkel dicht zusammen, die mittleren sind etwas voneinander entfernt.

Das Metasternum ist sehr kurz.

Der Hinterleib zeigt eine eigentümliche Form. Die Mitte desselben ist nämlich stark erhaben und wölbt sich nach den flach ausgebreiteten Seiten ab, die vollständig wagerecht daliegen; die einzelnen Segmente sind in der Mitte glatt, nur seitlich mit einigen grösseren, haartragenden Punkten besetzt.

Die Vordertibien haben aussen drei starke Zähne, ihr Enddorn ist schmal und spitz.

Die Mittel- und Hintertibien sind zur Spitze verbreitert, sie besitzen am Aussenrande zwei Querleisten, ihr Endrand tritt nach aussen stumpflappig hervor; die Enddorne der Hinterfüsse sind verbreitert, parallel und stumpf, der obere ist so lang als das erste Fussglied.

Die Tarsen sind fünfgliedrig und sehr kurz, das erste Glied ist nach aussen in eine dreieckige Spitze ausgezogen, die folgenden Glieder werden nach und nach schmaler, das letzte ist dünn und rundlich, nur wenig länger als das vorhergehende.

Die Klauen fehlen jedenfalls vollständig.

Hierher gehören kleine, meist dunkelbraun gefärbte Arten.

Geographische Verbreitung der Arten. — Australien.

1. *P. graniceps*, Broun, Man. New Zeal. Col. Vol. 3, p. 771 (1886).   Neu-Seeland.
   graniceps, Lea, Proc. Linn. Soc. N. S. Wales, Vol. 29, p. 90 (1904); Trans. Ent. Soc. Lond. p. 367 (1905).
2. *P. lobatus*, Broun, Man. New Zeal. Col. Vol. 5, p. 1114 (1893).   Neu-Seeland.
3. *P. sulcipennis*, Lea, Proc. Linn. Soc. N. S. Wales, Vol. 29, p. 89, t. 4,   Tasmanien.
   f. 10 (1904); Trans. Ent. Soc. Lond. p. 367 (1905).

2. GENUS ODOCHILUS, HAROLD

Odochilus. Harold, Ann. Mus. Stor. Nat. Genova, Vol. 10, p. 99 (1877).

Charaktere. — Diese Gattung ist nur durch eine Art vertreten. Dieselbe zeigt eine längliche, nach hinten verbreiterte, konvexe Gestalt, dadurch sowohl wie durch die Querwülste auf dem Thorax nähert sie sich den Arten aus der Gattung *Psammobius*, jedoch der verflachte Seitenrand des Halsschildes und die Skulptur des Kopfes verleihen ihr die Merkmale, die diese Gattung von allen anderen sofort unterscheidet und ihr Erkennen leicht ermöglichen.

Der Kopf ist stark herabgewölbt, breit, rauh punktiert und matt wie die ganze Oberfläche, am Hinterrande befinden sich vier etwas schrägstehende, kurze Leistchen, von denen die beiden vorderen, mehr in der Mitte befindlichen, nach hinten zusammenstossen und so einen nach vorn geöffneten Winkel bilden, vor diesem befinden sich zwei sehr schwache Längsleistchen, die nach vorn an eine scharfe, bis an den Seitenrand verlängerte Querleiste reichen, welche den Clipeus begrenzt, dieser ist an seinem Vorderrande abgestutzt, er ist glatt und glänzend. In diesem nach hinten durch eine Querleiste begrenzten Cļipeus ähnelt diese Gattung *Odontoderus,* doch ist bei letzterer Gattung der Clipeus nach unten umgeschlagen, also wagerecht liegend, während er bei *Odochilus* mehr senkrecht steht; die Wangen überragen die Augen sehr deutlich, letztere sind bei angezogenem Kopfe unsichtbar.

Das Halsschild ist breiter als der Kopf, nach hinten plötzlich verschmälert, die Seiten sind flach ausgebreitet und ihr Rand zeigt drei stumpfe Zähne, die Oberfläche hat drei scharfe und vor der Basis eine vierte, aber mehr stumpfe Querleiste, letztere ist in der Mitte unterbrochen, die Furchen zwischen ihnen sind rauh punktiert, Seiten und Basis sind ohne Rand, die letztere ist bis um die Hinterwinkel mit kurzen, gelblichen Borsten bewimpert.

Das Schildchen ist sehr klein und länglich.

Die Flügeldecken sind an der Basis viel breiter als das Halsschild daselbst, sie haben zehn Punktstreifen, die ungeraden Zwischenräume sind kielförmig und viel höher als die geraden, alle mit sehr kurzen, gelblichen Borsten besetzt.

Die Unterseite ist punktiert und behaart.

Die Mittelhüften stehen ziemlich dicht zusammen.

Die Vorderschenkel sind viel dicker als die anderen.

Die Tibien sind schlank und kaum zur Spitze verbreitert, die vorderen haben aussen drei Zähnchen und neben den Tarsen einen Enddorn, Mittel- und Hintertibien sind ohne Querleisten, haben aber zwei Enddorne.

Die Füsse sind fünfgliedrig, die Klauen normal.

Geographische Verbreitung der Art. — Die grossen Sunda-Inseln.

1. *O. syntheticus*, Harold, Ann. Mus. Stor. Nat. Genova, Vol. 10, p. 99 Celebes, Borneo, Java, Su-
   (1877). — **Taf. 3, Fig. 40.**   matra.

3. Genus PSAMMOBIUS, Heer

Psammobius. Heer, Fauna Col. Helvet. Vol. 1, p. 531 (1841).

Charaktere. — Mit den folgenden Gattungen hat *Psammobius* den gekörnten Kopf und die kurze Längsfurche auf dem Halsschilde gemein, die Form des Körpers aber, sowie die verbreiterten Hinterschenkel und die Form der Enddorne und des ersten Fussgliedes an den Hinterbeinen trennen sie.

Der Körper ist stark konvex, nach hinten verbreitert, mehr oder weniger glänzend und bräunlich gefärbt.

Der Kopf ist kappenförmig herabgebogen, deutlich gewölbt, zum grössten Teile rauh gekörnt, seltener nur punktiert; der Clipeus ist am Vorderrande deutlich eingeschnitten, die Ecken sind mehr oder weniger verrundet oder in spitze Zähnchen ausgezogen; die Wangen sind gross, sie überragen die Augen, letztere sind vom Vorderrande des Halsschildes fast ganz bedeckt.

Das Halsschild ist wenig breiter als der Kopf, immer stark quergewölbt, seine Seiten sind meist stark gerundet, nach hinten verschmälert, die Seiten und Basis sind gewöhnlich bewimpert, diese Wimperhaare sind entweder kurz, an der Spitze verdickt, oder länger und gleichstark, nur zuweilen fehlt die Bewimperung ganz; die Oberseite zeigt vier oder fünf deutliche Querwülste, die durch ebensoviele Querfurchen getrennt werden, oder nur zwei kurze, schwächere Eindrücke an den Seiten, der eine hinter den Vorderwinkeln, der andere mehr in der Mitte gelegen, immer jedoch ist eine kurze, mehr oder weniger vertiefte Längsfurche vor dem Schildchen vorhanden, die die hintern Querwülste scheidet; die Furche ist, sowie die Oberfläche, immer mehr oder weniger deutlich mit grösseren Punkten besetzt.

Das Schildchen ist klein, dreieckig.

Die Flügeldecken sind an der Basis gewöhnlich so breit als das Halsschild am Hinterrande, oft mit scharfer Basalkante und kleiner, zahnförmiger Schulter, sie verbreitern sich meistens sehr deutlich nach hinten und sind hier hochgewölbt, ihre Oberfläche ist deutlich punktiert-gestreift, die seitlichen Streifen erreichen nicht immer die Basis, die Zwischenräume sind flach oder konvex.

Die Unterseite ist glänzend und punktiert.

Die Hinterschenkel sind dicker als die andern, die mittlern stehen ziemlich dicht zusammen.

Die Vordertibien haben drei starke Aussenzähne und einen Enddorn neben den Tarsen.

Mittel- und Hintertibien sind an der Spitze stark erweitert, die letzten sind am obern Rande stark gezähnelt, am Spitzenrande beborstet und mit zwei Enddornen, dieselben sind gewöhnlich sehr stark verbreitert, am Ende schräg oder stumpf abgestutzt, seltener schlank und zugespitzt, sie sind aber stets länger als das erste Fussglied.

Das erste Tarsenglied der Hinterfüsse ist verlängert, an der Spitze nach aussen dreieckig erweitert, die drei folgenden Glieder sind sehr kurz, weniger stark dreieckig, das fünfte Glied trägt zwei sehr kleine, aber hornige Klauen.

Die Männchen sind durch längeren und stärkeren Enddorn an den Vordertibien, sowie durch stark vertiefte Hinterbrust ausgezeichnet.

Geographische Verbreitung der Arten. — Die Gattung kommt in allen Gebieten vor. .

1. *P. aegialioides*, Haldeman, Journ. Acad. Nat. Sc. Philad. (2), Vol. 1,   Mittelstaaten.
 p. 107 (1848).
    aegialioides, Horn, Trans. Amer. Ent. Soc. Vol. 3, p. 292 (1871); Vol. 14,   Südstaaten, Nordamerika.
      p. 74 (1887).
2. *P. ainu*, Lewis, Ann. Mag. Nat. Hist. (6), Vol. 16, p. 384 (1895).   Japan.
3. *P. ambiguus*, Fall, Trans. Amer. Ent. Soc. Vol. 33, p. 241 (1907).   El Paso.
4. *P. antipodum*, Panvel, Rev. d'Ent. Caen, Vol. 22, p. 366 (1903).   Neu-Kaledonien.
5. *P. australicus*, Blackburn, Proc. Roy. Soc. Victoria, Vol. 17, p. 173 (1904).   Neu-Südwales.
6. *P. basalis*, Mulsant & Rey, Hist. Nat. Col. France, Lamell. p. 396 (1871).   Provence.
    basalis, Reitter, Tab. p. 23; Brünn, 3o, p. 161.   Südfrankreich.
      sec. Semenow, Rev. Russe d'Ent. p. 37 (1902).   Krim.
      sec. Müller, München. Kol. Zeitschr. Vol. 2, p. 317 (1904).   Oesterreichisch. Küstenland.
7. *P. caelatus**, Le Conte, Pacific R. R. Rep. App. 1, p. 42 (1857).
    caelatus, Horn, Trans. Amer. Ent. Soc. Vol. 3, p. 292 (1871); Vol. 14,   Kalifornien, San Francisco.
      p. 97 (1887).
8. *P. catenatus*, Fauvel, Rev. d'Ent. Caen, Vol. 22, p. 366 (1903).   Neukaledonien.
9. *P. clypeatus**, Say. Long's Second Exped. p. 228; Edit. Lec. Vol. 1,
 p. 183.
    clypeatus, Horn, Trans. Amer. Ent. Soc. Vol. 14, p. 98 (1887).   Nordwestl. Vereinigte Staaten.
10. *P. comis*, Lewis, Ann. Mag. Nat. Hist. (6), Vol. 16, p. 384 (1895).   Japan.
11. *P. convexus*, Waterhouse, Trans. Ent. Soc. Lond. p. 94 (1875).   Japan
12. *P. cruentus*, Harold, Berl. Ent. Zeitschr. p. 282 (1867).   Mendoza.
    cruentus, Burmeister. Stett. Ent. Zeit. p. 407 (1877).   Mendoza.
    bidens, Horn. Trans. Amer. Ent. Soc. Vol. 3, p. 293 (1871); Vol. 14,   Südstaaten, Georgia, Florida.
      p. 94 (1887). .
      sec. Clouët, Bull. Soc. Ent. Fr. p. 188 (1898).
13. *P. culminatus*, Bates, Biol. Centr. Amer. Col. Vol. 2 (2), p. 103 (1887).   Mexiko. ʹ
14. *P. evanidus*, Péringuey, Trans. S. Afric. Philos. Soc 1901-03, Vol. 12,   Natal.
 Cat. p. 446 (1901).
15. *P. generosus*, Reitter, Tab. p. 23; Brünn, 3o, p. 161.   Ordubad.
16. *P. Gestroi*, Clouët, Ann. Soc. Ent. Belg. p. 13 (1900).   Birma.
17. *P. hydropicus*, Horn, Trans. Amer. Ent. Soc. Vol. 14, p. 97 (1887).   Georgia.
18. *P. indefensus*, A. Schmidt, Soc. Ent. Zürich, 1909-10, Vol. 24, p. 60 (1909).   Valparaiso.
19. *P. indicus*, Harold. Ann. Mus. Stor. Nat. Genova, Vol. 10, p. 100 (1877).   Celebes.
    sculpticollis, Fairmaire, Ann. Soc. Ent. Belg. p. 370 (1897).   Madagaskar.
      sec. Clouët, Ann. Soc Ent. Fr. p. 240 (1898).
20. *P. inscitus*, Walker, Ann. Mag. Nat. Hist. (3), Vol. 2, p. 207 (1858).   Ceylon.
21. *P. integer*, Bates, Biol. Centr. Amer. Col. Vol. 2 (2), p. 104 (1887).   Mexiko, Vera Cruz.
22. *P. interruptus**, Say, Boston Journ. Vol. 1 (2), p. 178 (1835); Edit. Lec.   Indiana.
 Vol. 2, p. 651.
    interruptus, Horn, Trans. Amer. Ent. Soc. Vol. 3, p. 292 (1871); Vol. 14,   Mittelstaaten, Dakota, Texas
      p. 95 (1887).
23. *P. japonicus*, Harold, Deutsche Ent. Zeitschr. p. 69 (1878).   Japan.
24. *P. laevicollis*, Klug, Symb. Phys. Vol. 5, t. 42, f. 10 (1845).   Arabien.
    laevicollis, Clouët, Ann. Ent. Soc. Belg. p. 13 (1900).   Abessinien, Bogos.
    desertorum, Fairmaire, Ann. Soc. Ent. Fr. p. 482 (1868).   Biskra.
      Marseul, L'Abeille, Vol. 9, p. 269 (1872-73).   Biskra.
      sec. d'Orbigny, ibidem, Vol. 28, p. 256 (1896).
    pallidus, Reitter, Tab. p. 23; Brünn, 3o, p. 161.   Syrien.
      sec. Clouët, Bull. Ent. Soc. Fr. p. 372 (1896).
    Chobauti, d'Orbigny, ibidem, p. 148 (1898).   Algier.
      sec. Clouët, Ann. Soc. Ent. Belg. p. 13 (1900).

25. *P. laevipennis**, Costa, Ann. Accad. Nat. Napoli, Vol. 2, p. 18 (1844).　　Italien.
　　laevipennis, Reitter, Tab. p. 22; Brünn, 30, p. 160.　　Südeuropa, Nordafrika, Syrien,
　　plicicollis, Erichson, Naturg. Ins. Deutschl. Vol. 3, p. 916 (1848).　　Sardinien.　[Transkaukasien.
　　rugicollis, Erichson, ibidem, p. 916 (1848).　　Italien, Euphrat.
　　　　sec. Weise, Deutsche Ent. Zeitschr. p. 192 (1878).
　　ciliatus, Küster, Käf. Europ. Vol. 18, p. 51.　　Südspanien.
　　accentifer, Mulsant & Rey, Opusc. d'Ent. Vol. 9, p. 172 (1859).　　Frankreich.
　　scutellaris, Mulsant & Wachanru, ibidem, p. 187 (1859).　　Südfrankreich.
　　　　sec. Reitter, Tab. p. 22; Brünn, 30, p. 160.
　　insculptus, Mulsant, Hist. Nat. Col. France, Lamell. p. 398 (1871).　　Provence.
　　planipennis, Reitter, Tab. p. 224; Brünn, 31, p. 103.　　Südeuropa.
　　　　sec. d'Orbigny, L'Abeille, Vol. 28, p. 255 (1896).
　　　　sec. Clouët, Bull. Ent. Soc. Fr. p. 373 (1896).

26. *P. micros*, Bates, Biol. Centr. Amer. Col. Vol. 2 (2), p. 103 (1887).　　Guatemala.

27. *P. modestus*, Péringuey, Trans. S. Afric. Philos. Soc. 1901-03, Vol. 12,　　Natal.
　　Cat. p. 446 (1901).

28. *P. nocturnus*, Reitter, Tab. p. 22; Brünn, 30, p. 160.　　Beirut.
　　nocturnus, d'Orbigny, L'Abeille, Vol. 28, p. 255 (1896).　　Tunis, Algier.

29. *P. obscurior*, Blackburn, Proc. Roy. Soc. Victoria, Vol. 17, p. 173 (1904).　　Süd- und Westaustralien.

30. *P. placidus*, A. Schmidt, Stett. Ent. Zeit. p. 38 (1911).　　Argentina.

31. *P. plicatulus*, Fairmaire, Rev. d'Ent. Caen, Vol. 11, p. 95 (1892).　　Obock.

32. *P. porcicollis*, Illiger, Mag. Vol. 2, p. 195 (1803). — **Taf. 3, Fig. 41.**　　Portugal.
　　porcicollis, Mulsant, Hist. Nat. Col. France, Lamell. p. 403 (1871).　　Südfrankreich.
　　　　Reitter, Tab. p. 21; Brünn, 30, p. 159.　　Südeuropa, Nordafrika, Syrien
　　　　d'Orbigny, L'Abeille, Vol. 28, p. 254 (1896).　　Mitteleuropa, Madeira, Kana-
　　var. rugosulus, Mulsant, Hist. Nat. Col. France, Lamell. p. 323 (1842).　　Südfrankreich.　[rische Inseln.

33. *P. quinqueplicatus*, Horn, Trans. Amer. Ent. Soc. Vol. 3, p. 292 (1871);　　Arizona, Westtexas.
　　Vol. 14, p. 95 (1887).
　　quinqueplicatus; sec. Bates, Biol. Centr. Amer. Col. Vol. 2 (2), p. 103 (1887).　　Mexiko.

34. *P. rotundipennis*, Reitter, Tab. p. 21; Brünn, 30, p. 159.　　Andalusien.
　　rotundicollis, d'Orbigny, L'Abeille, Vol. 28, p. 254 (1896).　　Algier.

35. P *scabrifrons**, Walker, List Coleopt. coll. Lord, p. 12 (1871).　　Kairo.

36. *P. Schwarzi*, Linell, Proc. U. S. Nat. Mus. Vol. 18, p. 721 (1896).　　Florida.

37. *P. subciliatus*, Harold, Col. Hefte, Vol. 5, p. 103 (1869).　　Südafrika.
　　subciliatus, Clouët, Ann. Soc. Ent. Belg. p. 12 (1900).　　Südafrika.

38. *P. sulcicollis*, Illiger, Mag. Vol. 1, p. 20 (1802).　　Königsberg.
　　sulcicollis, Sturm, Deutschl. Ins. Vol. 1, p. 173, t. 15, f. C (1805).　　Oesterreich.
　　　　Erichson, Naturg. Ins. Deutschl. Vol. 3, p. 915 (1848).　　Deutschland.
　　　　Mulsant, Hist. Nat. Col. France, Lamell. p. 401 (1871).　　Frankreich.
　　　　Reitter, Tab. p. 21; Brünn, 30, p. 159.　　Nord- und Mitteleuropa, Kauka-
　　asper, Paykull, Fauna Suec. Vol. 1, p. 29 (1798).　　Schweden.　[sus.
　　costatus, Stierlin, Bull. Soc. Nat. Mosc. Vol. 4, p. 489 (1863).　　Sarepta.
　　　　sec. d'Orbigny, L'Abeille, Vol. 28, p. 255 (1896).
　　var. canaliculatus, Mulsant, Hist. Nat. Col. France, Lamell. p. 321 (1842).　　Frankreich.

39. *P. veraecrucis*, Bates, Biol. Centr. Amer. Col. Vol. 2 (2), p. 103 (1887).　　Mexiko.

40. *P. Zietzi*, Blackburn, Trans. Roy. Soc. S. Austral. Vol. 19, p. 32 (1895);　　Südaustralien.
　　**Trans. Roy. Soc. Victoria, p. 172 (1904); Proc. Roy. Soc. Vic-
　　toria, Vol. 17, p. 174 (1904).

4. Genus DIASTICTUS, Mulsant

Diastictus. Mulsant, Hist. Nat. Col. France, Lamell. p. 318 (1842).

Charaktere. — In der gedrungenen, stark nach hinten verbreiterten Gestalt ist diese Gattung der vorigen ähnlich, das Halsschild ist aber stets ohne Querwülste über die ganze Scheibe, und das erste Glied der Hintertarsen ist nie stark dreieckig erweitert.

Der Kopf ist stark herabgebogen und gewölbt, vor der Stirnlinie gekörnt, hinter derselben rauh punktiert; der Clipeus ist eingeschnitten, die Ecken sind stumpf verrundet; die Wangen sind gross, sie überragen die Augen, die bei angezogenem Kopfe durch den Vorderrand des Halsschildes bedeckt werden.

Das Halsschild ist wenig breiter als der Kopf, seitlich ist dasselbe stark herabgewölbt, nach hinten gerundet erweitert, die Seiten und Basis sind gerandet, aber nicht mit Borsten besetzt, die ganze Oberfläche ist dicht und stark punktiert, vor dem Schildchen befindet sich eine Längsfurche, und an den Seiten sind zwei schwache Eindrücke, der vordere hinter den Vorderwinkeln, der hintere mehr in der Mitte.

Das Schildchen ist klein, schmal-dreieckig.

Die Flügeldecken sind vorn so breit als der Hinterrand des Halsschildes, an der Basis wenig ausgerandet, nach hinten verbreitert, an der Schulter schwach gedornt, die Oberfläche zeigt zehn stark punktierte Streifen, die durch konvexe Zwischenräume getrennt werden, die seitlichen derselben erreichen nicht ganz die Basis.

Die Unterseite ist mehr glänzend, der Hinterleib nur schwach punktiert.

Die Hinterschenkel sind schmäler als die vorderen.

Die Mittelhüften stehen ziemlich dicht zusammen.

Die Vordertibien sind wie gewöhnlich nach der Spitze verbreitert, ihr Aussenrand ist mit drei Zähnen, und der innere Spitzenwinkel neben der Tarsen mit einem Enddorn versehen.

Die Mittel- und Hintertibien sind ohne Querleisten, sie haben aber am obern Rande schwache, bedornte Kerbzähnchen, am Spitzenrande einen Borstenbesatz und zwei nicht verbreiterte und zugespitzte Enddorne.

Die Füsse sind fünfgliedrig, das erste Glied ist länger als das folgende, nach der Spitze ebenfalls verbreitert, aber nach beiden Seiten gleichmässig, während es bei *Psammobius* nur auf der äussern Seite dreieckig ausgezogen ist.

Die Männchen zeichnen sich durch breiteren Enddorn an den Vordertibien und stark vertiefte Metasternalplatte aus.

Geographische Verbreitung der Art. — Europa.

1. *D. vulneratus*, Sturm, Deutsche Ins. Vol. 1, p. 175, t. 15, f. D (1805). — Wien.
   Taf. 3, Fig. 42.

vulneratus, Gyllenhal, Ins. Suec. Vol. 4. p. 244 (1827).		
Heer, Fauna Col. Helvet. Vol. 1, p. 531 (1841).	Schweiz.	
Erichson, Naturg. Ins. Deutsch. Vol. 3, p. 914 (1848).	Deutschland.	
Reitter, Tab. p. 29; Brünn, 30, p. 167.	Europa.	
sec. Newbery, Ent. M. Mag. (2). Vol. 13, p. 253 (1902).	England.	
semipunctatus*, Bonelli, Spec. Fauna Subalp. p. 155, t. 1, f. 2 (1812).		
sabuleti, Mulsant, Hist. Nat. Col. France, Lamell. p. 319 (1842).	Frankreich.	
var. *latitans*, Mulsant, ibidem, p. 319 (1842).	Frankreich.	

5. GENUS SICARDIA, REITTER

Sicardia. Reitter, Deutsche Ent. Zeitschr. p. 318 (1896).

Charaktere. — Diese Gattung wurde auf eine Art gegründet, die in der ganzen Körperform, dem gekörnten Kopfe und dem Bau der Beine sich den beiden vorhergegangenen Gattungen anschliesst, aber durch andere Skulptur des Halsschildes und die haarförmigen Klauen entfernt.

Der Körper ist robust, konvex, nach hinten verbreitert, stark glänzend, rotbraun gefärbt.

Der Kopf ist herabgebogen, gewölbt, vorn ausgerandet und daneben verrundet, ohne Erhebungen, mit vertiefter Stirnlinie zwischen den Augen, vor derselben ist er deutlich gekörnt, hinter ihr nur punktiert.

Das Halsschild ist von der Breite der Flügeldecken, an den Seiten und der Basis fein gerandet, aber nicht mit Borsten besetzt, hinter den Vorderwinkeln und vor dem Schildchen, hier aber nur bei seitlicher Ansicht, bemerkt man einen Eindruck; Quer- und Längsfurchen fehlen, die Oberseite ist sehr fein und zerstreut punktiert.

Das Schildchen ist klein, länglich-dreieckig..

Die Flügeldecken sind vor der Spitze hochgewölbt, mit deutlichen Punktstreifen versehen, von denen der achte sowohl vor der Basis wie auch vor der Spitze stark verkürzt ist, die Zwischenräume sind konvex.

Die Vordertibien haben drei Aussenzähne und einen Enddorn neben den Tarsen.

Die Hinterschenkel sind stark verbreitert, ebenso auch die Hinterschienen, an den letzteren fehlen die Querleisten, sie haben am untern Endrande einen Borstenbesatz und zwei stark verbreiterte, am Ende abgestutzte Enddorne.

Die Tarsen sind fünfgliedrig, die Glieder der Hintertarsen sind sehr kurz, das erste ist dreieckig erweitert.

Die Klauen sind klein und haarförmig.

Hierher gehört eine kleine Art von 3 mm Länge.

Geographische Verbreitung der Art. — Tunis.

1. *S. psammodiformis*, Reitter, Deutsche Ent. Zeitschr. p. 318 (1896).   Tunis.
   psammodiiformis, Clouët, Ann. Soc. Ent. Belg. p. 14 (1900).

6. Genus RHYSSEMUS, Mulsant

Rhyssemus. Mulsant, Hist. Nat. Col. France, Lamell. p. 314 (1842).

Charaktere. — Diese und die drei folgenden Gattungen stehen in der Mitte zwischen *Psammobius* und *Pleurophorus*. Mit den ersteren haben sie die Skulptur des Kopfes und Halsschildes, mit den letzteren die Form des Körpers und den Bau der Beine gemein.

Der Körper ist schlank, mehr parallel, nach der Spitze nicht stark verbreitert und gewölbt; die Farbe der Arten variiert zwischen rotbraun und schwarz, meistens sind sie einfarbig, nur bei den dunklen Arten sind zuweilen Clipeus und Vorderwinkel des Halsschildes heller, sehr selten ist die Oberfläche zweifarbig (*R. bicolor* Clouët); sie sind meistens glänzend, seltener mehr oder weniger matt, immer aber unbehaart.

Der Kopf ist stark herabgewölbt, der vordere Teil desselben ist stärker oder feiner, gedrängter oder zerstreuter gekörnt, der Hinterkopf gewöhnlich nur punktiert und mit zwei oder vier kleinen, länglichen, schräggestellten Tuberkeln versehen; der Clipeus ist immer ausgerandet, daneben abgerundet oder zugespitzt; die Wangen sind gross; die Augen bleiben bei angezogenem Kopfe unsichtbar.

Der Thorax ist immer breiter als lang, an den Seiten stark herabgewölbt, von oben gesehen in der Mitte erweitert, bald stärker, bald schwächer nach vorn und hinten verjüngt, der Seitenrand ist entweder glatt oder fein gekerbt und wie die Basis gerandet, beide sind immer mit Borsten bewimpert, die Hinterwinkel sind verrundet und oft nach der Basis zu schwach ausgerandet, die Oberfläche ist immer mit Querwülsten, die den Seitenrand nicht erreichen, besetzt; dieselben sind entweder glatt oder durch grobe Punkte zerstochen oder mehr oder weniger in einzelne Tuberkeln aufgelöst, besonders die zwei oder drei hinteren, diese sind immer in der Mitte durch eine Längsfurche, seltener alle unterbrochen (*R. interruptus* Reitter), die zwischen ihnen gelegenen Querfurchen und die Längsfurche sind entweder punktiert, gerunzelt oder granuliert.

Das Schildchen ist klein und dreieckig.

Die Flügeldecken sind meistens etwas breiter als die Halsschildbasis, nach hinten nur schwach verbreitert, mässig gewölbt, ihre Schultern meistens mit einem Dorn bewaffnet, die Basis zeigt eine Randung, die Oberfläche ist von zehn Punktstreifen durchzogen, deren seitliche fast immer die Basis erreichen, die Zwischenräume sind konvex, gerippt, oder letztere wechseln mit flachen ab, dieselben sind meistens durch kleine Erhabenheiten rauh skulptiert.

Die Unterseite ist glänzend bis auf das durch dichtere Punktierung matte Mesosternum; die Mittelhüften sind wenig getrennt; das Metasternum ist in der Mitte gefurcht und mehr oder weniger vertieft, es ist glatt, punktiert oder gekörnt, manchmal auch kurz beborstet; die Hinterleibsringe zeigen gewöhnlich in der Mitte eine gekerbte Querlinie mit kurzer Borstenreihe oder ohne dieselbe, seltener ist die ganze Breite punktiert, das letzte Segment ist immer von den vorhergehenden durch eine tiefe, seitlich verkürzte Furche geschieden.

Die Vorderschenkel sind kurz und dick, dicht punktiert und behaart, die mittlern und hintern meistens deutlich schmaler und länger, mehr einzeln punktiert und behaart.

Die Vordertibien sind aussen dreizähnig und haben neben der Einlenkung der Tarsen einen Enddorn.

Die Mittel- und Hintertibien sind zur Spitze wenig verbreitert, aussen ohne Querleisten, nur einzeln beborstet, am Endrande mit dichtem Borstenbesatz und zwei spitzen Enddornen.

Die Füsse haben fünf Glieder, das erste Glied ist verlängert und schlank, meist so lang als die drei folgenden zusammen, der obere Enddorn ist so lang als das erste Glied oder kürzer, selten länger.

Die Klauen sind hornig.

Ueber die Lebensweise und die Entwicklung der Arten dieser Gattung und der folgenden sind bisher keinerlei sichere Beobachtungen gemacht worden; man nimmt an, dass sie sich teils von vegetabilischen Stoffen, teils tierischen, mehr trockenen Exkrementen ernähren.

Die sexuellen Unterschiede beruhen in der Form des Enddorns der Vordertibien, der beim Weibchen schlanker und länger, nie nach innen gebogen ist, und in der Form der Metasternalplatte, die beim Männchen mehr und breiter vertieft ist.

Geographische Verbreitung der Arten. — Die Gattung ist in allen Gebieten vertreten.

1. *R. algiricus*, Lucas, Explor. Algér. p. 266, t. 24, f. 3 (1846). — **Taf. 3, Fig. 43.** — Algier. [Kaukasus.
   algiricus, Reitter, Tab. p. 28 ; Brünn, 30, p. 166. — Morea, Andalusien, Marokko,
   Clouët, Monogr. Mém. Soc. Ent. Belg. Vol. 8, p. 89 (1901). — Südfrankreich, Griechenl., Spa-
   Marqueti, Reiche, Catal. Grenier, p. 76 (1863). — Béziers. [nien, Belgien.
   sec Clouët, Monogr. Mém. Soc. Ent. Belg. Vol. 8, p. 120 (1901).
   Mulsant, Hist. Nat. Col. France, Lamell. p. 382 (1871). — Béziers.
   Reitter, Tab. p. 27 ; Brünn, 30, p. 165. — Südfrankreich.
   meridionalis, Reitter, Deutsche Ent. Zeitschr. p. 391 (1890). — Morea, Algier, Marokko.
   sec Reitter, Tab. p. 28 ; Brünn, 30, p. 166.
   var. *caucasicus*, Clouët, Monogr. Mém. Soc. Ent. Belg. Vol. 8, p. 91 (1901). — Kaukasus.
2. *R. Alluaudi*, Clouët, Monogr. p. 53 (1901). — Madagaskar.
3. *R. atramentarius*, Péringuey, Trans. S. Afric. Philos. Soc. 1901-03, Vol. 12, Cat. p. 443 (1901). — Kapkolonie, Natal.
4. *R. Aurivilliusi*, Clouët, Monogr. Mém. Soc. Ent. Belg. Vol. 8, p. 55 (1901). — Kongo.
5. *R. Bedeli*, Clouët, ibidem, p. 94 (1901). — Algier.
6. *R. berytensis*, Marseul, L'Abeille, Vol. 16, p. 57, Nouv. et Fait. (2) 14-15 (1878). — Beirut.
   berytensis, Reitter, Tab. p. 27 ; Brünn, 30, p. 165. — Syrien.
   Clouët, Monogr. Mém. Soc. Ent. Belg. Vol. 8, p. 46 (1901). — Akbes, Jaffa, Persien.

7. *R. bicolor*, Clouët, Monogr. Mém. Soc. Ent. Belg. Vol. 8, p. 76   Kongo.
   (1901).
      var. inurbanus, A. Schmidt, Aphodiinen-Zusammenst. Deutsche Ent. Zeitschr.   Kongo.
         Beih. p. 113 (1907-08).
8. *R. biovatus,* Clouët, Monogr. Mém. Soc. Ent. Belg. Vol. 8, p. 48 (1901).   Madagaskar.
9. *R. birmensis,* Clouët, ibidem. p. 79 (1901).   Birma.
10. *R. Blackburnei,* Clouët, ibidem. p. 50 (1901).   Adelaïde.
11. *R. caelatus,* Péringuey, Trans. S. Afric. Philos. Soc. 1901-03, Vol. 12,   Südafrika.
    Cat. p. 445 (190:).
12. *R. californicus,* Horn, Trans. Amer. Ent. Soc. Vol. 3, p. 290 (1871);   Kalifornien.
    Vol. 14, p. 89 (1887).
      californicus, Clouët, Monogr. Mém. Soc. Ent. Belg. Vol. 8, p. 72 (1901).   Arizona, Georgia, Florida.
13. *R. capensis,* Clouët, ibidem,. p. 75 (1901).   Kap der guten Hoffnung.
14. *R. carinatipennis,* Péringuey, Trans. S. Afric. Philos. Soc. 1901-03,   Südrhodesia.
    Vol. 12, Cat. p. 443 (1901).
15. *R. coluber,* Mayet, Bull. Soc. Ent. Fr. p. 89 (1887).   Tunis.
      coluber, d'Orbigny, L'Abeille, Vol. 28, p. 250 (1896).   Algier, Obock.
      Clouët, Monogr. Mém. Soc. Ent. Belg. Vol. 8, p. 70 (1901).   Arabien.
      laesifrons, Fairmaire, Rev. d'Ent. Caen. Vol. 11, p. 94 (1892)   Obock.
      caesoides, Reitter, Ent. Nachr. p. 184 (1894).   Algier.
         sec. Reitter, Wien. Ent. Zeit. p. 312 (1894).
16. *R. congolanus,* Clouët, Monogr. Mém. Soc. Ent. Belg. Vol. 8, p. 86   Kongo.
    (1901).
17. *R. exaratus,* Marseul, L'Abeille, Vol. 16, p. 57, Nouv. et Fait. (2),   Aegypten.
    14-15 (1878).
      exaratus, Clouët, Monogr. Mém. Soc. Ent. Belg. Vol. 8, p. 100 (1901).   Obock, Djibouti.
      var. asperocostatus, Fairmaire, Rev. d'Ent. Caen, p. 94 (1892).   Obock.
      Clouët, Monogr. Mém. Soc. Ent. Belg. Vol. 8, p. 101 (1901).
18. *R. Fairmairei,* Clouët, ibidem, p. 111 (1901)   Diégo Suarez.
19. *R. Feae,* Clouët, ibidem, p. 91 (1901).   Birma.
20. *R. germanus,* Linné, Syst. Nat. (ed. 12), Vol. 1 (2), p. 566 (1767). Deutschland.
      germanus, Mulsant, Hist. Nat. Col. France, Lamell. p. 387 (1871). Frankreich.
      Harold, Col. Hefte, Vol. 8, p. 26 (1871).   Nordabessinien.
      Reitter, Tab. p. 27; Brünn, 30, p. 165.   Europa, Kaukasus, Kleinasien.
      Clouët, Monogr. Mém. Soc. Ent. Belg. Vol. 8, p. 115 (1901).   Afrika, Asien.
      Péringuey, Trans. S. Afric. Philos. Soc. 1901-02, Vol. 12, Cat.   Kapkolonie.
         p. 444 (1901).
         sec. Newbery, Ent. M. Mag. (2), Vol. 13, p. 254 (1902).   England.
      asper, Fabricius, Syst. Ent. p. 20 (1775).   Europa.
      Herbst, Fuessly, Archiv. Vol. 4, p. 8, t. 19, f. 10 (1783).   Berlin.
      Erichson, Naturg. Ins. Deutschl. Vol. 3, p. 910 (1848).   Deutschland.
         sec. Fairmaire, Ann. Soc. Ent. Fr. p. 34 (1871).   Madagaskar.
      aspericeps, Chevrolat, Rev. Mag. (2). Vol. 3, p. 266 (1861).   Algier.
      Mulsant, Hist. Nat. Col. France, Lamell. p. 391 (1871).   Algier.
      parallelus, Reitter, Tab. p. 28; Brünn, 30, p. 166.   Algier, Marokko.
         sec. d'Orbigny, L'Abeille, Vol. 28, p. 252 (1896).
      geminatus, Reitter, Deutsche Ent. Zeitschr. p. 390 (1890); Tab. p. 28;   Griechenland, Turkestan, Kau-
         Brünn, 30, p. 166.   kasus, Turkmenien.
         sec. Clouët, Monogr. Mém. Soc. Ent. Belg. Vol. 8, p. 121 (1901).
      obsoletus, Rey, L'Echange, p. 171 (1890).
         sec. Reitter, Cat. Eur. Col. p. 716 (1906).
      var. rufipes, Mulsant, Hist. Nat. Col. France, Lamell. p. 314 (1842).   Frankreich.
21. *R. Gestroi,* Clouët, Monogr. Mém. Soc. Ent. Belg. Vol. 8, p. 105   Nubien.
    (1901).
22. *R. Godarti,* Mulsant, Hist. Nat. Col. France, Lamell. p. 385 (1871). Narbonne, Béziers.
      Godarti, Reitter, Tab. p. 25; Brünn, 30, p. 163.   Frankreich.
      Clouët, Monogr. Mém. Soc. Ent. Belg. Vol. 8, p. 41 (1901).   Marokko, Algier.
      corrugatulus, Reitter, Tab. p. 26; Brünn, 30, p. 164   Marokko.
         sec. Clouët, Monogr. Mém. Soc. Ent. Belg. Vol. 8, p. 120
         (1901).

costipennis. Fairmaire, i. litt.?
 Reitter, Ent. Nachr. p. 183 (1894).   Marokko.
  sec. d'Orbigny, L'Abeille, Vol. 28, p. 251 (1896)
  A. Schmidt, Aphodiinen-Zusammenst. Deutsche Ent. Zeitsohr.
   Beih. p. 115. Anmerkung 1 (1907-08).

23. *R. Goudoti,* Harold, Col Hefte, Vol. 4, p. 85 (1868).   Madagaskar.
  Goudoti, Reitter, Tab. p. 28; Brünn, 30, p. 166.   Aegypten.
  d'Orbiguy, L'Abeille, Vol. 28, p. 253 (1896).   Obock.
  Clouët, Monogr. Mém. Soc. Ent. Belg. Vol. 8, p. 66 (1901). Madagaskar.

24. *R. granosus,* Klug, Doubl. Verz. Seneg. Ins. p. 7 (1842); Stett. Ent. Senegal.
 Zeit. p. 84, Abdruck (1859). — **Taf. 3, Fig. 44.**   [sche Inseln.
  granosus, Clouët, Monogr. Mém. Soc. Ent. Belg. Vol 8, p. 103 (1901). Abessinien, Indien, Kapverdi-
  rugatus, Wollaston, Col. Hesp. p. 92 (1867).   Kapverdische Inseln.
   sec. Clouët, Monogr. Mém. Soc. Ent. Vol. 8, p. 121 (1901).

25. *R. granulosocostatus,* Clouët, ibidem, p. 108 (1901).   Madagaskar.

26. *R. granulosus,* Ballion, Bull. Soc. Nat. Mosc. Vol. 44 (1), p. 154 (1871), •
 nom. nov.
  granulosus, Harold, Ann. Mus. Stor. Nat. Genova, Vol. 10, p. 97 (1877). Celebes.
  Clouët, Monogr. Mém. Soc. Ent. Vol. 8, p. 49 (1901).   Colombo.
  granosus ‖ Motschulsky, Bull. Nat. Mosc. Vol. 36 (2), p. 465 (1863). Colombo.

27. *R. Haroldi,* Clouët, Monogr. Mém. Soc. Ent. Belg. Vol. 8, p. 68 (1901). Diégo Suarez.

28. *R. Horni* 1), Clouët. ibidem, p. 78 (1901).

29. *R. inermis,* Clouët, ibidem, p. 98 (1901).   Madagaskar.

30. *R. interruptus,* Reitter. Tab. p. 27; Brünn, 30, p. 165.   Ordubad.
  interruptus. d'Orbigny, L'Abeille, Vol. 28, p. 253 (1896).   Ordubad.
  Clouët, Monogr. Mém. Soc. Ent. Belg. Vol. 8, p. 83 (1901). Ordubad.
  Reitteri, Koshantschikow, Hor. Soc. Ent. Ross. 1893-94, Vol. 28, p. 117
   (1894). nom. nov.

31. *R. madagassus.* Harold, Col. Hefte, Vol. 16, p. 228 (1879). Madagaskar.
  madagassus. Fairmaire, Ann. Soc. Ent. France, p. 33 (1886). Madagaskar.
  Clouët, Monogr. Mém. Soc. Ent. Belg. Vol. 8, p. 56 (1901). Madagaskar.

32. *R. malasiacus,* Lansberge, Notes Leyd. Mus. Vol. 8, p. 133 (1886). Sardang, Malakka.
  malasiacus, Clouët, Monogr. Mém. Soc. Ent. Vol. 8, p. 87 (1801). Bengalen, Java, Sumatra.

33. *R. maximus.* Clouët, ibidem, p. 74 (1901).   Kapkolonie.

34. *R. Mayeti,* Clouët. ibidem, p. 110 (1901).   Aegypten bis Mozambique.

35. *R. parallelicollis,* Clouët, ibidem. p. 101 (1901).   Natal.

36. *R. pectoralis,* Clouët, ibidem, p. 52 (1901).   Kongo.

37. *R. plicatus,* Germar, Reise Dalmat. p. 184 (1817).   Ragusa.
  plicatus, Reitter, Tab. p. 26; Brünn, 30, p. 164: Wien. Ent Zeit. p. 76 Dalmatien, Korfu.
   (1897).
   Clouët, Monogr. Mém. Soc. Ent. Belg. Vol. 8, p. 44 (1901). Westliche Mittelmeerländer.
  arenarius*, Costa, Ann. Accad. Aspir. Napoli. Vol. 2, p. 17 (1844).
   Reitter, Tab. p. 26; Brünn, p. 164; Wien. Ent. Zeit. p. 76 Italien, Korsika, Sardinien,
   (1897).   Sizilien, Frankreich.
   sec. d'Orbigny, L'Abeille, Vol. 28. p. 251 (1896).   Algier, Marokko.
  sulcigaster, Mulsant & Rey, Opusc. Ent. Vol. 9, p. 174 (1859 ; Hist. Nat. Korsika, Provence.
   Col. France, Lamell. p. 383 (1871).
   sec. Reitter, Tab. p. 26; Brünn, 30, p. 164.

38. *R. polycolpus,* Fairmaire, Ann. Soc. Ent. Fr. p. 34 (1886). Madagaskar.
  polycolpus, Clouët. Monogr. Mém. Soc. Ent. Belg. Vol. 8, p. 57 (1901). Madagaskar.

39. *R. promontorii,* Péringuey, Trans. S. Afric. Philos. Soc. 1901-03, Kapkolonie.
 Vol. 12, Cat. p. 444 (1901).

40. *R. Reitteri,* Clouët, Monogr. Mém. Soc. Ent. Belg. Vol. 8, p. 96 (1901). Kongo, Madagaskar, Java.

41. *R. Ritsemae,* Clouët, ibidem, p. 81 (1901).   Westafrika, Freetown.
  var. indica, Clouët, Monogr. p. 82 (1901).   Ostindien.

42. *R. rubeolus,* Harold, Col. Hefte, Vol. 8, p. 25 (1871).   Bogos.
  rubeolus, Clouët, Monogr. Mém. Soc. Ent. Belg. Vol. 8, p. 93 (1901). Nubien.

---

1) Vaterlandsangabe fehlt loc. cit. Eine diesbezügliche Anfrage liess der Autor unbeantwortet.

43. *R. scaber*, Haldeman, Journ. Acad. Nat. Sc. Philad. (2), Vol. 1, p. 107   Mittelstaaten.
    (1848).
        scaber, Horn, Trans. Amer. Ent. Soc. Vol. 3, p. 290 (1871) ; Vol. 14, p. 88   Oestliches Küstengebiet, Mittel-
        (1887).   staaten bis Texas.
44. *R. Sequensi*, Reitter, Wien. Ent. Zeit. p. 176 (1903).   Obock, Kairo.
45. *R. Severini*, Clouët, Monogr. Mém. Soc. Ent. Belg. Vol. 8, p. 40 (1901).   Kongo.
46. *R. sexcostatus*, A. Schmidt, Soc. Ent. Zürich. 1909-10, Vol. 24, p. 61   Dar-es-Salaam.
    (1909).
47. *R. sonatus**, Le Conte, Trans. Kans. Acad. Sc. p. 77 (1881).   Chicago.
        sonatus, Horn, Trans. Amer. Ent. Soc. Vol. 14, p. 89 (1887).   Kansas, Colorado, Montana.
48. *R. tarsalis*, Waterhouse, Ann. Mag. Nat. Hist. (4), Vol. 18, p. 115 (1876).   Insel Rodriguez.
        tarsalis, Clouët, Monogr. Mém. Soc. Ent. Belg. Vol. 8, p. 113 (1901).   Madagaskar, Neu-Kaledonien,
49. *R. Vaulogeri*, Clouët, ibidem, p. 84.   Tunis, Algier.   [Indien.
50. *R. verrucosus*, Mulsant, Hist Nat. Col. France, Lamell. p. 316 (1842);   Südfrankreich.
    p. 389 (1871).
        verrucosus, Jacquelin Du Val, Gener. Scarab. Atlas, t. 7, f. 35.
        Reitter, Tab. p. 27; Brünn, 30, p. 165.   Sizilien.
        d'Orbigny, L'Abeille, Vol. 28, p. 253 (1896).   Nizza, Cannes.
        Clouët, Monogr. Mém Soc. Ent. Belg. Vol. 8, p. 106 (1901).   Südfrankreich.

7. Genus RHYSSEMODES, Reitter

Rhyssemodes. Reitter, Verhandl. Naturf. Ver. Brünn, 1891, Vol. 30, p. 156 (1892); Best.-Tab. Eur. Col. Heft 24, p. 18, 23 (1892).

Charaktere. — Die Arten dieser Gattung sind ebenfalls kleine Tierchen wie die der vorhergehenden, auch von rotbrauner oder schwarzer Farbe, schlanker Gestalt und unbehaarter Oberseite.

Der Kopf ist gekörnt, hinten punktiert und am Vorderrande eingeschnitten.

Der Thorax hat dieselbe Bildung und Beschaffenheit der Oberfläche wie *Rhyssemus*.

Die Flügeldecken zeigen ähnliche Skulptur, doch ist dieselbe weniger ausgeprägt, deshalb erscheinen die Zwischenräume mehr glatt.

Die Unterseite zeigt nichts Abweichendes.

Der eigentliche Unterschied beider Gattungen liegt in der Bildung der Füsse. Das erste Glied der Hintertarsen ist allmählich nach der Spitze verbreitert, es ist nicht so lang als die drei folgenden Glieder und kürzer als das erste Glied an den Mitteltarsen, aber an der Spitze dicker als dieses, überhaupt sind die Hintertarsen deutlich kürzer als ihre Schiene, bei *Rhyssemus* nicht, der Enddorn der Hintertibien ist immer länger als das erste Glied.

Alles Uebrige stimmt mit *Rhyssemus* überein.

Geographische Verbreitung der Arten. — Nordafrika, Syrien, Kaukasus, Zentralasien.

1. *R. alutaceus*, Reitter, Tab. p. 24; Brünn, 30, p. 162.   Margljan.
        alutaceus, Clouët, Monogr. Mém. Soc. Ent. Belg. Vol 8, p. 19 (1901).   Margljan.
2. *R. Bouvieri*, Clouët, ibidem, p. 22 (1901).   Nordchina.
3. *R. opacus*, Reitter. Tab. p. 223; Brünn, 31, p. 102.   Turkestan.
        opacus, Clouët, Monogr. Mém. Soc. Ent Belg. Vol. 8, p. 17 (1901).   Margljan.
4. *R. orientalis*, Mulsant & Godart, Ann. Soc. Linn. Lyon, 1874, Vol. 21,   Beirut.
    p. 411 (1875); Opusc. Ent. Vol. 16, p. 75 (1875). — **Taf. 3, Fig. 45.**
        orientalis, Clouët, Monogr. Mém. Soc. Ent Belg. Vol. 8, p. 23 (1901).   Nordafrika, Turkestan, Kauka-
        gemmifer, Marseul, L'Abeille, Vol. 16, p. 58, Nouv. et Fait. 14-15 (1878).   Aegypten.   [sus, Zentralasien.
        Reitter, Tab. p. 28; Brünn, 30, p. 160.   Aegypten.
        obsoletus, Reitter, Hor. Soc. Ent. Ross. Vol. 21, p. 227 (1887); Tab. p. 24;   Chinesisch Turkestan, Zentral-
        Brünn, 30, p. 162.   asien.
        hybridus, Reitter, Tab. p. 29; Brünn, 30, p. 167.   Marokko.
        d'Orbigny, L'Abeille, Vol. 28, p. 252 (1896).   Marokko.

transversus, Reitter, Tab. p. 24; Brünn, 3o, p. 162.   Ordubad, Transkapien, Margl-
Reitteri, d'Orbigny, L'Abeille, Vol. 28, p. 254 (1896).   ljan.
aspericeps. Reitter (nec Chevrolat), Tab. p. 24; Brünn, 3o, p. 162.   Algier.
  sec. Clouët, Monogr. Mém. Soc. Ent. Belg.Vol. 8, p. 119 (1901).
5. *R. tenuisculptus*, Reitter, Tab. p. 24; Brünn, 3o, p. 162.   Margljan.
  tenuisculptus, Clouët, Monogr. Mém. Soc. Ent. Belg. Vol. 8, p. 20 (1901).   Margljan.

8. Genus RHYSSEMORPHUS, Clouët

Rhyssemorphus. Clouët, Bull. Soc. Ent. Fr. p. 122 (1900).

Charaktere. — Die Art dieser Gattung gewährt ganz den Anblick eines *Rhyssemus*, sie unterscheidet sich nur dadurch, dass bei ihr das letzte Segment von dem vorhergehenden nicht durch eine Furche getrennt ist wie bei *Rhyssemus*, *Rhyssemodes* und der folgenden Gattung.

Geographische Verbreitung der Art. — Madagaskar.
  1. *R. Mocquerysi*, Clouët, Bull. Ent. Soc. Fr. p. 122 (1900); Monogr. p. 117.   Madagaskar.

9. Genus TRICHIORHYSSEMUS, Clouët

Trichiorhyssemus. Clouët, Mém. Soc. Ent. Belg. Vol. 8, p. 15 (1901).

Charaktere. — Diese Gattung, die mit den drei vorhergehenden dieselbe Gestalt, Grösse, Farbe und Skulptur der Oberfläche zeigt, unterscheidet sich nur dadurch, dass die Oberseite kurz behaart ist.

Die Hinterschenkel sind ebenfalls dünner als die vorderen.

Das erste Glied der Hintertarsen ist den drei folgenden an Länge gleich wie bei *Rhyssemus*, es ist auch so lang als das erste Glied der Mitteltarsen.

Geographische Verbreitung der Arten. — Sizilien, Nordchina, Japan, Sunda-Inseln, Ceylon, Nord- und Mittelamerika.
  1. *T. asperulus*, Waterhouse, Trans. Ent. Soc. Lond. p. 94 (1875).   Japan.
    asperulus, Clouët, Monogr. Mém. Soc. Ent. Belg. Vol. 8, p. 28, 33 (1901).   Japan.
  2. *T. cristatellus*, Bates, Biol Centr. Amer. Col. Vol. 2 (2), p. 102 (1887).   Mexiko, Guatemala.
    cristatellus, Clouët, Monogr. Mém. Soc. Ent. Belg. Vol. 8, p. 27, 28 (1901).   Mexiko, Guatemala.
  3. *T. hirsutus*, Clouët, ibidem, p. 28, 35. — **Taf. 3, Fig. 46.**   Sunda-Inseln.
  4. *T. lasionotus*. Clouët, ibidem: p. 28, 32.   Nordchina.
  5. *T. riparius*, Horn, Trans. Amer. Ent. Soc. Vol. 3. p. 290 (1871);   Arizona.
    Vol. 14, p. 90 (1887).
    riparius, Clouët, Monogr. Mém. Soc. Ent. Belg.Vol. 8, p. 27, Note p. 29(1901).   Arizona.
    *caelatus**, Le Conte, Trans. Kans. Acad. Sc. p. 77 (1881).   Wyoming, Santa Fé.
      sec. Horn, Trans. Amer, Ent. Soc. Vol. 14, p. 110 (1887).
  6. *T. setulosus*, Reitter, Tab. p. 25; Brünn, 3o, p. 163.   Sizilien.
    setulosus, Clouët, Monogr. Mém. Soc. Ent. Vol. 8, p. 27, 30 (1901).   Sizilien.

10. Genus PLEUROPHORUS, Mulsant

Pleurophorus. Mulsant. Hist. Nat. Col. France, Lamell. p. 312 (1842).

Charaktere. — Kleine, glänzende Arten von schmaler, meist paralleler, wenig konvexer Gestalt und rotbrauner oder schwarzer Farbe bilden diese Gattung. Sie hat mit *Rhyssemus* den gekörnten

Kopf gemein. unterscheidet sich aber hauptsächlich von dieser durch den von Querwülsten entblössten Thorax und die glatten Flügeldecken.

Der Kopf ist stark herabgewölbt, konvex, am Vorderrande eingeschnitten und daneben mehr oder weniger verrundet, der Vorderteil ist gekörnt und wird von einer meistens deutlichen Stirnlinie begrenzt, hinter derselben ist der Kopf fein punktiert oder glatt; die Augen sind bei angezogenem Kopfe bedeckt.

Das Halsschild ist quer, an den Seiten stark herabgewölbt, mehr oder weniger parallel, besonders in der Hinterhälfte, vorn verschmälert, Seiten und Basis sind gerandet, aber ohne Wimpern, die Hinterwinkel gewöhnlich verrundet, die Scheibe hat vor dem Schildchen eine nach vorn abgekürzte Längsfurche und an den Seiten zwei schwächere und kurze Eindrücke, von denen der eine sich hinter den Vorderwinkeln, der andere mehr in der Mitte befindet, sie ist ausserdem zerstreut, ziemlich grob punktiert.

Das Schildchen ist klein und dreieckig.

Die Flügeldecken sind nicht breiter als das Halsschild, ihre Basis ist glatt gerandet, die Schultern sind scharfwinklig, sie sind meistens gleichbreit, gewöhnlich zweimal so lang als zusammen breit oder wenig kürzer, immer mit deutlichen Punktstreifen, die Zwischenräume sind entweder schwach konvex oder eben, punktiert sowohl wie glatt.

Die Unterseite ist glatt und glänzend.

Die Mittelhüften stehen nahe zusammen.

Das Metasternum ist in der Mitte gefurcht.

Die Bauchsegmente sind frei, das letzte ist durch eine tiefe Furche von dem vorhergehenden getrennt wie bei *Rhyssemus*.

Die Hinterschenkel sind schmaler als die vorderen.

Die Tibien sind nach der Spitze verbreitert, die vordern haben drei deutliche Aussenzähne und einen Enddorn, die vier folgenden sind ohne Querleisten an der Aussenseite, ihr Endrand ist mit Borsten und zwei Enddornen besetzt.

Die Tarsen sind fünfgliedrig, das erste Glied ist entweder sehr dünn und lang, den drei folgenden an Länge gleich, oder es ist kürzer und stärker, nur so lang als die zwei folgenden Glieder, der obere Enddorn ist länger oder kürzer als der Metatarsus.

Das Männchen hat ein Metasternum, welches besonders nach hinten stärker vertieft ist.

Geographische Verbreitung der Arten. — Europa, Nord- und Südafrika, Nord- und Südamerika, Kleinasien, Kaukasus, Turkestan, Ceylon, Sunda-Inseln.

1. *P. apicipennis*, Reitter, Tab. p. 29; Brünn, 30, p. 167; Wien. Ent. Zeit.   Taschkent.
p. 75 (1897).
2. *P. caesoides*, Fairmaire, Ann. Soc. Ent. Fr. p. 471 (1899).   Madagaskar.
3. *P. caesus*, Creutzer, Fauna Germ. p. 35 (2) (1796).   Wien.
    caesus, Sturm, Ent. Handb. Vol. 1, p. 57 (1800).   Wien.
     *Stephens, Ill. Brit. Ent. Vol. 3, p. 218 (1830).   England.
    Erichson, Naturg. Ins. Deutschl. Vol. 3, p. 913 (1848).   Oesterreich, Steiermark, Tirol.
    Horn, Trans. Amer. Ent. Soc. Vol. 3, p. 91 (1871); Vol. 14, p. 91 (1887).   Mittelstaaten, Baltimore, Washington.

    Reitter, Tab. p. 29; Brünn, 30, p. 167.   Europa, Nordafrika, Kleinasien,
      sec. Fairmaire, Ann. Soc. Ent. Fr. p. 34 (1871).   Madagaskar. [Kaukasus.
    angustus, Philippi, Stett. Ent. Zeit. p. 316 (1864).   Chile.
    rugiceps (*Ataenius*)*, Dury, journ. Cincinnati. Soc. Vol. 20, p. 154 (1902).   Cincinnati.
      sec. *Bedel, L'Abeille, Vol. 30, p. 152 (1904).
    var. *elongatulus*, Mulsant. Hist. Nat. Col. France, Lamell. p. 312 (1842).   Frankreich.
    Biologie : *Xambeu, L'Echange. Vol. 6, p. 107, Mœurs et Métam. — Larve
      beschrieben.
      sec. Wiegmann, Arch. f. Naturf. Ber. 1896, p. 191 (1899).

4. *P. capicola*, Péringuey, Trans. S. Afric. Philos. Soc. 1901-03. Vol. 12,   Kapkolonie.
   Cat. p. 448 (1901).
5. *P. cracens*, Motschulsky, Bull. Soc. Nat. Mosc. Vol. 36 (2), p. 464 (1863).   Ceylon.
6. *P. impressicollis*, Boheman, Freg. Eug. Res. Zool. Vol. 2 (1), Ins.   Java.
   p. 51 (1858). — **Taf. 3, Fig. 47.**
   impressicollis, Harold, Ann. Mus. Stor. Nat. Genova, Vol. 10, p. 100 (1877).   Celebes.
7. *P. laevistriatus*, Perris, L'Abeille, Vol. 7, p. 13 (1869-70).   Sardinien.
   laevistriatus, Reitter. Tab. p. 30; Brünn, p. 168.   Korsika, Italien.
   poricollis, Fairmaire, Ann. Soc. Ent. Fr. (4), Vol. 10, p. 374 (1870).   Nordafrika.
   sec. d'Orbigny, L'Abeille, Vol. 28, p. 250 (1896).
   porcicollis, Reitter, Tab. p. 30; Brünn, 30, p. 168.   Algier.
8. *P. laticeps*, Fairmaire, Ann. Soc. Ent. Fr. p. 34 (1871).   Madagaskar.
9. *P. natalensis*, Péringuey, Trans. S. Afric. Philos. Soc. 1901-03, Vol. 12,   Natal.
   Cat. p. 449 (1901).
10. *P. opacus*, Reitter, Tab. 224; Brünn, Vol. 31, p. 103.   Tunis.
    opacus, A. Schmidt, Aphodiinen-Zusammenst. Deutsche Ent. Zeitschr.
    Beih. p. 106, Anmerkung 1 (1907-08).
11. *P. parvulus* 1), Chevrolat, Ann. Soc. Ent. Fr. p. 415 (1864).   Kuba.   [Südamerika.
    parvulus, Bates, Biol. Centr. Amer. Col. Vol. 2 (2), p. 104 (1887).   Antillen, Mexiko, Guatemala,
    nanus, Horn (nec Degeer), Trans. Amer. Ent. Soc. Vol. 14, p. 96 (1887).   Arizona, Kalifornien, Massachu-
    A. Schmidt, Aphodiinen-Zusammenst., Deutsche Ent. Zeitschr.   [setts, Michigan, Texas.
    Beih. Anmerkung, p. 110 (1907-08).
12. *P. sabulosus*, Mulsant, Hist. Nat. Col. France, Lamell. p. 310 (1842);   Südfrankreich.
    p. 379 (1871).
    sabulosus, Reitter, Tab. p. 30; Brünn, 30, p. 168.   Südeuropa, Nordafrika, Syrien.
    sec. Wollaston, Cat. Coleopt. Canar. p. 192 (1864).   Kanarische Inseln.
    insculptus, Küster, Käf. Eur. Vol. 18, p. 49.   Sardinien.
    sec. Reitter, Cat. p. 716 (1906).
    *ovipennis**, Desbrochers, Col. Nord-Afr. Vol. 2, p. 98 (1884); Bull. Acad.   Bône.
    d'Hippone, Nr. 19, p. 98.
    sec. Bedel, Bull. Soc. Ent. Fr. p. 33 (1889).
    A. Schmidt, Aphodiinen-Zusammenst. Deutsche Ent. Zeitschr.
    Beih. p. 106, Note 2 (1907-08).
13. *P. tibialis*, Fabricius, Ent. Syst. Suppl. p. 24 (1798).   Tanger.
    tibialis, Illiger, Mag. Vol. 1, p. 325 1802).
14. *P. variolosus*, Kolenati, Melet. Ent. Vol. 5, p. 20 (1846).   Elisabethopol.
    variolosus, Reitter, Tab. p. 30; Brünn, 30, p. 168.   Kaukasus, Transkaspien, Turk-
    foveicollis, Ballion, Bull. Soc. Nat. Mosc. 1870, Vol. 43 (2), p. 333 (1871).   Chodshent.   [menien.
    sec. Reitter, Tab. p. 30; Brünn, 30, p. 168.
    multipunctatus, Marseul, L'Abeille, Vol. 16 (2), Nouv. et Fait. 14-15. p. 58   Batum, Imeretien.
    (1878).
    sec. Reitter, Tab. p. 30; Brünn, 30, p. 168.   [ton.
15. *P. ventralis*, Horn, Trans. Amer. Ent. Soc. Vol. 14, p. 92 (1887).   Kanada, Ontario, Washing-

4. GRUPPE RHYPARINA

Charaktere. — Diese Gruppe unterscheidet sich von den *Psammobiina* dadurch, dass der Kopf nicht gekörnt, sondern mit Längs- und Querleistchen und der Thorax und die Flügeldecken mit Längsrippen versehen sind.

Der Körper ist länglich, mehr oder weniger breit, flach gewölbt, schwärzlich, nicht vollglänzend, nackt oder fein behaart oder mit grauglänzendem Toment bedeckt.

Der Kopf ist flach, breit und kurz, fast senkrecht herabgebogen, glatt oder punktiert, nach vorn

---

1) Diese Art wurde bisher der Gattung *Psammobius* zugerechnet, sie gehört aber wegen ihrer Fussbildung zur Gattung *Pleurophorus*.

verschmalert, dort abgestutzt oder schwach ausgebogt, die Ecken jederseits sind stumpfwinklig oder stumpfzähnig, zuweilen bildet der Seitenrand auch noch vor den ziemlich grossen Wangen einen stumpfen Winkel, am Hinterrande. befinden sich vier Längs- oder Querleistchen oder eine vertiefte winklige Stirnlinie und dahinter zwei mit Haarbüscheln gezierte Tuberkeln, die Mitte des Kopfes ist entweder eben oder mit zwei Längsleistchen versehen.

Das Halsschild ist quer, an den wenig herabgewölbten Seiten und der Basis, wenigstens in der Mitte der letzteren, ohne deutliche glatte Randung, auf der Scheibe mit fünf oder sechs glatten oder fein behaarten Rippen, der Raum zwischen ihnen ist dichter oder zerstreuter punktiert.

Ein sichtbares Schildchen fehlt oder ist vorhanden, es ist spitz-dreieckig.

Die Flügeldecken haben scharfe Schultern, sie sind gewöhnlich etwas breiter als der Thorax und nach hinten erweitert, punktiert-gestreift, die abwechselnden Zwischenräume sind entweder flach und gerippt oder sie sind stärker und schwächer rippenförmig, es befinden sich auf jeder Flügeldecke drei, vier oder acht Rippen, die glatt oder behaart sind, vor der Spitze zeigt die Gattung *Rhyparus* je einen grossen Tuberkel.

Die Unterseite ist ebenfalls wenig glänzend, immer punktiert und zuweilen behaart.

Die Vorderschenkel sind meistens viel dicker als die andern, die hintersten zuweilen sehr schlank, sie sind immer deutlich punktiert.

Das Metasternum ragt zuweilen als scharfe Spitze zwischen die Mittelhüften hinein, es hat eine schmalere oder breitere Mittelfurche oder ist nach der Mitte breit vertieft.

Das fünfte Abdominalsegment ist das breiteste.

Das Pygidium ist frei, grösser oder kleiner, gefurcht oder mit Längskiêl.

Die Vordertibien sind zur Spitze wenig verbreitert, am Aussenrande mit einem oder zwei Zähnen besetzt, der vordere Innenwinkel ist zuweilen zahnförmig nach innen erweitert, und dann ohne Enddorn, oder der Innenwinkel ist normal und dann mit Enddorn versehen, zuweilen befindet sich auch am Vorderrande ein Zahn.

Die Mittel- und Hintertibien sind ohne Querleisten am Aussenrande und zuweilen auch ohne Enddorne, sie haben aber immer am untern Endrande einen Borstenbesatz.

Die Füsse sind drei- oder fünfgliedrig.

Die Klauen sind normal.

In diese Gruppe gehören fünf Gattungen : *Stereomera*, *Termitodius*, *Rhyparus*, *Sybacodes*, *Notocaulus*.

BESTIMMINGS-TABELLE DER GATTUNGEN

1. *Vordertibien an der Aussenseite ungezahnt, Schildchen vorhanden,*
   Füsse dreigliedrig, Pygidium frei, stark bauchwärts gebogen . . 1. Genus STEREOMERA, Arrow.

1'. *Vordertibien gezahnt, Schildchen vorhanden oder fehlend, Füsse fünf-*
   gliedrig, Pygidium frei, nur mehr oder weniger senkrecht.

2. *Schildchen nicht sichtbar, Vordertibien ohne Enddorn, innen mit oder*
   ohne zahnförmige Spitze, am Vorderrande mit einem, am Aussen-
   rande mit einem oder zwei Zähnen, Mittel- und Hintertibien ohne
   deutliche Enddorne, Hinterkopf mit Längsleisten oder Haarbüscheln,
   fünftes Segment breiter als das vierte.

3. *Beine sehr lang. Hinterschenkel sehr schmal, stark gebogen, das Ab-*
   domen überragend, Halsschild und Flügeldecken mit Längsrippen,
   ersteres ausserdem am Vorderrande mit kräftigen Längstuberkeln,
   Fühlerkeule sehr schmal, Hinterkopf mit Längsleisten, Vordertibien
   mit zahnförmiger Spitze innen, am Aussenrande mit einem Zahne,

Hinterkopf mit Längsleistchen, Metasternum nicht nach vorn in eine
Spitze ausgezogen . . . .   2. Genus TERMITODIUS, Wasmann.
3'. *Beine nicht besonders lang, Hinterschenkel kräftiger, das Abdomen*
nicht überragend, Halsschild am Vorderrande ohne Tuberkeln, aber
wie die Flügeldecken mit Längsrippen, Metasternum überragt als
Spitze das Mesosternum.
4. *Vordertibien innen mit zahnförmiger Spitze, am Vorder- und Aussen-.*
rande mit je einem Zahne, Kopf mit Längsleisten, Abdomen mit
Quereindrücken an der Seite . . . .   3. Genus RHYPARUS, Westwood.
4'. *Vordertibien innen ohne zahnförmige Spitze, am Vorderrande mit*
einem, am Aussenrande mit zwei Zähnen, Stirn mit Haarbüscheln,
Abdomen ohne Eindrücke. . . . .   4. Genus SYBACODES, Fairmaire.
2'. *Schildchen sichtbar, Vordertibien mit Enddornen, innen nicht zahn-*
förmig, am Vorderrande ohne, am Aussenrande mit zwei Zähnen,
Metasternum vorn ohne Spitze, Mittel- und Hintertibien mit zwei
deutlichen Enddornen, Hinterkopf mit Querleistchen, fünftes Seg-
ment nicht breiter als viertes . . . .   5. Genus NOTOCAULUS, Quedenfeldt.

1. GENUS STEREOMERA, ARROW

Stereomera. Arrow, Ann. Mag. Nat. Hist. (7), Vol. 15, p. 534 (1905).

Charaktere. — Diese Gattung weist nur einen einzigen Vertreter auf, eine kleine Art von
2 1/2 mm Länge, mit breitem, flachen Körper von rotbrauner Farbe, deren auffallendstes Merkmal die
dreigliedrigen Tarsen sind, eine Erscheinung, die sich bei keiner andern Art wiederholt.

Der Kopf ist eben und breit, ohne Höcker; der Clipeus breit abgerundet; die Augen sind
länglich.

Das Halsschild ist quer, nach vorn verschmälert, mit scharfen Winkeln, die Scheibe ist mit
Längsrippen bedeckt, die in der Mitte durch eine Querfurche unterbrochen werden.

Ein Schildchen ist vorhanden.

Die Flügeldecken sind ebenfalls längsgerippt, ihre Zwischenräume quer gefurcht.

Die Hüften stehen nahe beieinander.

Das Prosternum ragt nach hinten hervor.

Die Epipleuren sind breit.

Die Bauchsegmente sind in der Mitte verwachsen, das Pygidium ist frei und stark nach unten
gebogen.

Die Mittel- und Hintertibien sind ohne Querleisten.

Die dreigliedrigen Füsse sind kurz, alle Glieder stark verdickt.

Geographische Verbreitung der Art. — Halbinsel Malaka.

1. *S. pusilla*, Arrow, Ann. Mag. Nat. Hist (7), Vol. 15, p. 535 (1905).   Singapur.

2. GENUS TERMITODIUS, WASMANN

Termitodius. Wasmann, Krit. Verz. Myrmekoph. et Termit. Arthrop. p. 220 (1894).

Charaktere. — Diese Gattung nähert sich in der länglichen, schmalen Form und Skulptur der

Gattung *Rhyparus*, die schmale Fühlerkeule, die gebogenen und sehr langen Hinterschenkel und die Tuberkeln des Halsschildes unterscheiden sie hinlänglich.

Der Kopf ist herabgebogen, breit und flach, sein Vorderrand mit vier schwachen Zähnchen, am Hinterkopf sind vier kurze Längsleistchen und vor ihnen, in der Mitte sind zwei andere, zwischen und neben diesen sind drei glatte, glänzende Längsfurchen.

Der Thorax ist breiter als der Kopf, nach hinten schwach verschmälert, der Seitenrand hinter den Vorderwinkeln gebuchtet, mit sechs Längsrippen, als Fortsetzung von diesen befinden sich am Vorderrande sechs Längstuberkeln, dieselben sind viel höher, besonders die mittelsten, als die Längsrippen, die beiden seitlichen Längsrippen sind an ihrer obern Kante eingekerbt, dann folgen nach der Mitte zu zwei schwächere, die nach vorn abgekürzt sind, die beiden mittelsten nähern sich vorn, der Raum zwischen den Rippen ist glatt.

Ein sichtbares Schildchen fehlt.

Die Flügeldecken sind an der Basis so breit als der Thorax, bis zur Mitte wenig verbreitert, dann ziemlich stark konvergierend nach hinten, jede Decke mit drei starken Rippen, zwischen denen sich glänzende, breite Furchen befinden, die Rippen sind wie die des Halsschildes ziemlich dicht punktiert und sehr kurz hell behaart, die Naht ist nur wenig erhaben, vor der Spitze befindet sich jederseits zwischen der ersten und zweiten Rippe ein ziemlich starker, glänzender Tuberkel, der nach vorn durch eine Vertiefung von den Rippen getrennt ist.

Die Vorderschenkel sind am dicksten, sie werden durch eine schmale Leiste getrennt, die sich hinter denselben dreieckig erweitert.

Das Metasternum ist vorn nicht in eine das Mesosternum überragende Spitze ausgezogen, die Platte desselben ist ziemlich eben, mit einer mittlern und zwei seitlichen Vertiefungen.

Die Mittel- und Hinterschenkel sind dünn, die letzteren sehr lang und stark gebogen.

Das fünfte Bauchsegment ist breiter als eins der vorhergehenden.

Die Vordertibien haben je einen kleinen Zahn am Aussen- und Vorderrande, statt eines Enddorns ist die innere Spitze neben den sehr kurzen Tarsen in einen kleinen Zahn ausgezogen.

Die Mittel- und Hintertibien sind am untern Endrande kurz beborstet, Enddorne fehlen denselben, dagegen ist die innere Kante an der Spitze in einen kurzen Dorn verlängert, der aber schwer sichtbar ist.

Die fünf Tarsenglieder sind ziemlich kurz, die mittlern fast quer, nur erstes und letztes wenig verlängert.

Die Klauen sind klein, aber deutlich.

Die Männchen haben an der Innenkante der Mitteltibien, kurz vor der Spitze, ein kleines spitzes Zähnchen.

Geographische Verbreitung der Art. — Venezuela.

1. *T. coronatus*, Wasmann, Krit. Verz. Myrmekoph. et Termit. Arthr. p. 220 (1894). Venezuela.

3. GENUS RHYPARUS, WESTWOOD

Rhyparus. Westwood. Proc. Ent. Soc. Lond. p. 93 (1843); Trans. Ent. Soc. Lond. Vol. 4, p. 240 (1845-47).

Antrisis. Pascoe, Journ. Ent. Vol. 2, p. 447 (1866).

Charaktere. — Die kräftigen, das Abdomen nicht überragenden Hinterschenkel, die fehlenden Tuberkel am Vorderrande des Halsschildes, sowie das in eine Spitze ausgezogene Metasternum unterscheiden diese Gattung und die folgenden von *Termitodius*.

Die Oberseite der *Rhyparus*-Arten ist oft mit einem Ueberzuge behaftet, der sich nicht ganz entfernen und so die Skulptur nicht immer genau erkennen lässt.

Die Arten haben einen länglichen, parallelen oder nach hinten verschmälerten, wenig konvexen, auf dem Rücken flachgedrückten Körper, sie sind wenig glänzend und von dunkler Farbe.

Der Kopf ist kurz und verhältnismässig breit, senkrecht herabgebogen, wenig gewölbt, gewöhnlich mit sechs kurzen Längsleistchen, am Hinterkopf vier, in der Mitte davor zwei; der abgestutzte Clipeus ist meistens stumpf gezahnt; die Augen sind vom Halsschilde bedeckt; die Wangen sind deutlich.

Das Halsschild ist kaum breiter als der Kopf, wenig gewölbt, nach hinten verschmälert, die Vorderwinkel ragen ohrenförmig hervor, die Mitte der Seiten ist mehr oder weniger gerundet erweitert, zwischen beiden entsteht deshalb eine Einbuchtung, die Hinterwinkel sind deutlich, nicht verrundet, die Seiten und Basis haben einen scharfen Rand; die Oberfläche zeigt sechs scharfe Längsrippen, von denen die mittelsten jederseits in der vordern Hälfte durch einen Quereindruck unterbrochen sind.

Das Schildchen fehlt.

Die Flügeldecken sind nach der Spitze meistens deutlich verjüngt, vorn gewöhnlich so breit als die Basis des Halsschildes, sie haben statt der vertieften Streifen sehr deutliche Rippen, die sich vor ihrem Ende zuweilen ziemlich stark verbreitern, besonders die innern; die Spitze der Flügeldecken erhebt sich jederseits zu einem breiten, nach oben mehr oder weniger zugespitzten Tuberkel; der Raum zwischen den Rippen ist flach, zweireihig punktiert oder quergerieft, die Schultern sind scharf, bei einigen Arten sogar schwach gezähnt.

Die ganze Unterseite, auch die Schenkel, besonders die vorderen, sind sehr dicht punktiert, äusserst fein und kurz behaart.

Die verdickten Vorderschenkel werden durch eine schmale Leiste getrennt, die sich hinter ihnen winklig verbreitert.

Die Mittelhüften sind wenig getrennt.

Das Metasternum hat eine breite Mittelfurche, zuweilen jederseits noch einen schwächeren, länglichen Eindruck, es läuft nach vorn in eine Spitze aus, die das Mesosternum wagerecht überragt.

Die Bauchsegmente sind ausser der Punktierung noch an den Seiten mit Quereindrücken versehen, das fünfte Segment ist viel breiter als eins der vorhergehenden, das Pygidium ist unbedeckt, es steht senkrecht und ist in der Mitte gewöhnlich gekielt.

Die Vordertibien verbreitern sich wenig nach vorn, an ihrer Aussenseite befindet sich gewöhnlich nur ein deutlicher Zahn, ein zweiter ist am Vorderrande neben der Einlenkung der Tarsen, er ist kleiner, der Enddorn am innern Spitzenwinkel fehlt, dafür ist die Tibie hier mehr oder weniger deutlich und lang in eine zahnförmige, nach innen gerichtete Spitze ausgezogen, sie steht dem Aussenzahn gegenüber.

Die Vordertarsen sind fünfgliedrig und kurz.

Die Mittelschenkel sind schmaler als die vorderen, aber breiter als die längeren Hinterschenkel, sie sind zuweilen an der Unterkante stumpf gezahnt.

Die Mittel- und Hintertibien sind im grössten Teile ihrer Länge gleichbreit, nur an ihrer Basis innen bogig verschmälert, die Querleisten an der Aussenkante oder Zähnelung an dem obern Rande, wie bei *Psammobius,* fehlen, am Endrande sind sie mit kurzen, starren Borsten versehen, aber die Enddorne fehlen.

Die fünfgliedrigen Tarsen sind auch hier kurz, nur das erste Glied ist verlängert.

Die Klauen sind normal.

Die Männchen zeichnen sich dadurch aus, dass der innere Endrand der Mittel- und Hintertibien zahnförmig ausgezogen ist, gewöhnlich an den Mitteltibien etwas spitzer.

Geographische Verbreitung der Arten. — Grosse Sunda-Inseln, Philippinen, Hinterindien, afrikanische Inseln.

1. *R. approximans*, Fairmaire, Notes Leyd. Mus. Vol. 15, p. 145 (1893).   Borneo.
2. *R. birmanicus*, Fairmaire, ibidem, Vol. 19, p. 210 (1897).   Birma.
3. *R. comorianus*. Fairmaire, Ann. Soc. Ent. Belg. p. 452 (1896).   Komoren Inseln.
4. *R. dentatus*, Fairmaire, Notes Leyd. Mus. Vol. 18, p. 83 (1896).   Borneo,
5. *R. denticollis*, Fairmaire, ibidem, Vol. 15, p. 144 (1893).   Java.
6. *R. Desjardinsi*, Westwood, Trans. Ent. Soc. Lond. Vol. 4, p. 241, t. 17,   Mauritius.
   f. 5 (1847).
        Desjardinsi, Coquerel, Ann. Soc. Ent. Fr. p. 329 (1866).   Réunion.
7. *R. gracilis*, Arrow. Ann. Mag. Nat. Hist. (7), Vol. 15, p. 538 (1905).   Luisiade-Archipel.
8. *R. helephoroides*, Fairmaire, Notes Leyd. Mus. Vol. 15, p. 145 (1893).   Borneo.
9. *R. nilgirensis*, Arrow, Ann. Mag. Nat. Hist. (8), Vol. 4, p. 94 (1909).   Nilgiri Hills.
10. *R. obsoletus*, Fairmaire, Notes Leyd. Mus. Vol. 15, p. 145 (1893).   Sumatra.
11. *R. peninsularis*, Arrow, Ann. Mag. Nat. Hist. (7), Vol. 15, p. 537 (1905). Penang, Perak.
12. *R. philippinensis*, Arrow, ibidem, p. 538 (1905).   Philippinen.
13. *R. Saundersi (Antrisis)*, Pascoe. Journ. Ent. Vol. 2, p. 448, t. 18, f. 5 (1866). Sarawak.
        Saundersi, sec. Fairmaire, Notes Leyd. Mus. Vol. 18, p. 84 (1896).
14. *R. simplicicolis*, Fairmaire, ibidem, p. 84 (1896).   Sumatra.
15. *R. sumatrensis*, Fairmaire, ibidem, Vol. 15, p. 17 (1893).   Sumatra.
16. *R. Xanthi (Antrisis)**, Frivaldszky, Term. Füzet. Vol. 6, p. 138 (1883). Borneo.

4. Genus SYBACODES, Fairmaire

Sybacodes. Fairmaire, Notes Leyd. Mus. Vol. 18, p. 84 (1896).

Charaktere. — In dem grossen Kopf mit dem gezahnten Clipeus, den Längsleisten auf dem Halsschild und den Flügeldecken, zum Teil auch in der Form der Mittel- und Hintertibien, ferner in dem freien, mit Längskiel versehenem Pygidium stimmt diese Gattung mit *Rhyparus* überein, ihr fehlen aber die Längsleisten des Hinterkopfes, die Tuberkeln vor der Spitze der Flügeldecken, die *Rhyparus* auszeichnen, auch ist die Bewaffnung der Vordertibien eine andere.

Es sind mittelgrosse, konvexe, dunkel gefärbte und wenig glänzende Arten, die zuweilen mit seidenglänzendem Toment bekleidet sind; obwohl von länglicher Gestalt, sind die Vertreter dieser Gattung doch breiter und gedrungener als *Rhyparus*.

Der Kopf ist breit und flach, stark herabgebogen, punktiert, mit deutlich gebogener und unge-höckerter Stirnlinie, hinter derselben sind zwei schwache rundliche Erhöhungen, deren jede mit einem langen Borstenbüschel versehen ist, vor der Stirnlinie ist der Kopf beulig erhaben; der Clipeus zeigt am Vorderrande vier mehr oder weniger deutliche Zähne; die Wangen überragen als stumpfe Winkel die Augen; letztere sind bei angezogenem Kopfe unsichtbar.

Der Thorax ist breiter als der Kopf, wenig gewölbt, quer, von oben gesehen in der Mitte der Seiten rundlich erweitert, am Hinterrande etwas schmaler als vorn, die Vorderwinkel sind schwach vorgezogen, die hintern stumpfwinklig, Seiten und die Basis sind undeutlich gerandet, die Oberfläche ist mit sechs fein behaarten Rippen geschmückt, von denen die beiden mittlern dichter zusammenstehen, die folgenden werden durch eine Quervertiefung unterbrochen.

Ein sichtbares Schildchen fehlt.

Die Flügeldecken sind etwas breiter als der Thorax, an der Schulter scharfwinklig, aber ohne Dorn oder Zahn, ausser der Naht haben sie vier scharfe, behaarte Rippen, jede derselben wird seitlich von je einer Punktreihe begrenzt, der Raum zwischen zwei Punktreihen ist entweder vollständig eben oder schwach rippenförmig, besonders an den Seiten und vor der Spitze.

Die Unterseite ist wenig glänzend, punktiert und fein behaart.

Die Vorderschenkel stehen ziemlich dicht zusammen und werden wie bei *Rhyparus* durch eine schmale, nach hinten sich dreieckig erweiternde Leiste getrennt.

Die Mittelschenkel sind etwas weiter entfernt, das Metasternum spitzt sich zwischen ihnen zu und überragt das tieferliegende Mesosternum, nach hinten ist es mehr oder weniger breit und tief gefurcht.

Das zweite und dritte Abdominalsegment sind kurz, das vierte, noch schmalere, ist mit dem fünften, viel breiteren, in der Mitte fast vollständig verwachsen, nur an den Seiten ist ihre Trennung schwach angedeutet.

Das Pygidium ist gross, etwas nach unten gebogen, in der Mitte mit langbehaarter Längleiste versehen.

Die Schenkel sind ebenfalls fein punktiert, die hinteren sind wie in der vorhergehenden Gattung am schmalsten.

Die Vordertibien sind verbreitert und am Aussenrande zweizahnig, am Vorderrande neben den Tarsen ist ein drittes Zähnchen, der Enddorn am inneren Spitzenwinkel fehlt.

Die Mittel- und Hintertibien besitzen am Innenrande nahe der Basis einen stumpfen Zahn, am Aussenrande fehlen die Querleisten und am untern Spitzenrande, der beborstet ist, die beiden Enddorne

Die Tarsen an den vier Hinterbeinen sind kürzer als die Tibien, sie sind fünfgliedrig, das erste Glied ist sehr verlängert.

Die Klauen sind normal.

Das Männchen besitzt an den Mitteltibien am innern Spitzenwinkel einen Dorn.

Geographische Verbreitung der Arten. — Hinterindien.

1. *S. aureopilosus*, A. Schmidt. Soc. Ent. Zürich, 1909-10, Vol. 24, p. 60　Yünnan. (1909). — **Taf. 3, Fig. 48.**
2. *S. lutulentus*, Fairmaire, Notes Leyd. Mus. Vol. 18, p. 85 (1896). 　　Birma.
   lutulentus, Arrow, Ann. Mag. Nat. Hist. (7), Vol. 15, p. 539 (1905). 　Pandschab, Indien, Siam.
   var. alternatus, Fairmaire, Notes Leyd. Mus. Vol. 19, p. 211 (1897). 　Malabar.

5. Genus NOTOCAULUS, Quedenfeldt

Notocaulus. Quedenfeldt, Berl. Ent. Zeitschr. p. 285 (1884).

Charaktere. — Diese Gattung unterscheidet sich von *Stereomera* durch die fünfgliedrigen Tarsen, von den drei anderen Gattungen der *Rhyparina*-Gruppe auf den ersten Blick durch das Vorhandensein eines sichtbaren Schildchens.

Der Körper ist von länglicher, konvexer Gestalt, schwärzlich gefärbt und wenig glänzend, auf der Ober- und Unterseite unbehaart.

Der breite Kopf ist stark herabgezogen, aber nur flach gewölbt, in der vorderen Hälfte mehr glatt, hinten punktiert und daselbt mit vier quergestellten Höckerchen, die aber mehr die Form gebogener Leistchen haben, geschmückt; vor diesen, mehr in der Mitte des Kopfes befindlich, ist ein Längskiel, der vorn und seitlich von einer Vertiefung begrenzt wird; der Clipeus zeigt an seinem Rande zwei stumpfe Zähne; die Augen sind bei angezogenem Kopfe nicht vollständig vom Vorderrande des Halsschildes bedeckt; die Wangen sind ziemlich deutlich, sie werden nach vorn durch eine scharfe Leiste von der Kopffläche getrennt.

Das Halsschild ist quer, in der Mitte mit drei scharfen Rippen und ausserdem mit zwei Seitenràndern, die Oberfläche ist meistens vereinzelt punktiert, die Basis ist schwach zweibuchtig und kurz bewimpert, ohne eigentliche Randung.

Das Schildchen ist sehr schmal, dreieckig.

Die Flügeldecken sind etwas breiter als der Thorax an der Basis, sie sind parallel oder hinten etwas verbreitert und haben drei oder vier scharfe Rippen, der Raum zwischen je zwei derselben ist in Reihen punktiert.

Die Unterseite samt den Schenkeln ist punktiert, der Hinterleib am stärksten.

Das Mesosternum ist gekielt zwischen den weiter entfernten Mittelhüften.

Das flach vertiefte Metasternum hat eine vertiefte Mittellinie.

Die Hinterleibssegmente sind von gleicher Länge, das freie Pygidium ist klein, punktiert und behaart, mehr senkrecht stehend.

Die Vordertibien sind vorn etwas breiter, an der Aussenseite haben sie zwei deutliche Zähne, ihr Vorderrand ist ungezahnt, aber am innern Spitzenwinkel neben der Einlenkung der Tarsen befindet sich ein kurzer, kräftiger Enddorn.

Den schwach verbreiterten Mittel- und Hintertibien fehlen an der Aussenseite die Querleisten, ein Borstenbesatz und zwei Enddorne sind aber am untern Spitzenrande vorhanden.

Die Tarsen sind kürzer als die Tibien, sie sind fünfgliedrig und haben normale Klauen.

Hierher gehören kleine Tierchen von 3,5 bis 4,5 mm Länge.

Geographische Verbreitung der Arten. — Afrika und Hinterindien.

1. *N. auriculatus*, Quedenfeldt, Berl. Ent. Zeitschr. p. 287 (1884) . Port Natal.
2. *N. laticollis*, Arrow. Ann. Mag. Nat. Hist. (7), Vol. 18, p. 130 (1906). Huilla (Angola).
3. *N. Neumanni*, Felsche, Deutsche Ent. Zeitschr. p. 451 (1909). . Abessinien.
   Neumanni, sec A. Schmidt, Stett. Ent. Zeit. p. 49 (1911).
4. *N. nigropiceus*, Quedenfeldt, Berl. Ent. Zeitschr. p. 286, t. 8, f. 6 (1884). Angola.

5. GRUPPE CORYTHODERINA

Charaktere. — Diese letzte Gruppe ist die kleinste, sie umfasst nur zwei Gattungen mit wenigen Arten, die durchweg Ameisen- oder Termitengäste sind. Aus dieser versteckten Lebensweise und dem dadurch erschwerten Fange ist die geringe Artenzahl erklärlich.

Durch ihre zierliche Gestalt, die helle, stark glänzende Oberfläche, die höchstens sparsam aufstehend behaart ist, die sonderbare Gestaltung des Halsschildes, die langen, dünnen und gebogenen Schenkel fallen diese Arten besonders auf.

Der Kopf ist wenig herabgebogen, meist deutlich dreieckig, die Spitze nach vorn gerichtet, ohne Höcker, Leisten oder Haarbüschel, feiner oder stärker punktiert; die Wangen sind nur wenig deutlich; die Augen haben eine wenig gewölbte Oberfläche.

Das Halsschild weicht durch seine Bildung von allen andern Gattungen erheblich ab. Die Mitte und die Seiten desselben sind stark gefurcht und wulstig begrenzt, die beiden Wülste neben der Mittelfurche laufen nach hinten in je eine mehr oder weniger deutliche Spitze aus, zwischen welche die Basismitte zuweilen als dreieckige Spitze hineinragt, die Basis ist auch oft wulstig gebuchtet und tomentiert.

Das Schildchen fehlt.

Die Flügeldecken sind nach hinten verbreitert, vor der Spitze stark herabgewölbt und am Spitzenrande oft mit roten Haarbüscheln geziert, die Oberfläche zeigt breite, flache Rippen.

Die Unterseite ist glatt und glänzend und wie die Oberseite gefärbt.

Die Mittelhüften stehen ziemlich dicht beieinander.

Die vier vordern Hinterleibsringe sind kurz, das fünfte ist immer stark verbreitert.

Das kleine Pygidium ist unbedeckt.

Die Vorderschenkel sind meistens stumpf gezahnt, ihre Tibien sind schlank und haben am Aussenrande gewöhnlich einen Zahn, selten ist ein zweiter angedeutet, am innern Spitzenwinkel neben den Tarsen fehlt gewöhnlich der Enddorn.

Die Mittel- und Hinterschenkel, ganz besonders die letzteren, sind dünn, sehr lang und gebogen, sie überragen sehr deutlich die Hinterleibsspitze, ihre Tibien sind meistens breit und seitlich stark zusammengedrückt, ihnen fehlen immer an der Aussenseite die Querleisten, meistens auch die Borsten am untern Spitzenrande und die zwei Enddorne.

Die Füsse sind fünfgliedrig, das erste Glied ist meistens verlängert.

Die Klauen sind normal.

BESTIMMUNGS-TABELLE DER GATTUNGEN

1. *Körper kurz, gedrungen, Flügeldecken nicht zweimal so lang als das Halsschild, Basis des letzteren in der Mitte als dreieckige Platte in die Höhe ragend, Flügeldecken an der Basis mit Quertuberkeln, vor der Spitze stets ohne Haarbüschel, Mittel- und Hintertibien nie der ganzen Länge nach stark zusammengedrückt, nicht sehr breit, fünftes Bauchsegment wohl verbreitert, aber nie bis an das erste reichend.* . . . . 1. Genus CORYTHODERUS, Klug.

1'. *Körper länglich, Flügeldecken mehr als zweimal so lang als der Thorax, die dreieckige Spitze desselben an der Basis fehlt, die Flügeldecken sind ohne Quertuberkeln, ihre Spitze ist mit oder ohne Haarbüschel, die Tibien sind meistens seitlich stark zusammengedrückt und breit, das fünfte Segment ist halbkreisförmig oder dreieckig bis an das erste erweitert* . . . . 2. Genus CHÆTOPISTHES, Westwood.

I. GENUS CORYTHODERUS, KLUG

Corythoderus. Klug, Symb. Phys. Vol. 5, t. 42, f. 11 (1845).

Charaktere. — Die Arten dieser Gattung sind rötlichgelb gefärbt, glatt, glänzend, die Oberfläche ist mit einzelnen, aufstehenden Haaren besetzt.

Der Kopf ist meistens dreieckig zugespitzt, seltener verrundet, wenig gewölbt, einzeln punktiert, ohne eingedrückte oder erhabene Stirnlinie sowohl wie ohne Höcker; die Wangen sind klein und rundlich; die sehr flachen Augen werden von ihnen wenig überragt und vom Vorderrande des Halsschildes nicht vollständig bedeckt.

Der Thorax ist an den Seiten ziemlich stark herabgewölbt, in der Mitte und an den Seiten längs ausgehöhlt, die beiden seitlichen Furchen dehnen sich fast bis zur Mitte der Basis aus und verbreitern sich hier nach vorn, die mittelste wird hinten jederseits leistenförmig begrenzt, diese Leisten ragen hinten als Spitzen hervor, zwischen ihnen erhebt sich die Mitte der Basis als dreieckige Platte, die Basis ist mit gelbem Toment bekleidet.

Ein sichtbares Schildchen fehlt.

Die Flügeldecken sind stark gewölbt und nach der Spitze verbreitert, sie haben mehrere flache,

nach hinten sich verbreiternde, divergierende Längsrippen, die aber noch vor der Spitze wieder verschwinden und nahe der Basis sich zu einer scharfen Spitze erheben, daneben befindet sich ein
Quertuberkel, der bei den einzelnen Arten verschieden gestaltet ist.

Die Unterseite ist mit der Oberseite gleichfarbig. .

Die Vorderschenkel haben an der Vorderkante einen stumpfen Zahn, ihre Tibien sind an der
Spitze zahnartig nach aussen verlängert, zuweilen noch darüber mit der Spur eines zweiten Zähnchens,
an der Innenseite neben den Tarsen fehlt ihnen der Enddorn.

Die Mittelhüften sind gross, nach hinten konvergierend; die Mittel- und Hinterschenkel sind
sehr lang, dünn und gebogen, letztere überragen sehr deutlich die Spitze des Hinterleibes; ihre Tibien
sind seitlich zusammengedrückt, an der Innenseite nahe der Basis verengen sie sich bogenförmig und
sind hier mit einer Membrane bekleidet, sie sind aussen ohne Querleisten, nur einzeln behaart, am
Endrande fehlen ihnen der Borstenbesatz und die Enddorne, nur *Marshalli* zeigt zwei winzige Enddorne
und hat nach der Beschreibung von Brauns auch einen Enddorn an den Vordertibien; bei dem Exemplare, das mir vorlag, konnte ich keinen Enddorn finden.

Die Füsse sind fünfgliedrig, mit normalen Klauen, das erste Glied ist, ausser bei *Marshalli*,
kaum länger als das zweite.

Die vier ersten Bauchsegmente sind in der Mitte stark verkürzt, das fünfte ist verbreitert.

Das Pygidium ist gross, unbedeckt und nach unten gebogen.

Geographische Verbreitung der Arten. — Vorderindien und Afrika.

1. *C. gibbiger*, Wasmann, Deutsche Ent. Zeitschr. p. 153, t. 1, f. 4 (1899).   Vorderindien.
    gibbiger (Chaetopisthes), Wasmann, Zool. Jahrb. Vol. 26, p. 123, Note 1
        (1899) (olim.).
    sec. Wasmann, Deutsche Ent. Zeitschr. p. 154, Note (1899).
2. *C. loripes*, Klug, Symb. Phys. Vol. 5, t. 42. f. 11 (1845).   Dongola.
    loripes, sec. Gestro, Ann. Mus. Stor. Nat. Genova (2), Vol. 10, p. 906 (1890-91).   Nubien.
3. *C. Marshalli*, Brauns, Ann. K. K. Hofmus. Wien, Vol. 15, p. 164, t. 9,   Bothaville.
    f. 1 (1900).
    Marshalli, Péringuey, Trans. S. Afric. Philos. Soc. 1901-03, Vol. 12, Cat.   Orangefluss-Kolonie.
        p. 450 (1901).

2. GENUS CHÆTOPISTHES, WESTWOOD

Chætopisthes. Westwood, Trans. Ent. Soc. Lond. 1845-47, Vol. 4, p. 242 (1847).

Charaktere. — Durch die mehr längliche Körperform, das Fehlen der dreieckigen Platte an
der Halsschildbasis und der Quertuberkeln an der Basis der Flügeldecken ist diese Gattung von der
vorigen zu unterscheiden.

Die Arten sind etwas grösser, mehr hellbraun gefärbt, die Oberfläche ist glatt und glänzend,
einzeln aufstehend behaart.

Der Kopf ist wenig gewölbt, in der Mitte meist flach längsvertieft, ohne Stirnlinie, Höcker oder
Leisten, vorn breit stärker punktiert, hinten mehr fein, der Vorderrand ist in der Mitte in eine Spitze
ausgezogen, nur bei *Chaetopisthes* zeigt derselbe drei kleine Zähnchen, die Seiten sind entweder gerundet
oder schwach ausgerandet; die Augen sind meist ganz vom Vorderrande des Halsschildes bedeckt; die
Wangen sind klein und rundlich.

Das Halsschild ist wenig breiter als der Kopf, seitlich stark herabgewölbt, von oben gesehen
erscheint es in der Vorderhälfte parallel oder ausgerandet, in der Hinterhälfte durch den vorstehenden
Seitenwulst verbreitert, es hat drei Furchen, eine in der Mitte und je eine seitliche, die letztere ist fast

bis zur Mitte der Basis verlängert, letztere ist mit dichtem Toment bekleidet, in der Mitte nie zu einer dreieckigen Platte umgebildet wie bei *Corythoderus*.

Ein sichtbares Schildchen fehlt.

Die Flügeldecken sind an der Basis so breit als der Thorax, nach hinten aber deutlich verbreitert, jede Decke mit vier oder fünf stumpfgewölbten, glänzenden Rippen, die nach vorn verschmälert sind und bis zur Basis reichen, die Spitze der Flügeldecken ist mit Haarbüscheln geschmückt, die nur bei *Chaetop. termiticola* und *Wasmanni* fehlen.

Die Unterseite ist auch hellbraun gefärbt, sie ist glatt und glänzend. Das fünfte Bauchsegment ist in der Mitte meistens stark verbreitert, zuweilen hier bis an das erste heranreichend.

Das Pygidium ist gross und schräg abwärts gerichtet.

Die Vorderschenkel sind kurz und dick, am Vorderrande ausgebuchtet, dadurch entstehen an den Hüften und am Knie zwei mehr oder weniger deutliche Zähne; die Vordertibien haben einen Aussenzahn, selten darüber noch ein zweites Zähnchen angedeutet.

Die Mittel- und Hinterschenkel sind sehr dünn, lang und gebogen, letztere überragen die Spitze des Abdomens; die Tibien sind fast immer seitlich sehr stark zusammengedrückt, infolgedessen sehr breit, ihre innere Kante ist an der Basis mit einer Membrane versehen, dahinter zeigen sie eine stumpfwinklige Erweiterung, am untern Spitzenrande fehlen gewöhnlich die Borsten und die Enddorne, der untere Aussenwinkel ist zuweilen in eine längere oder kürzere Spitze ausgezogen.

Die Tarsen sind fünfgliedrig, mehr oder weniger kompress, das erste Glied ist minstens deutlich verlängert.

Die Klauen sind normal.

Ueber die Geschlechtsunterschiede ist bisher nichts bekannt.

Geographische Verbreitung der Arten. — Indien.

1. *C. fulvus*, Westwood, Trans. Ent. Soc. Lond. Vol. 4, p. 242, t. 17, f. 6   Zentralindien.
   (1847).
2. *C. Heimi**, Wasmann, Zool. Jahrb. Vol. 17, p. 149, t. 5, f. 3 (1902).   Vorderindien.
3. *C. simplicipes*, Gestro. Ann. Mus. Stor. Nat. Genova (2), Vol. 10, p. 907   Nordindien.
   (1890-91).
4. *C. sulciger*, Wasmann, Deutsche Ent. Zeitschr. p. 152, t. 1. f. 3 (1899).   Vorderindien.
5. *C. termiticola*, Gestro, Ann. Mus. Stor. Nat. Genova (2), Vol 10, p. 904   Birma.
   (1890-91).
6. *C. Wasmanni*, A. Schmidt, Stett. Ent. Zeit. p. 33 (1911).   Chota Nagpore.

FOSSILE ARTEN

Aphod. antiquus, Heer, Insektf. Oening. Käf. Vol. 1, p. 66, t. 7, f. 28 (1847).   Oeningen (Baden).
Aphod. ? Bosniashii, Handlirsch, Foss. Ins. p. 838 (1907).   Gabbro (Italien).
Aphod. brevipennis*, Heer, Verh. Holl. Maatsch. Wetensch. Vol. 16, p. 77,   Oeningen.
   t. 6. f. 21 (1862); Beitr. Insektf. Oening. Col. p. 77, t. 6, f. 21 (1870).
Aphod. fossor*, Robert, Bull. Soc. Géolog. Fr. Vol. 9, p. 114 (1838).   Baltischer Bernstein.
Aphod. Krantzi*, Heyden. Palæontogr. Vol. 15, p. 140, t. 22, f. 24 (1866).   Rott (Siebengebirge).
Aphod. Meyeri, Heer, Insektfauna Oening. Käf. Vol. 1, p. 67, t. 7, f. 27   Oeningen.
   (1847).
Aphod. praecursor, Horn, Trans. Amer. Ent. Soc. Vol. 5, p. 245 (1876).   Port Kennedy.
Aphod. succini, Zang, Sitzber. Gesellsch. Nat. Freunde, p. 204, f. 5 (1905).   Baltischer Bernstein.
Ataenius patescens*, Scudder, Mon. U. S. Geol. Surv. Vol. 21, t. 1, f. 14 (1893);   Colorado.
   Vol. 40, p. 104, t. 11, f. 5, 8, 10 (1900).

REGISTER DER GRUPPEN, GÄTTUNGEN, UNTERGATTUNGEN UND SYNONYME

REGISTER DER ARTEN, VARIETÄTEN UND SYNONYME

(Die Namen der Varietäten und Synonyme sind hursiv gedruckt und eingerückt)

ERKLÄRUNG DER TAFELN

TAFEL I

Fig. 1. *Turanella latevittis*, Reitter.
— 2. *Acanthaphodius Bruchi*, A. Schmidt; 2a, Hinterbein.
— 3. *Aphodius lunifer*, Solsky, ♂.
— 4. — *bimaculatus*, Laxmann.
— 5. — *Wahlbergi*, Boheman.
— 6. — *pulcherrimus*, Reiche.
— 7. — *rhinocerus*, Reiche; 7a, Seitenansicht von Kopf und Thorax.
— 8. — *magnificus*, A. Schmidt. Seitenansicht von Kopf und Thorax.
— 9. — *curvodilatatus*, A. Schmidt; 9a, Hinterbein, ♂.
— 10. — *amoenus*, Boheman.
— 11. — *senegalensis*, Klug.

Fig. 12. *Aphodius Ballioni*, A. Schmidt, ♂.
— 13. — *discoidalis*, Boheman.
— 14. — *hamatus*, Say, ♀.
— 15. — *peruanus*, Erichson.
— 16. *Oxyomus simillimus*, A. Schmidt.
— 17. — *costipennis*, Boheman.

Tafel 2

Fig. 18. *Heptaulacus alpinus*, Drapiez.
— 19. — *iniquus*, A. Schmidt.
— 20. *Lorditomaeus deplanatus*, Roth.
— 21. *Proctophanes sculptus*, Hope.
— 22. *Macrovetrus singularis*, Péringuey, ♀.
— 23. *Didactylia varia*, A. Schmidt, ♀.
— 24. — *cicotricosa*, A. Schmidt, ♀.
— 25. *Coptochirus pteropus*, Harold. ♂.
— 26. — *vulgatus*, Harold.
— 27. *Drepanocanthus lineatus*, Wiedemann, ♂.
— 28. *Harmogaster exarata*, Harold.
— 29. *Euparia excavaticollis*, Blanchard.
— 30. — *bitubericollis*, A. Schmidt.
— 31. *Ataenius angusticollis*, A. Schmidt.
— 32. — *sculptor*, Harold.
— 33. — *opatroides*, Blanchard.

Tafel 3

Fig. 34. *Ataenius platensis*, Blanchard.
— 35. *Saprosites dynastoides*, Walker.
— 36. — *parallelus*, Harold.
— 37. *Simogonius Beccarii*, Harold.
— 38. *Dialytes monstrosus*, Harold.
— 39. — *striatulus*, Say.
— 40. *Odochilus syntheticus*, Harold.
— 41. *Psammobius porcicollis*, Illiger.
— 42. *Diastictus vulneratus*, Sturm.
— 43. *Rhyssemus algiricus*, Lucas.
— 44. — *granosus*, Klug.
— 45. *Rhyssemodes orientalis*, Mulsant.
— 46. *Trichiorhyssemus hirsutus*, Clouët.
— 47. *Pleurophorus impressicollis*, Boheman.
— 48. *Sybacodes aureopilosus*, A. Schmidt.

———————————

Berlin, 15. December 1909.

uerittis Reitt.   *Acanthaphodius Bruchi. A. Schmidt.*   *Aphodius lunifer. Solsk, ♂.*   *Aphodius bimaculatus. Laxmann*

Aphodius pulcherrimus. Reiche.   *Aphodius rhinocerus Reiche, ♂.*   *Aphodius curvodilatatus. A. Schmidt, ♂.*

Aph. magnificus. A. Schmidt, ♂

noenus Bohem.   *Aphodius senegalensis. Klug.*   *Aphodius Ballioni. A. Schmidt, ♂.*   *Aphodius discoidalis. Bohem.*

hamatus Say, ♀   *Aphodius peruanus Erichs.*   *Oxyomus simillimus A. Schmidt.*   *Oxyomus costipennis Bohem.*

Heptaulacus alpinus.Drapier.

Heptaulacus iniquus.A.Schmidt.

Lorditomaeus deplanatus Roth.

Proctophanes sculptus.Hope.

Macroretrus singularis Péring.,♀

Didactylia varia A.Schmidt,♀

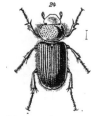

Didactylia cicatricosa.A.Schmidt, ♀

Coptochirus pteropus.Har.,♂

Coptochirus vulgatus Har.

Drepanocanthus lineatus.Wiedem., ♂

Harmogaster exarata Har.

Euparia exaraticollis.Blanch.

Euparia bituberinicollis.A.Schmidt.

Ataenius angusticollis.A.Schmidt.

Ataenius sculptor.Har.

Ataenius opatroides.Blanch.

FAM. APHODIIDÆ

2

Atænius platensis Blanch.

Saprosites dynastoides Walker

Saprosites parallelus Har.

Simogonius Beccarii Har.

Dialytes monstrosus Har.

Dialytes striatulus Say.

Odochilus syntheticus Har.

Psammobius porcicollis Illig

Diastictus vulneratus Sturm

Rhyssemus algiricus Luc.

Rhyssemus granosus Klug

Rhyssemodes orientalis Muls.

Trichiorhyssemus hirsutus Clouët.

Pleurophorus impressicollis Bohem.

Sybacodes aureopilosus A.Schmidt.

FAM. APHODIIDÆ

COLEOPTERA

FAM. IPIDÆ

COLEOPTERA

FAM. IPIDÆ

von Max HAGEDORN, Dr. Med.

MIT 14 SCHWARZEN TAFELN

I. — ALLGEMEINER TEIL

HISTORISCHES

INNÉ beschreibt in seinem *Systema Naturae*, Ed. 10, 1758, p. 355, die ersten erkennbaren Ipiden unter dem Gattungsnamen *Dermestes* und führt folgende Arten an : *D. typographus, D. micrographus, D. poligraphus, D. piniperda* und *D. domesticus*. In seiner *Fauna Suecica* 1761 fügt er noch hinzu : *D. chalcographus*. Dan folgt Fabricius in seiner *Mantissa* 1787, seiner *Entomologia Systematica* 1792 und seinem *Systema Eleutheratorum* 1801 schon mit einer Anzahl verschiedener Gattungen : *Apate, Bostrichus, Hylesinus* und Arten, achtundzwanzig an der Zahl.

Die erste systematische Aufstellung gab Latreille in der *Histoire Naturelle des Crustacés et Insectes* 1802, Vol. 3, p. 202, welcher seine 29. Familie der *Bostrichins* (*Bostrichini*) mit den Gattungen *Bostrichus* (Type *Apate capucinus* Fabricius), *Tomicus* (Type *Hylesinus piniperda* Fabricius), *Scolytus* (Type *Hylesinus scolytus* Fabricius), *Platypus* (Type *Platypus cylindrus* Herbst) und *Phloeotribus* (Type *Hylesinus oleae* Fabricius) mit den *Xylophagen* im weiteren Sinne zu einer Gruppe zusammenfasste.

Wenn wir von dieser auf die Anzahl der Tarsenglieder gegründeten Einteilung absehen, dann müssen wir Erichson 1836 als den ersten Borkenkäferforscher anführen, der eine brauchbare systematische Zusammenstellung der Ipiden gab. Dann kam Ratzeburg 1837, der die Borkenkäfer hauptsächlich von forstentomologischen Gesichtspunkten aus, Kirby 1837 und Perris 1856, die mehr im faunistischen Sinne die Ipiden bearbeiteten, bis schliesslich Lacordaire 1866 ein schönes ausführliches System schuf. Für die nordamerikanischen Borkenkäfer errichtete Le Conte 1876 ein neues System, das noch bis heute sich vielfacher Anerkennung erfreut. Als weitere Systematiker nenne ich noch Chapuis 1876, Eichhoff (*Ratio Tomicinorum* 1879 und *Europäische Borkenkäfer* 1881), Reitter 1894 für die paläarktischen Borkenkäfer, Blandford für die centralamerikanischen (*Biologia*

COLEOPTERA

Centrali-Americana 1895-1907), Escherich 1897, Trédl 1907 für die europäischen Borkenkäfer und Verfasser 1909 und 1910 im *Coleopterorum Catalogus* von Schenkling, für die Borkenkäfer der Welt.

Ueber die Anatomie der Borkenkäfer schrieben besonders : Lindemann, *Anatomische Untersuchungen des männlichen Begattungsgliedes der Borkenkäfer* 1875; Eichhoff, *Ueber Mundteile der Xylophagen* 1864 und *Ratio Tomicinorum* 1879; Schröder, *Studien über das männliche Genitalorgan einiger Scolytiden* 1902; Sedlaczek, *Ueber den Darmkanal der Scolytiden* 1902; Powell, *The Development of Wings* 1904, 1905; Scholz, *Der Tonapparat von Scolytiden* 1905. Besonders wichtig sind die anatomischen Untersuchungen von Verhoeff, *Ueber das Abdomen der Scolytiden* 1896, und Hopkins, *The Genus Dendroctonus* 1909.

Borkenkäferlarven und ihre Anatomie beschrieben Perris 1876, Eichelbaum 1903 und 1905 und Leisewitz, *Die chitinösen Fortbewegungsapparate von Insektenlarven* 1906.

Um die Erforschung der Biologie der Borkenkäfer haben sich besonders verdient gemacht Ratzeburg in *Die Waldverderber* 1841-42, Nördlinger in seinen *Nachträgen zu Ratzeburgs Forstinsekten* 1856, dann Altum in seiner *Forstzoologie* 1874, ferner Lindemann in seiner *Monographie der Borkenkäfer Russlands* 1875-79, ganz besonders aber Eichhoff in den *Europäischen Borkenkäfern* 1881, schliesslich Iudeich und Nitsche in der *Forstinsektenkunde* 1895, Knotek in verschiedenen Beiträgen zur Biologie der Borkenkäfer 1898 und 1899.

Die jüngste Periode der Forschung über die Borkenkäferbiologie wurde eingeleitet durch die bahnbrechenden Arbeiten von Pauly 1888-1906, Nüsslin 1882-1907, Knoch 1900-1908, Fuchs 1907, Hennings 1907 und 1908.

Die Biologie der nordamerikanischen Borkenkäfer erforschte besonders Hopkins in zahlreichen Arbeiten in den Jahren 1892-1909, die der ostindischen Stebbing in den Jahren 1903-1908.

Speciell mit der Biologie der pilzzüchtenden Ambrosiakäfer beschäftigten sich Hubbard 1897 und Neger 1908, 1909, denen wir grundlegende Anschauungen über die Lebensweise dieser hochinteressanten Tiere zu verdanken haben.

Ausführliche Zusammenstellungen der Nahrungspflanzen der Borkenkäfer gaben Eichhoff in den *Europäischen Borkenkäfern* 1881, Trédl in den *Entomologischen Blättern* 1907 und Kleine in der *Berliner Entomologischen Zeitschrift* 1908.

Man wolle den ausführlichen Literaturnachweis in des Verfassers *Ipidenkatalog* 1910 nachlesen; ich habe hier nur einige Autoren, welche gewissermassen Marksteine in der Borkenkäferforschung bezeichnen, anführen können.

Allgemeine Familienmerkmale

Wenn man eine kurze aber umfassende Diagnose der Ipiden geben will, so würde man am besten sich der von Iudeich in der Forstinsektenkunde gebrauchten bedienen können. Diese in ihrer Urform für die mitteleuropäischen Ipiden geschaffene würde nach ihrer Erweiterung auf die Exoten etwa so lauten können : Die Borkenkäfer, Ipidæ, sind den eigentlichen Rüsselkäfern zoologisch nahe verwandte, 1 bis 12 mm. lange, walzenförmige bis eirunde oder kugelförmige, kryptopentamere Käfer mit flachen querovalen, häufig ausgerandeten bis geteilten Augen, mit gebrochenen aus Schaft und Geissel mit Endknopf bestehenden Fühlern, mit nach unten verbreiterten Schienen und mit Fussgliedern, deren Sohlen bis auf wenige Ausnahmen nicht behaart oder gepolstert sind.

Die Familienmerkmale im einzelnen sind folgende :

Körpergrösse : durchschnittlich klein, nur wenige Arten erreichen eine Länge von 12 mm.

Farbe : wechselt von blasshellgelb bei nichtausgefärbten Individuen durch rostbraun, braun bis tiefschwarz. Im allgemeinen sind die Tiere einfarbig, selten zweifarbig wie *Aphanarthrum* und *Amphi-*

cranus. Metallische, grüne oder blaue Farben kommen nicht vor bis auf drei Ausnahmen, nämlich *Camptocerus aeneipennis* Fabricius, welcher metallisch grüne Flügeldecken hat, *Hexacolus unipunctatus* Blandford, bei welchem bei beiden Geschlechtern die Stirn blau opalescierend ist, und *Cnesinus teres* Blandford, wo im männlichen Geschlecht die Stirn iridisiert.

Skulptur wechselt von ganz glatt bis rauh durch Erhabenheiten und Vertiefungen.

Die *Bekleidung* des Körpers ist sehr wechselnd durch kürzere oder längere, spärlichere, oder dichtere Behaarung von grauer bis gelber und braungelber Farbe oder durch mehr weniger dichte Beschuppung von bald anliegenden, bald aufstehenden flachen bis keulenförmigen Schuppen von verschiedener Farbe, welche, da sie von weissgrau durch gelb, braun bis schwarz wechseln, manchen Arten ein buntscheckiges Aussehen verleihen.

Kopf ist klein, schmäler als der Vorderrand des Halsschilds, entweder kugelig oder mit einem mehr minder grossen Rüssel versehen.

Oberlippe ist quer-viereckig und dem vorderen Rande des Kopfschildes so innig verwachsen dass sie nur bei der Gattung *Problechilus* deutlich zu erkennen ist.

Die *Vorderkiefer* sind kurz, breit dreieckig konisch, kräftig mit meist scharfer Spitze und Zähnen am Innenrande, immer von dunkelbrauner, nach der Spitze zu dunkler häufig schwarz werdender Farbe.

Mittelkiefer sind mit einer einzigen und zwar Innenlade versehen, an deren inneren Rande, der Kaukante, die eigentlichen Werkzeuge zur Nahrungsaufnahme befestigt sind. Und zwar sind diese je nach der Beschaffenheit der Nahrung entweder einfache Haare oder schwache platte sichelförmig gebogene Borsten (bei den Pilzfressern oder Ambrosia-beetles) oder starke breite dolchartig-spitze Dornen oder Zähne (bei den Holzfressern oder bark-borers). Die einzelnen Teile des Mittelkiefers sind meist innig miteinander verwachsen, sodass die Grenzen von stipes, fulcrum oder mala nur bei sehr wenigen Gattungen zu unterscheiden sind. Die Taster sind kurz, konisch, bis auf eine Ausnahme (Genus *Dactylipalpus*) dreigliedrig.

Die *Hinterkiefer* verschmelzen zu einem vorgestreckten auf der Spitze des Submentum eingefügten Kinne (Mentum oder Labium), das eine frei Zunge trägt; die Form des Hinterkiefers und der Zunge, sowie der letzteren Ansatz ist fast bei jedem Genus anders. Die Taster sind bis auf eine Ausnahme (*Dactylipalpus*) dreigliedrig.

Die *Augen* sind bei keinem Borkenkäfer rund oder vorstehend, sondern immer flach, quergestellt, mehr oder weniger lang eiförmig, vorne ausgerandet oder nierenförmig oder bei manchen Gattungen durch einen Fortsatz der Stirn in zwei Hälften geteilt, welche mitunter soweit auseinanderstehen, dass ein Paar gänzlich isoliert vorn auf der Stirn, das andere auf der Unterseite des Kopfes neben den Vorderkiefern liegt.

Die *Fühler* sind kurz, gebrochen, neben den Vorderkiefern nur ausnahmsweise auf der Stirn eingelenkt, mit ein- bis siebengliedriger Geissel und grosser Keule.

Halsschild so breit wie die Flügeldecken; dessen Vorderrücken mit den Seiten der Vorderbrust innig verwachsen, nur selten durch eine Naht von ihr getrennt.

Vorderbrust sehr kurz, mit ihrem Episternum meistens innig verwachsen, häufig einen Fortsatz zwischen die Vorderhüften entsendend.

Das *Schildchen* ist von verschiedener Form und Grösse, bald punktförmig, gerundet oder länglich, dann auch grösser und dreieckig, liegt häufig tiefer als das Niveau der Flügeldecken.

Die *Mittelbrust* ist lang mit kleinen beinahe linienförmigen Epimeren.

Die *Hinterbrust* ist gross mit freien Episternen.

Die *Flügeldecken* sind je nach der allgemeinen Körperform mehr weniger gewölbt, kugelig bis cylindrisch. An der Basis sind sie entweder aufgeworfen und gekerbt oder glatt abgeschnitten; der Absturz ist entweder flach oder gewölbt oder ausgehöhlt und trägt sehr häufig in Form von Zähnen, Dornen u. s. w. sekundäre Geschlechtsmerkmale.

Die *Vorderhüften* sind vorgestreckt, beinahe kugelförmig, einander berührend oder voneinander entfernt.

Die *Mittel- und Hinterhüften* sind quer; alle Hüften sind ohne Trochantinen.

Die *Füsse* sind kräftig und kurz, die Schenkel zusammengedrückt, die Schienen länger als die Tarsen, an der Aussenkante meist bezähnt oder gedornt, selten glatt, und dann an der Aussenspitze mit einem einfachen oder doppelten starkgekrümmten Haken versehen.

Die *Tarsen* sind kryptopentamer, auf der Unterseite mit wenigen Ausnahmen nie haarig oder schwammartig gepolstert; das erste Glied ist kürzer als die folgenden zusammen, das vierte ist undeutlich.

Der *Bauch* besteht aus fünf Abschnitten, von denen die beiden ersten miteinander verwachsen und unbeweglich sind. Sie tragen häufig sekundäre Geschlechtsmerkmale und verlaufen im ganzen entweder wagerecht oder steigen in konkavem oder konvexem Bogen gegen den After an.

Die Geschlechtsmerkmale

Man unterscheidet primäre und sekundäre Geschlechtsmerkmale. Die ersteren geben die Genitalien der Borkenkäfer. Man kann an ihnen durch mikroskopische Untersuchung die Reife oder Unreife der Tiere, sowie ob sie Eier abgelegt haben oder noch nicht, an folgenden Merkmalen erkennen :

Unreif	Reif
♂. *Hoden :* Weiss ohne Spermatozoen.	Gelblich mit Spermaflocken.
Ektadenien : Klein.	Wachsen und füllen sich mit Sekret.
Samenblasen : Klein.	Wachsen enorm und enthalten Sperma.
♀. Kleine *Keimfächer*, die dem Eileiter (Eikelch) direkt aufsitzen.	Wachsen grösser und bilden als Keimlager einen Kolben, an dessen unterem Ende sich die Keimanlagen befinden. Die Keimfächer werden immer weiter hinaus in die Peritonealhüllen getrieben und sitzen schliesslich nur im oberen kleinen Teil des Ovariums. Unten sind die Eier am grössten, oben werden sie immer kleiner.
Kittdrüsen : Leer.	Mit erst weissem, dann citronengelbem Sekret gefüllt.
Begattungstasche *Receptaculum seminis* *Anhangsdrüse* der letzteren } Leer.	Mit Samenfäden gefüllt, auch noch nach beendeter Eiablage solche enthaltend.

Hat das ♀ die Eier schon abgelegt, dann findet sich am Grunde der Eiröhren das Corpus luteum.

Sekundäre Geschlechtsmerkmale : Ein von Verhoeff (« Ueber das Abdomen der Scolytiden » im *Archiv für Naturgeschichte*, Bd. 62, p. 134 und 135, 1896) angegebenes Merkmal zur äusserlichen Geschlechtsbestimmung der Borkenkäfer ist folgendes : « Auf Grund meiner Mitteilungen über die Abdominalsegmente sind also *alle* Borkenkäfer in Bezug auf ihr Geschlecht schon äusserlich leicht zu erkennen, denn wenn man die Elytren aufhebt oder besser noch ganz entfernt, kann man feststellen, ob die letzte äussere Dorsalplatte die siebente oder die achte ist (die siebente Dorsalplatte hat zwei Haarfelder, während die achte der Haarfelder entbehrt).

Ist sie die siebente Dorsalplatte, also verdecktes Pseudopygidium, so liegt ein ♀, ist sie die achte Dorsalplatte, also verdecktes Pygidium, so liegt ein ♂ vor ».

Ob das wirklich für *alle* Borkenkäfer, wie Verhoeff annimmt, auch zutrifft, muss erst noch nach-
geprüft werden. Ich habe es bisher nur bei wenigen Exoten prüfen können und zutreffend gefunden.

Ausser diesem vielleicht für sämtliche Ipiden gültigen sekundären Geschlechtsmerkmale kommen
noch eine ganze Reihe anderer an verschiedenen Körperteilen vor — Gattungen, bei denen keine
anderen sekundären Geschlechtsmerkmale gefunden wurden, gibt es nicht viele; ich nenne nur beispielsweise die Gattungen *Cryphalus*, *Liparthrum*, *Hypoborus*, *Hylurgus*, *Kissophagus*, *Sphärotrypes*, *Dendrosinus*.
Bei den meisten Gattungen treten Auszeichnungen verschiedener Art an verschiedenen Körperteilen
auf, so zum Beispiel :

> *Stirn* : Geringere Wölbung, Abflachung oder tiefere Aushöhlung;
> Glänzende Flecke, Knötchen oder Kiele;
> Dichtere oder längere Haarbürsten oder Haarbüschel.
> *Fühler* : Grössere Entwicklung des Schaftes oder der Keule;
> Verlängerung der Geissel;
> Lange oft sehr derbe Haare an einem oder mehreren Teilen des Fühlers.
> *Flügeldecken* : Stärkere Bezahnung, tiefere Aushöhlung oder Abflachung des Absturzes.
> *Bauch* : Abflachung oder Aushöhlung;
> Bezahnung der Ventralplatten.

Auszeichnungen an Flügeldecken und Bauch zugleich sind konstant männliche; an Stirn und
Fühlern zugleich konstant männliche bei den Subfamilien der *Spongocerinae*, *Eccoptogastrinae*, *Hylesininae*,
Hylocurinae; bei den übrigen Subfamilien sind sie je nach Gattungen und Arten wechselnd. Nachstehend
folgt eine Zusammenstellung der mir bekannten *sekundären Geschlechtsmerkmale* nach den Gattungen :

1. Durch Farbenunterschiede . . . . *Amphicranus.*
2. Durch die Körperform; ♂ und ♀ sind mehr weniger
   verschieden . . . . *Xyleborus, Coccotrypes.*
3. Körperform gleich, aber die Geschlechter unterscheiden
   sich durch Auszeichnungen an sehr vielen Körperteilen zugleich (an Stirn, Fühler, Halsschild, Flügeldecken, Vorderbrust, Beinen) . . . . . . *Scolytoplatypus.*
4. Auszeichnungen befinden sich an Stirn und zwei anderen
   Körperteilen :
   A. An Stirn, Fühlern und Flügeldecken . . . . . *Pterocyclon, Tricolus.*
   B. An Stirn, Fühlern und Halsschild· . . . . . . *Brachyspartus, Glochinocerus.*
   C. An Stirn, Halsschild und Beinen . . . . *Xyloterus.*
   D. An Stirn, Bauch und Beinen . . . . *Hylastes.*
5. Auszeichnungen befinden sich an Stirn und einem
   anderen Körperteil :
   A. An Stirn und Fühlern . . . . { *Camptocerus, Ceratolepis, Cnemonyx, Loga-*
   { *nius, Hexacolus, Corthylus, Metacor-*
   { *thylus.*
   B. An Stirn und Thorax . . . . { *Phloeoborus, Aricerus, Hyorrhynchus, Xy-*
   { *lechinus, Erineophilus, Dactylipalpus.*
   C. An Stirn und Flügeldecken . . . . { *Phloeosinus, Polygraphus, Coptonotus, Ips,*
   { *Taphrorychus, Pityophthorus.*
   D. An Stirn und Bauch . . . . *Eccoptogaster.*

6. Auszeichnungen befinden sich an Halsschild und Flügel-
    decken . . . . *Hylocurus.*
7. Auszeichnungen befinden sich an den Fühlern allein .   *Gnathotrichus.*

                                                 Cactopinus ,   Orthaspistes ,   Dryocoetes ,
                                               Prionosceles,   Chramesus,   Phloeotribus,
                                             Hylesinus, Dendroctonus, Dendroterus,
8. Auszeichnungen befinden sich an der Stirn allein . . *Problechilus, Eulytocerus, Eupagiocerus,*
                                             Phloeophthorus, Pycnarthrum, Scolytop-
                                             sis, Pagiocerus, Bothrosternus. Carpho-
                                             borus. Chortastus, Cnesinus.
9. Auszeichnungen befinden sich am Thorax allein . . . *Crypturgus.*
10. Auszeichnungen befinden sich auf den Flügeldecken
    allein . . . .   *Xylocleptes, Myelophilus, Thamnurgus.*

Biologie

Die Borkenkäfer brüten zum grössten Teile in Holzpflanzen (nur wenige Gattungen leben in krautartigen Pflanzen oder in harten Fruchtsamen), aber auch in diesen wieder nur in den verholzten Teilen. Sie legen ihre Eier in *Muttergänge*, d. h. in röhrenförmige oder platzförmige Aushöhlungen mit kreisrunden Eingängen, den *Bohrlöchern*, welche der hierbei mit seinem ganzen Körper in die Pflanze eindringende Käfer seinem Dickendurchmesser entsprechend nagt.

Die weissen fusslosen bauchwärts gekrümmten, nur am deutlich abgesetzten Kopfe stärker chitinisierten Larven sind denen der Rüsselkäfer äusserst ähnlich und schwer zu unterscheiden.

Dagegen sind die meistens durch das Zusammenwirken von Mutterkäfer nund Larven gebildeten Frassfiguren so eigentümlich, dass nicht nur der Borkenkäferfrass als solcher von jedem anderen Insektenfrass zu unterscheiden ist, sondern auch meistens aus der Gestalt des Frassbildes und der Holzart, in welcher sich dasselbe befindet, auf die Art, welcher der Täter angehört, geschlossen werden kann.

Man unterscheidet hinsichtlich der Art und Weise des Frasses mehrere Gruppen unter den Borkenkäfern, welche durch die Verschiedenartigkeit der Ausbildung ihrer Mundteile und die dadurch bedingte Verschiedenheit der Ernährung und sonstigen Lebensweise sich ganz natürlich voneinander abgrenzen.

Alle Borkenkäfer benutzen ihre kräftig gebauten Vorderkiefer lediglich zur Zertrümmerung der Pflanzensubstanz, indem sie mit ihnen die Holzteilchen abkneifen, wenn sie ihre Gänge hineinarbeiten. Die losgelösten Bohrspäne werden nun entweder durch die Mittelkiefer, welche in diesem Falle mit starken dornartigen Zähnen versehen sind, weiter zerschrotet und nach genügender Zerkleinerung dem Schlunde und dem Kaumagen zugeführt, woselbst sie behufs Ausnutzung der im Holze enthaltenen ziemlich spärlichen Nährstoffe durch die Kauplatten noch mehr zerrieben und ausgelaugt werden. Der unverdauliche Celluloserest geht durch den Darmkanal und wird entweder aus den Gängen entfernt oder bleibt in ihnen, sie hinter dem Käfer verstopfend, liegen. Dies ist bei den sogenannten *rindenbrütenden Borkenkäfern*, den *Phloeophagi* Eichhoff, oder *bark-borers* der Amerikaner, *Spinidentatae* Hagedorn, der Fall.

Bei einer anderen Gruppe werden die Bohrspäne nicht gefressen, sondern einfach als Abfall aus dem Bohrloch herausgeschafft. Die Tiere, welche sich des letzteren Verfahrens bedienen, müssen natürlich eine andere Nahrungsquelle als die Holz- oder Rindensubstanz haben. Sie sind meistens Pilzzüchter geworden, *Ambrosia-beetles* der Amerikaner, *Mycetophagae* Hagedorn, und zeichnen sich durch eine sehr schwache, aus feinen flachgedrückten Borsten bestehende Bewehrung der Mittelkiefer aus, wie sie zum Abweiden der Ambrosiapilze genügt : *Saetidentatae* Hagedorn.

Ob die Gruppe der *Phloeotrupinae*, welche weder Zähne noch Borsten, sondern nur einfache Haare an der Kaukante der Mittelkiefer tragen, auch von Pilzen lebt, was ja möglich wäre, oder vom Milchsaft der Kautschukbäume, muss mangels Kenntnis der Biologie dieser Tiere dahingestellt bleiben. Je nach der Nahrung ist nun auch die Lebensweise verschieden.

Was zunächst die von der Substanz des Baumes selbst lebenden Käfer betrifft, so legen diese, die sogenannten *rindenbrütenden Borkerkäfer*, ihre Frassfiguren zwischen Rinde und Holz des Baumes, den Splint mehr oder minder furchend, an. Von den in krautartigen Pflanzen lebenden *Thamnurgus*- und den in harten Fruchtsamen fressenden *Coccotrypes*- und *Stephanoderes*-Arten will ich zunächst absehen.

Die Rindenbrüter legen ihre Muttergänge entweder in der Längsrichtung der Bäume, *Lot- oder Langsgänge*, oder quer zu dieser, *Wage- oder Quergänge*, oder sternförmig ausstrahlend, *Sterngänge*, an.

Die Längs- und Quergänge werden von monogamisch oder bigamisch lebenden Tieren, die Sterngänge von polygamisch lebenden angelegt : jeder einzelne Gang entspricht dann einem ♀, während das ♂ sich in dem Mittelpunkte der Frassfigur, der geräumigeren Rammelkammer, aufhält und daselbst seinem Geschäfte, das von den Weibern losgelöste Bohrmehl herausenschaffen, nachgeht.

Die Begattung findet hier in der Rammelkammer statt, welche, wie auch das Einbohrloch vom ♂ angelegt wird, während jedes ♀ nur seinen Mutter- oder Brutgang macht. Anders ist es bei den monogam lebenden : hier fertigt das ♀ das ganze Frassbild an, auch das Einbohrloch, in welchem es während des Einbohrens meistens schon von dem auf dem Stamme ausser alb herankriechenden ♂ befruchtet wird, solange es noch mit der Hälfte des Körpers nach aussen hervorragt, wenn die Befruchtung nicht schon vor Anlage des Bohrloches auf dem Stamme stattgefunden hat.

Der Mutterkäfer legt die Eier entweder in Haufen in ein gemeinschaftliches Lager ab oder fertigt für jedes Ei eine kleine halbrunde Nische, in welche er das Ei mit dem Maule hineinbringt und dann den Eingang zu der Nische sorgfältig mit Bohrmehl verstopft.

Die Eiablage findet entweder in rascher Aufeinanderfolge, gewissermassen auf ein Mal statt : dann liegen die Eier entweder auf einem Haufen oder die Eiernischen stehen dicht nebeneinander ; oder es finden sich zwei oder mehrere räumlich voneinander getrennte Haufen wie bei *Dendroctonus micans* Kugelann und *Cryphalus Grothii* Hagedorn ; oder die Muttergänge sind sehr lang gestreckt, die Eiernischen durch weite Zwischenräume voneinander entfernt, z. B. bei *Pityophthorus macrographus* Eichhoff und *Ips acuminatus* Gyllenhal. Dieses letztere Verhalten ist ein Beweis dafür, dass zwischen den einzelnen Eiablagen der Mutterkäfer einer Erholung, eines *Regenerationfrasses* zwecks Reifung der Eier bedarf.

Nun entwickeln sich die Larven.

Diese fressen entweder gemeinschaftlich nebeneinander in Familiengängen wie bei *Dendroctonus micans* Kugelann und *Ips laricis* Fabricius, sowie bei verschiedenen *Cryphalus*-Arten, oder jede Larve frisst senkrecht zur Achse des Mutterganges ihren Larvengang, der entsprechend der Dickenzunahme des Tieres immer breiter wird und hinter dem Tiere mit dem Bohrmehl, welches den Darmkanal der Larve passiert hat, gefüllt ist.

Wenn das Wachstum der Larve beendet ist, nagt sie am Ende ihres Frassganges eine Wiege für die Puppe, die entweder senkrecht in den Splint hineinführt, wie bei *Myelophilus minor* Hartig und *Hylesinus fraxini* Panzer, oder mehr in der bisherigen Richtung des Larvenganges im Splint oder in der Rinde liegt.

Nach beendigter Puppenruhe, während derer keine Nahrung aufgenommen wird, entwickelt sich der Jungkäfer. Dieser braucht nun bei den meisten Arten eine gewisse, kürzere oder längere Zeit, bis er generationskräftig geworden und ausgehärtet ist, welche damit ausgefüllt wird, dass er mehr weniger Nahrung zu sich nimmt, also *Nachfrass* ausübt. Man kann hierbei verschiedene Gruppen unterscheiden,

je nach dem ob überhaupt Nachfrass geübt wird oder nicht, ferner ob der Nachfrass an der Geburtsstätte oder an frischem Nährmaterial, an anderen Pflanzen stattfindet.

Diese Gruppierung nach der Art des Nachfrasses der Jungkäfer würde folgende sein :

I. Tiere, die ohne Nachfrass ausschwärmen und sofort zur Brut schreiten, also eine zweite
Generation anlegen. Hierher gehören sämtliche Arten der Gattung *Eccoptogaster*, von *Hylesininen H. crenatus*
Fabricius, *H. oleiperda* Fabricius, *Pteleobius vittatus* Fabricius, dagegen keine *Ipinen*.

II. Tiere, die ohne Nachfrass aus ihrer Geburtsstätte ausschwärmen, dann aber anderweitig
Nachfrass üben, und erst nachdem sie eine längere oder kürzere Zeit dies getan, oder gar erst im
nächsten Jahre brüten. Dazu gehören von *Hylesininen* die sogenannten Wurzelbrüter (*Hylastes angustatus*
Herbst, *H. attenuatus* Erichson, *H. opacus* Erichson, *H. ater* Paykull, *H. cunicularius* Erichson, *H. linearis*
Erichson, ferner *Hylurgops decumanus* Erichson, *H. palliatus* Gyllenhal, *Hylesinus fraxini* Panzer, *Myelo-
philus piniperda* Linné und *M. minor* Hartig, dagegen keine *Ipinen*.

III. Tiere, die unter der Rinde an der Geburtsstätte nachfressen. Hierher gehören sämtliche
Ipinen, und von *Hylesininen* : *Dendroctonus micans* Kugelann, *Phthorophloeus spinulosus* Rey, *Hylastinus Fank-
hauseri* Reitter, *Xylechinus pilosus* Knoch, mitunter auch *Hylurgops decumanus* Erichson und *palliatus*
Gyllenhal; von *Crypturginen* : *Polygraphus poligraphus* Linné.

Natürlich finden vielerlei Modificationen und Abänderungen in der Art und Weise, sowie in der
Stärke des Nachfrasses statt. So z B. fressen in Gruppe II die wurzelbrütenden *Hylesinen* aussen an der
Rinde junger Nadelholzpflanzen nach und vernichten dadurch viele Anpflanzungen, während *Hylurgops
decumanus* Erichson und *H. palliatus* Gyllenhal unter der Rinde frischen Materiales weitere Ernährungs-
gänge fressen. Die beiden Waldgärtner *Myelophilus piniperda* Linné und *minor* Hartig bohren sich in die
frischen Zweigspitzen ein und fressen deren Mark aus, *Hylesinus fraxini* Panzer fliegt in die Kronen von
Eschenbäumen und bohrt sich dort in die Rinde gesunder. Baumteile ein, woselbst er das nächste
Frühjahr abwartet und durch seinen Frass Veranlassung zur Bildung der Rindenrosen der Esche abgibt.

In der Gruppe III wird verschieden starker Nachfrass geübt. Bei *Polygraphus poligraphus* Linné
und *Cryphalus abietis* Ratzeburg findet er mehr in der Rinde statt, bei den Käfern der Gruppe *Ips* furcht
er stark den Splint. Dann wird von einigen die Puppenwiege mehr minder platzförmig ausgefressen,
so von *Cryphalus abietis* Ratzeburg und *Cryphalus piceae* Ratzeburg, von *Ips acuminatus* Gyllenhal und *Ips
Mannsfeldi* Wachtl, oder die Käfer arbeiten in der Richtung des Larvenganges weiter, wie die *Pityophthorus*-
Arten, dann *Phthorophloeus spinulosus* Rey. häufig auch *Cryphalus fagi* Fabricius, oder es werden labyrin-
thische, gekrümmte, meist tief den Splint furchende Gänge gefressen, die oft das ganze Frassbild
zerstören, wie von *Ips typographus* Linné und seinen Verwandten.

Schwachen Nachfrass und diesen nur in der Rinde üben *Xylechinus pilosus* Knoch, *Phthorophloeus
spinulosus* Rey, *Polygraphus poligraphus* Linné, starken mit Angreifen des Splintes *Polygraphus grandiclava*
Thomson, *Dendroctonus micans* Kugelann und *Hylastinus Fankhauseri* Reitter.

Aber nicht nur die Jungkäfer fressen an ihrer Geburtsstätte oder anderswo zum Zwecke der
Erhärtung ihres Chitinpanzers und der Erzielung der Geschlechtsreife nach und richten dadurch viel
Schaden an, auch die abgebrunsteten alten Käfer tun das Gleiche in ausgedehntem Masse, damit ihre
Geschlechtsorgane wieder funktionsfähig werden.

Diesen Frass der Mutterkäfer bezeichnet man mit dem Namen « *Regenerationsfrass* »; er ist am
längsten bekannt bei den beiden Waldgärtnern, *Myelophilus piniperda* Linné und *M. minor* Hartig, wo die
alten Käfer, nachdem sie ihre erste Brut abgelegt haben, genau wie die Jungen, in die frischen Triebe
einbohren und deren Mark ausfressen. Aehnlich ist es bei *Hylesinus fraxini* Panzer : wie die Jungkäfer
so gehen auch die abgebrunsteten Mutterkäfer in die Kronen der Eschenstämme und bohren sich in
die grüne Rinde ein, um sich durch längeren Frass zu erholen und dort zu überwintern.

Sind die Mutterkäfer regeneriert und ihre Geschlechtsorgane wieder funktionstüchtig geworden, so können sie zur Anlage neuer Bruten schreiten, sei es im selben Jahre, je nach günstigen oder ungünstigen Witterungsverhältnissen, sei es im nächsten.

Diese dann entstehenden « *Geschwisterbruten* » (die zweite Brut des nämlichen Mutterkäfers stellt ja die Geschwister der in der ersten Brut entstandenen Jungkäfer dar) oder « *Sommerbruten* » waren Veranlassung, dass man dem *Hylesinus fraxini* Panzer und den beiden *Waldgärtnern* « *doppelte Generation* », d. h. Brüten der Jungkäfer in demselben Jahre, zuschrieb. Dies war ein Irrtum, weil man nicht wusste, dass nicht die Jungkäfer, sondern die Mutterkäfer die Sommerbrut anlegten, und weil man vor allen Dingen nicht wusste, dass die alten Käfer zum zweiten Mal brüten könnten. Man hielt nämlich dafür, dass die Käfer nach einmaliger Vollendung ihres Brutgeschäftes ihren Lebenslauf beendet hätten, weiss aber heute, dass sehr viele längere Zeit, bis ins nächste Jahr hinein und länger leben und mehrere Male brüten können. So wie bei den beiden Waldgärtnern verhält es sich unter anderen auch mit den Mutterkäfern des *Pityogenes bistridentatus* Eichhoff : diese brüten verhältnismässig früh im Jahre zum zweiten Male und täuschen dadurch doppelte Generation vor.

Was die « *doppelte Generation* » im allgemeinen betrifft, so ist das Vorkommen derselben einmal von der Art abhängig — ob sie bei der betreffenden Art je nach der schnelleren oder langsameren Reifung der Geschlechtsorgane physiologisch möglich oder nicht möglich ist — andererseits von der Temperatur, dem Klima und den lokalen Verhältnissen.

Früher, als das lange Leben der Käfer als solcher und die Fähigkeit der Muttertiere mehr als einmal zu brüten, nicht bekannt waren, musste man natürlich die Meinung haben, dass Sommerbruten nur durch doppelte Generationen zu erklären seien; daher war man bis resp. mit Eichhoff überzeugt, dass bei den meisten Borkenkäfern doppelte Generation die Regel sei.

Dem ist aber nicht so. Die Forschungen von Pauly, Nüsslin, Knoche und Fuchs haben ergeben, dass man die rindenbrütenden Borkenkäfer nach der genetischen Generationsfolge in einem Jahr biologisch in drei Gruppen einteilen kann :

I. Wärmebedürftige Tiere, denen doppelte Generation besser zuzusagen scheint als einfache, weil man findet, dass in solchen kühleren Gegenden, wo wegen der Temperatur und des Klimas nur einfache Generation möglich wäre, die Käfer nicht mehr vorzukommen scheinen. Hierher gehören die Arten der Gattung *Eccoptogaster*, ferner *Hylesinus crenatus* Fabricius und *H. oleiperda* Fabricius.

II. Solche Tiere, die unter den gegebenen dafür nötigen Verhältnissen doppelte Generation erzeugen, unter anderen weniger günstigen nur einfache. Hierher gehören sämtliche *Ipinen*, ferner *Hylastinus Faukhauseri* Reitter. *Hylurgops decumanus* Erichson und *H. palliatus* Gyllenhal, die Gattungen *Polygraphus* und *Crypturgus* von den *Crypturginen*, die Untergattung *Pteleobius* von den *Hylesininen*.

III. Solche Tiere, die unter keinen Umständen doppelte Generation erzeugen, also sich immer nur einfach vermehren, wie *Dendroctonus micans* Kugelann, *Myelophilus piniperda* Linné und *M. minor* Hartig, *Hylesinus fraxini* Panzer und die wurzelbrütenden *Hylesininen*, vielleicht auch die in krautartigen Pflanzen lebenden *Thamnurgus*-Arten.

Wenn man nun die Gruppierung der *Jungkäfer* in bezug auf den *Nachfrass* und die der *Mutterkäfer* in Beziehung auf den *Regenerationsfrass* und mehrmaliges Brüten miteinander vergleicht, so sieht man, wie eigenartig, aber doch folgerichtig. diese beiden Gruppen zueinander in Verbindung stehen und es ergibt sich dann folgende sehr interessante Zusammenstellung :

I. Wo die Jungkäfer keinen Nachfrass üben, können in günstiger Lage doppelte Generationen erzeugt werden — die Mutterkäfer brüten nur einmal und haben eine kurze Lebensdauer (*H. crenatus* Fabricius, *oleiperda* Fabricius, Gattung *Eccoptogaster*).

II. Wo die Tiere nur kürzere Zeit Nachfrass üben, werden je nach den äusseren Umständen doppelte oder einfache Generationen erzeugt (Gattung *Ips*).

III. Wo die Tiere einen sehr starken und lange Zeit währenden Nachfrass brauchen um reif zu werden, kann keine doppelte Generation im selben Jahr erzeugt werden. Hier haben die Käfer eine kurze Entwicklungszeit, ein langsames Reifen der Geschlechtsorgane, während dessen die Käfer Nachfrass üben, ein langes Imaginalleben (*Ips typographus* Linné bis zwanzig Monate) und die Fähigkeit öfter zu brüten (*D. micans* Kugelann, *M. piniperda* Linné, *M. minor* Hartig, *H. fraxini* Panzer).

Eine schemastische Darstellung der verschiedenen biologischen Gruppen der Borkenkäfer für unsere gewöhnlichsten Schädlinge würde aussehen wie folgt :

Mutterkäfer	**Jungkäfer**

I. *M. piniperda* Linné und *minor* Hartig (Frühschwärmer); *H. fraxini* Panzer (Spätschwärmer) :

Mutterkäfer	Jungkäfer
Lange Lebensdauer.	Kurze Entwicklungszeit bis zur Imago, aber
Langer Regenerationsfrass.	langsames Reifen der Genitalien, daher starker
Mehrmalige Bruten.	Nachfrass und einfache Generation.
Sommer- oder Geschwisterbruten.	

II. *H. crenatus* Fabricius und *oleiperda* Fabricius, Gattung *Eccoptogaster* :

Mutterkäfer	Jungkäfer
Kurze Lebensdauer.	Kurze Entwicklungszeit bis zur vollkommenen Reife.
Einmalige Brut.	Kein Nachfrass.
Kein Regenerationsfrass.	Doppelte Generation.

III. Gattung *Ips* je nach dem Klima und der Witterung :

Mutterkäfer	Jungkäfer
Lebensdauer mehr weniger lang.	Kurze Entwicklungszeit, c^a acht bis zehn Wochen.
Kurzer Regenerationsfrass.	Kurzer Nachfrass.
Ein- oder mehrmalige Bruten.	Schnelleres Reifen der Genitalien.

Einfache oder doppelte Generation.

Es geht aus diesen Zusammenstellungen ohne weiteres hervor, dass diejenigen Borkenkäfer sich am stärksten vermehren und dadurch auch den grössten Schaden in den Wäldern verursachen, welche sowohl doppelte Generation als auch Sommerbruten erzeugen, und das sind die seit alters schon berüchtigten Ipinen : *Ips typographus* Linné und seine Verwandten.

Eine ganz andere Lebensweise als die rindenbrütenden Borkenkäfer, die *Phloeophagae, Spinidentatae* oder *bark-borers* führen die *Holzbrüter, Mycetophagae*, « *Saetidentatae* » oder « *Ambrosiakäfer* ».

Hier sind es die Weibchen, welche das ganze Wohnhaus anfertigen. Nachdem sie von den bei der Gattung *Xyleborus* flugunfähigen Männchen bereits an ihrer Geburtsstäte oder in der Nähe derselben befruchtet sind, schwärmen sie aus, um eigene neue Braträume anzulegen. Radiär zur Achse des Baumes bohren sie ein Eingangsloch und treiben einen röhrenförmigen Gang in derselben Richtung soweit vor, bis sie geeigneten, nämlich sterilen Nährboden für ihre Nahrung, die von ihnen in Reinkultur gezüchteten Pilze finden; denn da sie mit ihren schwachen Kauwerkzeugen und mit ihrer mangelhaften Darmverdauung nicht imstande sind die grossen Massen nährstoffarmer Holzsubstanz, welche zu ihrer Ernährung erforderlich sind, zu bewältigen, müssen sie versuchen mittelst der Pilze, welche sie zu diesem Zweck aussäen und züchten, die Nährstoffe auszuziehen, aufspeichern und verdaulich machen zu lassen. Dass von diesen Pilzzüchtern wirklich keine Holzfaser gefressen und verdaut wird, beweist ausser der direkten Beobachtung auch die chemische Untersuchung des Darminhaltes (Ausfall der Phloroglucinreaktion auf Lignin nach Sedlaczek).

Die Gänge dieser Tiere sind röhrenförmig, ihr Durchmesser der Dicke des Tieres entsprechend.

Bei der Eiablage verhalten sich nun die verschiedenen Gattungen und Arten wieder ähnlich wie die rindenbrütenden Borkenkäfer. Es gibt atavistische, in ihrer biologischen Entwicklung zurückgebliebene Arten, die keine geordnete Brutpflege haben, sondern ihre Eier in der gemeinsamen Familienwohnung in regellosen Haufen ablegen, wie z. B. *Xyleborus dispar* Fabricius, *X. dryographus* Ratzeburg, *X. monographus* Fabricius, *X. xylographus* Say, und solche, welche jedes Ei in eine eigene halbkugelige Nische betten, deren Oeffnung sie mit abgenagten Holzspänen und Pilzmycel verstopfen, wie z. B. die Gattungen *Corthylus, Gnathotrichus* und *Xyloterus.*

Auch ist die Beteiligung der Larven an dem Bau der Frassbilder eine verschiedene : bei den Käfern, welche einfache Gabelgänge ohne besondere Brutröhren anlegen, also gemeinschaftliche Familienwohnungen schaffen, wie *Xyleborus monographus* Fabricius und *dryographus* Ratzeburg, beteiligen . sich die Larven bei der Anlage der Wohngänge nicht, während bei den *Xyloterus*-Arten die Larve ihre Wiege mit zunehmendem Wachstum selbst vergrössert, aber nur soweit, dass sie gerade eben Platz darin hat, und bei *X. xylographus* Say die Larven den blattförmig flachen gemeinsamen Wohnraum wohl erweitern helfen, aber ebenfalls, wie die ersteren, die Holzspäne nicht zu Enährungszwecken abnagen, sondern dazu der Pilze bedürfen.

Diese Pilze werden von den Mutterkäfern in die Gänge mitgebracht — in Form von Sporen — und an geeigneten Stellen ausgesät, um sie in Reinkultur zu züchten.

Dazu ist die Auswahl eines passenden, keimfreien Nährbodens erforderlich, weshalb von den *Ambrosiakäfern* nur lebende oder doch eben erst gefällte Stämme, die den nötigen Wassergehalt besitzen, angegangen werden.

Um das Sauerstoftbedürfnis der aëroben Pilze zu befriedigen, schaffen die *Ambrosiakäfer* sorgfältig das bei der Anlage der Brutstätten freiwerdende Holzmehl heraus und sorgen so für genügende Durchlüftung der Gänge. Ausserdem werden diese, um das Eindringen von parasitischen Pilzen möglichst zu verhüten, meistens mit winkligen Abbiegungen angelegt.

Daher findet man wohl im Beginn der radialen Eingangsröhre fremde, d. h. nicht ambrosiabildende Schmarotzerpilze, während in der Nähe der Larvenwiegen, also nahe dem Ende der Muttergänge, die Ambrosia in prachtvoller Reinheit zu beobachten ist.

Ein weiterer Grund für die gabelförmig sich teilenden und winklig abgeknickten Gänge liegt darin, dass nur das Splintholz, in welchem sie meistens verlaufen, genügende Bedingungen für das Wachstum der Ambrosiapilze gewährt (es ist am reichsten an Nährstoffen und Feuchtigkeit).

Die Pilze, welche die verschiedenen Käferarten züchten, um von ihnen selbst zu leben und ihre Larven mit ihnen zu füttern, sind wohl je nach der Art des Käfers, aber nicht nach der Art des Wirtspflanze verschieden, d. h. jede Käferart hat ihren specifischen Ambrosiapilz.

Diesen kann sie in jedem Baume, den sie bewohnt, in Reinkultur züchten, was sehr erstaunlich erscheint, da wir unter den Pilzzüchtern polyphage Arten haben, die wie *X. dispar* Fabricius und *X. xylographus* Say sowohl in Laubhölzern, als auch in Nadelhölzern leben und doch überall ihren specifischen Ambrosiapilz züchten, der also sowohl in Laub- als auch in Nadelholz gedeiht.

Wenn nun die weiblichen Jungkäfer in den Familien- oder Einzelhäusern generationstüchtig geworden sind und ihren Chitinpanzer erhärtet haben, werden sie von ihren Männchen, sei es der nämlichen, sei es der vorhergehenden Generation im gemeinsamen Wohnraume oder in der Nähe desselben befruchtet und fliegen dann fort, um neue Bruten anzulegen, indem sie abweichend von den Rindenbrütern die ursprüngliche Eingangsöffnung zum Ausflug benutzen, nicht aber, wie jene, direkt aus der Puppenwiege resp. dem Platze des Nachfrasses ins Freie sich herausbohren. '

Ueber Nachfrass der Jungkäfer und über Regenerationsfrass der Mutterkäfer ist bei den Ambrosiakäfern noch nichts bekannt, ebensowenig welche Folgen die ständige Inzucht nach sich zieht und ob nicht vielleicht bei einigen Arten Parthenogenesis vorkommt.

Auch über das Schicksal der Männchen, die ja erheblich weniger zahlreich bei den Ambrosiakäfern sind als die Weibchen, wissen wir noch nichts. Viele von ihnen, besonders die Männchen der

Gattung *Xyleborus*, zeichnen sich ja durch eine äusserst abweichende Form vor den Weibchen aus, besonders auch dadurch, dass sie keine oder verkümmerte Unterflügel haben. Von ihnen wissen wir noch nicht, ob sie lange Zeit in der gemeinsamen Familienwohnung verbleiben und verschiedene Generationen befruchten, was möglich ist, da im allgemeinen bei den *Xyleborus*-Arten das Verhältnis der Männchen zu den Weibchen 1 : 4 ist. Wenn sie hier absterben, kommen sie bei einigen Arten, wie bei *X. xylographus* Say, in eine eigene Totenkammer oder werden bei anderen Arten einfach aus dem Hause herausgeworfen. Ob die jungen Männchen nicht vielleicht auch freiwillig ihre Geburtstätte verlassen, um andere Familienheime zu suchen und so die Inzucht zu vermeiden, ist nicht sicher : jedenfalls sind von Eichhoff, Schreiner und dem Verfasser mehrfach junge Männchen in grösserer Anzahl auf der Wanderschaft angetroffen worden.

Nicht von allen Gattungen der Pilzzüchter sind die Männchen ungeflügelt, z. B. die *Xyloterus*-Männchen haben wohl entwickelte Unterflügel, schwärmen mit den Weibchen zusammen aus und begatten sie auf dem Stamme beim Einbohren.

Ob die Ambrosiakäfer nach ihrem Ausschlüpfen aus der Puppenruhe noch längere Zeit Nachfrass üben müssen, um generationskräftig zu werden, und ob sie einfache oder mehrfache Generationen erzeugen, ist noch nicht soweit erforscht wie bei den Rindenbrütern, bei welchen diese Frage, welche jahrzehntelang die Gemüter der Forstleute und Biologen sehr erregte, jetzt einigermassen geklärt ist.

Eine andere Frage, welcher seinerzeit auch viel Streit verursachte, die nämlich, ob die Borkenkäfer gesunde oder kranke Bäume angehen, ist jetzt wohl ziemlich übereinstimmend dahin entschieden :

1° Das kein Borkenkäfer in abgestorbenes Holz geht;

2° Dass die Ambrosiakäfer (Pilzzüchter) häufig gesunde, frohwüchsige oder allenfalls frisch gefällte Stämme zur Anlage ihrer Brutgänge wählen;

3° Dass die rindenbrütenden Borkenkäfer im allgemeinen Bäume vorziehen, welche in ihrer Ernährung etwas zurückgeblieben sind, aber bei starker Vermehrung und sonst günstigen Verhältnissen das gesunde Holz keineswegs verschonen, sondern gerade dann ihre verderblichste Tätigkeit entfalten und den stärksten Schaden verursachen.

Was die Lebenweise der Borkenkäfer betrifft, die in *harten Fruchtsamen* leben, so ist über diese zu bemerken, dass es sich bei ihnen in der Hauptsache um *Coccotrypes*-Arten handelt. Von diesen ist erst bei einer Art, nämlich *C. Eggersi* Hagedorn, welche in den Steinnusssamen (*Phytelephas macrocarpa*) lebt, die Entwicklung beobachtet worden. Die Tiere machen in der Nähe der grössten Kante der Nuss mehrere, etwa drei oder vier isolierte stehende Bohrlöcher, welche senkrecht ins Innere der Nuss hineinführen. Die Gänge verlaufen nicht gradlinig, sondern in verschiedenen Biegungen, verzweigen sich spärlich und führen an ihrem Ende in eine zu der bisherigen Gangrichtung senkrecht stehende ovale Höhle, in welcher die Puppe ruht. Die Larven halten sich in den Verzweigungen auf, welche von dem Hauptgang abgehen und fressen von der Substanz der Nuss, bis sie vollwüchsig die Puppenwiege ausnagen und sich daselbst, mit dem Kopfe vom Gange abgewendet, verpuppen. Die in den Brutgängen sich aufhaltenden männlichen und weiblichen Käfer sind sehr besorgt um die Reinhaltung der Gänge, denn diese sind alle äusserst sauber, blendend weiss, frei von Larvenkot und zeigen keine Spur von Pilzrasen. Das jedenfalls ist sicher, dass *C. Eggersi* Hagedorn keine Pilzzucht betreibt, sondern sich von dem Sameneiweiss ernährt.

Da dies mit der Bewaffnung der Kaukante der Mittelkiefer übereinstimmt, welche Art der Bewaffnung auch die übrigen *Coccotrypes*-Arten zeigen, so darf wohl angenommen werden, dass deren Lebensweise eine ähnliche sein wird. Bekannt ist darüber meines Wissens noch nichts, insbesondere nicht, ob sie in den Fruchtsamen brüten oder bloss Nachfrass und Regenerationsfrass ausüben.

Die sonst in harten Fruchtsamen aufgefundenen Borkenkäfer gehören der Untergattung *Stephanoderes* an. Hier ist nur von dem in Kaffebohnen in Uganda, Angola und kürzlich auch in Java aufgefundenen *Stephanoderes coffeae* Hagedorn nachgewiesen, dass er in den Bohnen des Kaffebaums tatsächlich brütet.

In *krautartigen Gewachsen* leben in Labiaten, europäischen Euphorbien, ferner in Delphinium und Aconitum, die Arten der Gattung *Thamnurgus*.

Von diesen ist *Th. Kaltenbachi* Bach von Buddeberg genauer beobachtet worden (*Jahrbücher des Nassauischen Vereins fur Naturkunde,* Jahrgang 35, 1880; Jahrgang 36, 1881, p. 394).

Das überwinterte Weibchen frisst im Frühling, gewöhnlich im Mai, ein Loch in den Stengel von *Teucrium scorodonia* oder *Origanum vulgare* oder *Betonica officinalis* oder *Lamium album,* bohrt sich, mit dem Kopf voran abwartssteigend, weiter nach unten, nagt neben der Bohrung drei bis fünf Grübchen aus, kriecht dann zurück und legt in jedes ein Ei. Dann verlässt es diese Pflanze und verfährt ebenso mit einer Anzahl anderer Pflanzen der gleichen Art, bis es sämtliche Eier untergebracht hat. Während die Spitze des Stengels über der angebohrten Stelle meistens umknickt und dann abstirbt, schwillt der unter dieser liegende Stengelteil, soweit der Muttergang reicht, infolge des lebhaften Saftzuflusses an und bildet insbesondere über den Grübchen, in denen die Eier liegen, knorpelartige oder gallenartige Auswüchse. Die Larven ernähren, entwickeln und verpuppen sich in ihren Wiegen.

Die Eiablage dehnt sich von Anfang Mai bis in den Juni aus. Da die Entwicklung vom Ei bis zum Käfer je nach den klimatischen und Witterungsverhältnissen zwei bis drei Monate dauert, so können die ersten Käfer schon im Juli auskommen. Nachdem sie durch eigens genagte Fluglöcher ihren Ausgang gefunden haben, bohren die Jungkäfer im August wieder neue Pflanzen an. Sie brüten aber nicht darin, sondern halten nur Nachfrass und überwintern im Inneren ihrer Nährpflanzen.

Diese Lebensweise bringt die *Thamnurgus*-Arten in eine gewisse Parallele zu den mehrmals brütenden Borkenkäfern, wie *Dendroctonus micans* Kugelann und *Myelophilus piniperda* Linné und *M. minor* Hartig. Der Regenerationsfrass bei den letzteren Arten findet sich in modificierter Weise auch bei den *Thamnurgus*-Käfern. Diese regenerieren sich jedes Mal, wenn sie ihre drei bis fünf Eier in eine Pflanze abgelegt haben, dadurch dass sie immer neue Pflanzen in längeren Zwischenräumen anbohren und während dieser Zeit immer neue Nahrung erhalten. Daher dürfte *Thamnurgus Kaltenbachi* Bach zu der Gruppe I der Rindenbrüter, welche Regenerationsfrass übt, Sommerbruten erzeugt und nur einfache Generation hat, zu stellen sein.

Als ursprüngliche altertümliche Formen im Leben der Borkenkäfer müsste man wohl diejenigen bezeichnen, welche sich durch primären Angriff auf frohwüchsige Pflanzen, Anlage von platzförmigen Gängen oder von Längsgängen mit spärlichen weit voneinander entfernten Einischen, haufenweise Eiablage und damit geringe Brutpflege als rückständig erwissen, während das Anlegen von Quer- und Sterngängen behufs Abschneidung des Saft- und Harzstromes, das Ablegen der Eier in einzelne nahe beieinanderstehende Nischen, besonders aber die ausgebildete Brutpflege der Ambrosiakäfer den höchsten, am weitesten fortgeschrittenen, also jüngsten Entwicklungsstand ausdrücken würden.

Geographische Verbreitung der Borkenkäfer

Das heutige Vorkommen der Borkenkäfer stellt das Ergebnis einer lange bestehenden Entwicklung dar, die von den Lebenseigentümlichkeiten der Tiere selbst, von den zeitlich nicht gleichmässigen physikalischen Bedingungen und namentlich von den langsam aber in weiten Umfage vorsichgehenden Aenderungen des Oberflächenbildes der Erde sehr stark beeinflusst und abgeändert ist. In vergangenen Perioden sind nachweislich Ausprägungen unserer jetzigen Borkenkäfertypen vorhanden gewesen, die wir jetzt vergebens suchen, oder es gab Vertreter der letzteren an Orten wo sie nachträglich ausgestorben sind und wo die gegenwärtigen Verhältnisse auch ohne weiteres keinerlei Rückschluss auf das frühere Vorhandensein jener ausgestorbenen Arten zulassen.

Andererseits könnte aus der früheren Verteilung von Land und Wasser, Höhen und Tiefen, Pflanzenwuchs und unfruchtbarem Boden die Möglichkeit erschlossen werden, zu erkennen, wie manche auffallende Züge in der jetzigen Verteilung durch mehr oder minder ausgedehnte Wanderung von Gattungen und Arten zustande kamen.

Neben dem Studium der heutigen geographischen Verbreitung ist deshalb eine möglichst ausgedehnte Berücksichtigung der Verhältnisse in der Vergangenheit nötig. Durch schrittweises Verfolgen der Veränderungen, welche die Ausbreitung der Borkenkäfer im Laufe der Zeiten erfahren hat. kann die Erklärung der heutigen Verbreitung angestrebt werden. Deshalb ist es nötig, dass bei der Darstellung der Verbreitung der Borkenkäfer nicht nur die heutigen, sondern auch die vergangenen Erscheinungen berücksichtigt werden.

Leider sind wir nur höchst unvollkommen davon unterrichtet, wie sich die Verbreitung der Borkenkäfer in der Vorwelt gestaltete.

Fossile Borkenkäfer sind aus keiner älteren erdgeschichtlichen Periode als aus der Tertiärzeit bekannt. Und auch hier sind die Funde nur spärlich. In Nordamerika sind von Scudder zwei sichere Hylesinus-Arten und ein Xyloterus beschrieben worden, von Heer aus Aix in der Provence ein Hylesinus, von Förster aus dem Elsass ebenfalls ein Hylesinus. Die übrigen fossilen Borkenkäfer stammen alle aus dem baltischen Bernstein : ein Hylesinus ist von Germar beschrieben worden; von dem Verfasser ein Hylastes, ein Myelophilus, ein Xylechinus und drei Phloeosinus-Arten.

Aus sehr viel jüngerer Zeit, und zwar dem Alluvium, hat Verfasser aus dem afrikanischen fossilen Copal sieben Xyleborus-Arten, zwei Premnobius-Arten und eine noch nicht veröffentlichte Cryphalus-Art festgestellt. Das ist alles, was uns die Paläontologie an Material liefert, und doch können wir einige wichtige Schlüsse aus diesen geringen Funden ziehen.

Schon a priori drängt sich der Gedanke auf. dass gemäss der Verschiedenheit des umhüllenden Materiales (Bernstein und Copal) nach Alter, Herkommen und Fundort auch die eingeschlossenen Tiere in ihren Arten und in ihren Lebensweise werden verschieden sein müssen.

Wenn man berücksichtigt, dass der Bernstein ein Harz ist, welches aus Nadelhölzern floss, die in der älteren Tertiärzeit, dem Oligocaen, grünten, welches somit ein Alter von vielen Jahrtausenden, wenn nicht Jahrmillionen haben muss, während die afrikanischen fossilen Copale von Laubhölzern, Caesalpiniaceen, besonders Trachylobium, Guibourtia herstammen, die zum Teil heute noch an den Copalfundorten existieren, zum Teil erst kürzlich ausgestorben zu sein scheinen, und dass der im Alluvium sich findende Copal höchstens zwei bis drei tausend Jahre alt sein kann, so ergibt sich zunächst, dass die in beiden Harzen gefundenen Tiere je nach den Nährbäumen andere sein werden : im Bernstein Nadelholzbewohner, im Copal Laubholzbewohner. Es ergibt sich ferner, dass bei dem ungeheuren Altersunterschied zwischen den beiden Harzen wohl auch die Arten, welche sich in ihnen vorfinden, nicht nur in Bezug auf die durch Nahrung und Wohnung gegebenen Kennzeichen, sondern auch in ihrer allgemeinen Gestaltung verschieden sein werden, indem die einen noch die Bildung der Jetztzeit, die anderen die einer längst entschwundenen Vorzeit an sich bemerken lassen werden.

Dieser aprioristische Schluss trifft nun auch wirklich zu. Ich habe unter den allerdings auffallend wenigen Borkenkäfern des baltischen Bernsteins, wie ich in den Schriften der physikalisch-ökonomischen Gesellschaft zu Königsberg in Preussen, 47. Jahrgang, 1906. p. 115 u. f. mitgeteilt habe, keinen gefunden, der heute noch existierte. Die Arten sind sämtlich ausgestorben; die Gattungen sind noch gut erkennbar und dieselben die heute auch vorkommen.

Auffallend ist das Fehlen sämtlicher Ipinen, besonders der Gattungen, welche heute mit Vorliebe in Nadelhölzen leben, so der Gattungen Ips und Pityophthorus. Auch die heute weitverbreiteten Nadelholz-bewohnenden Gattungen Polygraphus und Cryphalus sind bisher im Bernstein nicht aufgefunden worden.

Alle bisher gefundenen fossilen Borkenkäfer mit einer Ausnahme gehören zu den *Hylesininen*. Eigentümlich ist die Beziehung der Borkenkäfer des baltischen Bernsteins zu der heutigen nordamerikanischen Fauna : die drei von mir aufgefundenen *Phloeósinus*-Arten haben ihre nächsten Verwandten im N. W. der Vereinigten Staaten, wo diese in *Sequoia* und *Cupressus* wohnen.

Im afrikanischen Copal dagegen habe ich nur, bis auf eine neue Art aus Madagaskarcopal, Tiere gefunden, welche noch heute existieren. Kein ausgesprochener Nadelholzbewohner ist dabei; alle bis auf einen noch nicht publizierten *Cryphalus* und zwei *Premnobius*-Arten gehören in die Unterfamilie der *Saetidendaten* oder *Ambrosiakäfer*, d. h. sie leben nicht zwischen Rinde und Holz, sondern bohren ihre Gänge senkrecht ins Holz hinein, ernähren sich auch nicht von der Holzfaser, sondern von Pilzen, welche sie in ihren Wohnungen züchten und mit denen sie ihre Larven füttern.

Es haben sowohl im tertiären Bernsteinwald wie auch im diluvialen resp. alluvialen Copalwald anscheinend vice versa die nämlichen Verhältnisse für die Borkenkäfer vorgelegen, welche heute ihre charakteristische Verbreitung in den verschiedenen Zonen bedingen und auch zu einer ähnlichen Verteilung der Gattungen und Arten geführt, wie sie heute augenscheinlich ist.

Während in den nördlicheren Gebieten die Nadelholzbewohner, seien es *Hylesininen* oder *Ipinen*, überwiegend häufig vorkommen, fehlen sie in den Tropen oder sind nur spärlich vorhanden, wohl weil ihre Nährbäume, die Coniferen, in den Tropen seltener werden.

Dagegen nimmt die Gattung *Xyleborus*, welche im Norden nur spärlich vertreten ist, nach den Tropen hin allmählich zu, sowohl was die Zahl der Arten als auch die Häufigkeit des Vorkommens anbetrifft und herrscht in der Aequatorialzone durch Arten- und Individuenzahl durchaus unter allen Borkenkäfern vor, teilt sich darin an einigen Orten höchstens mit der *Cryphalinen*-Untergattung *Hypothenemus*.

Aus den geringen fossilen Borkenkäferfunden lassen sich zwingende Schlüsse auf das geologische Alter der Tiere nicht ziehen. Wenn auch aus dem Umstand, dass die ältesten aufgefundenen Borkenkäfer *Hylesininen* gewesen sind, im Vergleich mit der nahen Verwandtschaft dieser Tiere mit den Rüsselkäfern geschlossen werden könnte, dass die Hylesininen die ältesten Borkenkäfer seien, so ist dieser Schluss doch nicht beweisend. Denn seit dem Tertiär hat unsere Flora keine wesentlichen Veränderungen erfahren, ihr Aussehen war im grossen und ganzen damals so wie heute : und es kann ein Zufall sein, dass die bekannt gewordenen spärlichen Ueberreste nur aus der einen einzigen Unterfamilie stammen.

Richtiger wird aber der Schluss sein, den wir aus den Copalfunden ziehen können, nämlich der, dass die biologisch am meisten fortgeschrittenen, in ihrer Bruptflege aus höchsten entwickelten Pilzzüchter allmählich, und besonders in klimatisch günstigen Gegenden, das Uebergewicht über die rückständigeren rindenbrütenden Borkenkäfer erlangen.

Eine faunistische Einteilung der Erde nach den *Ipiden* der Gegenwart wird nach folgendem Schema aufzustellen sein :

Geographische Einteilung

1. Altes Nordreich : Europa, Nordasien bis Himalaya, Japan, Nordafrika bis Atlas.
2. Neues Nordreich : Amerika nördlich von Mexiko.
3. Aethiopisches Reich : Afrika südlich vom Atlas.
4. Makronesisches Reich : Azoren, Canarien, Cap Verde-Inseln.
5. Madegassisches Reich : Madagascar, Mascarenen, Seychellen.
6. Indo-Malayisches Reich : Asien südlich vom Himalaya, Sunda Inseln mit Philippinen and Neu-Guinea.
7. Suedreich : Mexico, Central- und Südamerika.

8. AUSTRALISCHES REICH : Australien und Tasmanien.
9. NEU-SEELAENDISCHES REICH : Neu-Seeland.
10. POLYNESISCHES REICH : Polynesien und Sandwichs-Inseln.

Geographische Verbreitung der Subfamilien

1. *Phloeotrupinae* : Reich 3. 6, 7.
2. *Diamerinae* :   »   3, 5, 6.
3. *Hylesininae* ⎫
4. *Crypturginae* ⎪
5. *Cryphalinae* ⎬ Kosmopolitisch.
6. *Ipinae*   ⎭

7. *Hylocurinae* : Reich 2, 3, 7.
8. *Eccoptogastrinae* : Kosmopolitisch.
9. *Corthylinae* : Reich 2 und 7.
10. *Xyleborinae* : Kosmopolitisch.
11. *Spongocerinae* : Reich 1, 3, 5, 6.

Geographische Verbreitung der Gattungen

KOSMOPOLITISCH resp. SUBKOSMOPOLITISCH sind (13 Gattungen) : *Hylastes, Cryphalus, Ips, Xyleborus, Pityophthorus, Hylesinus, Phloeosinus, Phloeotribus, Xylocleptes, Dryocoetes, Coccotrypes, Eccoptogaster, Polygraphus.*

Nur in einem Reich kommen vor ausser den kosmopolitischen Gattungen :

1. Im ALTEN NORDREICH (6 Gattungen) : *Hyorrhynchus, Myelophilus, Cisurgus, Taphrorychus, Thamnurgus, Eidophelus.*
2. Im NEUEN NORDREICH (7 Gattungen) : *Renocis, Thysanoes, Chaetophloeus, Micracis, Dolurgus, Cactopinus, Erineophilus.*
3. Im ÆTHIOPISCHEN REICH (13 Gattungen) : *Bothryperus, Rhopalopselion, Strombophorus, Chortastus, Dacryostactus, Styracopterus, Lissoclastus, Adiaeretus, Tiarophorus, Poecilips, Orthaspistes, Xyloctonus, Ctonoxylon.*
4. Im MAKRONESISCHEN REICH (2 Gattungen) : *Aphanarthrum, Triotemnus.*
5. Im MADEGASSISCHEN REICH (2 Gattungen) : *Cryphalomorphus, Hyloscyllus.*
6. Im INDOMALAYISCHEN REICH (8 Gattungen) : *Craeniodicticus, Spongotarsus, Cryptarthrum, Ozopemon, Lepicerus, Scolytomimus, Scolytogenes, Olonthogaster.*
7. Im SUEDREICH (28 Gattungen) : *Phloeoborus, Phloeotrupes, Coptonotus, Dendrosinus, Meringopalpus, Dryotomus, Problechilus, Ctenophorus, Epomadius, Prionosceles, Pycnarthrum, Microborus, Dendroterus, Phrixosoma, Eulytocerus, Eupagiocerus, Metacorthylus, Tricolus, Glochinocerus, Cnemonyx, Ceratolepis, Camptocerus, Brachyspartus, Phthorius, Amphicrauus, Anchonocerus, Steganocranus, Styphlosoma.*
8. Im AUSTRALISCHEN REICH (1 Gattung) : *Aricerus.*
9. 1m NEU-SEELAENDISCHEN REICH (5 Gattungen) : *Inosomus, Acrantus, Dendrotrupes, Mesoscolytus, Pachycotes.*
10. Im POLYNESISCHEN REICH (keine Gattung).

Nur in zwei Reichen kommen vor :

Im 1. ALTEN NORDREICH und 2. NEUEN NORDREICH (5 Gattungen) : *Dendroctonus, Carphoborus, Phloeophthorus, Crypturgus, Xyloterus.*
Im 1. ALTEN NORDREICH und 3. ÆTHIOPISCHEN REICH (1 Gattung) : *Kissophagus.*
Im 1. ALTEN NORDREICH und 4. MAKRONESISCHEN REICH (1 Gattung) : *Liparthrum.*
Im 1. ALTEN NORDREICH und 6. INDO-MALAYISCHEN REICH (4 Gattungen) : *Hylurgus, Hypoborus, Cosmoderes, Acanthotomicus.*

Im 1. ALTEN NORDREICH und 7. SÜDREICH (1 Gattung) : *Xylechinus*.

Im 2. NEUEN NORDREICH und 7. SÜDREICH (7 Gattungen) : *Bothrosternus, Pagiocerus, Cnesinus, Loganius, Corthylus, Pterocyclon, Gnathotrichus.*

Im 3. ÆTHIOPISCHEN und 6. INDO-MALAYISCHEN REICH (1 Gattung) : *Dactylipalpus.*

Im 3. ÆTHIOPISCHEN und im 7. SÜDREICH (2 Gattungen) : *Araptus, Premnobius.*

Im 5. MADEGASSISCHEN und 6. INDO-MALAYISCHEN REICH (1 Gattung) : *Triarmocerus.*

Nur in drei Reichen kommt vor :

Im 3. ÆTHIOPISCHEN, 5. MADEGASSISCHEN und 6. INDO-MALAYISCHEN REICH (1 Gattung) : *Diamerus.*

Im 1. ALTEN NORDREICH, 3. ÆTHIOPISCHEN und 6. INDO-MALAYISCHEN REICH (1 Gattung) : *Sphaerotrypes.*

Nur in vier Reichen kommt vor :

Im 1. ALTEN NORDREICH, 3. ÆTHIOPISCHEN, 5. MADEGASSISCHEN, und 6. INDO-MALAYISCHEN REICH (1 Gattung) : *Scolytoplatypus.*

Zusammenstellung der in der einzelnen Reichen, ausser den (13) Kosmopoliten, vorkommenden Gattungen

1. ALTES NORDREICH (20 Gattungen) : *Hyorrhynchus, Hylurgus, Myelophilus, Spaerotrypes, Dendroctonus, Carphoborus, Kissophagus, Xylechinus, Liparthrum, Hypoborus, Phloeophthorus, Crypturgus, Cisurgus, Cosmoderes, Acanthotomicus, Taphrorychus, Thamnurgus, Eidophelus, Xyloterus, Scolytoplatypus.*

2. NEUES NORDREICH (20 Gattungen) : *Renocis, Chaetophloeus, Chramesus, Dendroctonus, Carphoborus, Phloeophthorus, Crypturgus, Dolurgus, Cactopinus, Micracis, Thysanoes, Bothrosternus, Pagiocerus, Cnesinus, Loganius, Erineophilus, Corthylus, Pterocyclon, Gnathotrichus, Xyloterus.*

3. ÆTHIOPISCHES REICH (20 Gattungen) : *Dactylipalpus, Bothryperus, Diamerus, Rhopalopselion, Strombophorus, Sphaerotrypes, Chortastus, Kissophagus, Dacryostactus, Styracopterus, Lissoclastus, Adiaeretus, Premnobius, Tiarophorus, Poecilips, Orthaspistes, Araptus, Xyloctonus, Ctonoxylon, Scolytoplatypus.*

4. MAKRONESISCHES REICH (3 Gattungen) : *Aphanarthrum, Liparthrum, Triotemnus.*

5. MADEGASSISCHES REICH (5 Gattungen) : *Diamerus, Triarmocerus, Cryphalomorphus, Hyloscyllus, Scolytoplatypus.*

6. INDO-MALAYISCHES REICH (17 Gattungen) : *Dactylipalpus, Diamerus, Craniodicticus, Hylurgus, Sphaerotrypes, Hypoborus, Spongotarsus, Cryptarthrum, Cosmoderes, Triarmocerus, Acanthotomicus, Ozopemon, Lepicerus, Scolytomimus, Scolytogenes, Scolytoplatypus, Olonthogaster.*

7. SÜDREICH (40 Gattungen) : *Phloeoborus, Phloeotrupes, Coptonotus, Dendrosinus, Meringopalpus, Xylechinus, Dryotomus, Problechilus, Styphlosoma, Hexacolus, Araptus, Premnobius, Hylocurus, Epomadius, Prionosceles, Pycnarthrum, Microborus, Dendroterus, Phrixosoma, Eulytoceras, Eupagiocerus, Metacorthylus, Tricolus, Gnathotrichus, Glochinocerus, Bothrosternus, Pagiocerus, Cnesinus, Cnemonyx, Loganius, Ceratolepis, Camptocerus, Scolytopsis, Corthylus, Brachyspartus, Pterocyclon, Amphicranus, Phthorius, Anchonocerus, Steganocranus.*

8. AUSTRALISCHES REICH (1 Gattung) : *Aricerus.*

9. NEUSEELAENDISCHES REICH (5 Gattungen) : *Inosomus, Acrantus, Dendrotrupes, Mesoscolytus, Pachycotes.*

10. POLYNESISCHES REICH : keine.

Das interessanteste Vorkommnis ist wohl die Verbreitung der Gattung *Aphanarthrum.* Sie bildet eins der klarsten Beispiele harmonischer Artenverteilung über einen Inselschwarm.

Die Gattung mit ihren achtzehn Arten und Varietäten ist hauptsächlich auf Madeira und den Canarischen Inseln verteilt; nur wenige Arten kommen auf den Capverdischen Inseln vor. Sie leben nur in den baum- oder kaktusartigen Euphorbien und sind so verteilt, dass neun Arten nur auf je einer

Insel vorkommen, zwei Arten auf je zwei Inseln, zwei Arten auf drei Inseln und fünf Arten auf vier und mehr Inseln.

Da diese Gattung bisher nirgend anders auf der Erde gefunden ist, als auf diesen Felsinseln, welche doch wohl die übers Wasser emporragenden Bergspitzen eines untergegangenen Landblockes darstellen, der vielleicht eine Verbindung der heutigen restirenden Ländermassive bewerkstelligt hat, so möchte man wohl annehmen können, dass diese Tiere autochthon und endemisch sind und vielleicht die ältesten Typen ihres Geschlechts darstellen. Allerdings sind es keine *Hylesininen*, sondern sie gehören zu den *Crypturginen*, die ein Verbindungsglied zwischen *Hylesininen* und *Ipinen* bilden.

Wie die Verteilung dieser kleinsten Euphorbienbewohner auffällig ist, so ist beachtenswert auch die Verbreitung der Subfamilie der *Phloeotrupinen*, der grössten Tiere unter den Borkenkäfern. Von diesen kommen zwei Gattungen nur in Südamerika vor, eine in Afrika und auf den grossen Sundainseln. Die letztere zeichnet sich noch dadurch besonders aus, dass sie in der Umbildung begriffen ist. Sie ist die einzige Borkenkäfergattung, die zweigliedrige Taster hat : es finden sich nun Arten in Afrika, bei welchen die allmähliche Differenzierung des letzten Tastergliedes in zwei sich deutlich verfolgen lässt!

Von den Subfamilien sind eine Reihe kosmopolitisch oder doch beinahe kosmopolitisch, wenn man auch nicht sagen kann, dass sie überall autochthon wären : denn z. B. das Vorkommen von *Ips curvidens* Germar am Cap der guten Hoffnung und in Argentinien ist doch sicher auf Einschleppung dieses Bewohners des alten Nordreiches zurückzuführen. Ausgesprochener Bewohner der neuen Welt, nämlich des neuen Nordreichs und des Südreichs ist die Subfamilie der *Corthylinen*, während wir keine Subfamilie haben, die allein auf *ein* Reich beschränkt wäre.

Sehr eigenartig ist die Verbreitung der Gattungen in der Subfamilie der *Spongocerinen*. Die Gattung *Scolytoplatus* s. str. findet sich nur in Afrika und Madagaskar, also im äthiopischen und madegassischen Reiche; die beiden anderen Untergattungen, *Spongocerus* und *Taeniocerus*, kommen nur in Japan und im indo-malayischen Reich vor.

Das australische Reich hat nur eine Gattung, welche ihm eigentümlich ist, das neuseeländische fünf, während dem Südreich allein achtundzwanzig Gattungen eigentümlich sind. Das mag aber wohl auch daran liegen, dass die Borkenkäfer des Südreiches besser durchforscht sind als die von Australien und Neuseeland.

Durch grossen Reichtum an *Spongocerinen* zeichnet sich die Fauna von Japan aus, welche auch sonst manche Eigentümlichkeiten aufweist, die auf den Ursprung der Fauna aus einer Vermischung von Formen des alten Nordreichs mit denen des indo-malayischen Reiches hindeuten.

So finden wir in Japan aus dem alten Nordreich vor : *Hylastes attenuatus* Erichson und *H. decumanus* Erichson, *Myelophilus piniperda* Linné und *M. minor* Hartig, *Crypturgus pusillus* Gyllenhal, *Ips cembrae* Heer, *Dryocoetes autographus* Ratzeburg. *Xyloterus signatus* Fabricius. *Xyleborus adumbratus* Blandford und *X. sobrinus* Eichhoff sind wohl nur Lokalformen von *X. Pfeilii* Ratzeburg und *X. xylographus* Say.

Orientalische Formen sind *X. obliquecauda* Motschulsky, der sonst in Ceylon vorkommt, und *X. badius* Eichhoff, den wir aus Madagaskar und Tahiti kennen. Auch haben wir in den Gattungen *Sphaerotrypes* und *Cosmoderes* characteristische indo-malayische Typen.

Es scheint eine Eigentümlichkeit der Borkenkäfer zu sein, dass wir in verschiedenen Reichen Gattungen vorfinden, welche das Faunenbild beherrschen und ihm gewissermassen ihren Stempel aufdrücken : sei es durch die Zahl der Arten und Individuen, sei es durch ausgedehnte Verbreitung oder durch eigenartige, hervorragende Gestalt, teils schliesslich durch hervorragende Schädlichkeit.

So möchte ich als charakteristische Type des alten Nordreiches die Gattung *Myelophilus* bezeichnen, welche diesem Reiche eigentümlich ist und sich überall vorfindet, wo die Kiefer (*pinus silvestris*) wächst und die sich durch grosse Schädlichkeit auszeichnet : daher würde man das alte Nordreich auch das « Reich der Waldgärtner » oder das « Myelophilusreich » nennen können.

Im neuen Nordreich ist die bezeichnende Gattung *Dendroctonus* : alle Arten dieser Gattung bis auf eine kommen nur dort vor und sind die Hauptschädlinge der Nadelholzforsten! Also das neue Nordreich = « Dendroctonusreich ».

Dass für das makronesische Reich die Euphorbienbewohnende Gattung *Aphanarthrum* die Ipidenfauna beherrscht, ist schon oben angeführt : daher ist das makronesische Reich füglich als « Aphanarthrumreich » zu bezeichnen.

Für das Südreich würde ich die Kennzeichnung als « Amphicranusreich » vorschlagen, nach der eigentümlichen, schönen und in zahlreichen Arten nur dort vorkommenden Gattung gleichen Namens.

Für das indo-malayische Reich scheint die Gattung *Sphaerotrypes* charakteristisch zu sein : daher « Sphærotrypesreich ».

In den übrigen Reichen finde ich keine Borkenkäfergattung, welche so ausgeprägt eigentümlich wäre, dass sie das Faunenbild beherrschte.

Systematik

Im Jahre 1836 hat Erichson die erste brauchbare systematische Einteilung der Borkenkäfer gegeben. Er nannte die ganze Familie *Bostrichidae* und machte drei Unterabteilungen :

I. *Hylesinen.*

Caput exsertum, rostro brevi crasso auctum. Antennæ (excepto Phlœotribo) rostri lateribus insertæ. Thorax subtus antice emarginatus, et excipiendo capite (sæpe obsoletius), impressus. Tarsorum articulus tertius plerumque emarginatus vel bilobus.

         Genera : 1. *Hylastes* Erichson, 2. *Hylurgus* Latreille, 3. *Dendroctonus* Erichson, 4. *Phloeotrupes* Erichson, 5. *Phloeoborus* Erichson, 6. *Hylesinus* Fabricius, 7. *Phloeotribus* Latreille, 8. *Diamerus* Erichson, 9. *Polygraphus* Erichson, 10. *Eccoptogaster* Herbst, 11. *Camptocerus* Latreille.

II. *Eigentliche Bostrichen.*

Caput in thoracem retractum, globosum. Antennæ capitis lateribus inter mandibularum basin et oculos insertæ. Thorax antice supra caput productum. Coxæ anticæ semper aproximatæ. Tarsi in omnibus articulis simplicibus.

         Genera : 1. *Xyloterus* Erichson, 2. *Crypturgus* Erichson, 3. *Hypothenemus* Westwood, 4. *Cryphalus* Erichson, 5. *Hypoborus* Erichson, 6. *Bostrichus* Fabricius, 7. *Amphicranus* Erichson, 8. *Corthylus* Erichson.

III. *Platypus* Herbst.

Dann folgte Lacordaire 1866, welcher folgende Einteilung gab :

Scolytides vrais

I. Abdomen de forme normale.

    a. Tête non globuleuse, visible d'en haut au repos.

    b. Yeux finement granulés.

        c. Pronotum confondu avec les flancs du prothorax . . . .   1. *Hylésinides.*

        c'. Pronotum distinct des flancs du prothorax . . . .   2. *Camptocérides.*

    bb. Yeux fortement granulés.

        cc. Pronotum distinct des flancs du prothorax . . . .   3. *Eutomides.*

        Pronotum confondu avec les flancs du prothorax . . . .   4. *Phloeotrupides.*

    aa. Tête globuleuse, le plus souvent invisible d'en haut . . . .   5. *Tomicides.*

II. Abdomen retroussé à partir du deuxième segment . . . .   6. *Scolytides vrais.*

Er zählte zu den *Hylesiniden* die Gattungen *Hylastes, Hylurgus, Blastophagus, Dendroctonus, Carpho-borus, Hylesinus, Phloeophthorus, Phloeotribus* und *Polygraphus*, zu den *Camptocérides* die Genera *Diamerus* und *Camptocerus*, zu den *Phloeotrupiden* die Gattungen *Phloeotrupes* und *Phloeoborus*, zu den *Tomiciden Cryplurgus, Hypothenemus, Aphanarthrum, Triotemnus, Liparthrum, Trypodendron, Xyloterus, Hypoborus, Xyleborus, Dryocoetes, Pityophthorus, Thamnurgus, Tomicus* und *Amphicramus*, zu den *Scolytides vrais* nur die. Gattung *Scolytus*.

Chapuis machte im Jahre 1873 folgende Einteilung der *Scolityden*, mit Ausnahme der *Tomicinen*, welche Eichhoff bearbeitete, im *Coptonotiden, Phloeotrupiden, Hylesiniden, Phloeotribiden, Polygraphiden, Onychiiden, Ctenophoriden, Camptoceriden* und *Scolytidae verae*. Er entfernte also die *Eutomiden* aus dem System, setzte aber dafür die *Onychiiden* hinein, obwohl die Gattung *Onychius* unzweifelhaft zu den. *Cossoniden* gehört.

Weit umfassendere und die Verwandtschaft zwischen Borkenkäfern und Rüsselkäfern mehr berücksichtigende Systeme stellten Thomson 1868, welcher als Unterabteilung seiner *Rhynchophori* auch die *Tomicidae* als den übrigen Rüsselkäferabteilungen gleichwertige Unterordnung ansetzte, und ganz besonders Lindemann 1875. Dieser legte auf Grund seiner sehr genauen anatomischen Unter--suchungen, besonders des Kaumagens und der männlichen Genitalien, die nahe Verwandtschaft zwischen Rüsselkäfern und Borkenkäfern fest, indem er die Gruppe der *Curculionites* Latreille in zwölf kleinere, einander ganz vollkommen gleichwertige Gruppen einteilte. Diese zwölf kleineren Gruppen sind folgende : *Bruchidae, Anthribidae, Rhinomaceridae, Attelabidae, Apionidae, Curculionidae, Rhynchänidae, Rhyncolidae, Scolytidae, Hylesinidae, Tomicidae, Platypidae.*

Als Unterscheidungsmerkmale für die Gruppen, die wir heute zu den *Ipiden* rechnen, gibt er an ::

II. Ein Kauapparat im Proventriculus ist immer vorhanden.

    2. Der Kauapparat besteht aus Kauladen und einem unpaaren vorderen Teil, welcher mit Borsten. oder Querrillen bewaffnet ist.

       d. Genitalplatte des ♀ ohne Stengel und ohne Palpen . . . . . . *Hylesinidae.*

    3. Der Kauapparat besteht aus paarigen Kauplatten und Kauladen.

       e. Kauladen ohne Bürsten . . . . *Scolytidae.*

       f. Kauladen mit Bürsten . . . . *Tomicidae.*

Leider führt er das System specieller nur für die *Tomicidae* aus, welche er in vier Subfamilien teilt, nämlich : 1° *Cryphaloidae*, 2° *Tomicoideae*, 3° *Dryocoetoideae*, 4° *Xyloteroideae.*

Die Unterschiede dieser hier von ihm begründeten Subfamilien drückt er in folgender Tabelle aus ::

I. Im Begattungsglied besteht der Aufsatz bloss aus den Endplatten . . . . . *Cryphaloideae.*

II. Der Aufsatz ist zusammengesetzt aus den Endplatten und der Rinne.

    * Die Füsschen des Penis sind angewachsen an den Körper desselben . *Dryocoetoideae.*

    * Die Füsschen des Penis sind mit dem Körper desselben beweglich verbunden . . . . *Tomicoideae.*

III. Der Aufsatz ist zusammengesetzt aus Endplatten, Rinne und Anker. . . . . *Xyloteroideae.*

Weiter gibt Lindemann noch eine Klassificierung der europäischen Gattungen der *Crypha-loideae*, wie folgt :

I. Die Kauapparate besitzen keine Kauplatten; dieselben sind hier durch einen unpaaren Ansatz vertreten, welcher ebenso zusammengesetzt ist wie bei den *Hylesiniden*. Das Copulationsorgan hat sehr verbreitete Füsschen, welche mit ihren Spitzen gegenseitig verwachsen sind.

    * Mandibeln ohne Anhang . . . . *Ernoporus.*

II. Jeder Kauapparat besitzt zwei Kauplatten. Die Füsschen des Copulationsorganes sind nie verwachsen, immer stabförmig frei.

1. Mandibeln mit Anhang.
   * Die Genitalplatte ist beim ♀ chitinisiert, behaart und mit einem Stengel
   versehen . . . . *Stephanoderes.*
2. Mandibeln ohne Anhang.
   * Die Genitalplatte ist beim ♀ ganz chitinisiert. Sieben Paar Bauchstigmen sind vorhanden . . . . *Cryphalus.*
   * Die Genitalplatte ist beim ♀ häutig, weich; nur der Stengel derselben
   ist chitinisiert. Nur fünf Paar Bauchstigmen sind vorhanden . . . *Hypoborus.*
   * Die Genitalplatte des ♀ ist wie bei *Hypoborus.* Sieben Paar Bauchstigmen sind vorhanden . . . . *Pityophthorus.*

Soweit die Ausführungen Lindemanns; es ist schade, dass die Untersuchungen unvollständig
geblieben sind, denn es hätten sich durch dieselben gewiss noch interessante Verwandstchaftsver-
hältnisse zwischen verschiedenen Gattungen ergeben.

Gemeinsam mit Chapuis und ursprünglich nach dem gleichen Plane, der auf eine gemeinsam
von beiden Forschern herzustellende Monographie der Borkenkäfer hinausging, bearbeitete Eichhoff
die *Tomicinen,* während jener die übrigen *Ipiden*-Gattungen beschreiben wollte, aber nur zu einer Synopsis
gekommen ist.

Eichhoff war in seiner *Ratio Tomicinorum* 1879 der erste, der den Versuch gemacht hat, seiner
Einteilung ein biologisches Princip zugrunde zu legen. Er teilt nämlich die *Tomicinen* in *Phloeophagi* und
Xylophagi ein, indem er zu der ersten Gruppe die Tiere rechnet, welche nicht ins Holz gehen, sondern
zwischen Rinde und Splint ihre Frassgänge machen, auch von der Rindensubstanz leben und daher ihre
Mittelkiefer mit dornartigen Zähnen besetzt haben; zu der zweiten die Tiere, welche tief hinein ins
Holz ihre Gänge machen, aber nur eine zarte, aus Borsten bestehende Mittelkieferbewaffnung besitzen.

Bevor aber Eichhoff seine *Ratio Tomicinorum* im Jahre 1879 veröffentlichte, erschien die
Beschreibung der nordamerikanischen Borkenkäfer von Le Conte 1876, welches Werk einer
genaueren Erwähnung bedarf.

Wie Thomson unter dem Namen *Rhynchophori* die sämtlichen Rüsselkäfer mit den Borkenkäfern zusammenfasste, so stellte auch Le Conte die *Scolytidae* als Abteilung seiner *Rhynchophora*
zwischen die *Rhyncolini,* Familie *Calandridae* und Familie *Anthribidae,* indem er die natürlichen verwandt-
schaftlichen Beziehungen zu diesen beiden Rüsselkäfergruppen hervorhob.

Die *Scolytidae* teilte er in zwei Unterfamilien : *Platypodidae* und *Scolytidae genuinae.* Die letzteren
zerlegte er in drei Hauptgruppen : *Tomicini, Scolytini* und *Hylurgini.*

Zu den *Tomicini* rechnete er die *Corthyli, Xyloteri, Xylebori, Tomici* und *Micracides.* Zu den *Scolytini*
nur die Gattung *Scolytus,* schliesslich zu den *Hylurgini* die *Polygraphi, Phloeotribi, Hylurgi, Crypturgi* und
Hylastes.

Von Besonderheiten seines Systems ist zu erwähnen, dass er in die Gruppe der *Corthyli* die Gattungen *Pityophthorus* und *Hypothenemus,* in die Gruppe der *Xylebori* ausser *Xyleborus* noch *Dryocoetes* und
Cryphalus stellte.

Es folgte Eichhoff, der 1881 für die europäischen Borkenkäfer ein System aufstellte, in welchem er die *Scolytidae* und *Platypodae* als gleichwertige Familien voneinander schied. In der ersten
Familie stellte er die *Scolytini* zwischen die *Hylesinini* und *Tomicini* und teilte die letzteren nach der
Lebensweise in Rindenbewohner und Holzkäfer. Reitter setzte in seiner *Bestimmungstabelle für die
paläarktischen Borkenkäfer* 1894 die *Scolytini* an die Spitze des Systems und schob zwischen *Hylesinini*
und *Ipini (Tomicini)* eine neue Abteilung *Hylastini,* bestehend aus den Gattungen *Hylastes* Erichson,
Crypturgus Erichson, *Cisurgus* Reitter und *Thamnurgus* Eichhoff, ein.

Blandford, der 1895-1907 in der *Biologia Centrali-Americana* eine umfassende Bearbeitung der centralamerikanischen Borkenkäfer gab, vereinfachte die alte Lacordaire'sche Einteilung, indem er für die Centralamerikaner vier Gruppen aufstellte. nämlich : 1° *Scolytides*, 2° *Hylesinides*, 3° *Hexacolides*, 4° *Tomicides*.

Endlich machten Escherich 1897 für die deutschen und Trédl 1907 für die europäischen Borkenkäfer die Gruppierung in *Eccoptogastridae*, *Ipidae* und *Platypodidae*, wobei in die erste Gruppe die einzige Gattung *Eccoptogaster (Scolytus)*, in die zweite alle übrigen *Scolytiden* kamen.

Eine der wichtigsten Fragen in der Systematik des *Rhynchophoren* ist die nach der Stellung der *Platypinen* im System. Diese isolierte und wohlumgrenzte Insektengruppe zeigt eine Reihe von Besonderheiten ihres Baues, welche sie ebensoweit von den Borkenkäfern wie von den Rüsselkäfern entfernt. Die Bildung der Mundwerkzeuge, der Beine, der Vorderbrust und des Metasternums sind so abweichend von der der Borkenkäfer, dass sie dadurch viel weiter von irgend einem Borkenkäfer entfernt erscheint als z. B. die morphologische Bildung der Gattung *Hylastes* diese von den *Cossoniden* entfernt.

Trotz der unleugbaren grossen Verschiedenheiten sind die *Platypinen* bisher meistens als Teil der Borkenkäfer rubriciert worden.

Eichhoff war wohl der erste, welcher in der *Berl. Ent. Zeitschr.* 1867 auf die fundamentalen Unterschiede zwischen *Platypiden* und *Scolytiden* hinwies und dieselben auch in seinen Europäischen Borkenkäfern 1881 als gleichwertige Familien behandelte.

Alber noch Bedel in seinen *Coléoptères du Bassin de la Seine* Vol. 6 *Rhynchophores* 1888, trennte wohl in der Familientabelle auf page 3 die *Platypiden* als eine wohlunterschiedene Familie von den übrigen *Scolytiden*, wagte aber im speciellen Teil page 385 doch nicht diese Trennung durchzuführen.

Es scheint mir aber, als ob gegen den Vorschlag Eichhoffs die *Platypiden* als selbständige Familie zu betrachten und gegen dessen Begründung bisher nichts durchschlagendes vorgebracht worden sei. Ich halte es daher für richtig, die notwendige Consequenz zu ziehen und die *Platypiden* von einer systematischen Besprechung der *Ipiden* auszuschliessen.

Da die Morphologie und die Biologie der Borkenkäfer noch zu wenig bekannt sind — die erstere ist nur für einige wenige Gattungen (*Ips*, *Cryphalus*, *Dendroctonus*, *Hypoborus*, etc.) teilweise, die letztere nur für die europäischen und nordamerikanischen Arten genauer erforscht — so sind naturgemäss alle vorgenannten Systeme nicht vollkommen und können auch nicht die natürliche Verwandtschaft der Gattungen und Arten untereinander ausdrücken. Es sind eben nur Zusammenfassungen von einzelnen Gattungen und einzelnen Gruppen, die je nach der Auffassung des Autors, aber wohl ohne ein höheres ordnendes Princip bald so, bald so nebeneinander gestellt sind.

Ein solches höheres ordnendes Princip nach der natürlichen Verwandtschaft der einzelnen Gattungen untereinander aufzufinden. ist auch heute mangels unserer Kenntnis der Borkenkäfer noch nicht möglich. Wir sind noch weit entfernt davon, die Verwandtschaftsgrade der einzelnen Gattungen und Gruppen durch genügende anatomische Untersuchungen zu belegen. Daher müssen wir uns leider immer noch mit einem künstlichen, mit einem Arbeitssystem begnügen.

Wenn ich um den Versuch wage den von Eichhoff zuerst ausgesprochenen Gedanken, der systematischen Einteilung ein biologisches Princip zugrunde zulegen, den er nur für die *Tomicinen* ausgeführt hat auf die ganze Familie der *Ipiden* auszudehnen, so bin ich mir wohl bewusst, dass das nur ein Versuch ist, der sich erst bewähren soll. d. h. dass die Richtigkeit meiner vorzuschlagenden Einteilung erst noch durch zahlreiche anatomische und biologische Untersuchungen gestützt werden muss.

Doch ermutigen mich die heute bereits bekannten Tatsachen, diesen Versuch für einen nicht ganz unberechtigten zu halten. Nachdem wir nämlich die Lebensweise der von Eichhoff sogenannten *Xylophagen*, der *Ambrosiakäfer*, etwas genauer kennen gelernt und gefunden haben, dass sie nicht von der Substanz des Baumes leben, sondern Pilze züchten, mit denen sie sich und ihre Larven ernähren und zu deren Zerkleinerung sie selbstverständlich nicht eine solch starke Bezahnung nötig haben, wie die übrigen Borkenkäfer, scheint mir durch die verschiedenartige Lebensweise und den dadurch bedingten Bau der Mundteile ein Princip gegeben zu sein, auf Grund dessen man eine Neuordnung der *Ipiden* wagen könnte.

Wir würden dabei folgende Tatsachen festzuhalten haben : sämtliche *Ipiden* besitzen stark gebaute kräftige Vorderkiefer. Diese benutzen sie in jedem Falle, sei es dass sie ihre Gangsysteme in der Rinde, oder zwischen Rinde und Holz im Splint, oder senkrecht gegen die Baumachse tief ins feste Holz anlegen, zur Ausbohrung der dem Körperumfange entsprechenden röhrenförmigen Gänge. Zur Zerkleinerung ihrer Nahrung dienen die Mittelkiefer. Diese sind je nach der Verschiedenheit der Ernährung mit verschieden starken Werkzeugen versehen. Diejenigen Tiere, welche von der Rinden- respekt. Splintsubstanz selbst leben — die sogenannten *bark-borers* der Amerikaner — besitzen starkge- baute mehr oder minder breite sichel- oder dolchförmige Dorne an der Kaukante : ich nenne sie daher *Spinidentatae*.

Diejenige Tiere, welche Pilznahrung zu sich nehmen, haben sehr viel schmälere, dünnere und schwächere, meist sichelförmig gebogene aber immer noch etwas breitgedrückte Borsten an der Innen- kante der Mittelkiefer — *Saetidentatae*.

Wieder eine andere Gruppe hat weder Zähne noch Borsten an der Kaulade, sondern nur einfache runde oder platte Haare an der Kaulade — *Pilidentatae*. Ob diese Tiere auch von sehr zarten Pilzen leben oder vielleicht von dem Milchsaft von Kautschukbäumen, ist bei unserer Unkenntnis der Lebens- weise der Exoten nicht zu sagen.

Eine vierte Gruppe endlich trägt an der Kaukante eine gemischte Bewehrung, die aus breiten Borsten und dazwischengestelten Haaren besteht — *Mixtodentatae*. Sie umfasst nur die Tribus *Spongo- cerinae*, welche wieder die unter dem Gattungsnamen *Scolytoplatypus* bekannten, nach Blandfords Vorschlag in drei Gattungen resp. Untergattungen zu zerlegenden Tiere enthält. Nach den Untersu- chungen von Niijima in Sapporo, Japan, leben diese Tiere in ähnlichen Wohnungen wie unsere *Xyloterus*-Arten, deren Gänge auch ebenso geschwärzt sind. Sie ernähren sich also wahrscheinlich auch von Pilzen.

Die Bewehrung der Kaukanten an den Mittelkiefern, welche ich in Haare, Borsten, Zähne oder Dornen getrennt habe, ist natürlich nur eine graduell verschiedene : im Grunde sind die genannten Gebilde alle des nämlichen Stammes und nur verschieden stark entwickelt.

Ich stelle mir die Entwicklung des Zahnbaues der Borkenkäfer so vor, dass die ursprünglichsten oder ältesten *Ipiden* auch die einfachste Bezahnung, nämlich Haare, an den Kaulaben besessen und vielleicht in saftigen, nicht baumartigen Pflanzen oder auch in milchsaftführenden Bäume gelebt haben. Sobald sie es versuchten zu festerer Nahrung überzugehen, mussten sich die Haare an den Kaukanten entsprechend verändern, indem sie dicker, breiter, kürzer wurden : ich finde bei den Gattungen *Phloeo- trupes* und *Phloeoborus* sowie bei *Dactylipalpus* bereits vereinzelte Uebergangsbildungen von den Haaren zu den Dornen — vielleicht kann man auch die rudimentär erscheinende Zahnbildung bei *Diamerus impar* Chapuis und *D. tuberculatus* Hagedorn hierher rechnen.

Wenn nun die Nahrung eine immer festere wurde, musste die Umbildung der Haare an der Kaukante in festere Gebilde fortschreiten. Dies ist der Zustand, wie wir ihn heute bei allen rindenbrü- tenden Borkenkäfern — *Phloeophagae* — vorfinden.

Bei einzelnen Gruppen ist aber wohl keine besondere Neigung vorhanden gewesen Baumsubstanz selbst zu verzehren und sich die dazu nötigen Zähne anzubeissen. Diese zogen es vor, weiche saftige Pilze zu geniessen, welche sie sich selbst züchteten : Nach der Beschaffenheit ihrer Nahrung brauchte daher die Bewaffnung ihrer Kaulaben sich nicht so stark zu entwickeln; sie blieb auf der Mitte zwischen Haar- und Dornbildung stehen, es bildeten sich nur Kauborsten, die zur Zerkleinerung der Pilze aus- reichend waren — *Mycetophagae*.

Von diesen eben entwickelten Gesichtspunkten ausgehend, schlage ich vor die Ipiden in folgende Unterfamilien und Tribus einzuteilen :

I. Subfamilie **Pilidentatæ** . .	1. Tribus PHLŒOTRUPINÆ . .	(Galactophagæ ?).
	2. Tribus DIAMERINÆ . . .	
	3. Tribus HYLESININÆ . .	
	4. Tribus CRYPTURGINÆ . .	
II. Subfamilie **Spinidentatæ** . .	5. Tribus CRYPHALINÆ . . .	Phlœophagæ.
	6. Tribus IPINÆ	
	7. Tribus HYLOCURINÆ. . .	
	8. Tribus ECCOPTOGASTRINÆ .	
III. Subfamilie **Sætidentatæ** . .	9. Tribus CORTHYLINÆ. . .	
	10. Tribus XYLEBORINÆ. . .	Mycetophagæ.
IV. Subfamilie **Mixtodentatæ** .	11. Tribus SPONGOCERINÆ . .	

Unterscheidungstabellen

Familienreihe : RHYNCHOPHORA — Familie : IPIDÆ

UEBERSICHT DER UNTERFAMILIEN

1. *Kaukante der Mittelkiefer mit Haaren besetzt* . . . . I. Subfam. PILIDENTATÆ.
2. *Kaukante der Mittelkiefer mit Dornen besetzt* . . . . II. Subfam. SPINIDENTATÆ.
3. *Kaukante der Mittelkiefer mit Borsten besetzt* . . . . III. Subfam. SÆTIDENTATÆ.
4. *Kaukante der Mittelkiefer mit Haaren und Dornen besetzt* . . . . . . IV. Subfam. MIXTODENTATÆ.

UEBERSICHT DER GATTUNGSGRUPPEN (TRIBUS)

I. Subfamilie **PILIDENTATÆ** . . . . 1. Tribus PHLŒOTRUPINÆ.

II. Subfamilie **SPINIDENTATÆ** :

1. *Schienen mit glatter Aussenkante, Vorderschienen an der äusseren Ecke in einen ein- oder zweigliedrigen Haken ausgezogen.*
  2. *Bauch ansteigend* . . . . 8. Tribus ECCOPTOGASTRINÆ.
  2'. *Bauch wagerecht.* . . . . 2. Tribus DIAMERINÆ.
1'. *Schienen niemals an der äusseren Ecke in einen Haken oder Fortsatz ausgezogen.*
  2. *Kopf mit Rüssel versehen.*
    3. *Drittes Tarsenglied einfach rund.*
      4. *Halsschild gleichmässig sculptiert* . . . . 4. Tribus CRYPTURGINÆ.
      4'. *Halsschild ungleichmässig sculptiert* . . . . 7. Tribus HYLOCURINÆ.
    3'. *Drittes Tarsenglied verbreitert* . . . . 3. Tribus HYLESININÆ.
  2'. *Kopf kugelig.*
    3. *Flügeldeckenabsturz bewehrt* . . . . 6. Tribus IPINÆ.
    3'. *Flügeldeckenabsturz nicht bewehrt* . . . . 5. Tribus CRYPHALINÆ.

III. Subfamilie **SÆTIDENTATÆ** :

1. *Erstes Lippentasterglied geschwollen und auf der Innenseite mit einem Bart von Haaren schräg besetzt* . . . . 10. Tribus XYLEBORINÆ. .
1'. *Erstes Lippentasterglied nicht geschwollen, sondern cylindrisch, nicht bebartet.* 9. Tribus CORTHYLINÆ.

IV. Subfamilie **MIXTODENTATÆ** . . . . 11. Tribus SPONGOCERINÆ.

II. — SPECIELLER TEIL

I. SUBFAM. PILIDENTATÆ

I. TRIBUS PHLŒOTRUPINÆ

UEBERSICHT DER GATTUNGEN

1. *Mittelkiefertaster zweigliedrig, Fühlerkeule eiförmig* . . . . . 1. Genus Dactylipalpus, Chapuis.
1'. *Mittelkiefertaster dreigliedrig.*
    2. *Die drei Glieder ziemlich gleich lang, Fühlerkeule zugespitzt* . 2. Genus Phlœoborus, Erichson.
    2'. *Das letzte Glied doppelt so lang als die beiden andern zusammen,*
        Fühlerkeule gerundet . . . . 3. Genus Phlœotrupes, Erichson.

I. Genus DACTYLIPALPUS, Chapuis

Dactylipalpus. Chapuis, Mém. Soc. Science Liége. p. 68 (1869); Synops. Scolyt. p. 220 (1873).
Dactylopselaphus. Gemminger & Harold, Cat. Col. Vol. 9, p. 2678 (1872).
Ethadopselaphus. Blandford, Ann. Mag. Nat. Hist. (6), Vol. 17, p. 320 (1896).

ORIGINALDIAGNOSE : Chapuis, loc. cit.
« Antennarum funiculus 7-articulatus, clava annulata. Oculi transverse reniformes, grosse gra-nulati. Tibiæ extus spinulosæ. Corpus ovatum vel oblongo-ovatum, staturæ maioris. Maxillarum palpi Zart gelb biarticulati, articulo 2º longissimo. »

Charaktere. — Körperform länglich bis länglich-eiförmig, Grösse bis 12 mm. Farbe schwarz; zart gelb beborstet bis grobflockig gelb behaart.

Kopf in einen kurzen breiten Rüssel verlängert.

Augen quer-nierenförmig, sehr gross, nach unten bis beinahe zum Kehlausschnitt, nach oben bis auf die Stirn reichend.

Fühler mit siebengliederiger Geissel, Keule eiförmig zugespitzt, solide.

Vorderkiefer derb, mit drei starken Zähnen.

Mittelkiefer hornig, Kaukante nicht mit Zähnen, sondern nur mit Haaren, wie an den übrigen Teilen, besetzt; an der Spitze derselben mit kürzerem oder längerem Lappen.

Kiefertaster zweigliedrig, zweites Glied länger als das erste; bei den afrikanischen Arten finden sich deutliche Spuren von Teilung desselben.

Hinterkiefer sind zu einen schmalen, langgestreckten Kinne verschmolzen, welches nur wenig von der Zunge, die in der Mitte des Kinnes angesetzt ist, überragt wird; diese ist an der Basis schmal, nach der Spitze verbreitert und stark mit Haaren besetzt.

Lippentaster zweigliedrig, letztes Glied sehr lang, zugespitzt.

Halsschild querbreiter, ohne Seitenrand, grob sculptiert, beim ♀ in einigen Arten mit eine Querfurche versehen; mit zarten bis groben gelben Borsten bedeckt.

Schildchen dreieckig, gross, von Halsschild und Flügeldeckenbasis überragt, so dass es wenig sichtbar ist.

Flügeldecken an der Basis erhaben und gekerbt, hinten abschüssig, gleichmässig abgewölbt. Sculptur : tiefe Punktstreifen und grobe Körnung der Zwischenräume, bei einigen (neuen) Afrikanern mit grober, mitunter flockiger, gelber Behaarung.

Vorder- und Mittelhüften kugelig, Hinterhüften quer, von einander abstehend, die vorderen durch einen geknopften Fortsatz der Vorderbrust getrennt.

Schienen verbreitert, mit gezähnten Aussenrand, das vorderste Paar auf der Innenfläche tief ausgehöhlt.

Fussglieder mit starker Haarbürste auf den Sohlen; drittes Glied zweilappig.

Bauch horizontal.

Die Gattung bildet eine Ausnahme unter den Borkenkäfern wegen der Zahl ihrer Tasterglieder. Während alle Borkenkäfer sonst dreigliedrige Taster haben, finden wir bei einer Art, *D. transversus* Chapuis, zweigliedrige Kiefertaster, häufig aber mit angedeuteter Abschnürung auf dem letzten Gliede. Bei den anderen Arten ist die Teilung des letzten Gliedes mehr weniger deutlich, findet sich auch einmal mehr in der Nähe der Basis, dann wieder mehr in der Nähe der Spitze. Die Lippentaster sind bei allen zweigliedrig; ich habe nirgends eine beginnende Abschnürung beobachtet.

Blandford hat für einige Tiere mit deutlicher Abschnürung eines dritten Kiefertastergliedes eine eigene Gattung, *Ethadopselaphus*, gemacht; ich kann ihm darin nicht folgen, weil ausser dieser einen Eigentümlichkeit vollständige generische Uebereinstimmung der Tiere besteht. Ich bin viel mehr der Meinung, dass die Gattung in der Umbildung begriffen ist, wofür mir zwei Umstände zu sprechen scheinen. nämlich : 1° dass man bei einigen Exemplaren von *D. transversus* Chapuis Andeutungen einer Teilung des letzten Kiefertastergliedes bemerkt, bei anderen nicht, und 2° dass die Abschnürung an verschiedenen Stellen des letzten Kiefertastergliedes erfolgt.

Geographische Verbreitung der Arten. — Von den fünf beschriebenen und zwei im Besitze des königlichen Museums in Berlin befindlichen, demnächst zu veröffentlichen Arten kommen sechs in Afrika im äthiopischen Reich und nur eine im indo-malayischen vor. Die letztere ist von Malakka und Ternate sowie Sumatra bekannt, während von den Afrikanern vier Kameruner und eine Ashanti, also an der Westküste, und nur einer an der Ostküste vorkommen.

1. *D. transversus*, Chapuis, Synops. Scolyt. p. 220 (1873). — **Taf. I, Fig. I.** Malakka.
   quadratocollis, ♂, Chapuis, ibidem, p. 220 (1873).
2. *D. camerunus*, Hagedorn, Deutsche Ent. Zeitschr. p. 370 (1908). Kamerun.
3. *D. similis*, Hagedorn, ibidem. p. 370 (1908). — **Taf. I, Fig. I a, I b.** Kamerun.
4. *D. africanus*, Schaufuss. in litt. — **Taf. I, Fig. 2.** Kamerun.
5. *D. floccosus*, Hagedorn, in litt. Kamerun.
6. *D. Grouvellei*, Blandford, Ann. Mag. Nat. Hist. (6), Vol. 17, p. 322 Ashanti.
   (1896).
7. *D. cicatricosus*, Blandford, ibidem. p. 321 (1896). Natal.

2. Genus PHLŒOBORUS, Erichson

Phlœoborus. Erichson, Arch. f. Naturg. (2), Vol. 1, p. 54 (1836): Blandford, Biol. Centr. Amer. Col. Vol. 4 (6), p. 149 (1897); Chapuis, Synops. Scolyt. p. 220 (1873).

Originaldiagnose : Erichson, loc. cit.

« Antennæ funiculo 6-articulato, capitulo 4-annulato, oblongo, acuminato. Tibiæ compressæ, extus denticulatæ. Maxillæ extus pilosæ, mala minuta, apice pilorum fasciculo instructa. Palpi maxillares conici, articulo primo brevissimo, secundo brevi, quarto minuto, obtuse subulato. Labium parvum, angustum, subcompressum. Palpi labiales articulis decrescentibus, ultimo obtuse acuminato. Antennæ scapo brevi, clavato : funiculi articulo primo subgloboso, secundo sequentibus paulo longiore, his sensim latioribus : capitulum segmento primo minuto, polito, reliquis subæqualibus pubescentibus. Corpus maioris magnitudinis. Rostrum perbreve. Oculi in fronte spatio tenui distantes. Prosternum antice leviter impressum. Coxæ anticæ distantes. Tibiæ compressæ, extus denticulatæ, postice levissime excavatæ. Tarsi articulo tertio bilobo. »

Charaktere. — Körperform länglich-walzenförmig, oder länglich-eiförmig, Grösse bis 12 mm., grobskulptiert, unbekleidet, Farbe schwarz.

Kopf mit kurzem breitem Rüssel.

Augen quer-oval, reichen von der Kehlnaht bis zur Stirn; bei einigen Arten stossen sie auf der Stirn beinahe zusammen.

Fühler mit siebengliedriger Geissel; Keule dreigliedrig, zugespitzt; kaum zusammengedrückt. Vorderkiefer derb, zweizähnig.

Mittelkiefer hornig, stark behaart, Kaukante mit etwas breitgedrückten Haaren, die mitunter Uebergänge zu Spinen zeigen, besetzt. Stipes und Fortsatz der Lade deutlich getrennt.

Kiefertaster dreigliedrig, die beiden ersten Glieder beinahe gleichlang, das letzte etwas kürzer, zugespitzt, das mittlere am längsten.

Hinterkiefer sind zu einem schmalen länglichen Kinne verschmolzen, auf dem die eben so breite Zunge aufsitzt.

Lippentaster dreigliedrig, Glieder drehrund, ziemlich gleich an Grösse, letztes Glied zugespitzt. Halsschild quer breiter, grob skulptiert, nicht seitlich gerandet.

Schildchen knopfförmig, klein

Flügeldecken an der Basis gekerbt und aufgeworfen, an der Spitze gewölbt abfallend, mit groben Punktstreifen und derber Skulptur der Zwischenräume.

Vorderbrust mit einem knopfförmigen Fortsatz, der sich zwischen die Vorderhüften erstreckt. Bei einigen Arten befindet sich auf den Propleuren rechts und links eine tiefe Grube, welche eine Anzahl von runden Löchern in ihrem Grunde aufweist, zwischen denen lange gelbe Haare stehen. Aus diesen Löchern dringt ein fettiges gelbes Sekret, welches an der Luft erstarrt und bei einer Reihe von Tieren auch im getrockneten Zustand sichtbar 1) ist. Vermutlich ist dieses ein sekundäres Geschlechtsmerkmal, doch ist darüber nichts authentisches bekannt.

Vorder- und Mittelhüften kugelig, Hinterhüften quer mit grossen Trochanteren. Zwischen den Vorderhüften erstreckt sich ein knopfförmiger Prosternalfortsatz.

Meso- und Metasternum sind kanalförmig ausgehöhlt.

Schienen derb, aussen gezähnt, mit Furchen zum Einlegen der Tarsen.

Fussglieder haben starke Haarbürsten unter den Sohlen, drittes Fussglied zweilappig. Bauch horizontal.

---

1) Cf. **Taf. 1, Fig. 3b.**

Geographische Verbreitung der Arten. — Es sind zweiundzwanzig Arten bekannt, welche alle auf das Südreich beschränkt sind.

1. *P. asper*, Erichson, Arch. f. Naturg. (2), Vol. 1, p. 55 (1836). — Brasilien.
2. *P. aspericollis*, Strohmeyer, Ent. Blätter, Vol. 5, p. 248 (1909). — Ecuador.
3. *P. Belti*, Blandford, Biol. Centr. Amer. Col. Vol. 4 (6), p. 151 (1897). — Nicaragua.
4. *P. breviusculus*, Chapuis, Synops. Scolyt. p. 222 (1873). — Cayenne.
5. *P. cristatus*, Chapuis, ibidem. p 221 (1873). — Bogotá.
6. *P. ellipticus*, Chapuis, ibidem, p. 223 (1873). — Brasilien.
7. *P. elongatus*, Chapuis, ibidem. p. 221 (1873). — Brasilien.
8. *P. Gaujonii*, Fairmaire, Bull. Soc. Ent. Fr. p. 16 (1887). — Ecuador.
9. *P. granosus*, Eichhoff, Berl. Ent. Zeitschr. Vol. 12, p. 148 (1868). — Brasilien.
10. *P. grossus*, Chapuis, Synops. Scolyt. p. 221 (1873). — Columbien.
11. *P. imbricornis*, Eichhoff, Berl. Ent. Zeitschr. p. 148 (1868). — Mexico.
12. *P. mamillatus*, Chapuis, Synops. Scol. p. 222 (1873). — Brasilien.
13. *P. nitidicollis*, Chapuis, ibidem, p. 222 (1873). — Brasilien.
14. *P. ovatus*, Chapuis, ibidem, p. 223 (1873). — Cayenne.
15. *P. punctato-rugosus*, Chapuis, ibidem, p. 222 (1873). — Neu-Granada.
16. *P. radulosus*, Blandford, Biol. Centr. Amer. Col. Vol. 4 (6), p. 153 (1897). — Ecuador und Centraleamerika.
17. *P. rudis*, Erichson, Arch. f. Naturg. (2), Vol. 1, p. 55 (1836). — **Taf. I, Fig. 3, 3a.** — Brasilien. [rika.
18. *P. rugatus*, Blandford, Biol. Centr. Amer. Col. Vol. 4 (6), p. 151 (1897). — Nicaragua.
    rugatus, ♂, Strohmeyer, Ent. Blätter, Vol. 5, p. 248 (1909). — Guyana.
19. *P. scaber*, Erichson, Arch. f. Naturg. (2), Vol. 1, p. 55 (1836). — **Taf. I, Fig. 3c.** — Brasilien.
    sericeus, ♂, Chapuis, Synops. Scolyt. p. 221 (1873). — Centralamerika.
20. *P. signatus*, Strohmeyer, Ent. Blätter, Vol. 5, p. 248 (1897). — Brasilien.
21. *P. Sipolisii*, Fairmaire, Bull. Soc. Ent. Fr. p. 16 (1887). — Brasilien.
22. *P. sulcifrons*, Eichhoff, Berl. Ent. Zeitschr. Vol. 12. p. 148 (1868). — Brasilien.

3. Genus PHLŒOTRUPES, Erichson

Phlœotrupes. Erichson, Arch. f. Naturg. Vol. 1, p. 53 (1836); Chapuis, Synops. Scolyt. p. 219 (1873).

ORIGINALDIAGNOSE : Erichson loc. cit.

« Antennæ funiculo 6-articulato, capitulo 4-annulato, orbiculari, compresso. Tibiæ extus convexæ, muricatæ, intus concàvæ. Maxillæ pilosæ extus dilatatæ : mala parva setosa. Palpi maxillares cylindrici, articulis tribus brevissimis, quárto reliquis coniunctis æquali. Labium parvum, compressum, lineare. Palpi labiales articulis duobus primis æqualibus, tertio utroque paulo longiore tenuioreque. Antennæ scapo breviusculo, subarcuato, funiculi articulo primo crassiore, reliquis sensim latioribus ; capitulum segmento primo parvo polito, reliquis subæqualibus, pubescentibus. Corpus magnum. Rostrum breve planum. Mandibulæ validæ. Prosternum antice parvum impressum, dein inter coxas anticas distantes obtuse elevatum. Pedes validi. Tibiæ posteriores extus convexæ, spinulis crebris muricatæ, intus excipiendis tarsis excavatæ : anticæ antice profunde canaliculatæ. Tarsi minuti articulo tertio bilobo. »

Charaktere. — Körperform kurz oval, plump, dick.

Länge : 12-13 mm.; Breite : 7-8 mm.

Farbe : tiefschwarz.

Bekleidung nur auf Hüften, Schenkeln und Schienen mit längeren blassgelben Haaren. Skulptur stark ausgeprägt aber nicht grob.

Kopf mit kurzem breitem Rüssel, der häufig gekielt ist.

Augen quer oval, schmal, nierenförmig, von der Kehlnaht bis auf die Stirne reichend.

Fühler mit siebengliedriger Geissel, Keule mit Nähten, gerundet, zusammengedrückt und stumpf.

Vorderkiefer sehr derb mit zwei Zähnen.

Mittelkiefer hornig, stark behaart, Kaukante mit verbreiterten platt-borstenförmigen Haaren besetzt.

Kiefertaster dreigliedrig, das letzte Glied ist noch einmal so lang als die beiden andefen zusammengenommen.

Hinterkiefer zu einem schmalen linearen Kinne verschmolzen; Zunge ebenfalls schmal, bis zur Spitze des Mentum reichend.

Lippentaster stark behaart, dreigliedrig, letztes Tasterglied lang, dünn, kegelförmig.

Halsschild quer breiter, seitlich gerandet, an der Basis doppelt gebuchtet, Scheibe meist glatt und glänzend mit spärlicher Punktierung.

Schildchen dreieckig, mässig gross.

Flügeldeckenbasis aufgeworfen und gekerbt, Spitze abschüssig gewölbt, mit tiefen Punktstreifen, Zwischenräume mit grossen queren Erhöhungen besetzt.

Vorderbrust mit stark geknopftem und behaartem Fortsatz zwischen den kugeligen Vorderhüften, auf den Propleuren befinden sich bei einzelnen Stücken von *P. grandis* Erichson rechts und links tiefe Gruben, deren Grund siebartig durchlöchert und mit ziemlich langen, blassgelben Haaren besetzt ist : eine ähnliche Bildung wie bei *Phloeoborus* und auch hier vermutlich ein sekundäres Geschlechtsmerkmal.

Vorderhüften kugelig, durch den stark geknopften Fortsatz der Vorderbrust, Mittelhüften und Hinterhüften durch kanalikulierte Fortsätze des Meso- und Metasternums getrennt.

Schienen an der Aussenkante gezähnt, ihre Aussenfläche mit groben Erhabenheiten besetzt, ihre Innenfläche mit tiefer Aushöhlung versehen, welche an den Vorderschienen besonders tief kanalartig erscheint.

Fussglieder mit stark bebürsteten Sohlen, drittes Glied zweilappig.

Bauch horizontal.

Geographische Verbreitung der Arten. — Es sind nur drei Arten aus dem Südreich bekannt. Sie heissen :

1. *P. caelatus*, Blanchard, Voy. d'Orbigny, p. 204 (1846).   Bolivia.
2. *P. grandis*, Erichson, Arch. f. Naturg. (2),Vol. 1, p. 54 (1836). — **Taf. I**,   Brasilien.
   Fig. 4, 4a; Taf. I I, Fig. 77, 78.
3. *P. procerus*, Erichson, ibidem, p. 54 (1836).   Brasilien.

II. SUBFAM. SPINIDENTATÆ

2. TRIBUS DIAMERINÆ

UEBERSICHT DER GATTUNGEN

1. *Fühlerkeule solid, ohne Borstenbinden.*
    2. *Vorderhüften zusammenstehend* . . . . 4. Genus BOTHRYPERUS, Hagedorn.
    2'. *Vorderhüften auseinanderstehend.* . . . . 5. Genus DIAMERUS, Erichson.
1'. *Fühlerkeule mit Borstenbinden.*
    2. *Kopf ohne Rüssel* . . . . 6. Genus RHOPALOPSELION, Hagedorn.
    2'. *Kopf mit Rüssel* . . . . 7. Genus STROMBOPHORUS, Hagedorn.

4. Genus BOTHRYPERUS, Hagedorn

Bothryperus. Hagedorn, Deutsche Ent. Zeitschr. p. 742 (1909).

ORIGINALDIAGNOSE : Hagedorn, loc. cit.

« Caput in rostellum hand productum, oculi bipartiti, antennæ lateraliter inter mandibulas et oculos insertæ, breves, funiculo 6 articulato, articulis latitudine crescentibus, clava ovata rotundata compressa, sutura unica transversa ornata. Prothorax transversus, lateraliter immarginatus, basi bisinuatus. Elytra ad apicem angustata. Coxæ anticæ contiguæ, mediæ et posticæ late distantes. Tibiæ extus spinulosæ, tarsorum articuli primus et secundus æquales, tertius bilobus, subtus pilosus. Abdomen adscendens. »

Charaktere. — Körperform : eiförmig nach hinten zugespitzt, von pechschwarzer Farbe mit gelbbraunen Schuppen bedeckt. Grösse 3 mm.

Kopf ohne Rüssel.

Stirn mit einem Längskiel versehen.

Vorderkiefer kräftig, schwach gezähnt.

Mittelkiefer pergamentartig, ziemlich stark behaart und bedornt mit beilförmigem Lappen, an dessen Kaukante fünfzehn bis achtzehn breite zugespitzte dolchförmige derbe Zähne sitzen.

Kiefertaster dreigliedrig, Glieder von ungefähr gleicher Länge, an Dicke abnehmend.

Hinterkiefer zu einem breiten beinahe dreieckigen Kinne verschmolzen, an dessen Basis die lanzenförmige, starkgerunzelte und behaarte, mit ihrer ziemlich scharfen Spitze bis zum ersten Drittel des ersten Tastergliedes reichende Zunge entspringt.

Lippentaster-Glied 1 am längsten und dicksten, so lang wie die beiden anderen zusammengenommen, walzenförmig; Glied 2 stark verschmälert, quadratisch; Glied 3 kegelförmig, schmal.

Halsschild quer, vorne eingeschnürt, seitlich nicht gerandet, Basis durch einen mittleren Fortsatz zweibuchtig, auf der Scheibe gleichmässig punktiert.

Schildchen klein, halbkreisförmig.

Flügeldecken an der Basis aufgeworfen und gekerbt, nach hinten verschmälert, Absturz flach abgewölbt, mit tiefen Punktstreifen und ebenen, schuppenbedeckten Zwischenräumen versehen.

Vorderhüften kugelig, einander berührend, mässig behaart.

Mittel- und Hinterhüften voneinander getrennt.

Schienen an der Aussenkante bedornt und verbreitert.

Fussglieder 1 und 2 gleich, rund; 3 zweilappig ; unten behaart.

Bauch mit blassen Schuppen bedeckt, gegen die Flügeldeckenspitze etwas ansteigend.

Geographische Verbreitung der Arten. — Es ist nur eine Art aus Kamerun bekannt; sie heisst :

1. *B. psaltes*, Hagedorn, Deutsche Ent. Zeitschr. p. 742 (1909). — **Taf. 8.** Kamerun.

Fig. 11.

5. Genus DIAMERUS, Erichson

Diamerus. Erichson, Arch. f. Naturg. Vol. 1, p. 57 (1836); Chapuis, Synops. Scolyt. p. 257 (1873).
Acanthurus. Eichhoff, Notes Leyd. Mus. Vol. 8, p. 24 (1886).

ORIGINALDIAGNOSE : Erichson, loc. cit.

« Antennæ funiculo 6-articulato, capitulo solido subovali, compresso, tibiæ compressæ, extus

-obsolete denticulatæ. Maxillæ latæ pilosæ, extrorsum dilatatæ. Labium oblongum, planum. Antennæ
·scapo leviter clavato, funiculi articulo primo crasssiusculo, fere obconico, reliquis coactis, ægerrime
distinguendis; capitulum oblongo-subovale, obtusius acuminatum. Corpus breve convexum. Coxæ
.anticæ late distantes; prosterno interposito latissimo, brevi, apice truncato. Mesosternum antice truncatum. Tibiæ compressæ, extus obsolete denticulatæ, posteriores postice canaliculatæ. Tarsi articulo
tertio haud dilatato, emarginato. Elytra margine antico valde elevato. »

    Charaktere. — Körperform kurz eiförmig, gedrungen, meistens dicht und bunt beschuppt,
von 3-4 mm. Länge und 2-3 mm. Breite.

    Kopf in einen kurzen Rüssel ausgezogen.

    Augen quer oval, ganzrandig.

    Fühler mit siebengliedriger Geissel, Keule zusammengedrückt, oval. ohne Nähte, aber mit
dunklem Sensitivstreifen schräg durchsetzt.

    Vorderkiefer derb, dreizähnig.

    Mittelkiefer hornig, breit, stark behaart und bedornt, Kaukante mit längeren wohlausgebildeten,
oder wie bei *impar* Chapuis und *tuberculatus* Hagedorn mit spärlichen kleinen, rudimentär erscheinenden
Zähnen besetzt.

    Kiefertaster dreigliedrig, erstes Glied am grössten.

    Hinterkiefer zu einem länglich schmalen oben stark bedornten Kinne verschmolzen; Zunge nur
·wenig das Mentum überragend und kaum breiter als dieses.

    Lippentaster : Glied 1 am längsten und dicksten, Glied 2 quadratisch, Glied 3 kurz kegelförmig.

    Halsschild fast quadratisch, seitlich gerandet, gleichförmig punktiert und beschuppt.

    Schildchen klein, punktförmig.

    Flügeldecken stark gewölbt und nach hinten abfallend, Basis aufgeworfen und gekerbt; Skulptur
unter der starken bunten Beschuppung meistens verschwindend; Spitze gerundet oder zugespitzt.

    Hüften weit voneinander abstehend, die vorderen sind durch einen kurzen, breiten, platten-
förmigen Fortsatz der Vorderbrust voneinander getrennt.

    Schienen an der Aussenkante schwach gezähnt oder glatt verbreitert, an der Vorderspitze mit
-einem einfachen Haken oder einer mehrspitzigen Schaufel versehen.

    Füsse mit gleichgrossen, mit Sohlenbürsten versehenen ersten drei Gliedern.

    Bauch horizontal.

    E i c h h o f f hat unter dem Namen *Acanthurus* in den *Notes of the Leyden Museum*, p. 24 1886,
eine neue Gattung mit folgenden Worten beschrieben : « Caput prominulum, rostello brevi auctum,
· oculis oblongis integris. Antennarum funiculus 7-articulatus, clava compressa ovalis solida. Tarsi
articulis 1-3 æqualibus. Tibiæ extus obsolete denticulatæ, antice apice unco solido armatæ. »

    Nach dieser Beschreibung müssen die von E i c h h o f f unter diesem Gattungsnamen beschrie-
benen Arten *spinipennis* und *Ritsemae* sehr nahe verwandt sein mit der Gattung *Diamerus*. So nahe, dass
schon B l a n d f o r d in der *Biologia Centrali-Americana*, Col. Vol. 4 (6), p. 124, 1896, *Acanthurus* zu
Diamerus zieht. Die beiden Arten unterscheiden sich mit meinen Arten *dissimilis, ater* und *caesius* durch
die Zuspitzung der Flügeldecken von den übrigen Arten. Auch im Bau der Mundteile finde ich Unterschiede. Das einzige Tier von den Arten mit zugespitzten Flügeldecken welches ich untersucht habe,
nämlich *caesius*, weicht im Bau des Hinterkiefers sehr auffällig ab. Während das Mentum bei *D. impar*
und *D. tuberculatus* lang. nach vorne verschmälert ist, die Zunge fast vom Grunde aus beginnend bis
·zur Mitte des ersten Tastergliedes reicht und gerundet oder zugespitzt gerundet ist, ist der Bau des
Hinterkiefers von *caesius* folgender : das Mentum ist sehr lang und schmal, an beiden Enden verbreitert,
-die Zunge beginnt an der Basis, überragt die Mentumspitze nur wenig, die Taster sind sehr lang

gestreckt, besonders das Grundglied ist lang und schmal walzenförmig, das zweite ist kürzer, das dritte ist wieder lang und kegelförmig. Auch der Mittelkiefer von *caesius* unterscheidet sich sehr bedeutend durch seine lange derbe Bezahnung von den winzigen Zähnchen des *impar* und *tuberculatus;* er ähnelt am meisten dem von *luteus*, dessen Hinterkiefer aber wieder viel mehr mit denen von *impar* und *tuberculatus* übereinstimmt. Sollte sich bei der notwendigen genaueren Untersuchung der übrigen Arten der Bau der Mundteile von *caesius* als typisch für die Arten mit zugespitzten Flügeldecken erweisen, so wird man wohl die Eichhoffsche Gattung *Acanthurus* wieder herstellen müssen.

Geographische Verbreitung der Arten. — Von den vierzehn bekannten Arten gehören acht dem indo-malayischen, vier dem æthiopischen und zwei dem madegassischen Reiche an. Es sind folgende :

1. *D. ater*, Hagedorn, Deutsche Ent. Zeitschr. p. 735 (1909). — **Taf. I**, Nilgiri Hills.
   Fig. 6.
2. *D. caesius*, Hagedorn, ibidem, p. 735 (1909).—**Taf. 8, Fig. 8, 9, 10.**   Sumatra.
3. *D. curvifer*, Walker, Ann. Mag. Nat. Hist. p. 261 (1859).   Ceylon.
4. *D. dissimilis*, Hagedorn, Deutsche Ent. Zeitschr. p. 735 (1909).   Birma.
5. *D. fici*, Blandford, Trans. Ent. Soc. Lond. p. 426 (1898).   Himalaya.
6. *D. luteus*, Hagedorn, Deutsche Ent. Zeitschr. p. 735 (1909). — **Taf. 8,**   Sumatra.
   Fig. 5, 6, 7.
7. *D. Ritsemae*, Eichhoff, Notes Leyd. Mus. Vol. 8, p. 24 (1886).   Sumatra.
8. *D. spinipennis*, Eichhoff, ibidem, p. 24 (1886).   Sumatra.
9. *D. ericius*, Schaufuss, Tijdschr. v. Ent. Vol. 40, p. 217 (1897).   Natal.
10. *D. impar*, Chapuis, Synops. Scol. p. 258 (1873). — **Taf. I, Fig. 5;**   Guinea, Senegal, Kamerun.
    Taf. 8, Fig. I, 2, 3.
    var. nanus, Hagedorn, Deutsche Ent. Zeitschr. p. 734 (1909).   Togo.
11. *D. pulverulentus*, Gerstäcker, Arch. f. Naturg. Vol. 37, p. 76 (1870).   Zanzibar.
12. *D. tuberculatus*, Hagedorn, Deutsche Ent. Zeitschr. p. 734 (1909). —   Kamerun.
    Taf. 8, Fig. 4.
13. *D. hispidus*, Klug, in Abhandl. Berl. Akad. Wiss. Vol. I, p. 202 (1833).   Madagaskar.
14. *D. cinerascens*, Fairmaire, Ann. Soc. Ent. Belg. Vol. 41, p. 195 (1897).   Madagaskar.

6. GENUS RHOPALOPSELION, HAGEDORN

Rhopalopselion. Hagedorn, Deutsche Ent. Zeitschr. p. 740 (1909).

ORIGINALDIAGNOSE : Hagedorn, loc. cit.

« Caput oblongum, in rostellum haud productum. Oculi transverse reniformes. Antennæ lateraliter inter mandibules et oculos insertæ, breves, funiculo 7-articulato, articulis latitudine crescentibus, clava ovata rotundata compressa, sutura unica transversa. vittis setarum septem annulata. Prothorax lateraliter adangulum posticum fortiter, dein leviter marginatus. Coxæ anticæ et mediæ late distantes. Tibiæ anteriores ad apicem dilatatæ, spinula unica extus producta armatæ et superficie anteriore excavatæ. Tibiæ posteriores spinulosæ; tarsorum articuli primus et secundus æquales, tertius bilobus, subtus pilosi. Sphærotrypi similis. »

Charaktere. — Körperform kurz eiförmig, stumpf, Länge 3mm., Farbe braun, Skulptur auf Halsschild und Flügeldeckenabsturz grob, Bekleidung mit dunkeln und helleren kurzen Borsten.

Kopf ohne Rüssel.

Augen schmal, quer, langgestreckt, von der Kehlnath bis zur Stirn reichend.

Fühler mit siebengliedriger Geissel, die kürzer als die Keule ist; diese ist eiförmig beinahe dreieckig stumpf gerundet, mit einer Quernath und sieben queren Haarbinden.

Vorderkiefer kräftig mit zwei Zähnen.

Mittelkiefer mit hornartigem ziemlich schmalem Lappen, an dessen Kaukante zwölf bis vierzehn breite, dolchartige Zähne sitzen. Sonst reichlich behaart.

Kiefertaster dreigliedrig. Erstes Glied breiter als lang, zweites Glied fast quadratisch, drittes Glied stumpf kegelförmig, mit Längsstreifen versehen.

Hinterkiefer und Lippentaster gingen bei der Präparation verloren.

Halsschild quer, fast quadratisch, stark vorwärts über die Fläche gebogen, Vorderwinkel durch scharfe Dornen bezeichnet, Basis durch Vorspringen der Mitte zweibuchtig, Scheibe mit Tuberkeln, besonders an den Seiten, und kurzen hellgelben Börstchen besetzt.

Schildchen gross, quadratisch.

Flügeldecken an der Basis aufgeworfen und gekerbt, ziemlich derb skulptiert mit einzelnen Tuberkeln besetzt; nach hinten stark gewölbt und steil abfallend. Spitzen gerundet.

Hüften weit voneinander abstehend.

Vorderschienen verbreitert, an der Aussenecke mit einem Dorn; Vorderfläche vertieft.

Hinterschienen an der Aussenkante gezähnt.

Fussglieder 1 und 2 gleichrund. 3 zweilappig, Sohlen mit Haarbürsten.

Bauch wenig ansteigend.

Geographische Verbreitung der Art. — Es ist nur eine Art aus Kamerun bekannt.

1. *R. bituberculatum*, Hagedorn, Deutsche Ent. Zeitschr. p. 740 (1909). Kamerun.

7. Genus STROMBOPHORUS, Hagedorn

Strombophorus. Hagedorn, Deutsche Ent. Zeitschr. p. 740 (1909).

ORIGINALDIAGNOSE : Hagedorn, loc. cit.

« Caput in rostellum lateraliter marginatum productum. Oculi transverse reniformes, antennæ lateraliter in oculorum emarginatione et sub margine rostri insertæ, breves, funiculo 7-articulato, articulis latitudine crescentibus, clava rotundata compressa sutura unica transversa, vittis setarum 7-annulata. Prothorax lateraliter marginatus, coxæ anticæ subcontiguæ, processu brevi prosterni seiunctæ, mediæ et posticæ distantes. Tibiæ anticæ ad apicem dilatatæ, excavatæ, extus dentatæ. Tarsorum articuli primus et secundus æquales, tertius bilobus, subtus pilosus. »

Charaktere. — Körperform länglich nach hinten verschmälert, 3-4 mm. lang, Skulptur mässig schwach, Bekleidung mit kurzen dunklen und hellen Borsten.

Kopf in einen Rüssel verlängert, dessen Seiten gerandet sind.

Stirn flach oder vertieft.

Augen schmal und lang, von der Kehle bis zur Stirn sich hinziehend, vorn ausgerandet.

Fühler mit siebengliedriger Geissel, die kürzer als der Schaft sowohl wie die Keule ist.

Keule rund, mit einer Naht, welche, in steilem winkligem Bogen sich erhebend, in der Nähe der Basis entspringt. Ausserdem befinden sich mehrere Borstenbinden auf der Keule.

Vorderkiefer kräftig gezähnt.

Mittelkiefer mit breitem, beilförmigem Lappen, an dessen Kaukante fünfzehn bis siebzehn breite messerförmige Zähne sitzen.

Kiefertaster dreigliedrig, erstes Glied am grössten, walzenförmig, ebenso das kleinere zweite; das dritte Glied ist stumpf kegelförmig und mit Längsstreifen versehen.

Hinterkiefer sind zu einem dreieckigen, mit ausgeschweiften Seiten und gerader Spitze versehenen Kinne verschmolzen, an dessen Basis die schmale nach der Spitze sich stark verbreiternde und bis zur Basis der Taster reichende Zunge entspringt.

Lippentaster : Glied 1 am grössten, cylindrisch, etwas geschwellt; Glied 2 am kleinsten, Glied 3. schmal kegelförmig.

Halsschild seitlich gerandet, nach vorn etwas verschmälert, Basis gerandet und doppelt gebuchtet. Scheibe stark gewölbt, an den Vorderecken mit Knötchen besetzt.

Schildchen nicht sichtbar.

Flügeldecken an der Basis aufgeworfen und gekerbt, mit Punktstreifen, ebenen Zwischenraûmen,. die leicht gerunzelt resp. gehöckert sind, und mit bräunlichen Schuppen versehen. Nach der Spitze zu sind die Flügeldecken verschmälert.

Vorderhüften beinahe einander berührend, nur durch einen kurzen und schmalen Vorderbrust-- fortsatz unten getrennt. Mittel- und Hinterhüften voneinander entfernt.

Schienen verbreitert, Aussenkante schwach gekerbt.

Fussglieder 1 und 2 gleichrund, 3 zweilappig, Sohlen behaart.

Bauch horizontal.

Geographische Verbreitung der Arten. — Es sind drei Arten aus dem Æthiopischen Reich bekannt. Sie stammen alle aus Kamerun. Es sind :

1. *S. camerunus*, Hagedorn, Deutsche Ent. Zeitschr. p. 742 (1909). — Kamerun.
   Taf. 8, Fig. 13.
2. *S. cordatus*, Hagedorn, ibidem, p. 741 (1909). — **Taf. 8, Fig. 12.**   Kamerun.
3. *S. crenatus*, Hagedorn. ibidem, p. 740 (1909).   Kamerun.

3. TRIBUS HYLESININÆ

UEBERSICHT DER GATTUNGEN

1.   *Halsschild seitlich gerandet und zur Aufnahme der Vorder-*
        schenkel ausgehöhlt; Flügeldeckenbasis eben.
    2.   *Kopf mit starkem Rüssel, Fühlergeissel siebengliedrig.*
        3.   *Augen zweigeteilt.* . . . .   8. Genus HYORRHYNCHUS, Blandford..
        3'. *Augen ganz* . . . .   9. Genus COPTONOTUS, Chapuis.
    2'. *Kopf mit schwachem Rüssel, Fühlergeissel fünfgliedrig* . .   10. Genus CRANIODICTICUS, Blandford..
1'   *Halsschild seitlich nicht gerandet oder ausgehöhlt; Flügeldecken-*
        basis aufgeworfen oder gekerbt.
    2.   *Fühler mit loser Keule.*
        3.   *Fühler zwischen den Augen auf der Stirn eingefügt, Keule*
                mit drei Lamellen.
            4.   *Drittes Tarsenglied einfach* . . . .   11. Genus DRYOTOMUS, Chapuis.
            4'. *Drittes Tarsenglied herzförmig verbreitert.*
                5.   *Basalglied der Fühlerkeule dreieckig, so lang als breit.*   12. Genus EULYTOCERUS, Blandford.
                5'. *Basalglied der Fühlerkeule lang und schräg* . . .   13. Genus PHLŒOTRIBUS, Latreille.
        3'. *Fühler an den Seiten vor den Augen eingefügt, Keule ohne*
                Lamellen.
            4.   *Fühlergeissel fünfgliedrig* . . . .   14. Genus PHLŒOPHTHORUS, Wollaston..
            4'. *Fühlergeissel sechsgliedrig* . . . .   15. Genus ARICERUS, Blandford.
    2'. *Fühler mit fester Keule.*
        3.   *Fühlergeissel siebengliedrig.*

4. *Vorderhüften einander berührend.*

   5. *Fühlerkeule oval, nicht zusammengedrückt* . . . . 16. Genus HYLASTES, Erichson.

   5'. *Fühlerkeule länglich, zusammengedrückt* . . . . 17. Genus DENDROTRUPES, Broun.

4'. *Vorderhüften getrennt.*

   5. *Drittes Tarsenglied zweilappig.*

     6. *Fühlerkeule zugespitzt* . . . . 18. Genus HYLESINUS, Fabricius.

     6'. *Fühlerkeule stumpf-oval.*

       7. *Fühlerkeule ohne Haarbinden* . . . . . . 19. Genus INOSOMUS, Broun.

      . 7'. *Fühlerkeule mit Haarbinden* . . . . . . 20. Genus SPHÆROTRYPES, Blandford.

      7''. *Fühlerkeule nur an der basis mit Nähten.* . . 21. Genus DENDROSINUS, Chapuis.

   5'. *Drittes Tarsenglied einfach.*

     6. *Fühlerkeule solid.* . . . . 22. Genus MERINGOPALPUS, Hagedorn.

     6'. *Fühlerkeule mit Nähten.*

      7. *Fühlerkeule mit mehreren Nähten* . . . . . 23. Genus PROBLECHILUS, Eichhoff.

      7'. *Fühlerkeule mit einer Naht.* . . . . . . 24. Genus LISSOCLASTUS, Schaufuss.

3'. *Fühlergeissel sechsgliedrig.*

  4. *Vorderhüften einander berührend.*

    5. *Fühlerkeule mit Nähten.*

      6. *Fühlerkeule kugelig.* . . . . 25. Genus HYLURGUS, Latreille.

      6'. *Fühlerkeule länglich-eiförmig* . . . . 26. Genus MYELOPHILUS, Eichhoff.

    5'. *Fühlerkeule solid* . . . . 27. Genus CHORTASTUS, Schaufuss.

  4'. *Vorderhüften getrennt.*

    5. *Erstes Tarsenglied kürzer als die anderen* . . . . 28. Genus KISSOPHAGUS, Chapuis.

    5'. *Erstes Tarsenglied länger oder so lang als die anderen.* 29. Genus ACRANTUS, Broun.

3''. *Fühlergeissel fünfgliedrig.*

  4. *Vorderhüften einander berührend.*

    5. *Augen ganzrandig.*

      6. *Fühlergeisselglieder an Breite gleichmässig wachsend.* 30. Genus DENDROCTONUS, Erichson.

      6'. *Fühlergeisselglieder an Breite abwechselnd* . . . 31. Genus HYPOBORUS, Erichson.

    5'. *Augen nierenförmig.*

      6. *Augen nierenförmig stark ausgerandet.* . . . . 32. Genus CARPHOBORUS. Eichhoff.

      6'. *Augen nierenförmig schwach ausgerandet.* . . . 33. Genus RENOCIS, Casey.

  4'. *Vorderhüften getrennt.*

    5 *Fühlerkeule mit Nähten.*

      6. *Fühlerkeule klein, nicht zusammengedrückt* . . . 34. Genus XYLECHINUS, Chapuis.

      6'. *Fühlerkeule breit, zusammengedrückt.*

        7. *Geisselglieder an Breite wachsend* . . . . . 35. Genus PHLŒOSINUS, Chapuis.

        7'. *Geisselglieder gleichbreit bleibend* . . . . . 36. Genus CHÆTOPHLŒUS, Le Conte.

    5'. *Fühlerkeule solid* . . . . 37. Genus CHRAMESUS, Le Conte.

3'''. *Fühlergeissel viergliedrig* . . . . 38. Genus LIPARTHRUM, Wollaston.

3''''. *Fühlergeissel dreigliedrig.*

  4. *Keule ohne Nähte* . . . . 39. Genus DACRYOSTACTUS, Schaufuss.

  4'. *Keule mit Nähten.* . . . . 40. Genus STYRACOPTERUS, Blandford.

1''. *Halsschild seitlich gerandet, aber nicht ausgehöhlt, Fühlergeissel siebengliedrig, Vorderhüften getrennt, Flügeldeckenbasis aufgeworfen, Schienenaussenkante glatt* . . . . 41. Genus HYLOSCYLLUS, Schaufuss.

8. Genus HYORRHYNCHUS, Blandford

Hyorrhynchus. Blandford, Trans. Ent. Soc. Lond. Vol. 1, p. 60 (1894).

ORIGINALDIAGNOSE : Blandford, loc. cit.

« Caput rostratum, rostello lateraliter marginato. Oculi bipartiti; antennæ sub carina rostrali inter partes oculorum interiores et mandibulas insertæ, scapo recto, funiculo 7-articulato, articulo 1° magno, 2° obconico, ceteris transversis latitudine crescentibus, clava magna oblonga, subcompressa, 3-articulata, suturis rectis notata, pilosa. Prothorax subdepressus, lateribus determinatis, non tamen marginatis, basi immarginata. Elytra ad basin singulatim convexa, thoracem superantia. Coxæ anticæ magnæ globosæ, a processu prosterni angusto superatæ. Pedes longi, tibiis subcompressis, leviter dilatatis, ad apicem oblique truncatis, margine exteriore inermi. Tarsi articulo 1° brevi, 2° paullo longiore incrassato, 3° brevi, subtus producto et profunde emarginato, 4° minimo, 5° magno ceteris coniunctis æquali. »

Charaktere. — Mir ist die Gattung unbekannt geblieben; Gründe siehe bei Genus 10.

Geographische Verbreitung der Art. — Eine Art aus Japan ist beschrieben.

1. *H. Lewisi*, Blandford, Trans. Ent. Soc. Lond. Vol. 1, p. 60 (1894).   Japan.

9. Genus COPTONOTUS, Chapuis

Coptonotus. Chapuis, Synops. Scolyt. p. 219 (1873).

ORIGINALDIAGNOSE : Chapuis, loc. cit.

« Antennarum funiculus 7-articulatus, clava 3-annulata, suturis flexuosis. Pronotum lateraliter emarginatum. Tarsi cylindrici, articulo 1° elongato, 2° et 3° coniunctis æquali. »

Charaktere. — Körperform langgestreckt, aber schmal; Länge 10 mm.; Farbe schwarz; Skulptur auf den Flügeldecken kräftig; Bekleidung mit gelben Schuppen nur auf dem Flügeldecken-absturz.

Kopf frei, mit kurzem Rüssel, an welchem seitlich grosse Fühlergruben sich befinden.

Stirn beim ♀ flach, einfach punktiert; beim ♂ zeigt sich folgendes Bild : auf der Stirn mitten zwischen den Augen sieht man eine dreieckige Stelle, die Spitze des Dreieckes ist nach vorn, nach den Mandibeln zu, gerichtet, die Basis nach hinten, nach dem Scheitel zu. Dicht vor diesem Dreieck liegt ein längliches Grübchen, welches nach hinten zu, also dicht vor der Spitze des Dreieckes, stärker vertieft ist.

Auf diesem dreieckigen Felde stehen in ziemlich regelmässigen, mit der Längsachse des Körpers parallelen Reihen kleine schwach erhabene vollkommen rundliche helle Körnchen, nicht sehr dicht, nirgends sich berührend, überall Zwischenraum zwischen sich, in ihrer Mitte tragen sie einen rötlich dunklen Fleck, aus welchem ein sehr kurzes, steifes Härchen entspringt. Diese Körnchen unterscheiden sich sehr wesentlich von den umgebenden Nabelpunkten der Stirn- und Scheitelgegend und noch viel deutlicher von den Facetten des Auges, welche dicht aneinander gedrängt stehen, sechseckig sind und mit einer gewölbten Cornea überzogen sind. Die Körnchen gleichen durchaus nicht den einfachen Augen (Ozellen) bei Käferlarven oder bei den *Omaliinen (Staphylinidae)*, welche stets eine Cornea besitzen. Das weibliche Tier zeigt diese Stelle nicht, auch ist bei ihm das Grübchen auf der Vorderstirn anders gebaut. Ein Auge bedeutet die Einrichtung auf keinen Fall, ich neige zu der Ansicht, dass es ein sekundäres Geschlechtsmerkmal ist, welches sich nur bei den Männchen findet (Dr. Eichelbaum

4. 2., 1909, i. l.). Meine Untersuchung dieses merkwürdigen Gebildes hat mich zu dem nämlichen Resultat geführt. Es dürfte daher die Auffassung, welche Chapuis in dem Artnamen *cyclopus* ausspricht, und die, welche Schaufuss in der *Insektenbörse*, Vol. 22, p. 89 (1905) mitteilt, eine irrtümliche sein.

Fühler mit siebengliedriger ziemlich langer Geissel; Keule geringelt, zugespitzt, gross.

Augen quer-oval, stossen an der Kehlnaht zusammen und ziehen sich bis auf die Stirn; vor ihnen die grossen tiefen Fühlergruben.

Vorderkiefer derb mit zwei Zähnen.

Mittelkiefer hornartig derb, mit kurzen beilartigen Lappen, an dessen Kaukante zwölf bis fünfzehn kurze breite lanzettartige Zähne zitzen. Die Aussenseite des Kiefers trägt sehr lange starre Borsten.

Kiefertaster dreigliedrig, überragt weit die Spitze des Lappens. Glied 1 und 2 umgekehrt kegelförmig, breiter als lang, zusammen so lang als das dritte walzenförmige Glied.

Hinterkiefer sind zu einem kurzen dicken beinahe kugelförmigen Kinne verschmolzen, an dessen Spitze die einwärts gekrümmte mit langen Haaren besetzte ovale kurze Zunge entspringt.

Kiefertasterglieder : 1 kugelig, am kürzesten, 2 und 3 gleichlang cylindrisch.

Halsschild kegelförmig, nach vorne verschmälert, seitlich gerandet und daselbst mit tiefen Gruben zum Einlegen der Vorderbeine. Auf der Scheibe gleichmässig punktiert.

Schildchen nicht sichtbar, weil es von Halsschild und Flügeldeckenbasis überragt wird. Es ist flach, gross, dreieckig.

Flügeldecken an der Basis nur wenig aufgeworfen aber gekerbt, an der Spitze flach (beim ♀) oder eingedrückt (beim ♂) abfallend. Auf ihrer Oberfläche sind sie grob skulptiert. Die Hinterkante ist gerandet, beim ♂ ist der Absturz tiefer gekerbt und die Zwischenräume mit mehreren Reihen dichter gelber Schuppen bedeckt, ähnlich wie bei *Chapuisia* D u g è s .

Vorder- und Mittelhüften kugelig.

Hinterhüften quer.

Die Vorderbrust entsendet einen langen dreieckigen Fortsatz zwischen die Vorderhüften, welcher sich hinter denselben verbreitert und eine tiefe Grube von rhombischer Gestalt mit erhöhten und verdickten Rändern bildet. Die Mittel- und Hinterhüften sind auseinanderstehend; zwischen den Hinterhüften ein zungenförmiger Fortsatz des dritten Sternits.

Vorderschienen schmal, mit zwei Haken und zwei oder drei kleinen Zähnen an der Aussenkante und einem grossen Haken an der inneren Spitze. Mittel- und Hinterschienen aussen gezähnt und verbreitert.

Fussglieder sind rund, auch das dritte; erstes, zweites und drittes Glied gleichgross; viertes Glied kaum sichtbar.

Bauch horizontal.

Geographische Verbreitung der Art. — Es ist nur eine Art aus dem Südreich bekannt.

1. *C. cyclopus*, Chapuis, Synops. Scolyt. p. 219 (1873). — **Taf. I, Fig. 7, 7a,** Columbia. **7b, 8; Taf. II, Fig. 79, 80, 81, 82.**

10. Genus CRANIODICTICUS, Blandford

Craniodicticus. Blandford, Ann. Mag. Nat. Hist. Vol. 15, p. 317 (1895).

Originaldiagnose : Blandford, loc. cit.

« Caput globosum exsertum ; oculi ovales late emarginati ; antennæ breves, lateraliter insertæ, scapo clavato, funiculo paullo longiore, 5-articulato, articulo 1° magno, 2° obconico, ceteris transversis, latitudine haud crescentibus, clava ovali. haud compressa triarticulata, articulo 1° magno hemisphærico, sequentibus coniunctim longiore, his transversis latitudine subabrupte decrescentibus. Mentum ad basin angustum, versus apicem dilatatum, lateribus sinuatis; palpi labiales articulis 1° et 2° tumidis, 3° cylindrico.

» Prothorax cylindricus, lateribus pro receptione femorum impressis, immarginatis.

» Prosternum et mesosternum brevia, metasternum elongatum, episternis angustis. Abdominis segmenta 1um et 5um ceteris singulis longiore.

» Coxæ anticæ magnæ, globosæ, distantes; intermediæ distantes. Femora compressa, anteriora medio dilatata; tibiæ breves, extus dilatatæ, ad apicem oblique truncatæ, margine externo subtiliter dentato; tarsi tibiis longiores, articulis 2° primis brevibus, 3° paullo longiore ad apicem incrassato, 5° ceteris coniunctim fere æquali. »

Charaktere. — Mir ist die Gattung leider unbekannt geblieben, da meine Versuche mich zwecks Kennenlernens seiner Gattungen und Arten mit Herrn Blandford in Verbindung zu setzen, von diesem nicht beantwortet wurden.

Geographische Verbreitung der Art. — Es ist eine Art aus Ceylon beschrieben.

1. *C. mucronatus*, Blandford, Ann. Mag. Nat. Hist. Vol. 15, p. 317 (1895). Ceylon.

II. Genus DRYOTOMUS, Chapuis

Dryotomus. Chapuis, Synops. Scolyt. p. 254 (1873).

Originaldiagnose : Chapuis, loc. cit.

« Antennarum clava articulis tribus liberis, intus productis formata. Tarsorum articulus tertius cylindricus, integer ».

Charaktere. — Körperform eiförmig, nach hinten zugespitzt, 4.5 mm. lang, schwach skulptiert und bekleidet; mit auffällig langen Beinen.

Kopf mit kurzem breitem Rüssel.

Fühler vor den Augen, oberhalb des Vorderkiefers eingelenkt, Schaft fast ebenso lang als die fünfgliedrige Geissel, Keule mit drei Gliedern, die nach innen verbreitert sind.

Halsschild breiter als lang, seitlich gerandet.

Schildchen klein, dreieckig.

Flügeldecken an der Basis erhaben und gekörnelt, nach hinten verschmälert und steil abfallend.

Vorderhüften durch kurzen knopfförmigen Fortsatz der Vorderbrust getrennt.

Mittel- und Hinterhüften : die ersteren sehr weit, die letzteren weniger voneinander abstehend.

Beine auffällig lang, Schienen verbreitert, an der Aussenkante gerundet und gezähnt.

Fussglieder 1-3 gleich rund.

Bauch horizontal.

Geographische Verbreitung der Art. — Es ist nur eine Art aus Cayenne bekannt.

1. *D. puberulus*, Chapuis, Synops. Scolyt. p. 254 (1873). Cayenne.

12. Genus EULYTOCERUS, Blandford

Eulytocerus. Blandford, Biol. Centr. Amer. Col. Vol. 4 (6), p. 161 (1897).

Originaldiagnose : Blandford, loc. cit.

« Caput rostratum; oculi oblongi, integri; antennarum funiculus 5-articulatus, articulis latitudine paulo crescentibus, clava oblonga, subreniformis, articulis tribus liberis composita, 1° subtriangulari angulo apicali inferiore producto. 2° et 3° transversis subtus productis. Coxæ anticæ anguste separatæ; tibiæ superne rotundatæ serratæ; tarsorum articulus tertius simplex. »

Charaktere. — Körperform länglich eiförmig; braun; Länge 4 mm.; Bekleidung : spärliche kurze Haare.

Kopf in das Halsschild zurückgezogen mit Rüssel; Stirn beim ♂ ausgehöhlt.

Augen länglich, nicht ausgebuchtet.

Fühler in einer Grube, die durch eine Falte der vorderen Rüsselfläche gebildet wird, oberhalb der Vorderkiefer, vor dem unteren Augenwinkel eingelenkt; ihr Schaft ist stark gekeult, die Geissel kurz, fünfgliedrig, erstes Glied kugelig, die anderen quer, nach der Keule breiter werdend; Keule länglich nierenförmig, behaart, dreigliedrig, die Glieder voneinander getrennt, erstes dreieckig, so lang als breit mit abgeschrägter Spitzenkante, am inneren Winkel vorgezogen, zweites und drittes Glied einfach abgeschrägt.

Halsschild an den Seiten tief eingedrückt, aber ohne Rand nach dem Rücken hin.

Schildchen klein, abgerundet.

Flügeldecken einzeln gerundet, an der Basis erhöht.

Vorderhüften durch einen schmalen Fortsatz der Vorderbrust getrennt.

Mittelhüften breit, kugelig, voneinander abstehend.

Mittelbrust und Hinterbrust kurz.

Bauch : erstes Segment so lang als das zweite und dritte zusammen, mit einem spitzwinkligen Fortsatz zwischen den Hinterhüften.

Schienen gekrümmt, am oberen Rand gerundet und gesägt, unterer Spitzenwinkel mit kurzem Haken.

Fussglieder 1-3 gleich und einfach.

Geographische Verbreitung der Art. — Es ist nur eine Art aus Panama bekannt.

1. *E. Championis*, Blandford, Biol. Centr. Amer. Col. Vol. 4 (6), p. 161 (1897). Panama.

13. Genus PHLŒOTRIBUS, Latreille

Phlœotribus. Latreille, Précis Caract. Génér. Ins. p. 50 (1796).

Originaldiagnose : Latreille, loc. cit.

« *Phloiotribe.* — Phloiotribus, Bostrichus, Fabricius, antennes flabellées. Corps oblong, convexe, presque cylindrique. Tête grande inclinée pointue; yeux peu saillants. Corselet sans rebords. Elytres rebordées. Jambes triangulaires, larges, ciliées ou dentées. »

Charaktere. — Körperform oval, gewölbt; Länge 1 bis 3.5 mm.; Farbe gelb durch braun bis schwarz; glanzlos, meist stark beschuppt.

Kopf von oben sichtbar, Rand des Clipeus vorn dreieckig vorspringend.

Fühler oberhalb der Vorderkiefer seitwärts auf der Stirn eingefügt, mit fünfgliedriger Geissel und viel längerer, nach innen in drei mehr weniger lange Blätter aufgelöster Keule, die also an die der Lamellicornier erinnert.

Augen quer-oval, nicht ausgerandet.

Vorderkiefer kurz und breit, scharf zugespitzt.

Mittelkiefer mit mässig gerundeter Innenlade, deren Spitze stumpf gerundet ist und deren Kaukante mit etwa zwölf steifen geraden Stachelzähnen besetzt ist.

Kiefertaster mit drei an Stärke allmählich abnehmenden Gliedern.

Hinterkiefer zu einem fast gleichseitig dreieckigen, nach der Basis stark verschmälerten Kinne verschmolzen. Die Zunge ragt als dreieckiges vorne abgerundetes Läppchen fast bis zur Spitze des ersten Lippentastergliedes empor und entspringt ziemlich an der Basis des Kinnes.

Lippentaster : Glied 1 länger als die beiden anderen zusammen, Glied 2 am kleinsten.

Halsschild breiter als lang, nach vorne verschmälert oder cylindrisch, meist körnig punktiert.

Schildchen kaum sichtbar.

Flügeldecken cylindrisch, Vorderrand aufgeworfen und gekerbt; Absturz gewölbt; Skulptur meist kräftig; Bekleidung : reichliche Schuppenhaare.

Vorderbrust sehr kurz, bis zu den Hüften ausgerandet.

Vorderhüften kugelig, weit voneinander getrennt.

Schienen aussen.gerundet und gezähnt.

Fussglied 3 herzförmig verbreitert.

Bauch gewölbt, gegen den After ansteigend.

Geographische Verbreitung der Arten. — Es sind dreissig Arten beschrieben worden, von denen die Hauptmasse, nämlich einundzwanzig, im Südreich vorkommt. Neben fünf Nordamerikanern sind zwei Europäer, ein Ceyloner und ein Südafrikaner bekannt.

1. *P. armatus*, Blandford, Biol. Centr. Amer. Col. Vol. 4 (6), p. 166 (1897).   Centralamerika.
— Taf. 2, Fig. 9a.
2. *P. asperatus*, Blandford, ibidem, p. 166 (1897).   Centralamerika.
3. *P. biguttatus*, Blandford, ibidem, p. 169 (1897).   ·   Centralamerika.
4. *P. collaris*, Chapuis, Synops. Scolyt. p. 254 (1873).   Neu-Granada.
5. *P. contractus*, Chapuis, ibidem, p. 254 (1873).   Brasilien.
6. *P. demessus*, Blandford, Biol. Centr. Amer. Col. Vol. 4 (6), p. 165 (1897).   Centralamerika.
7. *P. discrepans*, Blandford, ibidem, p. 163 (1897).   Centralamerika.
8. *P. mexicanus*, Lacordaire, Gen. Col. Vol. 7, p. 365, Nota 2 (1866).   Mexico.
9. *P. nubilus*, Blandford, Biol. Centr. Amer. Col. Vol. 4 (6), p. 163 (1897).   Centralamerika.
10. *P. obesus*, Kirsch, Deutsche Ent. Zeitschr. p. 283 (1875).   Peru.
11. *P. obliquus*, Chapuis, Synops. Scolyt. p. 253 (1873).   Mexico.
12. *P. puncticollis*, Chapuis, ibidem, p. 253 (1873).   Brasilien.
13. *P. rudis*, Eichhoff, Berl. Ent. Zeitschr. Vol. 12, p. 149 (1868).   Brasilien.
14. *P. scabratus*, Blandford, Biol. Centr. Amer. Col. Vol. 4 (6), p. 164 (1897).   Centralamerika.
15. *P. setulosus*, Eichhoff, Berl. Ent. Zeitschr. Vol. 12, p. 149 (1866). —   Centralamerika.
Taf. 2, Fig. 9.
16. *P. Schoenbachi*, Kirsch, Berl. Ent. Zeitschr. Vol. 10, p. 214 (1866).   Bogotá.
17. *P. sodalis*, Blandford, Biol. Centr. Amer. Col. Vol. 4 (6), p. 168 (1897).   Centralamerika.
18. *P. subovatus*, Blandford, ibidem, p. 167 (1897).   Centralamerika.
19. *P. sulcifrons*, Chapuis, Synops. Scolyt. p. 253 (1873).   Neu-Granada.
20. *P. transversus*, Chapuis, ibidem, p. 252 (1873).   Columbien.
21. *P. villosulus*, Lacordaire, Gen. Col. Vol. 7, p. 365, Nota 2 (1866).   Cayenne.
22. *P. americanus*, Dejean, Cat. (ed. 3). p. 531 (1837).   Nordamerika.
23. *P. frontalis*, Olivier, Ent. Vol. 4, p. 78 (1795).   Nordamerika.
24. *P. liminaris*, Harris, Report Inj. Ins. Veg. p. 78 (1852).   Nordamerika.
25. *P. puberulus*, Le Conte, Bull. U. S. Geolog. Survey, Vol. 5, p. 519 (1879).   Colorado.
26. *P. texanus*, Herrich-Schäffer, Journ. New York. Ent. Soc. Vol. 16,   Texas.
p. 222 (1908).
27. *P. caucasicus*, Reitter, Deutsche Ent. Zeitschr. p. 32 (1891).   Russland.
28. *P. scarabaeoides*, Bernard, Mém. Hist. Nat. Provence, Vol. 2, p. 270 (1788).   Südeuropa.
29. *P. subquadratus*, Motschulsky, Bull. Soc. Nat. Moscou, Vol. 39 (2),   Ceylon.
p. 402 (1866).
30. *P. fuscipennis*, Chapuis, Synops. Scolyt. p. 252 (1873).   Caffraria.

14. Genus PHLŒOPHTHORUS, Wollaston

Phlœophthorus. Wollaston, Ins. Madeir. p. 299 (1854).
Hylesinus. Nördlinger, Stett. Ent. Zeit. p. 250 (1848).
Subgenus : **Phthorophlœus.** Rey, Rev. d'Ent. Caën, Vol. 2, p. 127 (1883).
(**Elzearius.** Guillebeau, Ann. Soc. Ent. Fr. Vol. 43, p. 64 (1894).

ORIGINALDIAGNOSE : Wollaston loc cit.

« Corpus parvum subcylindricum : capite leviter producto : prothorace amplo convexo, antice minus producto et haud scabroso : elytris apice rotundatis integris : alis amplis. Antennæ longiusculæ clavatæ; scapo elongato subclavato, basi flexuoso; funiculo 5-articulato, articulo 1º robusto, apice truncato, ad basin constricto, sinuato, reliquis brevissimis longitudine subæqualibus, a basi angusta latitudine paulatim crescentibus; clava elongata laxa, valde perfoliata, triarticulata, articulis longitudine subæqualibus (1º et 2º latioribus, illo leviter, hoc vix intus producto, ultimo subacuminato-ovato). Labrum obsoletum. Mandibulæ corneæ validæ, basi latæ, apicem versus parum angustæ acutæ, infra apicem dente minutissimo obscurissimo instructæ. Maxillæ lobo singulo, lato, brevissimo, setoso instructæ (interno obsoleto). Palpi subretuso conici; maxillares minuti, articulis 1º, 2º et 3º brevissimis transversis, ultimo longiore, graciliore, subcylindrico-conico; labiales longiores, articulo primo crasso, secundo paulo breviore crassiusculo, ultimo graciliore elongato-subovato. Ligula membranacea subelongata, basi angustata, apice truncata. Pedes longiores validi tibiis compressis, apicem versus extus dentatis nec non subito et valde dilatatis, ad apicem internum spina recta (in anticis robusta obtusa, in pósteriobus gracili acuta) armatis : tarsis pseudotetrameris (id est 5-articulatis, articulo 3º valde bilobo, quartum minutissimum inter lobos recipiente) articulis tribus baseos longiusculis crassiusculis, 5º elongato crasso, clavato, unguiculis simplicibus minuto. »

UEBERSICHT DER UNTERGATTUNGEN

1. *Fühlerkeule lose gegliedert, Halsschild vorne gegen die Seiten zu mit erhabenen Körnchen besetzt* . . . . Subg. PHLŒOPHTHORUS, s. str.

1'. *Fühlerkeule fest gegliedert, Halsschild ohne erhabene Körnchen.* . . . Subg. PHTHOROPHLŒUS.

Charaktere. — Körperform klein, länglich, fast walzenförmig; Farbe schwarz mit ziemlich reichlicher Beschuppung, respektive borstenartiger Behaarung.

Kopf klein.

Fühler oberhalb der Vorderkiefer seitwärts auf der Stirn eingefügt, mit langgestreckter aus drei getrennten Gliedern gebildeter Keule, welche viel länger als die fünfgliedrige Geissel ist.

Augen lang, quer oval, vorne wenig ausgerandet.

Vorderkiefer kräftig.

Mittelkiefer mit breiter kurzer Innenlade, an deren Kaukante etwa zwölf gerade scharf zugespitzte Stachelzähne mit dazwischenstehenden, mitunter gewimperten, Haarborsten stehen.

Kiefertaster : Glied 2 kürzer als die etwa gleichlangen einschliessenden; Glied 3 doppelt so lang als breit, cylindrisch.

Hinterkiefer sind zu einem pergamentartigen, kurzen, oval-herzförmigen, nach der Basis hin bauchig erweitertem, verschmälerten, kaum länger als breiteren, Kinne verschmolzen. Die Zunge ragt als gleichseitig dreieckiges, vorn etwas abgerundetes Läppchen etwa bis zur Spitze des ersten Lippentastergliedes, ist etwa halb so breit als das Kinn und lässt sich abwärts bis in die Hälfte des letzteren deutlich verfolgen.

Lippentaster : Glied 1 so lang wie 2 und 3 zusammen, 2 breiter aber kürzer als 3, dieses abgestutzt kegelförmig, doppelt so lang als breit.

Halsschild viel breiter als lang und nach vorn in ziemlich gleichem Bogen verschmälert, bald höckerig, bald runzlig punktiert.

Schildchen dreieckig, klein.

Flügeldecken mit aufgeworfener und gekerbter Basis; auf der Oberfläche punktiert-gestreift, Zwischenräume breiter, runzlig punktiert, mit Haarbörstchen bekleidet.

Vorderbrust sehr kurz; bis zu den Hüften ausgerandet.

Schienen aussen gerade und gezähnt, an der Spitze abgestutst, an dem inneren Winkel mit einem kleinen Dorn versehen.

Fussglieder : Glied 3 zweilappig.

Bauch horizontal.

Geographische Verbreitung der Arten. — Es sind acht Arten bekannt, welche in der Mehrzahl um das Mittelmeer herum wohnen; eine davon mit sechs Varietäten. Zwei Arten kommen in Mitteleuropa vor, zwei sind nur aus dem Kaukasus bekannt und eine findet sich im Mexico.

1. *P. Abeillei*, Guillebeau, Ann. Soc. Ent. Fr. Vol. 63, p. 58 (1894) (Subg. Corsica. *Phloeophthorus*).

2. *P. cristatus*, Fauvel, Rev. d'Ent. Caen, Vol. 8, p. 71 (1889) (Subg. Algier, Frankreich. *Phloeophthorus*).

    var. corsicus, Guillebeau, Ann. Soc. Ent. Fr. Vol. 63, p. 58 (1894).   Corsica.
    var. helveticus, Guillebeau, ibidem, p. 58 (1894).   Schweiz.
    var. lineigera, Guillebeau, ibidem, p. 58 (1894).   Dalmatien.
    var. Mayeti, Guillebeau, ibidem, p. 62 (1894).   Oram.
    var. pubifrons, Guillebeau, ibidem, p. 59 (1894).   Algier.
    var. Sharpi, Guillebeau, ibidem, p. 59 (1894).   Algier.

3. *P. maroccanus*, Guillebeau, Bull. Soc. Ent. Fr. p. 152 (1896) (Subg. Tanger. *Phloeophthorus*).

4. *P. rhododactylus*, Marsham, Ent. Brit. p. 58 (1802) (Subg. *Phloeophthorus*). Mitteleuropa.
— **Taf. 12, Fig. 1.**
    var. austriacus, Guillebeau, Ann. Soc. Ent. Fr. p. 54 (1896).   Oesterreich.

5. *P. spinulosus*, Rey, Rev. d'Ent. Caen, Vol. 2, p. 27 (1883) (Subg. *Phthorophloeus*). — **Taf. 12, Fig. 2.** Mitteleuropa.

6. *P. brevicollis*, Kolenati, Melet. Ent. Vol. 3, p. 38 (1846) (Subg. *Phloeophthorus*). Kaukasus, Krim.

7. *P. Vinogradowi*, Semenow, Rev. Russe d'Ent. Vol. 2, p. 269 (1901) (Subg. Transkaukasien. *Phloeophthorus*).

8. *P. moriperda*, Hopkins, Proc. Ent. Soc. Wash. Vol. 7, p. 77 (1895). Mexico. (Subg. *Phloeophthorus*)

15. GENUS ARICERUS, BLANDFORD

Aricerus, Blandford, Ann. Soc. Ent. Belg. Vol. 38, p. 133 (1894).

ORIGINALDIAGNOSE : Blandford, loc. cit., p. 133.

« Novum genus (Chapuis, in litt.).

Oculi elongati, oblongi, integri. Antennæ lateraliter supra mandibulas insertæ, funiculo brevissimo, 6-articulato, clava magna, 3-articulata, articulis liberis, compressis, pilosis, primo subtriangulari, secundo sublunato, intus breviter producto, tertio ovato-acuminato. Coxæ anticæ processu prosterni quadrato separatæ. Tibiæ anticæ versus apicem dilatatæ, extus rectæ, versus apicem dentibus duabus armatæ, ceteræ dilatatæ, margine externo arcuatim rotundato et dentibus obtuse serrato. Tarsorum articulus tertius bilobus. »

Und loc. cit., p. 134 :

« Mâchoires à lobe interne étroit, peu convexe, armé d'épines plates à peine plus longues que larges; palpes maxillaires courts, à articles transversaux. Sous-menton échancré au milieu, prolongé à chaque côté du menton en lobe arrondi; menton oblong; palpes labiaux presque aussi longs que larges, diminuant peu en largeur; languette attachée à la base du menton qu'elle dépasse, atténuée vers le sommet et bisinuée à chaque côté, fournie de cils très courts. »

Charaktere. — Körperform mittelgross, kurz und breit; Länge 4 mm; mit bunten Schuppen dicht sammetartig bekleidet, sodass von einer Skulptur der Oberfläche nichts zu sehen ist.

Kopf rüsselförmig ausgezogen.

Augen quer gestellt, länglich, nicht ausgebuchtet.

Fühler über der Basis der Vorderkiefer eingelenkt, Schaft sehr lang, sechsgliedrige Geissel sehr kurz; Keule dreigliedrig mit freien Gliedern, zugespitzt, flach, stark behaart.

Vorderkiefer stark entwickelt, dreizähnig.

Mittelkiefer mit schmaler Innenlade, deren Kaukante mit langen breiten Dornen besetzt ist.

Kiefertaster kurz mit queren Gliedern.

Hinterkiefer zu einem länglichen Kinne verschmolzen, an dessen Basis die Zunge angeheftet ist, welche gegen die Spitze verschmälert und mit kurzen Haaren besetzt ist.

Lippentaster : die einzelnen Glieder sind beinahe so lang als breit.

Halsschild breiter als lang, seitlich gerandet.

Schildchen klein, dreieckig, glänzend, unter der Flügeldeckenbasis versteckt.

Flügeldecken an der Basis aufgeworfen und gekerbt, stark gewölbt, nach hinten abfallend, die Skulptur durch die dichte sammetartige Beschuppung vollkommen verdeckt.

Vorderbrust entsendet einen quadratischen Fortsatz zwischen die Vorderhüften, welche ebenso wie die anderen weit voneinander abstehen.

Vorderschienen gegen die Spitze verbreitert, daselbst innen mit einem grossen Haken, an der Aussenkante mit zwei Zähnen besetzt; Mittel- und Hinterschienen verbreitert, mit bogenförmig gerundetem und gezähntem Aussenrand.

Fussglied 3 zweilappig, die Fusssohle mit Bürste versehen.

Geographische Verbreitung der Arten. — Es sind nur zwei Arten aus Australien bekannt.

1. *A. Chapuisii*, Blandford, Ann. Soc. Ent. Belg. p. 134 (1894).   Australien.
2. *A. Eichhoffii*, Blandford, ibidem, p. 135 (1894). — **Taf. 2, Fig. 10.**   Australien.

16. Genus HYLASTES, Erichson

Hylastes. Erichson, Arch. f. Naturg. Vol. 1, p. 47 (1836).

Tomicus. Bedel, Faune Col. Seine, Vol. 6, p. 388 (1888).

Hylastites. Hagedorn, Schrift. der Phys.-Oekonom. Ges. Königsberg, Vol. 57, p. 117 (1906).

Subgenera : **Hylurgops.** Le Conte, Proc. Amer. Philos. Soc. Vol. 15, p. 389 (1876).

Scierus. Le Conte, ibidem, p. 390 (1876).

Hylastinus. Bedel, Faune Col. Seine, Vol. 6, p. 388 (1888).

Originaldiagnose : Erichson, loc. cit.

« Antennæ funiculo 7-articulato, capitulo 4-articulato, orbiculari, compresso. Tibiæ extus denticulatæ.

Palpi maxillares mala breviores, conici. Labium nudum, planum, subcordatum. Palpi labiales articulo 1⁰ maximo, 2⁰ tertioque minimis, ægre distinguendis. Antennæ scapo elongato, articulo 2⁰ globoso, 3⁰ obconico, reliquis brevissimis, sensim latioribus. Corpus elongatum vel oblongum, cylindricum. Rostrum distinctum, prosternum antice profunde impressum. Coxæ anticæ approximatæ. »

Es zerfällt diese Gattung in zwei Abteilungen, nämlich :

« A. Mesosternum antice truncatum. Tarsorum articulus tertius cordatus, non dilatatus. Type : *H. ater* Paykull. und

» B Mesosternum antice conico-prominulum. Tarsorum articulus tertius dilatatus, bilobus. Type : *H. decumanus* Erichson. »

UEBERSICHT DER UNTERGATTUNGEN

1. *Prosternum mit grossem Fortsatz, Vorderhüften weit getrennt.* . . . . . . Subg. SCIERUS.

1'. *Prosternum mit kleinem oder keinem Fortsatz, Vorderhüften genähert.*

   2. *Mesosternum gerade abgestutzt, ohne Fortsatz, drittes Tarsenglied nur ausgerandet* Subg. HYLASTES, s. str.

   2'. *Mesosternum mit Fortsatz, drittes Tarsenglied zweilappig.*

      3. *Der erste Ring der Fühlerkeule ist gross, die drei anderen gleich klein* . Subg. HYLURGOPS.

      3'. *Die beiden unteren Ringe der Fühlerkeule sind gleich gross, die beiden letzten sehr klein.* . . . . Subg. HYLASTINUS.

Charaktere. — Körperform walzenförmig bis kurz-eiförmig. Farbe meistens schwarz, Skulptur derb, Bekleidung in spärlichen Haaren bestehend.

Kopf geneigt, von oben zum Teile sichtbar, Rüssel deutlich verlänge t, breit und kurz. Auf ihm wie auf der Stirn sind häufig Artmerkmale, Furchen oder Kiele vorhanden. Die Fühler sind in tiefen Gruben seitwärts an der Spitze des Rüssels eingelenkt, mit siebengliedriger Geissel und kurz eiförmiger, nicht zusammengedrückter, geringelter Keule.

Augen quer-oval, vorne ganzrandig.

Vorderkiefer stark, zwei- oder dreizähnig.

Mittelkiefer mit vorne abgerundetem, dann zugespitztem Lappen, der am Innenrande (der Kaukante) mit starken Stachelzähnen besetzt und ausserdem mit Haarborsten, die an der Spitze etwas dichter stehen, gewimpert ist.

Kiefertaster fast so lang als der Lappen, Glied 1 so lang als 2 und 3 zusammen, Glied 3 am kürzesten, cylindrisch.

Hinterkiefer zu einem fast herzförmigen Kinne verschmolzen, das zwei Drittel so breit als lang und nach der Basis mit stark gerundetem Bogen verschmälert ist. Zungenspitze schmal, bis zum ersten Drittel des Lippentasterbasalgliedes reichend.

Lippentaster kegelförmig, Glied 1 gross, eiförmig, länger als 2 und 3 zusammen.

Halsschild länglich, fast walzenförmig bis quer-oval und nach vorne stark verengt, so breit oder schmäler als die Flügeldecken, punktiert bis lederartig gerunzelt.

Schildchen dreieckig, nicht unter den Flügeldeckensaum herabgedrückt.

Flügeldecken gerade abgestutzt oder einzeln abgerundet, kräftig skulptiert, meistens haarlos, Absturz einfach gewölbt ohne besondere Auszeichnung.

Vorderbrust vor den nahe zusammenstehenden Vorderhüften mit beiderseits scharfkantig gerandeter Vertiefung, oder mit grossem Fortsatz; dann sind die Vorderhüften weit getrennt.

Vorderhüften genähert oder weit getrennt.

Mittelhüften getrennt, entweder ohne oder mit knopfförmigen Mesosternalfortsatz.

Hinterhüften getrennt.
Schienen mit bezahnter Aussenkante.
Fussglieder : die beiden ersten gleich und drehrund, das dritte herzförmig oder zweilappig.
Bauch horizontal.

Geographische Verbreitung der Arten. — Die Gattung ist subkosmopolitisch, doch bevorzugt sie wegen ihrer Lebensweise in Coniferen die nördlichen Reiche. Es sind zweiundfünfzig Arten bekannt: davon in Europa dreizehn (darunter eine fossil in Bernstein), in Nordamerika dreiundzwanzig, in Nordafrika vier. in Asien sieben, in Südamerika zwei, in Australien zwei.

1. *H. Achillei,* Reitter, Verh. Naturw. Ver. Brünn, Vol. 23, p. 54 (1894) (Subg. *Hylastinus*). Algier.

2. *H. ambiguus,* Blandford, Trans. Ent. Soc. Lond. p. 57 (1894) (Subg. *Hylastes*). Japan. [Kauskasus, Ostsibirien.

3. *H. angustatus,* Herbst, Käfer, Vol. 5, p. 111 (1793) (Subg. *Hylastes*). Mitteleuropa. Schweden,

4. *H. annectens,* Le Conte, Proc. Amer. Philos. Soc. Vol. 4, p. 390 (1876) (Subg. *Scierus*). Anticosti, Vancouver, British Columbia.

5. *H. ater,* Paykull, Fauna Sueç. Vol. 3, p. 153 (1800) (Subg. *Hylastes*). Europa und Kaukasus.
   var. brunneus. Erichson, Arch. f. Naturg. Vol. 1, p. 48 (1836).
   var. rotundicollis, Reitter, Verh. Naturw. Ver. Brünn, Vol. 23, p. 60 (1894).

6. *H. attenuatus,* Erichson, Arch. f. Naturg. Vol. 1, p. 30 (1836) (Subg. *Hylastes*). Mitteleuropa, Frankreich, Kaukasus.

7. *H. batnensis,* Brisout de Barneville, Rev. d'Ent. Caen, Vol. 2, p. 146 (1883) (Subg. *Hylastes*). Algier.

8. *H. Bonvouloiri,* Chapuis. Synops. Scolyt. p. 230 (1873) (Sub. *Hylurgops*). Algier.

9. *H. contractus,* Chapuis. ibidem. p. 231 (1873) (Subg. *Hylastinus*). Brasilien.

10. *H. cristatus,* Mannerheim, Bull. Soc. Nat. Moscou, Vol. 27 (3), p. 239 (1853) (Subg. *Hylastes*). Alaska.

11. *H. cunicularius,* Erichson, Arch. f. Naturg. Vol. 1, p. 49 (1836) (Subg. *Hylastes*). Europa.

12. *H. decumanus,* Erichson, ibidem, p. 51 (1836) (Subg. *Hylurgops*). Europa, Siberien, Nord-

13. *H. exilis,* Chapuis, Synops. Scolyt. p. 228 (1873) (Subg. *Hylastes*). Nordamerika. [amerika.

14. *H. Fankhauseri,* Reitter, Best.-Tab. Borkenkäfer, p. 54 (1894). (Subg. *Hylastinus*). Schweiz.

15. *H. Fiorii,* Eggers. Ent. Blätter, p. 215 (1908) (Subg. *Hylastinus*). Genua.

16. *H. glabratus,* Zetterstedt. Fauna Ins. Lappon. p. 343 (1828) (Subg. *Hylurgops*). Lappland.

17. *H. gracilis,* Le Conte, Trans. Amer. Ent. Soc. App. p. 174 (1868). (Subg. *Hylastes*). Kalifornien.

18. *H. granulatus,* Le Conte. ibidem, p. 175 (1868) (Subg. *Hylurgops*). Oregon, Kalifornien.

19. *H. humilis,* Blanchard in Gay, Hist. de Chile, Vol. 5, p. 427 (1851). (Subg. *Hylurgops*). Chile.

20. *H. imitator,* Reitter, Deutsche Ent. Zeitschr. p. 59 (1900) (Subg. *Hylastes*). Sibirien.

21. *H. incomptus,* Blandford, Biol. Centr Amer. Col. Vol. 4 (6), p. 145 (1897) (Subg. *Hylurgops*). Mexico.

22. *H. interstitialis,* Chapuis, Ann. Soc. Ent. Belg. Vol. 18, p. 196 (1875). (Subg. *Hylurgops*). Japan.

23. *H. lifuanus,* Fauvel, Bull. Soc. Linn. Normandie, Vol. 2, p. 199 (1867) (Subg. *Hylastes*). Lifu.

24. *H. linearis,* Erichson, Arch. f. Naturg. Vol. 1, p. 49 (1836) (Subg. *Hylastes*). Mitteleuropa.
    var. corticiperda, Erichson, ibidem, p. 50 (1836). Südeuropa, Nordafrica, Klein-

25. *H. longipennis,* Blandford, Biol. Centr. Amer. Col. Vol. 4 (6). p. 143 (1897) (Subg. *Hylastes*). Mexico. [asien. Madeira.

26. *H. longipillus,* Reitter. Best.-Tab. Borkenkäfer. p. 63 (1824) (Subg. *Hylurgops*). Sibirien.

27. *H. longus*, LeConte, Proc. Amer. Philos. Soc. p. 389 (1876) (Subg. *Hylastes*)   Colorado.
28. *H. Lowei*, Paiva, Ann. Mag. Nat. Hist. Vol. 8, p. 211 (1861) (Subg.   Kanarische Inseln.
    Hylastes).
29. *H. macer*, Le Conte, Trans. Amer. Ent. Soc. App. p. 175 (1868)   Nebraska.
    (Subg. *Hylastes*).
30. *H. nigrinus*, Mannerheim, Bull. Soc. Nat. Moscou, Vol. 25 (2), p. 356   Alaska.
    (1852) (Subg. *Hylastes*).
31. *H. opacus*, Erichson. Arch. f. Naturg. Vol. 1, p. 51 (1836) (Subg.   Mitteleuropa.
    Hylastes). — **Taf. 2, Fig. 12.**
32. *H. palliatus*, Gyllenhal, Ins. Suec. Vol. 3. p. 340 (1813) (Subg *Hylurgops*).   Europa.
    — **Taf. 12, Fig. 3.**
33. *H. parallelus*, Chapuis, Ann. Soc. Ent. Belg. Vol. 18, p. 196 (1875)   Japan.
    (Subg. *Hylastes*).
34. *H. peregrinus*, Chapuis, Synops. Scolyt. p. 229 (1873) (Subg. *Hylurgops*).   Neu-Seeland.
35. *H. pinifex*, Fitch, Trans. New York Agric. Soc. p. 43 (1851) (Subg.   Ohio, Canada.
    Hylurgops). — **Taf. 2, Fig. 11.**
36. *H. planirostris*, Chapuis. Synops. Scolyt. p. 229 (1873) (Subg. *Hylurgops*).   Mexico, Guatemala.
37. *H. plumbeus*, Blandford, Trans. Ent. Soc. Lond. p. 57 (1894) (Subg.   Japan.
    Hylastes).
38. *H. porculus*, Erichson, Arch. f. Naturg. Vol. 1, p. 49 (1836) (Subg.   Pennsylvanien.
    Hylastes).
39. *H. porosus*, Le Conte, Trans. Amer. Ent. Soc. App. p. 175 (1868)   Kalifornien.
    (Subg. *Hylastes*).
40. *H. rufipes*, Eichhoff, Berl. Ent. Zeitschr. Vol. 12, p. 147 (1868) (Subg.   Vereinigte Staaten v. Nord-
    Hylurgops).   amerika.
41. *H. rugipennis*, Mannerheim, Bull. Soc. Nat. Moscou, Vol. 16 (2), p. 297   Sitka.
    (1843) (Subg. *Hylurgops*).
42. *H. salebrosus*, Eichhoff, Berl. Ent. Zeitschr. Vol. 12, p. 146 (1868)   Carolina.
    (Subg. *Hylastes*).
43. *H. scobinosus*, Eichhoff, ibidem, p. 146 (1868) (Subg. *Hylates*).   Carolina.
44. *H. Schellwieni*, Hagedorn. Schrift. Phys.-Oekon. Ges. Königsberg,   Ostpreussen.
    Vol. 47. p. 117 (1906) (Subg. *Hylastes*); fossil im Bernstein.
45. *H. sericeus*, Mannerheim. Bull. Soc. Nat. Moscou, Vol. 16 (2), p. 296   Alaska, Kenai, Kalifornien.
    (1843) (Subg. *Hylurgops*).
46. *H. subcostulatus*, Mannerheim, ibidem, Vol. 26 (3), p. 239 (1853) (Subg.   Oregon, Mexiko.
    Hylurgops).
47. *H. tenuis*, Eichhoff, Berl. Ent. Zeitschr. Vol. 12, p. 147 (1868) (Subg.   Texas, Georgia.
    Hylastes).
48. *H. tiliae*, Semenow, Rev. Russe d'Ent. Vol. 2, p. 271 (1902) (Subg.   Transkaukasien.
    Hylastinus).
49. *H. trifolii*, Ph. L. St. Müller. Mém. Soc. Départ. du Mont Tonnerre, à   Mitteleuropa, Madera, Kau-
    Mayence, Vol. 1. p. 47 (1803) (Subg. *Hylastinus*).   kasus, Nordamerika.
50. *H. variegatus*, Blandford, Biol. Centr. Amer. Col. Vol. 4 (6), p. 145   Panama.
    (1897) (Subg. *Hylurgops*).
51. *H. vastans*, Chapuis, Synops. Scolyt. p. 225 (1873) (Subg. *Hylastes*).   Mexiko, Guatemala.
52. *H. alni*, Niijima, Journ. Coll. Agric. Tohoku Imp. Univ. Sapporo,   Japan.
    Vol. 3 (2), p. 137 (1909).

17. Genus DENDROTRUPES, Broun

Dendrotrupes. Broun, Man. New Zeal. Col. Vol. 2, p. 741 (1881).

ORIGINALDIAGNOSE : Broun, loc. cit.

« Body cylindric. Head vertical in front, produced in the form of a quadrangular muzzle, carinated laterally, concave or plane. Eyes narrow, transverse, distant above, distinctly granulated. Antennæ inserted at the sides close to the base of the mandibles, pilose; shape rather longer than funiculus, flexuose, gradually thickened; funiculus 7-articulate; first joint robust, obconical, about half the length of the following ones collectively; club somewhat flattened, large, oblong-oval, triarticulate. Prothorax longer than broad, contracted anteriorly, base subtruncate. Scutellum distinct. Elytra cylindric, individually rounded at the base, moderately declivous behind. Legs long and robust; femora dilated; tibiæ straight inwardly, somewhat arcuated outwardly, armed with a stout hook at the apex, and denticulated along the external edge; tarsi stout, second joint subtriangular and emarginated at apex, third bilobed, fourth joint shorter than the preceding three; claws stout. Mesosternum abbreviated and depressed, metasternum moderately long, somewhat elevated. Abdomen rather longer than metasternum, its basal segment as long as the following two, triangularly produced between the coxæ; 2-4 nearly equal, their sutures distinct. Anterior coxæ large, prominent, almost contiguous, separated by a linear space only; intermediate distant, small, their outer margin not extending beyond that of the front pair; posterior not so far apart. »

Charaktere. — Die Gattung ist mir unbekannt geblieben.

Geographische Verbreitung der Arten. — Es sind zwei Arten aus Neu-Seeland beschrieben.
1. *D. costiceps*, Broun, Man. New Zeal. Col. Vol. 2, p. 741 (1881).   Neu-Seeland.
2. *D. vestitus*, Broun, ibidem, p. 741 (1881).   Neu-Seeland.

18. Genus HYLESINUS, Fabricius

Hylesinus. Fabricius, Syst. Eleuth. Vol. 2, p. 390 (1801).
Hylesinites. Germar, Mag. Ent. Vol. 1, p. 15 (1813).
Subgenus : **Pteleobius.** Bedel, Faune Col. Seine, Vol. 6, p. 388 (1888).

ORIGINALDIAGNOSE : Fabricius, loc. cit.

« Antennæ clava solida acuminata, rostro obsoleto discedens. »

UEBERSICHT DER UNTERGATTUNGEN

1. *Flügeldecken von der Mitte zur Spitze allmählich abfallend. Bauch aufsteigend* . . . Subg. HYLESINUS.
1'. *Flügeldecken hinten steil abfallend, Bauch horizontal* . . . . Subg. PTELEOBIUS.

Charaktere. — Körperform walzenförmig bis kurz-oval, Länge 2 bis 6 mm., Skulptur schwach bis rauh, Bekleidung spärlich bis zu dichter bunter Beschuppung.

Kopf geneigt, in einen kurzen Rüssel verlängert.

Augen längs-oval, querstehend, nicht ausgerandet.

Fühler mit sehr langem Schaft, siebengliedriger Geissel, deren Glieder von ziemlich gleicher Breite; Keule länger als die Geissel, geringelt und zugespitzt.

Vorderkiefer stark, zwei- oder dreizähnig.

Mittelkiefer am Innenrand des stumpf zugespitzten Lappens mit zehn bis zwölf geraden, lang gespitzten Stachelzähnen, zwischen denen feine Haare stehen.

Kiefertaster : Glieder an Grösse abnehmend.

Hinterkiefer zu einem herzförmigen, an der Basis verschmälerten Kinne verschmolzen; Zunge viel schmäler als das Kinn, vorn abgerundet, bis zur Mitte des ersten Lippentastergliedes reichend.

Lippentaster : Glied 1 länger als 2 und 3 zusammen, diese gleichlang.

Halsschild meist nach vorn verengt, an der Basis gerade abgeschnitten oder scharfwinkelig gegen das Schildchen vorspringend, vorn meistens mit Körnchen besetzt.

Schildchen ziemlich klein, dreieckig.

Flügeldecken an der Basis aufgeworfen und gekerbt, hinten allmählich und flach oder plötzlich und steil abfallend, grob skulptiert oder buntscheckig beschuppt.

Vorderbrust sehr kurz, mit breitem Fortsatz zwischen den Vorderhüften.

Hüften alle weit voneinander abstehend.

Schienen an der Aussenkante gezähnt.

Fussglieder : drittes herzförmig verbreitert.

Bauch horizontal oder aufsteigend.

Geographische Verbreitung der Arten. — Eine kosmopolitische Gattung : fünfunddreissig Arten sind bekannt, von denen fünf fossil (zwei in Nordamerika, drei in Europa) sind. Von den übrigen sind acht Europäer, vier Nordamerikaner, vier Südamerikaner, sechs Japaner, drei Indo-Malayen, drei Afrikaner, zwei Australier, ein Canarïer.

1. *H. aculeatus*, Say, Journ. Acad. Nat. Sc. Philad. Vol. 3, p. 322 (1823)   Nordamerika.
   (Subg. *Pteleobius*).

2. *H. aspericollis*, Le Conte, Proc. Amer. Philos. Soc. Vol. 15, p. 380   Californien.
   (1876) (Subg. *Hylesinus*),

3. *H. atomarius*, Chapuis, Synops. Scolyt. p. 237 (1873) (Subg. *Hylesinus*).   Brasilien.

4. *H. bicolor*, Philippi, Stett. Ent. Zeit. Vol. 25, p. 375 (1864) (Subg. *Hyle-*   Chile.
   sinus).

5. *H. cingulatus*, Blandford, Trans. Ent. Soc. Lond. p. 67 (1864) (Subg.   Japan.
   Hylesinus).

6. *H. costatus*, Blandford, ibidem, p. 63 (1864) (Subg. *Hylesinus*).   Japan.

7. *H. crenatus*, Fabricius, Mant. Ins. Vol. 1, p. 37 (1787) (Subg. *Hylesinus*).   Europa.

8. *H. despectus*, Walker, Ann. Mag. Nat. Hist. Vol. 3, p. 251 (1859) (Subg.   Ceylon.
   Hylesinus).

9. *H. dromiscens*, Scudder, U. S. Geol. Survey, Mon. Vol. 21, p. 159 (1893)   Colorado.
   (Subg. *Hylesinus*); fossil.

10. *H. electrinus*, Germar, Mag. Ent. Vol. 1, p. 15 (1813) (Subg. *Hylesinus*);   Ostpreussen.
    fossil im Baltischen Bernstein.

11. *H. elegans*, Thomson, Arch. f. Ent. Vol. 2, p. 145 (1858) (Subg. *Hyle-*   Gabun.
    sinus).

12. *H. extractus*. Scudder, U. S. Geol. Survey, Mon. Vol. 21, p. 159 (1893)   Colorado.
    (Subg. *Hylesinus*); fossil.

13. *H facilis*, Heer, Vierteljahrschrift Naturw. Ges. Zürich, Vol. 1, p. 25   Aix in der Provence.
    (1859) (Subg. *Hylesinus*); fossil.

14. *H. fasciatus*, Le Conte, Trans. Amer. Ent. Soc. Vol. 2, p. 170 (1868)   Pennsylvania.
    (Subg. *Hylesinus*).

15. *H. fici*, Lea, Proc. Linn. Soc. N. S. Wales, Vol. 29, p. 103 (1904)   Australien.
    (Subg. *Hylesinus*),

16. *H. fraxini*, Panzer, Faun. Ins. Germ. 1793-1809, p. 66, 15 (1799)   Europa.
    (Subg. *Hylesinus*). — **Taf. 2, Fig. 13; Taf. 12, Fig. 4.**

17. *H. imperialis*, Eichhoff, Berl. Ent. Zeitschr. Vol. 12, p. 149 (1868)   Nordamerika.
    (Subg. *Hylesinus*).

18. *H. indigenus*, Wollaston, Cat. Col. Canar. p. 267 (1864) (Subg. *Hylesinus*).   Ferro.

19. *H. Kraatzi*, Eichhoff, Berl. Ent. Zeitschr. Vol. 8, p. 30 (1864) (Subg.   Mitteleuropa.
    Pteleobius).

20. *H. laticollis*, Blandford, Trans. Ent. Soc. Lond. p. 65 (1894) (Subg.   Japan.
    Hylesinus).

21. *H. lineatus*, Förster, Abhandl. Geolog. Specialkund. Elsass, Vol. 3,   Elsass.
    p. 401 (Subg. *Hylesinus*).

22. *H. nobilis*, Blandford, Trans. Ent. Soc. Lond. p. 64 (1894) (Subg.   Japan.
Hylesinus).
23. *H oleiperda*, Fabricius, Ent. Syst. Vol. 1 (2), p. 366 (1792) (Subg.   Mitteleuropa.
Hylesinus).
24. *H. pilula*, Erichson, Arch. f. Naturg. Vol. 13 (1), p. 138 (1847) (Subg.   Peru.
Hylesinus).
25. *H. porcatus*, Chapuis, Synops. Scolyt. p. 239 (1873) (Subg. *Hylesinus*).   Australien.
26. *H. pusillus*, Gerstäcker, Monatsb. Berl. Akad. Wiss. p. 639 (1855)   Mozambique.
(Subg. *Hylesinus*).
27. *H. reticulatus*, Chapuis, Synops. Scolyt. p. 237 (1873) (Subg *Hylesinus*).   Bogotâ.
28. *H. scutulatus*, Blandford, Trans. Ent. Soc. Lond. p. 67 (1894) (Subg.   Japan.
Pteleobius).
29. *H. sericeus*, Motschulsky. Bull. Soc. Nat. Moscou, Vol. 39 (2), p. 402   Ceylon.
(1866) (Subg. *Hylesinus*).
30. *H. tristis*. Blandford, Trans. Ent. Soc. Lond. p. 66 (1894) (Subg.   Japan.
Hylesinus).
31. *H. vestitus*, Mulsant & Rey, Ann. Soc. Linn. Lyon, Vol. 7, p. 340   Südeuropa.
(1860) (Subg. *Pteleobius*).
32. *H. vicinus*, Comolli, De Coleopter. Prov. Novecomi (1837) (Subg.   Mitteleuropa.
Hylesinus).
33. *H. vittatus*, Fabricius, Mant. Ins. Vol. 2, p. 38 (1787) (Subg. *Pteleobius*).   Mitteleuropa.
34. *H. Wachtli*, Reitter, Wien. Ent. Zeit. Vol. 6, p. 193 (1887) (Subg.   Südeuropa.
Hylesinus).
35. *H. Wallacei*, Blandford. Trans. Ent. Soc Lond. p. 197 (1896) (Subg.   Mysol.
Hylesinus).

19. Genus INOSOMUS, Broun

Inosomus. Broun, Ann. Mag. Nat. Hist. Vol. 9, p. 409 (1889).
Stenopus. Broun, Man. New Zeal. Col. p. 739 (1881).

ORIGINALDIAGNOSE : Broun, loc. cit.

« Body cylindrical, robust, coarsely sculptured, hirsute. Head large, globular, produced so as to form a broad but very evident rostrum. Eyes invisible from above, situated below at the base of the snout, moderately facetted, vertically oval, depressed. Antennæ rather long, gradually incrassated, so that the small ovate but not acuminate club is by no means well-limited; scape gradually thickened; funiculus 7-articulate, first joint longest; club pubescent, apparently three-jointed; they are inserted in deep scrobes, which are hardly capable of receiving the whole of the scape, so that it just touches the eye; the funiculus when bent at right angles rests under the rostrum, the scrobe being feebly prolonged as a shallow cavity for the stout first joint. Prothorax large, nearly conical, scarcely constricted anteriorly, of the same width at the base as the elytra, but narrowed in front to that of the head. Scutellum small, but distinct. Elytra cylindric, longer than the thorax, obtusely rounded posteriorly. Legs moderate, femora robust; front tibia straight, not at all expanded, its outer angle prolonged and curved outwardly, the inner also a little produced in the form of a spine; the others are flexuous and terminate externally in a projection as long as the basal tarsal joint, and from the inner edge of that projection there proceeds a spine-like spur, whilst its inner angle is likewise prolonged, but not to the same extent, the tarsus being inserted in the hollow; tarsi narrow, the basal and apical joints about equal; second and third, conjointly, hardly as long as the fourth, third entire, or with only an apical excision for the claw-joint; claws simple. Prosternum rather long, semicircularly excised in front; mesosternum moderate; metasternum rather short, convex. Abdomen composed of five segments, the basal one as long

COLEOPTERA

as the next two, so elevated as to be on a different plane from the others, truncate behind, produced in front so as to separate the posterior coxae; the second short, sloping from the first to the third; third and fourth very short; the last three with deep basal sutures; front coxæ prominent, not contiguous, but separated by a very narrow space, the intermediate not widely distant, having only a mesosternal process between them.

This genus makes a nearer approach to the *Cossonideous* pattern than any other I am acquainted with. There is much similarity to a very robust *Cossonid* in the shape of the body, whilst the antennæ very much resemble those of *Eutomus*, but possess a shorter shape. »

Charaktere. — Mir ist diese Gattung unbekannt.

Geographische Verbreitung der Art. — Eine Art aus Neu-Seeland.

1. *I. rufopiceus*, Broun, Man. New Zeal. Col. p. 739 (1881). Neu-Seeland.

20. GENUS SPHÆROTRYPES, BLANDFORD

Sphærotrypes. Blandford, Trans Ent. Soc. Lond. p. 61 (1894).

ORIGINALDIAGNOSE : Blandford, loc. cit.

« Caput oblongum, in rostellum haud productum. Oculi bipartiti. Antennæ lateraliter inter mandibulas et partem inferiorem oculorum insertæ, breves, funiculo 7-articulato, articulis latitudine crescentibus, clava ovata, rotundata, compressa, 3-articulata, vittis setarum transversis annulata; suturis transversis. Prothorax lateraliter marginatus. Mesosternum brevissimum, inflexum; metasternum breve. Coxæ anticæ et mediæ late distantes. Tibiæ anticæ ad apicem spinula unica extus producta armatæ, posteriores spinosæ. Tarsorum articuli 1-3 æquales, 3° bilobo. »

Charaktere. — Körperform kurz-eiförmig, beinahe kugelig; Skulptur mässig derb; Farbe schwarz, unter der verschiedenfarbigen Beschuppung verdeckt; Länge 2.5 bis 5 mm.

Kopf ohne Rüssel, länglich, Stirn flach, oder eingedrückt, oder gekielt, oder gehöckert.

Augen in zwei Teile zerlegt, diese dreieckig ; die beiden oberen Augen sitzen vorn auf der Stirn, die unteren unterhalb des Vorderkiefergelenks.

Fühler vor dem obern Winkel der untern Augenhälfte unterhalb der Vorderkiefer eingelenkt, Schaft gekrümmt und keulenförmig verdickt; Geissel siebengliedrig, deren erstes Glied kugelförmig, dick, zweites kegelförmig, 3-7 quer, nach der Keule zu verbreitert; Keule flach gedrückt, rundlich-eiförmig mit zwei Quernähten und fünf oder sechs queren Haarbändern versehen; die Spitze unregelmässig mit kurzen, dicken, gefiederten Haaren besetzt.

Vorderkiefer stark, hervorragend, ungezähnt.

Mittelkiefer hornartig, aussen stark behaart; Kaukante konvex mit kurzen breiten Zähnen besetzt.

Kiefertaster kurz, Glieder gleich lang.

Hinterkiefer zu einem länglich-viereckigen, an den Seiten eingebogenen, an der Spitze gerade abgestutzten Kinne verschmolzen; Zunge auf der Spitze des Kinnes eingefügt, klein, spitz-eiförmig, stark beborstet.

Lippentaster : Glied 1 und 3 so breit als lang, Glied 2 querbreiter, behaart.

Halsschild an den Seiten und hinten gerandet, hinterer Rand in der Mitte mehr weniger spitz vorgezogen.

Schildchen linear, gewölbt und runzelig.

Flügeldecken : Basis mehr weniger gekerbt und aufgeworfen; Skulptur kräftig; Beschuppung meist reichlich; Form halbkugelig.

Vorderbrust mit einem queren breiten Fortsatz zwischen den Vorderhüften.

Hüften voneinander enfernt.

Schienen : die vorderen nach der Spitze verbreitert, Aussenkante nur mit einem starken Dorn am Aussenwinkel und einem kleineren am Innenwinkel; die Mittel- und Hinterschienen haben eine bedornte Aussenkante.

Fussglieder : drittes Glied zweilappig mit schmalen und langen Lappen; Sohlen bebürstet.

Bauch horizontal.

Geographische Verbreitung der Arten. — Es sind neun Arten bekannt, davon fünf aus Ostindien und Himalaya, eine kommt sowohl in Sumatra wie in Kamerun vor; eine in Birma, eine in Japan, eine in Deutsch-Ostafrika

1. *S. assamensis*, Stebbing, India For.-Mem. Vol. 1, p. 5 (1908).　　　　Ostindien.
2. *S. coimbatorensis*, Stebbing, Departm. Not. Ins. aff. Forestry, Vol. 3,　Ostindien.
　p. 395 (1903).
3. *S. querci*, Stebbing, India For. Mem. Vol. 1, p. 5 (1908).　　　　　　Ostindien.
·4. *S. siwalikensis*, Stebbing, Departm. Not. Ins. aff. Forestry, Vol. 3, p. 389　Ostindien.
　. (1903).
5. *S. globulus*, Blandford, Trans. Ent. Soc. Lond. p. 63 (1893).　　　　　Ostindien.
6. *S. barbatus*, Hagedorn, Deutsche Ent. Zeitschr. p. 739 (1909).— **Taf. 2,**　Sumatra, Kamerun.
　Fig. 15.
7. *S. Blandfordi*, Schaufuss, Berl. Ent. Zeitschr. Vol. 42, p. 102 (1897).　Birma.
8. *S. pila*, Blandford, Trans. Ent. Soc. Lond. p. 62 (1893).　　　　　　　Japan.
9. *S. tanganus*, Schaufuss, Berl. Ent. Zeitschr. Vol. 42, p. 101 (1897).　Deutsch-Ostafrika

21. Genus DENDROSINUS, Chapuis

Dendrosinus. Chapuis, Synops. Scolyt. p. 236 (1873).

ORIGINALDIAGNOSE : Chapuis, loc. cit. p. 223, 236.

« Antennæ lateraliter insertæ, antennarum funiculus 7-articulatus, articulis sensim latitudine crescentibus, clava magna, basi annulata, apice truncata. Oculi transversi reniformes, minute granulati. Tibiæ extus spinulosæ. Tarsorum articuli subæquales, 3 bilobus. »

Charaktere. — Körperform eiförmig bis kugelig; Farbe schwarz, doch meist durch kurze farbige Behaarung verdeckt; Skulptur mässig derb; Länge 2 bis 4.5 mm.

Kopf breit, ohne Rüssel.

Augen länglich, querstehend, vorne ausgerandet.

Fühler kurz, mit siebengliedriger Geissel, mit flacher, breiter, runder, oder länglicher an der Spitze abgestutzter Keule mit drei behaarten Nähten; letztes Keulenglied stark behaart.

Vorderkiefer kräftig.

Mittel- und Hinterkiefer sind mir nicht bekannt.

Halsschild ohne Seitenränder, querbreiter, nach vorn eingeschnürt, seitlich stark gerundet, Basis zweibuchtig, rückwärts zwischen die Flügeldecken vorgezogen.

Schildchen nicht eingedrückt, klein, konvex.

Flügeldecken : Basis aufgeworfen und gekerbt, breiter als das Halsschild, Spitzen einzeln abgerundet. Skulptur mässig derb, auf dem Absturz körniger, häufig durch dichte kurze bunte Behaarung verdeckt.

Vorderbrust mit einem breiten queren Fortsatz zwischen den Vorderhüften.

Mittelbrust senkrecht, Hinterbrust sehr kurz.

Hüften weit voneinander getrennt.

Schienen verbreitert und an der Spitze abgestutzt, die Aussenkante mit zwei oder drei Dornen.
Fussglieder kurz, das dritte zweilappig.
Bauch horizontal bis konvex.

Geographische Verbreitung der Arten. — Fünf Arten aus dem Südreich sind beschrieben.

1. *D. Bonnairei*, Reitter, Best.-Tab. Borkenk. p. 45 (1894).   Patria latet.
2. *D. globosus*, Eichhoff, Berl. Ent. Zeitschr. Vol. 12. p. 149 (1868).   Columbia, Venezuela.
3. *D. puncticollis*, Blandford, Biol. Centr. Amer. Col. Vol. 4 (6), p. 156 (1897).   Columbia.
4. *D. transversalis*, Blandford, ibidem, p. 156 (1807).   Mexiko.
5. *D. vittifrons*, Blandford, ibidem, p. 156 (1897).   Brasilien.

22. Genus MERINGOPALPUS, Hagedorn

Meringopalpus. Hagedorn, Bull. Mus. Nat. Hist. Paris, Vol. 8, p. 547 (1904).

ORIGINALDIAGNOSE : Hagedorn, loc. cit.

« Caput subexsertum, rostello brevi auctum. Mentum oblongum versus basin sensim angustatum, lateribus rectis, apice truncato, ligula basi inserta, mento angustior, spinis compressis acutis dense ornata; palpi articulo 1⁰ magno sequentibus minoribus, 1⁰ et 2⁰ intus spinis compressis acutis rigidis, in linea semiorbiculari positis, notatis; maxillæ mala versus apicem angustata et producta, margine interno membranaceo spinulis viginti compressis obtusis et pilis subtilibus, extus pilis longissimis ciliata. squama palpigera distincta; oculi antici emarginati. Antennæ inter basin mandibularum et emarginationem oculorum insertæ funiculo 7-articulato, articulo 1⁰ globoso, apice truncato, magno, 2⁰ multo minore, obconico, ceteris transversis, latitudine crescentibus; capitulo magno solido, ovali, spongioso, vittis duabus obscuris notato; prothoracis superficies et inferior pars margine acuto distincto sejunctæ sunt; prosternum processu nullo. Coxæ anteriores subcontiguæ, mediæ late distantes, posteriores approximatæ. Tibiæ anteriores ad apicem dilatatæ, extus spinis duabus ornatæ, ceterum integræ, ad tarsos recipiendos sulcatæ, mediæ et posticæ valde dilatatæ compressæ extus serratæ. Tarsi recepti articulis 1⁰, 2⁰, 3⁰ subæqualibus. Corpus ovale, elytra declivia, stria suturali impressa. »

Charaktere. — Körperform länglich-eiförmig, breit; Farbe dunkel pechbraun, wenig behaart; Skulptur schwach; Länge 5, Breite 3 mm.

Kopf mit kurzem Rüssel, der gekielt ist.

Fühler, zwischen der Einlenkung der Vorderkiefer und der Ausrandung der Augen eingefügt, haben einen langen Schaft, eine siebengliedrige Geissel, deren erstes Glied kugelförmig, ziemlich gross, an der Spitze abgestutzt ist, das zweite viel kleiner, kegelförmig, die übrigen quer-breiter, an Breite zunehmend; Keule oval, gross, solide mit zwei kaum wahrnehmbaren dunklen Binden.

Augen quer-oval, vorne ausgerandet.

Vorderkiefer kräftig gezähnt.

Mittelkiefer ziemlich breit; Kaukante mit circa zwanzig breiten messerförmigen Stachelzähnen besetzt. An der Aussenseite befinden sich längere gefiederte Haare, die innere Fläche des Mittelkiefers ist mit kurzen derben Dornen ziemlich dicht besetzt.

Kiefertaster mit drei ziemlich gleichen, walzenförmigen Gliedern, die auf einem ziemlich isolierten, zwischen den Fortsätzen der Mala und der Squama sich erhebenden Tasterträger sitzen.

Hinterkiefer sind zu einem länglichen, gegen die Basis allmählich verschmälerten Kinne verschmolzen, dessen Seiten gerade, dessen Spitze abgestutzt sind. In der Nähe der Basis ist die Zunge, welche schmäler als das Kinn und stumpf lanzettförmig zugespitzt ist, eingefügt : sie ist ebenso wie die Lippentasterglieder an der Innenfläche mit kurzen spitzen derben Dornen dicht besetzt.

Lippentaster : Glied 1 gross, die folgenden kleiner; auf Glied 1 und 2 ist in der Mitte je eine Reihe halbkreisförmig angeordneter kurzer starrer Dornen aufgestellt.

Halsschild quer breiter, an der Basis abgestutzt, seitlich scharf gerandet, nach vorne etwas verschmälert, Oberfläche bucklig gewölbt, vorderer Rand und vordere Oberfläche durch grössere Knötchen rauh, hinten dicht punktiert.

Schildchen dreieckig, sehr klein, braun.

Flügeldecken von der Breite des Halsschildes und halbmal so lang als dieses, an der Basis abgestutzt, an der Spitze gemeinschaftlich gerundet; Absturz beginnt in der Mitte und ist dichter behaart als die übrigen Teile.

Vorderbrust ohne Fortsatz.

Vorderhüften einander berührend, Mittelhüften weit abstehend, Hinterhüften wieder genähert.

Schienen sind nach der Spitze zu verbreitert; die vorderen haben eine glatte Aussenkante, auf der nur zwei Dornen sitzen und sind auf ihrer Hinterfläche ausgehöhlt zur Aufnahme der Füsse. Mittel- und Hinterschienen sind an der Aussenkante gesägt.

Fussglieder sind einander gleich.

Bauch horizontal.

Geographische Verbreitung der Art. — Es ist nur eine Art aus Venezuela beschrieben.

1. *M. fallax*, Hagedorn, Bull. Mus. Hist. Nat. Paris, Vol. 8, p. 547 (1904). Venezuela.

23. Genus PROBLECHILUS, Eichhoff

Problechilus. Eichhoff, Ratio Tomic. p. 167 (1879).
Gymnochilus. Eichhoff, Berl. Ent. Zeitschr. Vol. 11, p. 399 (1867).

Originaldiagnose : *Gymnochilus*, Eichhoff, loc. cit.

« Tarsorum articulis tribus primis simplicibus. Capite prominulo, labro transverso. Antennarum funiculo 7-articulato, clava compacta. »

Problechilus, Eichhoff, loc. cit.

« Caput subexsertum, in rostrum breve productum. Labrum distinctum, transversum, subquadratum. Maxillæ lobo intus setis rigidis ciliato. Mentum oblongum, versus basin æqualiter angustatum ligula prope medium menti inserta : Oculi oblongi integri. Antennæ funiculo 7-articulato; huius articulo primo crassiusculo, secundo multo minore, obconico, sequentibus transversis, arcte coactis, latitudine sensim crescentibus, capitulo ovali, imbricato, subsolido. Pronotum a prosterno sutura elevata seiunctum, dorso anterius rugoso-exasperato, posterius punctato. Prosternum processu lato, apice rotundato, inter coxas producto. Coxæ anteriores late distantes. Scutellum maiusculum semi-orbiculare. Episterna metathoracis latiora, oblongo-quadrata. Tibiæ anticæ versus apicem dilatatæ, apice truncato, bispinato; posteriores apice valde compressæ, extus rotundato-ampliatæ, serratæ. Prothorax transversus, semi-orbicularis, basi et lateribus marginatus. Elytra pube sericea dense vestita. Corpus ovale convexum. »

Charaktere. — Mir ist die Gattung unbekannt geblieben.

Geographische Verbreitung der Arten. — Es sind vier Arten aus dem Südreich bekannt.

1. *P. consocius*, Blandford, Biol. Centr. Amer. Col. Vol. 4 (6), p. 171 (1897).   Guatemala.
2. *P. minor*, Blandford, ibidem, p. 172 (1897).   Guatemala.
3. *P. Reitteri*, Eichhoff, Stett. Ent. Zeit. Vol. 39, p. 388 (1878).   Guatemala. Mexiko.
4. *P. zonatus*, Eichhoff, Berl. Ent. Zeitschr. Vol. 11, p. 399 (1867).   Columbia.

24. Genus LISSOCLASTUS, Schaufuss

Lissoclastus. Schaufuss, Insektenbörse, p. 71 (1905).

Originaldiagnose für : *L. pimeloides*, Schaufuss, loc. cit.

« Ovatus aterrimus, elytris pedibusque nitidissimus; ore antennis pedibus rufopiceus; subtus setis brevibus albidis aspersus, supra brevissime rufo-setosus.

» Antennæ in fovea profunda semicirculari ante oculos sub frontis carina insertæ, setis longæ. Scapus duplicis funiculi longitudinis, apice modice clavatus, hoc clava duplicis latitudinis funiculi, articuli primi globosi. Funiculus brevis, robustus, 7(?)-articulatus, articulus secundus conicus, ceteri transversi breves. Capitulum ovale, solidum, compressum, aureo-pruinosum, supra sutura una, flexa, non procul basi notatum, subtus vix cavum.

» Caput late rostratum, dense punctatum, Frons truncata, subconcava, anterius excavata; posterius breviter rufosetosa, anterius griseo-pilosa; in versura verticis linea longitudinali abbreviata elevata; carina foveæ antennalis antice utrinque angulatim elevata ibique rufescens.

» Os aureo-ciliosum. Oculi elongato-ovales, tenues, parvi. Prothorax transversus, apice declivis; supra visus lateribus ex basi subito parum rotundato-ampliatus, dum fere recte et denique rotundato-angustatus, apice constrictus; lateraliter obtuse carinatus et subcarina truncatus nec non impressus. Totus densissime rugulose punctatus, subnitidus; linea longitudinalis mediana ex basi elevata; apice griseo-ciliatus.

» Elytra thorace latiora et plus duplo longiora, lateraliter in nono insterstitio carinato subtus fracta. Basis elevata et carinata, vix crenulata et subtus ciliosa, scutellum versus rotundato-inducta. Elytra punctato-striata, stria prima ex basi ad apicem profunda, interstitia omnia ante basin tuberculose-scabrata, tota rugulose punctulata, tertium, quintum, septimum ex basi ad apicem irregulariter spinis distantibus armata, secundum, quartum, octavum solum in disco usque ad versuram. Sutura carinata.

» Coxæ anticæ globosæ distantiores, intus aureo-setosæ; mediæ magis distantes quam posticæ.

» Abdomen griseo-pilosum, ruguloso-subopacum, transverse vix convexum, omnium segmentorum margo posticus carinatus.

» Femora simplicia, antica subtus solum pro receptione tibiæ excisa, setis albidis adspersa, item tibiæ. Tibiæ anticæ triangulares, in apice intus supra tarsorum insertionem acuta spina intus curvata armatæ, subspina aureo-setosæ apice incisæ, extus spina mutica extus versa armatæ, extus denticulatæ.

» Tarsi longi, articuli tres primi conici longitudine decrescentes, quartus longissimus, biunguiculatus. Longitudo 4.6 mm. Latitudo 2.3 mm. »

Charaktere. — Mir ist die Gattung unbekannt geblieben.

Geographische Verbreitung der Art. — Es ist nur eine Art aus Kamerun beschrieben.

1. *L. pimeloides*, Schaufuss, Insektenbörse, p. 71 (1905).   Kamerun.

25. Genus HYLURGUS, Latreille

Hylurgus. Latreille, Gen. Crust. Ins. Vol. 2, p. 274 (1807).
Hylesinus. Fabricius, Ent. Syst. Vol. 1 (2), p. 367 (1792).
Tomicus. Latreille, Gen. Crust. Ins. Vol. 3, p. 203 (1802) (pars).

Originaldiagnose aus Cuvier. Règne Animal, Vol. 5, Ins. p. 91 (1829), par Latreille :

Les Scolytes. — « Tantôt le pénultième article des tarses est bilobé. Les antennes ont sept ou huit articles avant la massue. Les Hylurgues ont la massue des antennes solide, presque globuleuse, obtuse, peu ou point comprimée, annelée transversalement et le corps presque cylindrique. »

Charaktere. — Körperform lang gestreckt. walzenförmig; Lange 2-5 mm., Farbe braun bis schwarz, Skulptur mässig derb mit starker langer Behaarung.

Kopf wenig vorgestrekt, meist stark punktiert oder auch glatt.

Fühler mit sechsgliedriger Geissel, deren Glieder nach vorne zu an Breite zunehmen; Keule kugelig mit drei Nähten.

Augen schmal, quer-oval, nicht ausgerandet.

Vorderkiefer stark, dreieckig mit einem stumpfen starken Zahn vor der Spitze.

Mittelkiefer mit stumpf zugespitztem Lappen, der am Innenrande kräftige Stachelzähne und steife gerade, breite Borsten besitzt.

Kiefertaster : Glied 1 und 2 quer, das dritte schlankere kegelförmig.

Hinterkiefer sind zu einem breit herzförmigen Kinne verschmolzen, welches kaum länger als breit, beiderseits backenartig erweitert und nach unten stark verengt ist. Die Zunge ist kaum zwei Drittel so breit als das Kinn, reicht bis zur Hälfte des ersten Lippentastergliedes, ist vorn abgerundet und sehr dicht pinselförmig mit feinen Haaren besetzt.

Lippentaster : Glied 1 fast doppelt so lang wie 2 und 3 zusammen, Glied 3 kurz kegelförmig.

Halsschild abgestumpft kegelförmig, langer als breit, ohne Seitenrand.

Schildchen nicht sichtbar.

Flügeldecken walzenförmig. vorne gerandet, aber nicht aufgeworfen. Absturz einfach abschüssig abgewölbt, durch sehr starke Behaarung ausgezeichnet.

Vorderbrust nicht bis zu den Hüften ausgeschnitten und ohne Fortsatz.

Vorderhüften dicht zusammenstehend, Mittel- und Hinterhüften voneinander getrennt.

Schienen an der Aussenkante gezähnt.

Fussglieder : Glied 1 länger als die folgenden, Glied 3 herzförmig.

Bauch horizontal.

Geographische Verbreitung der Arten. — Es sind fünf Arten bekannt, davon zwei aus Mitteleuropa, eine aus Kaukasus, eine von Madeira und eine von Ceylon.

1. *H. ligniperda*, Fabricius. Ent. Syst. Vol. 1, p. 367 (1792). — **Taf. 2, Fig. 16.**
2. *H. Micklitzi*, Wachtl, Deutsche Ent. Zeitschr. Vol. 25, p. 227 (1881).
3. *H. longulus*, Kolenati, Melet. Ent. Vol. 3, p. 38 (1846).
4. *H. destruens*, Wollaston, Col. Atlant. App. p. 45 (1865).
5. *H. determinans*, Walker, Ann. Mag. Nat. Hist. Vol. 3, p. 261 (1859).

Mitteleuropa, Frankreich, St. Helena, Kaukasus.
Dalmatien, Griechenland, Kaukasus. [Kaukasus.
Madeira.
Ceylon.

26. Genus MYELOPHILUS, Eichhoff

Myelophilus. Eichhoff, Stett. Ent. Zeit. Vol. 40, p. 400 (1870).
Dermestes. Linné, Syst. Nat. (ed. 9). p. 355 (1756).
Bostrichus. Fabricius, Ent. Syst. Vol. 1, p. 967 (1792).
Hylurgus. Latreille, Gen. Crust. Ins. Vol. 2, p. 274 (1807).
Hylesinus. Fabricius, Syst. Eleuth. Vol. 2, p. 390 (1801).
Tomicus. Latreille, Gen. Crust. Ins. Vol. 3, p. 203 (1802).
Blastophagus. Eichhoff, Berl. Ent. Zeitschr. p. 25 (1864).
Myelophilites. Hagedorn, Schrift. Physik.-Oekon. Ges. Königsberg, Vol. 47. p. 118 (1906).

ORIGINALDIAGNOSE : Eichhoff, Berl. Ent. Zeitschr. p. 25 (1864).

« Tarsorum articulus tertius bilobus. Antennarum funiculo 6-articulato, articulis clavam versus latitudine subæqualibus, clava oblongo-ovata, annulata, ligulæ fulcrum ovale, illa haud latius. »

Charaktere. — Körperform walzenförmig, Farbe braun bis schwarz, glänzend, Länge 3-5 mm., Skulptur mässig. Behaarung sparsam.

Kopf weitläufig punktiert, mit gekieltem schwachem Rüssel.

Fühler mit sechsgliedriger, fadenförmiger Geissel und eiförmig zugespitzter, nicht zusammengedrückter, geringelter Keule.

Augen lang-eiförmig, querstehend, nicht ausgerandet.

Vorderkiefer derb, zwei- oder dreizähnig.

Mittelkiefer mit vorn abgerundetem Lappen, dessen Kaukante mit etwa zwölf geraden Stache-zähnen besetzt ist.

Kiefertaster : Glied 1 so lang als 2 and 3 zusammen, diese gleichlang, drittes abgestutzt.

Hinterkiefer zu einem länglich-eiförmigen Kinn verschmolzen, Zunge vor der Mitte des Kinnes eingefügt. so breit als letzteres, bis zur Mitte des ersten Tastergliedes reichend.

Lippentaster Glied 1 so lang als 2 und 3 zusammen.

Halsschild breiter als lang, kegelförmig, mässig punktiert.

Schildchen klein, dreieckig.

Flügeldecken : Basis gerandet und gekerbt, Absturz einfach abgewölbt, hinten gekörnt.

Vorderbrust sehr kurz, vorne bis zu den Hüften ausgeschnitten.

Vorderhüften einander berührend, Mittel- und Hinterhüften getrennt.

Schienen an der Aussenkante gezähnt.

Fussglieder : Glied 1 länger als 2; Glied 3 breit, zweilappig.

Bauch horizontal.

Geographische Verbreitung der Arten. — Es sind vier Arten bekannt, drei davon Europäer, darunter eine fossil im Baltischen Bernstein; eine Art ist nur aus Sibirien beschrieben. Die beiden recenten Europäer kommen auch in Japan, Ostasien, Kaukasus, Nordamerika und den Canarien vor.

1. *M. dubius*, Hagedorn, Schrift. Physik.-Oekon. Ges. Königsberg, Vol. 47, p. 118 (1906); fossil im Baltischen Bernstein.   Ostpreussen.
2. *M. minor*, Hartig, Forstliches Conversationslexikon, p. 413 (1834).   Europa, Japan, Ostasien.
3. *M. piniperda*, Linné. Syst. Nat. (ed. 10), p. 563 (1758). — **Taf. 2, Fig. 16a, 16b.**   Europa, Japan, Ostasien, Nordamerika, Canarien.
4. *M. puellus*, Reitter, Best.-Tab. Borkenkäfer, p. 53 (1899).   Sibirien.

27. GENUS CHORTASTUS, SCHAUFUSS

Chortastus. Schaufuss, Insektenbörse, p. 15 (1905).

ORIGINALDIAGNOSE : Schaufuss, loc. cit.

« Habitus generis *Dendroctoni* Erichson. Caput vix rostratum. Oculi forma irregulari elongata, integri, parum solum ad frontis projecturam excisi, aterrimi subnitidi.

» Antennæ sub mandibulis insertæ; funiculo 6-articulato, articulis 2-6 obconicis, longitudine descrescentibus, latitudine crescentibus ; clava magna elongata, ovali cultriforme, compressa, pubescente, supra striis duabus valde transversis, indistinctis, notata.

» Apex elytrorum rotundatus, declivitate ornata.

» Coxæ anteriores approximatæ, posticæ antice approximatæ.

» Tibiæ apicem versus dilatatæ, extus excavatæ: apice fere recte truncato, excavationis lateribus productis. Tarsorum articulo ultimo bilobato. »

Charaktere. — Körperform lang-eiförmig, Länge 1.5 bis 5.5 mm., Farbe braun, Skulptur grob, Behaarung schwach.

Kopf mit schwachem Rüssel.

Stirn beim ♀ konkav mit Kiel und Knötchen versehen, länger behaart; beim ♂ flach.

Fühler unterhalb der Vorderkiefer eingefügt, mit langem dünnem Schaft und sechsgliedriger Geissel. Die Keule ist gross, lang-oval, hackmesserförmig, zusammengedrückt, behaart mit schwacher querer Naht. An der hinteren äusseren Ecke ist die Geissel angefügt.

Augen gross, quer-oval, durch eine scharfe Seitenkante des Rüssels ausgerandet.

Vorderkiefer stark, schwarz, gezähnt.

Mittelkiefer breit, mit grosser Lade, die nach vorn etwas verschmälert, nach innen stark gerundet ist, mit circa achtzehn breiten derben Stachelzähnen an der Kaukante.

Kiefertäster lang, die drei Glieder von gleicher Länge, die unteren cylindrisch, das letzte kegelförmig.

Hinterkiefer zu einem länglichen, an der Basis verengten, an den Seiten geraden, an der Spitze abgestumpften Kinne verschmolzen; die Zunge ist in der Mitte angefügt, nach der Spitze verschmälert und schwach zugespitzt, mit starken Haaren besetzt.

Lippentaster : Glied 1 lang cylindrisch, Glied 2 klein und quer, Glied 3 lang kegelförmig.

Halsschild quer, nach vorn verengt, gleichmässig punktiert. Schildchen gross, dreieckig, nicht zwischen die Flügeldecken reichend.

Flügeldecken parallel, nach der Spitze etwas verbreitert, an der Basis mit aufgeworfenem und gekerbtem Rand; Oberfläche stark punktiert gestreift, auf dem konvexen Absturz mit Knötchen resp. Kielen versehen.

Vorderhüften berührend, Mittel- und Hinterhüften voneinander abstehend.

Beine kräftig; Schienen gegen die Spitze verbreitert, dreikantig, auf der Aussenseite für die Aufnahme der Füsse ausgehöhlt, mit Dornen an den Ecken versehen; Aussenrand schwach gesägt.

Fussglied 3 zweilappig.

Bauch gerade.

Geographische Verbreitung der Arten. — Es sind vier Arten aus Kamerun beschrieben; sie heissen :

1. *C. camerunus*, Schaufuss, Insektenbörse, p. 15 (1905). — **Taf. 8, Fig. 16,** Kamerun.
   17, 18, 19.
2. *C. minimus*, Hagedorn, Deutsche Ent. Zeitschr. p 738 (1909).   Kamerun.
3. *C. Schenklingi*, Hagedorn, ibidem, p. 737 (1909). — **Taf. 2, Fig. 17, 17a;** Kamerun.
   Taf. 8, Fig. 15.
4. *C. serrifer*, Hagedorn. ibidem, p. 739 (1909).   Kamerun.

28. Genus KISSOPHAGUS, Chapuis

Kissophagus. Chapuis, Synop. Scolyt. p. 242 (1873).
Hylurgus. Gemminger & Harold, Cat. Col. Vol. 9, p. 2671 (1872).
Hylesinus. Schmitt. Stett. Ent. Zeit. p. 108 (1843).
Cissophagus. Bedel, Faune Col. Seine, Vol. 6, p. 391 (1888).

ORIGINALDIAGNOSE : Chapuis, loc. cit.

« Antennarum funiculus 6-articulatus, articulis latitudine subæqualibus, clava ovalis annulata. Tarsorum articuli minuti, subæquales, tertius bilobatus. Mentum basi rotundato-ovatum. »

Charaktere. — Körperform walzenförmig; Länge 2 bis 3 mm.; Farbe schwarzbraun, aber meist verdeckt durch starke Bekleidung mit dichten kurzen Haarbörstchen; Skulptur kräftig.

Kopf mit kurzem Rüssel.

Fühler neben den Vorderkiefern eingelenkt, mit sechsgliedriger Geissel und eiförmig zugespitzter voller Keule mit abgesetzten Ringeln.

Augen quer-oval, ganzrandig.

Vorderkiefer derb.

Mittelkiefer mit stark gerundeter oben zugespitzter Innenlade, an deren Kaukante zehn bis zwölf breite gerade Stachelzähne sitzen.

Kiefertaster : Glied 1 und 2 quer breiter, Glied 3 länger, kegelförmig.

Hinterkiefer zu einem herzförmig-dreieckigen, vorn abgestutzten Kinne verschmolzen; mit sehr kleiner nahe dem Vorderrande eingefügter Zunge.

Lippentaster sehr lang, Glied 1 sehr gross, die beiden folgenden klein, das zweite quer.

Halsschild fast so lang als breit, vorn eingeschnürt, punktiert und schuppenartig beborstet.

Schildchen länglich, zwischen den Flügeldecken versteckt.

Flügeldecken walzenförmig, an der Basis mit erhabenem Zähnchenkamm, hinten einfach abgewölbt; punktiert gestreift, Zwischenräume mit Borstenreihen.

Vorderbrust mit langem Fortsatz zwischen den Vorderhüften.

Hüften sind sämtlich weit voneinander getrennt.

Schienen aussen gezähnt.

Fussglieder : 1 am kürzesten, 3 herzförmig.

Bauch gerade.

Geographische Verbreitung der Arten. — Es sind zwei Arten aus Südeuropa und eine aus Deutsch-Ostafrika bekannt, nämlich :

1. *K. hederae*, Schmitt, Stett. Ent. Zeit. p. 108 (1843). — **Taf. 2, Fig. 18a.**   Mittel- und Südeuropa.
2. *K. Novaki*, Reitter, Wien. Ent. Zeit. Vol. 13, p. 45 (1844).   Südeuropa.
3. *K. fasciatus*, Hagedorn, Deutsche Ent. Zeitschr. p. 737 (1909). —   Deutsch-Ostafríka.
   Taf. 2, Fig. 18, 18b.

29. Genus ACRANTUS, Broun

Acrantus. Broun, Ann. Mag. Nat. Hist. p. 417 (1895).
Homarus. Broun, Man. New Zeal. Col. Vol. 2, p. 740 (1881).

ORIGINALDIAGNOSE : Broun, loc. cit

« Body cylindrical squamose. Head vertical in front, with a quadrangular muzzle Eyes narrow, transverse, remote, distinctly facetted. Antennæ short; scape as long as funiculus, gradually incrassated; funiculus 6-articulate; first joint stout, subglobular; joints 2-6 small, compact, gradually widened, second obconical; club pubescent, oval, triarticulate, the terminal joint rather long and somewhat pointed. Prothorax subquadrate, slightly narrowed anteriorly, its base truncate. Scutellum distinct. Elytra cylindric, a little broader than thorax, moderately declivous posteriorly, individually obtusely rounded, slightly raised and crenulated, and overlapping the base of the thorax. Legs stout; femora dilated; tibiæ expanded apically, dentate externally, considerably produced inwardly at the extremity; tarsi stout, their basal joints about equal, third almost bilobed, fourth as long as the preceding three conjointly; claws stout, thickened at the base. Prosternum plane, depressed between the broadly separated anterior coxæ, these latter prominent; mesosternum short, depressed, middle coxæ more distant than the front pair; metasternum moderate, a little elevated, posterior coxæ least remote. Abdomen not twice the length of the metasternum; its basal segment as long as the three following short ones, their sutures distinct; its process produced between the coxæ. »

Charaktere. — Die Gattung ist mir unbekannt geblieben.

Geographische Verbreitung der Art. — Es ist nur eine Art aus Neu-Seeland beschrieben.

1. *A. mundulus*, Broun, Ann. Mag. Nat. Hist. p. 417 (1895).   Neu-Seeland.

30. Genus DENDROCTONUS, Erichson

Dendroctonus. Erichson, Arch. f. Naturg. Vol. 2 (1), p. 45-65 (1836).

Bostrichus. Kugelann, Schneiders Mag. Vol. 5, p. 523 (1794).

Scolytus. Olivier, Ent. Vol. 4, (gen. 78), p. 6 (1795).

Hylurgus. Mannerheim, Bull. Soc. Nat. Moscou, Vol. 25, p. 283 (1852).

Hylurgus. Kirby, Fauna Bor. Amer. Vol. 4, p. 195 (1837).

Die genaue Biobliographie dieser Gättung findet sich in der hervorragenden Monographie : Hopkins, A. D.: The genus *Dendroctonus* in *U. S. Dep. Agric. technical* (17), Vol. 27, Pt. 1, p. 1-158 (1909) und loc. cit. Bulletin No. 83, Pt. 1, p. 1-169 (1909), woselbst Anatomie, Systematik, Biologie und praktische Information erschöpfend behandelt sind.

Die feinere Anatomie der innern Organe ist ausführlich bearbeitet von : L i n d e m a n n , *Monographie der Borkenkäfer Russlands*, p. 53-87 (1875).

ORIGINALDIAGNOSE : Erichson, loc. cit.

« Antennæ funiculo 5-articulo, capitulo 4-annulato, suborbiculari, compresso. Tibiæ extus denticulatæ. Palpi maxillares articulo 1° brevissimo, 2ⁿ maximo, sequentibus duobus sensim minoribus. Labium fortiter compressum. Palpi labiales articulo 1° longiore, subclavato, 2° tenuiore, cylindrico, minuto, 3° obtuse subulato. Antennæ breves, scapo clavato, funiculi articulo 1° breviter clavato, 2° obconico, reliquis brevibus transversis; capituli segmentum 1ᵘᵐ reliquis coniunctis æquale, politum. Corpus oblongum, cylindricum. Rostrum brevissimum Mesosternum antice obsolete impressum. Coxæ anticæ approximatæ. Tibiæ compressæ, extus denticulatæ. Tarsi articulo 3° dilatato, bilobo. Elytra margine antico elevato. »

Charaktere. — Körperform lang-walzenförmig; Länge 2.5 bis 9 mm., Farbe gelbrot bis braun und schwarz; Bekleidung : kurze bis sehr lange Haare von hellbrauner bis dunkelbrauner Färbung.

Kopf : Labrum und Clipeus fehlen, Stirn ist mit oder ohne Eindrücke und Knötchen.

Fühler : Schaft, Geissel und Keule sind beinahe einander gleich lang. Schaft ist nach der Spitze zu keulenförmig, cylindrisch bis kantig. Geissel fünfgliedrig, ein wenig länger als die Keule; erstes Glied zwiebelförmig, so lang oder länger als das zweite. Dieses ist so lang wie 3, 4 und 5 zusammen und becherförmig. Die drei letzten Glieder nehmen nach der Keule an Breite zu. Keule ist gerundet, zusammengedrückt, mit zwei oder drei konxexen Nähten. Der Fühler ist in einer ziemlich tiefen Grube, welche zwischen Auge, Basis der Vorderkiefer und Seitenwinkel des Epistoma liegt, eingelenkt.

Augen : oblong-oval bis herz-eiförmig, ganzrandig, hinter der Basis der Fühler gelegen.

Vorderkiefer kurz, kräftig, mit drei Zähnen an der Innenkante.

Mittelkiefer mit grosser, nach vorne verschmälerter Innenlade, deren Innenrand mit circa sechszehn langen starken Stachelzähnen und einzelnen Haaren besetzt ist.

Kiefertaster : Glied 1 nach der Basis verschmälert und so lang als 2 und 3 zusammen, 3 am kürzesten.

Hinterkiefer bilden ein lang eiförmiges, nach der Basis etwas verengtes Kinn, in dessen Mitte die dicke, breite, bis zur Mitte des ersten Tastergliedes reichende Zunge entspringt, die so dicht mit dicken langen fast keulenförmig angeschwollenen stumpfen Borsten besetzt ist, dass man ihre Innenfläche nicht zu Gesicht bekommt 1).

Lippentaster stehen weit voneinander ab, um für die dicke Zunge Raum zu lassen, Glied 1 sehr lang, nach vorne beinahe keulenförmig, anderthalbmal so lang als die beiden anderen zusammen, Glied 3 kurz kegelförmig.

Halsschild breiter als lang, nach vorne verengt, Mitte des Vorderrandes ausgeschnitten, mit oder ohne Mittellinie, mehr weniger punktiert, vorne mit kleinen Tuberkeln besetzt.

Schildchen dreieckig, eingedrückt zwischen den Flügeldeckenrändern.

Flügeldecken oblong, an der Basis abgeschnitten, diese gekerbt und aufgeworfen, hinten konvex abfallend, grob skulptiert und stark behaart.

Vorderbrust nicht bis zu den Hüften ausgeschnitten.

Vorderhüften einander berührend, Mittelhüften abstehend, Hinterhüften genähert.

Schienen nach vorne verbreitert, dorsal ausgehöhlt, Aussenkante gezähnt.

Bauch gerade.

Geographische Verbreitung der Arten. — Es sind vierundzwanzig Arten bekannt, von denen nur eine (*D. micans* Kugelann) sich durch Europa und Nordasien verbreitet. Die übrigen sind sämtlich Bewohner des neuen Nordreichs und gehen nach Süden hinunter bis nach Guatemala.

1. *D. adjunctus*, Blandford, Biol. Centr. Amer. Col. Vol. 4 (6), p. 146 (1897). Guatemala.
2. *D. approximatus*, Dietz, Trans. Amer. Ent. Soc. Vol. 17, p. 27 (1890). Nordamerika.
3. *D. arizonicus*, Hopkins, Monogr. p. 95 (1909). Nordamerika.
4. *D. Barberi*, Hopkins, ibidem, p. 85 (1909). Nordamerika.
5. *D. borealis*, Hopkins, ibidem, p. 133 (1909). Alaska
6. *D. brevicomis*, Le Conte, Proc. Amer. Philos. Soc. Vol. 15, p. 386 (1876). Nordamerika.
7. *D. convexifrons*, Hopkins, Monogr. p. 87 (1909). Nordamerika.
8. *D. Engelmanni*, Hopkins, ibidem, p. 130 (1909). Nordamerika.
9. *D. frontalis*, Zimmermann, Trans. Amer. Ent. Soc. p. 149 (1868). Nordamerika.
10. *D. Jeffreyi*, Hopkins, Monogr. p. 114 (1909). Kalifornien.
11. *D. mexicanus*, Hopkins, Proc. Soc. Ent. Wash. Vol. 7, p. 80 (1906). Mexiko.
12. *D. micans*, Kugelann, Schneiders Mag. Vol. 5, p. 523 (1794). — Taf. 2, Fig. 19; Taf. 11, Fig. 83, 84; Taf. 12, Fig. 5, 6. Europa, Nordasien.
13. *D. monticolae*, Hopkins, Bull. U. S. Dep. Agric. Vol. 56, p. 11 (1905). Nordamerika.
14. *D. murrayanae*, Hopkins, ibidem, p. 140 (1905). Nordamerika.
15. *D. obesus*, Mannerheim, Bull. Soc. Nat. Moscou, Vol. 16, p. 286 (1843). Nordamerika.
16. *D. parallelocollis*, Chapuis, Synops. Scolyt. p. 244 (1873). Mexiko.
17. *D. piceaperda*, Hopkins, Bull. U. S. Dep. Agric. Vol. 28, p. 16 (1901). Nordamerika.
18. *D. pondevosae*, Hopkins, ibidem, Vol. 22, p. 1 (1902). Nordamerika.
19. *D. pseudotsugae*, Hopkins, Proc. Meet. Soc. Prom. Agric. Sc. Denver, p. 67 (1901). Nordamerika.
20. *D. punctatus*, Le Conte, Trans. Amer. Ent. Soc. Vol. 2, p. 173 (1868). Nordamerika.
21. *D. rufipennis*, Kirby, Fauna Bor. Amer. Vol. 4, p. 195 (1837). Nordamerika.
22. *D. simplex*, Le Conte, Trans. Amer. Ent. Soc. Vol. 2, p. 173 (1868). Nordamerika.
23. *D. terebrans*, Olivier, Ent. Vol. 4, Genus 78, p. 6 (1795). Nordamerika.
24. *D. valens*, Le Conte, Rep. of Explor. and Survey from the Mississipi River to the Pacific Ocean, p. 59 (1860). Nordamerika.

---

1) Cf. Taf. 11, Fig. 84.

31. GENUS HYPOBORUS, ERICHSON

Hypoborus. Erichson, Arch. f. Naturg. Vol. 1, p. 62 (1836).

ORIGINALDIAGNOSE : Erichson, loc. cit.

« Antennæ funiculo 5-articulato, capitulo 4-annulato. Labium subovatum. Maxillæ mala extus setis rigidis ciliata. Palpi maxillares malæ subæquales, articulo primo brevi, secundo tertioque æqualibus, crassis, quarto cylindrico, præcedente tenuiore longioreque. Labium basin versus leviter angustatum, apice rotundatum. Palpi labiales articulis duobus primis magnis subovalibus, secundo primo parum minore, tertio elongato, tenui, cylindrico. Antennæ scapo elongato subclavato, funiculi articulo primo reliquis maiore, clavato, secundo obconico, tertio quartoque subglobosis, quinto introrsum producto : capitulo ovali, 4-annulato. Corpus parvum villosum subcylindricum. Thorax antrorsum angustatus. Tibiae compressæ, ciliatæ, extus obsolete denticulatæ. Tarsi articulo tertio antecedentibus longiore. »

Charaktere. — Körperform klein, oval; Länge 1-2 mm; Farbe schwarz, ganzlos; Bekleidung in greisen Haaren bestehend; Skulptur nur schwach ausgeprägt.

Kopf mit schwachem Rüssel.

Fühler mit fünfgliedriger Geissel, deren Glieder abwechselnd breiter und schmäler sind, und ovaler derber undeutlich geringelter Keule.

Augen vorne ganzrandig.

Vorderkiefer derb.

Mittelkiefer mit beilförmiger, vorn zugespitzter Innenlade, die an der Kaukante mit starren Borstenzähnen besetzt ist.

Kiefertaster mit beinahe gleich langen, an Dicke abnehmenden Gliedern.

Hinterkiefer zu einem oblongen, gegen die Spitze verbreiterten Kinne verschmolzen, dessen Seiten gerade und dessen Spitze gerundet ist. Die Zunge ist klein, schmal, fast an der Spitze des Kinnes angesetzt.

Lippentaster wie Kiefertaster.

Halsschild breiter als lang, vorn mit zerstreuten Höckern besetzt, an der Basis gerandet.

Schildchen versteckt.

Flügeldecken an der Basis mit geraden Zähnchenkamm, nach hinten schwach konvex abschüssig, ohne Auszeichnungen.

Vorderbrust ohne Fortsatz.

Vorderhüften einander berührend, die anderen abstehend.

Schienen : die vorderen zusammengedrückt, aussen ganzrandig, nach der Spitze zu verschmälert und in einen Enddorn auslaufend, die hinteren verbreitert, ihre Spitze aussen gerundet; an der Aussenkante tragen die vorderen kurze breite, die hinteren lange Schuppen.

Fussglieder : das erste Glied ist sehr kurz, das zweite zweimal so lang, das dritte am längsten. Bauch gerade.

Geographische Verbreitung der Arten. — Es sind vier Arten bekannt, davon zwei von Ceylon, eine um das Mittelmeer herumwohnend und eine aus Ostindien.

1. *H. cinereo-testaceus*, Motschulsky, Bull. Soc. Nat. Moscou, Vol. 39 (2), Ceylon. p. 403 (1866).
2. *H. dorsalis*, Motschulsky, ibidem, p. 403 (1866). Ceylon.
3. *H. ficus*, Erichson, Arch. f. Naturg. Vol. 1, p. 62 (1836). Südeuropa, Nordafrika, Sy-
   var. *siculus*, Ferrari, Borkenkäfer, p. 18 (1867). Sizilien. [rien.
4. *H. nebulosus*, Motschulsky, Bull. Soc. Nat. Moscou, Vol. 39 (2), p. 403 (1896). Ostindien.

32. Genus CARPHOBORUS, Eichhoff

Carphoborus. Eichhoff, Berl. Ent. Zeitschr. p. 27 (1864).
Dendroctonus. Zimmermann, Trans. Amer. Ent. Soc. p. 148 (1868).

ORIGINALDIAGNOSE : Eichhoff, loc. cit.

« Tarsi articulo 1º minuto, 2º maiore, 3º cordato. Antennarum funiculo 5-articulato clava ovalis annulata. Palpi labiales articulo 1º subquadrato, hoc 2º vix longiore. »

Charaktere. — Körperform klein, gestreckt, walzenförmig; Länge von knapp 1 bis 2 mm.; Farbe schwarz; Bekleidung : dicht schuppenartig behaart; Skulptur des Halsschildes schwach, der Flügeldecken gröber, besonders am Absturz.

Kopf klein, kugelig, grösstenteils in das Halsschild eingefügt.

Fühler mit fünfgliedriger Geissel und gerundeter zusammengedrückter, geringelter Keule.

Augen nierenförmig, vorne tief ausgerandet.

Vorderkiefer kräftig, gezähnt.

Mittelkiefer mit hautartiger kurzer Innenlade, die an der Kaukante fast kreisförmig gebogen, nach vorne abgerundet und mit acht bis zehn geraden Stachelborsten ziemlich gleichmässig besetzt ist.

Kiefertaster kegelförmig, Glied 1 quer, fast quadratisch, Glied 2 kurz, breiter als lang. Glied 3 so lang als 1.

Hinterkiefer zu einem herzförmig dreieckigen Kinne, dessen Seiten gerundet erweitert sind, verschmolzen.

Zunge als vorn halbkreisförmig abgerundetes Läppchen bis zur Hälfte des ersten Lippentastergliedes emporragend.

Lippentaster dicht zusammenstehend, erstes Glied kaum länger als zweites, fast quadratisch, drittes länger als zweites, abgestutzt kegelförmig.

Halsschild nicht länger als breit, vorn ganzrandig, nach der Spitze verschmälert, dicht und fein punktiert mit mehr weniger deutlicher Mittellinie.

Schildchen kaum sichtbar.

Flügeldecken mit ziemlich tiefen Kerbstreifen und kielartigen oder kammförmigen Erhöhungen der Zwischenräume auf dem Absturz. Basis gerandet und kammartig gekerbt.

Hüften : Vorderhüften einander berührend, die anderen voneinander entfernt.

Schienen verbreitert, am Aussenrand bezahnt.

Fussglieder : Glied 1 viel kürzer als die folgenden, Glied 3 schwach herzförmig; Füsse kürzer als die Schienen.

Bauch gerade.

Geographische Verbreitung der Arten. — Es sind zehn Arten bekannt, die sich in der Weise auf das alte und neue Nordreich verteilen, dass drei Europäer, drei Asiaten, ein Nordafrikaner und drei Nordamerikaner vorhanden sind. Sie heissen :

1. *C. minimus*, Fabricius, Syst. Eleuth. Vol. 2, p. 395 (1801).   Mitteleuropa.
2. *C. Perrisii*, Chapuis, Synops. Scolyt. p. 239 (1873).   Südeuropa.
3. *C. pini*, Eichhoff, Europ. Borkenk. p. 131 (1881).   Südeuropa.
4. *C. Henscheli*, Reitter, Wien. d'Ent. Zeit. Vol. 6, p. 192 (1887).   Smyrna.
5. *C. Jurinskii*, Eggers, Ent. Blätter. Vol. 6, p. 36 (1910).   Irkutsk.
6. *C. rossicus*, Semenow, Rev. Russe Ent. Vol. 2, p. 272 (1902).   Selabuga.
7. *C. Bonnairei*, Brisout de Barneville, Ann. Soc. Ent. Fr. Vol. 4, p. 52   Algier.
   (1884). — **Taf. 2, Fig. 20.**

8. *C. bicristatus*, Chapuis, Synops. Scolyt. p. 249 (1873). Nordamerika.
9. *C. bifurcus*, Eichhoff, Berl. Ent. Zeitschr. Vol. 12, p. 147 (1868). Nordamerika.
10. *C. simplex*, Le Conte, Proc. Amer. Philos. Soc. Vol. 15, p. 383 (1875). Nordamerika.

33. Genus RENOCIS, Casey

Renocis. Casey, Bull. Calif. Acad. Sc. Vol. 2, p. 257 (1886).

ORIGINALDIAGNOSE : Casey, loc. cit.

« Body subcylindrical. Head prominent, not concealed by the prothorax; inserted in the prothorax nearly to the eyes; slightly deflexed, not at all produced, beak entirely obsolete; eyes rather finely granulated, not at all prominent, on the sides, extending slightly under the head, short, very strongly transverse, with a small feeble sinuation in the anterior margin. Antennæ inserted on the sides of the head, just before the eyes, short ten-jointed. Basal joint longer than wide, rather robust; second not one-half as long, subglobular, 3 to 6 very small, joints 7 to 10 forming a very abrupt, elongate, oval club, longer than the entire preceding portion, strongly compressed, sparsely pubescent. Mandibles prominent, short and stout, perfectly chisel-shaped, apex transversaly truncate, straight; inner face at apex obliquely truncate. Mentum short transverse; maxillæ ligula et palpi very small, invisible under a mass of coarse hair surrounding the mentum. Labrum wanting. Anterior coxæ prominent, subglobular contiguous; middle coxæ widely distant, small, not prominent; posterior separated tranverse, attenuated laterally, only attaining the metasternal episternum, which is long, rather wide, sides parallel, epimeron not visible. Anterior coxæ in contact with the head beneath; prosternum entirely obsolete before them; femora rather robust simple; tibiæ very narrow at base, rapidly dilated and compressed towards apex, margined externally with a row of short, very robust spinules; obliquely truncate at apex. Tarsi rather short, slender, not at all dilated, but rather compressed, five-jointed; third obliquely truncate and slighthy produced beneath, not bilobed; fourth very minute; fifth slender, longer than the preceding united. Abdominal segments five in number, first two subequal, each nearly as long as the third and fourth together. Elytra covering the entire abdomen; pygidium invisible; prothorax strongly rounded at the sides, transverse, convex; sides continuous in curvature from the dorsal surface to the anterior coxæ. Integuments with a dense scabrous mass of scales; base of elytra elevated and tuberculate. Scutellum not distinctly visible. »

Charaktere. — Mir ist die Gattung unbekannt geblieben.

Geographische Verbreitung der Art. — Es ist nur eine Art aus Kalifornien beschrieben.
1. *R. heterodoxus*, Casey, Bull. Calif. Acad. Sc. Vol. 2, p. 257 (1886). Kalifornien.

34. Genus XYLECHINUS, Chapuis

Xylechinus. Chapuis, Synops. Scolyt. p. 244 (1873).
Xylechinites. Hagedorn, Schrift. Physik.-Oekonom. Ges. Königsberg, p. 120 (1906).

ORIGINALDIAGNOSE : Chapuis, loc. cit.

« Antennarum funiculus 5-articulatus, articulis vix latitudine crescentibus, clava ovalis annulata. Tarsorum articuli subæquales, tertius cordatus. Mentum cordiforme. Palporum labialium articulus primus elongatus, duobus aliis coniunctis longior. »

COLEOPTERA

Charaktere. — Körperform walzenförmig; Länge 2 bis 3 mm.; Farbe schwarzbraun, aber durch kurze starke borstenförmige Behaarung verdeckt. Mässig kräftig skulptiert.

Kopf mit kurzem Rüssel.

Fühler mit fünfgliedriger Geissel und kurz eiförmiger, nicht zusammengedrückter Keule.

Augen vorn in der Mitte kaum merklich ausgerandet.

Vorderkiefer derb.

Mittelkiefer mit beilförmiger Innenlade, an deren Kaukante zehn bis zwölf spitze Stachelzähne stehen.

Kiefertaster so lang wie die Spitze der Lade, Glied 1 und 2 kurz und breit, Glied 3 länger, kegelförmig.

Hinterkiefer zu einem dreieckig herzförmigen, an der Basis verschmälerten, an der Spitze breit abgerundeten Kinne verschmolzen; Zunge in der Mitte des Kinnes angesetzt, eben über seinen Rand reichend.

Lippentaster : Glied 1 sehr lang und dick, die beiden folgenden klein, zweites quer, drittes kegelförmig.

Halsschild so lang als breit, meist runzlig punktiert und mit Haarbörstchen besetzt.

Schildchen klein, dreieckig.

Flügeldecken walzenförmig, Basis erhaben gerandet und gekerbt, Skulptur kräftig; Zwischenräume mit Haarborstenreihen versehen.

Vorderbrust mit langem Fortsatz zwischen den Vorderhüften.

Hüften sämtlich weit voneinander getrennt.

Schienen aussen gezähnt; an der Aussenkante mitunter mit langen Schuppen besetzt.

Fussglieder : die drei ersten gleichgross, das dritte entweder einfach oder herzförmig.

Bauch gerade.

Geographische Verbreitung der Arten. — Es sind acht Arten bekannt, davon sechs aus dem Südreich, zwei aus Mitteleuropa, davon eine fossil im Bernstein. Die fossile Art steht der argentinischen am nächsten.

1. *X. irrasus*, Blandford, Biol. Centr. Amer. Col. Vol. 4 (6), p. 158 (1896).   Panama.
2. *X. fuliginosus*, Blandford, ibidem, p. 158 (1897).   Panama.
3. *X. marmoratus*, Blandford, ibidem, p. 159 (1897).   Guatemala.
4. *X. scabiosus*, Blandford, ibidem, p. 158 (1897).   Panama.
5. *X. tesselatus*, Blandford, ibidem, p. 159 (1897).   Guatemala.
6. *X. nigrosetosus*, Hagedorn, Deutsche Ent. Zeitschr. p. 737 (1909). —   Argentinien.
   Taf. 3, Fig. 21, 21a, 21b.
7. *X. anceps*, Hagedorn, Schrift. Physik.-Oekonom. Ges. Königsberg, p. 120   Ostpreussen.
   (1906); fossil im baltischen Bernstein.
8. *X. pilosus*, Knoch. Beitr Insektengesch. (1781-1801). — **Taf. 8, Fig. 14;**   Nord- und Mitteleuropa.
   Taf. 12, Fig. 7.

35. Genus PHLŒOSINUS, Chapuis

Phlœosinus. Chapuis, Synops. Scolyt. p. 245 (1873).

Phlœosinites. Hagedorn, Schrift. Physik. Oekonem. Ges. Königsberg, Vol. 47, p. 119 (1906).

ORIGINALDIAGNOSE : Chapuis, loc. cit.

« Antennarum funiculus 5-articulatus, articulis subæqualibus, clava ovalis annulata. Tarsorum articulus tertius integer. Mentum elongatum, basi angustatum. Palporum labialium articulus primus longior. »

Charaktere. — Körperform kurz eiförmig, nach vorn verschmälert; Farbe gelbbraun bis schwarz; Bekleidung gelbe kurze Borstenhaare; Skulptur ziemlich derb; Länge 2 bis 4 mm.

Kopf geneigt, in einen kurzen breiten Rüssel verlängert; Stirn bei den ♂ konkav, bei den ♀ konvex.

Fühler seitlich eingefügt mit fünfgliedriger Geissel und grosser länglich ovaler stumpfzugespitzter zusammengedrückter geringelter Keule.

Augen nierenförmig, vorn tief ausgerandet.

Vorderkiefer kräftig, gezähnt.

Mittelkiefer mit breiter, an der bis zur Höhe des zweiten Tastergliedes ragenden Spitze gerundeten Innenlade, deren Kaukante mit zehn bis zwölf schwach gebogenen sehr langen Stachelzähnen besetzt ist. Kiefertaster mit drei ziemlich gleichlangen, an Dicke abnehmenden cylindrischen Gliedern.

Hinterkiefer sind zu einem verlängerten, an der Basis verschmälerten Kinne verschmolzen.

Lippentaster : Glied 1 länger als die anderen.

Halsschild breiter als lang, nach vorne verengt, meist dicht punktiert, mit oder ohne Mittellinie. Schildchen klein.

Flügeldecken walzenförmig, an der Basis aufgeworfen und kammförmig gekerbt, am Schildchen unterbrochen. Oberfläche punktiert gestreift, die Zwischenräume auf dem Absturz gekielt und gehöckert, beim ♂ stärker als beim ♀.

Vorderbrust bis zu den Vorderhüften ausgeschnitten.

Vorderhüften weit, Mittelhüften noch weiter voneinander entfernt.

Schienen an der Aussenkante gezähnt.

Fussglieder fadenförmig, drittes Glied einfach.

Bauch gerade.

Geographische Verbreitung der Arten. — Es sind vierunddreissig Arten beschrieben. Vier von ihnen sind fossil und zwar drei im Baltischen Bernstein, eine im nordamerikanischen Interglacial gefunden. Die Hauptmasse der Arten kommt im alten Nordreich vor, nämlich siebzehn, etwas weniger im neuen Nordreich, nämlich neun. Aus dem Südreich ist eine, aus dem indo-malayischen sind sieben Arten bekannt geworden.

1. *P. armatus*, Reitter, Wien. Ent. Zeit. Vol. 6, p. 192 (1887).   Syrien.
2. *P. Aubei*, Perris, Bull. Soc. Ent. Fr. p. 78 (1855).   Südeuropa und Araxes.
3. *P. Brunni*, Hagedorn, Schrift. Physik.-Oekonom. Ges. Königsberg,   Ostpreussen.
   Vol. 47, p. 119 (1906); fossil im Baltischen Bernstein.
4. *P. cedri*, Brisout de Barneville, Rev. d'Ent. Caen, Vol. 2, p. 146 (1883).   Algier.
5. *P. dubius*, Blandford, Trans. Ent. Soc. Lond. p. 70 (1894).   Japan.
6. *P. Henschi*, Reitter, Wien. Ent. Zeit. Vol. 20, p. 201 (1901).   Hercegovina.
7. *P. Lewisii*, Chapuis, Ann. Soc. Ent. Belg. Vol. 28, p. 198 (1874).   Japan.
8. *P. minutus*, Blandford, Trans. Ent. Soc. Lond. p. 71 (1894).   Japan
9. *P. perlatus*, Chapuis, Ann. Soc. Ent. Belg. Vol. 28, p. 198 (1874).   Japan.
10. *P. pulchellus*, Blandford. Trans. Ent. Soc. Lond. p, 69 (1894).   Japan.
11. *P. regimontanus*, Hagedorn, Schrift. Physik.-Oekonom. Ges. Königsberg,   Ostpreussen.
    Vol. 47, p. 119 (1906); fossil im Baltischen Bernstein.
12. *P. Rehi*, Hagedorn, ibidem, p. 118 (1906); fossil im Baltischen Bern-   Ostpreussen.
    stein.
13. *P. rudis*, Blandford, Trans. Ent. Soc. Lond. p. 73 (1894).   Japan.
14. *P. seriatus*, Blandford, ibidem. p. 72 (1894).   Japan.
15. *P. thujae*. Perris. Bull. Soc. Ent. Fr. p. 77 (1855).   Mitteleuropa.
16. *P. transcaspicus*, Semenow, Revue Russe d'Ent. Vol. 2, p. 278 (1902).   Kopet-Dagh.
17. *P. turkestanicus*, Semenow, ibidem, p. 269 (1902).   Buchara.
18. *P. Baumanni*, Hopkins, Proc. Ent. Soc. Wash. Vol. 7. p. 80 (1905).   Mexiko.
19. *P. coronatus*, Chapuis, Synops. Scolyt. p. 247 (1873).   Mexiko, Yucatan.
20. *P. cristatus*, Le Conte, Trans Amer. Ent. Soc. Vol. 2, p. 170 (1868).   Kalifornien.

21. *P. cupressi*, Hopkins, Bull. U.S. Bureau of Forests. Vol. 38, p. 35 (1903).   Kalifornien.
22. *P. dentatus*, Say, Journ. Acad. Nat. Sc. Philad. Vol. 5, p. 258 (1825).   Nordamerika.
23. *P. punctatus*, Le Conte, Proc. Amer. Philos. Soc. Vol. 15, p. 381 (1876).   Nordamerika.
24. *P. sequoiae*, Hopkins. Bull. U.S. Bureau of Forests, Vol. 38, p. 33 (1903).   Kalifornien.
25. *P. squalidens*, Scudder, The Canad. Entom. Vol. 18, p. 194 (1889);   Ontario.
    fossil im Interglacial.
26. *P. tacubayae*, Hopkins, Proc. Ent. Soc. Wash. Vol. 7, p. 78 (1904).   Mexiko.
27. *P. variegatus*, Chapuis, Synops. Scolyt. p. 248 (1873).   Chile.
28. *P. concinnulus*, Walker, Ann. Mag. Nat. Hist. Vol. 3, p. 260 (1859).   Ceylon.
29. *P. cribratus*, Blandford, Trans. Ent. Soc. Lond. p. 198 (1896).   Sumatra.
30. *P. detersus*, Chapuis, Synops. Scolyt. p. 246 (1873).   Ceylon.
31. *P. maior*, Stebbing. Calcutta Forest. Bull. Nº 2, p. 36, 37 (1907).   Assam.
32. *P. minor*, Stebbing, ibidem, p. 36, 37 (1907).   Assam.
33. *P. squamulatus*, Chapuis, Synops. Scolyt. p. 247 (1873).   Himalaya.
34. *P. vilis*, Blandford, Trans. Ent. Soc. Lond. p. 199 (1896).   Sumatra.

36. GENUS CHÆTOPHLŒUS, LE CONTE

Chætophlœus. Le Conte, Proc. Amer. Philos. Soc. Vol. 15, p. 382 (1876).

ORIGINALDIAGNOSE : Le Conte, loc. cit.

« This genus is founded upon *Hylesinus hystrix*, a singular species from California, of robust oval form, thickly clothed with coarse erect hair. It differs from *Phloeosinus* by the four joints, which constitute the outer part of the funicle of the antennæ being slender, and increasing much less rapidly in thickness; the club is equally large, subovate, compressed, obtusely rounded at tip and the sutures are also straight. The mouth is clothed with long coarse hair. The prosternum is very short in front of the coxæ, which are very narrowly separated. The first ventral segment is longer than the second and the third; fourth and fifth are short. The tibiæ are broadly dilated, rounded and finely serrate at tip; the tarsi are not plainly visible in the unique specimen in my collection, but the third joint is emarginate, rather than bilobed. »

Charaktere. — Die Gattung ist mir unbekannt.

Geographische Verbreitung der Art. — Es ist nur eine Art aus Kalifornien beschrieben.
1. *C. hystrix*, Le Conte, Proc. Acad. Natur. Sc. Philad. p. 51 (1858).   Kalifornien.

37. GENUS CHRAMESUS, LE CONTE

Chramesus. Le Conte, Trans. Amer. Ent. Soc. App. p. 168 (1868).
Rhopalopleurus. Chapuis, Synops. Scolyt. p. 255 (1873).

ORIGINALDIAGNOSE : Le Conte, loc. cit.

« Body oval, convex, covered with erect short bristles, head large, prominent, concave in the male, slightly convex in the female : eyes transverse, feebly emarginate, finely granulated; antennæ with a scape long and slender, nearly as long as the head, and very gradually enlarged towards the tip; funiculus of but one distinct joint, which is conical, not langer than wide; the remaining joints are obsolete, and visible only as a corneous ridge ou the upper edge of the base of the club, which is very much compressed, uniformly pubescent, without trace of articulation on either face, as long as the head, less than half as wide as its length, oval, subsecuriform, lower outline nearly straight, upper one curved, obtusely rounded at tip. Prothorax one-half wider than long, much narrowed in front, rounded on the sides, and less so at the tip. Elytra about twice as long as the thorax, convex, obtusely rounded behind, basal margin acute and subserrate, as in *Hylesinus*. Tibiæ dilated gradually, feebly serrate; tarsi with the joints 1-3 very short, third scarcely dilated, fourth joint nearly as long as the others united, with large claws. »

Charaktere. — Körperform kurz eiförmig, Farbe schwarz, aber verdeckt durch kleine Schuppen und dicke aufrechte Borsten, Skulptur derb, Länge 1.5 bis 3.5 mm.

Kopf mit kurzem breitem Rüssel, der beim ♂ meistens eine konkave Grube zeigt, beim ♀ flach ist.

Augen quer oval, leicht ausgerandet um die Einlenkung der Fühler herum.

Fühler stehen vorne auf der Stirn, Schaft lang, zart, gebogen, Geissel fünfgliedrig, erstes Glied dick, etwas länger als breit, die vier anderen sind kleiner und an Grösse einander gleich; Keule sehr gross, breitgedrückt, ohne Nähte, auf beiden Seiten kurz behaart, länglich, die untere Kante ist gerade, die obere konvex, oberes wie unteres Ende abgerundet. Insertion der Geissel seitlich im untern Drittel des untern Randes.

Vorderkiefer derb, schwarz, dreizähnig.

Mittelkiefer rund, fast kreisförmig, mit schmalem Fortsatz der Kaulade; Kaukante mit acht bis zehn, unten geraden, dolchartigen, oben sichelförmigen, breiten Stachelzähnen besetzt. Aussenrand der Squama palpigera stark gerundet, mit langen, groben Haaren versehen.

Kiefertaster winkelig geknieet, Glieder walzenförmig, Glied 1 so lang als 2 und 3 zusammen.

Hinterkiefer zu einem herzförmigen, an der Spitze beiderseits breit gerundeten, nach der Basis stark und plötzlich verschmälerten Kinne verschmolzen, an dessen gerade abgestutzter Spitzenfläche die kleine, nur eben bis zur Mitte des ersten Tastergliedes reichende, stumpfgerandete schmale Zunge eingefügt ist.

Lippentaster gekniet; Glied 1 verkehrt kegelförmig, so lang als 2 und 3 zusammen, breit; Glied 2 fast quadratisch, etwas nach unten verschmälert; Glied 3 länger und schmäler, walzenförmig.

Halsschild halbkugelig, an den Seiten nicht oder kaum gerandet, an der Basis doppelt gebuchtet, in der Mitte ein Vorsprung gegen die Flügeldeckennaht.

Schildchen klein, punktförmig.

Flügeldecken an der Basis aufgeworfen und gekerbt, konvex, nach der Spitze stark abfallend.

Vorderhüften kugelig, einander berührend.

Schienen verbreitert, Aussenkante gesägt, Spitze breit gerundet und gesägt.

Fussglieder 1-3 rund, gleichgross, viertes klein, aber deutlich.

Bauch mässig konvex ansteigend.

Geographische Verbreitung der Arten. — Es sind elf Arten beschrieben, welche sich in der Weise auf die Neue Welt verteilen, dass sieben in Nordamerika, vier in Südamerika vorkommen. Es sind folgende :

1. *C. acuteclavatus*, Hagedorn. Deutsche Ent. Zeitschr. p. 742 (1909). — Argentinien.
   Taf. II, Fig. 88, 89, 90.
2. *C. asperatus*, Herrich-Schäffer, Journ. New York Ent. Soc. Vol. 16, p. 220 Arizona.
   (1908).
3. *C. Chapuisi*, Le Conte, Proc. Amer. Philos. Soc. Vol. 15, p. 375 (1876). Louisiana.
4. *C. dentatus*, Herrich-Schäffer, Journ. New York Ent. Soc. Vol. 16, p. 221 (1908). Arizona.
5. *C. globosus*, Hagedorn, Deutsche Ent. Zeitschr. p. 742 (1909). Argentinien.
6. *C. icoriae*, Le Conte, Trans. Amer. Ent. Soc. p. 168 (1868). — **Taf. 3,** Pennsylvania.
   Fig. 22, 22b.
7. *C. pumilus*, Chapuis. Synops. Scolyt. p. 255 (1873). Nordamerika.
8. *C. rotundatus*. Chapuis, ibidem, p. 255 (1873). Mexiko.
9. *C. subopacus*, Herrich-Schäffer, Journ. New York Ent. Soc. Vol. 16, p. 221 (1908). Arizona.
10. *C. tuberculatus*, Chapuis. Synops. Scolyt. p. 255 (1873). Neu-Granada.
11. *C. tumidulus*, Blandford, Biol. Centr. Amer. Col. Vol. 4 (6), p. 170 (1897). Guatemala, Panama.

38. Genus LIPARTHRUM, Wollaston

Liparthrum. Wollaston, Ins. Madeir. p. 294 (1854).

Originaldiagnose : Wollaston, loc. cit.

« Corpus minutum cylindricum : Prothorace amplo convexo, antice producto, haud scabroso, sed plerumque tuberculis minutissimis obsito : elytris apice rotundatis integris : alis amplis. Antennæ capitatæ; scapo elongato clavato subflexuoso; funiculo 4-articulato, articulo primo robusto apice truncato, secundo et tertio minutis, quarto paulo latiore transverso; capitulo solidissimo, elongato-ovato, piloso, obscurissime 4-annulato. Labrum obsoletum. Mandibulæ corneæ, validæ, triangulares, obtusæ, infra apicem dente parvo obtuso obscuro instructæ, ad basin integræ. Maxillæ lobo singulo latissimo, brevi, rotundato, setoso instructæ (interno obsoleto). Palpi subsetoso-conici; maxillares minuti, articulis primo, secundo et tertio brevissimis transversis, ultimo longiore, graciliore, subconico; labiales longiusculi articulo primo crasso, secundo paulo breviore, crassiusculo, ultimo elongato, gracili, subcylindrico. Ligula membranacea subelongata pilosa, basi angustata, apice truncata. Pedes brevissimi parum validi : tibiis compressis, apicem versus leviter dilatatis, anticis simplicibus, posterioribus subcurvatis, extus 4-dentatis, omnibus ad apicem internum spina (in anticis elongata, robustissima, valde obtusa, recta, in posterioribus minore, angustiore, leviter acuta, subrecta) armatis. Tarsis quadriarticulatis, articulis secundis baseos longiusculis, crassis, subæqualibus (primo paulo longiore basi angusto subflexuoso, secundo apice obscure emarginato), tertio minutissimo, quarto elongato, unguiculis simplicibus munito. »

Charaktere. — Körperform : sehr kleine Tiere von 0.7 bis 1.3 mm. Länge; länglich oval; von meist schwarzer Färbung mit verschiedenfarbiger kurzer Behaarung und schwacher Skulptur.

Kopf kugelig, in das Halsschild zurückgezogen.

Fühler mit kurzer viergliedriger Geissel und geringelter Keule.

Augen oval, vorne ganzrandig.

Vorderkiefer kurz dreieckig, kräftig, mit einem Zahn.

Mittelkiefer mit breiter, kurzer gerundeter Innenlade, an deren Kaukante mehrere Borstenzähne sitzen.

Kiefertaster : Glied 1 und 2 sehr kurz und quer, das letzte etwas schlanker.

Hinterkiefer zu einem an der Spitze verbreiterten und abgestutzten, nach der Basis verschmälerten Kinne verschmolzen.

Lippentaster länger als die Kiefertaster, erstes Glied ziemlich dick, das zweite kürzer, das dritte am längsten.

Halsschild quer, auf dem Rücken punktiert, vorne mit Höckerchen besetzt, die häufig in zwei Reihen angeordnet sind.

Schildchen versteckt.

Flügeldecken an der Basis mit kammartig zurückgeschlagenem Rande; die Streifen der Flügeldecken sind mit kürzeren oder längeren Haarreihen besetzt, die Zwischenräume mit kurzen, dicken, aufgerichteten borstenartigen Schuppenreihen.

Vorderbrust mit kurzem scharfem Fortsatz.

Vorderhüften sich fast berührend, Mittelhüften weit voneinander getrennt.

Schienen zusammengedrückt, die vorderen nach der Spitze verschmälert und aussen ganzrandig, die hinteren verbreitert mit einem Endhaken.

Fussglieder : d̦as 'erste Glied ist sehr kurz, das zweite etwas grösser, das dritte am längsten, nicht verbreitert.

Bauch : die beiden ersten Bauchsegmente sind lang, das dritte und vierte sehr kurz.

Geographische Verbreitung der Arten. — Es sind sechszehn Arten bekánnt. Davon leben neun nur auf den Kanarien, fünf in Mittel- und Südeuropa und zwei im Kaukasus.

1. *L. artemisiae*, Wollaston. Ins. Madeir. p. 299 (1854).   Madeira.
2. *L. bicaudatum*, Wollaston, Col. Atlant. App. p. 44 (1865).   Gomera.
3. *L. bituberculatum*, Wollaston, Ins. Madeir. p. 267 (1854).   Madeira.
4. *L. curtum*, Wollaston, ibidem, p. 298 (1854).   Madeira und Tenerifa.
5. *L. inarmatum*, Wollaston, Am. Mag. Nat. Hist. Vol. 5, p. 364 (1860).   Tenerifa.
6. *L. Loweanum*, Wollaston, Col. H̦esper. p. 118 (1867).   Hesperiden.
7. *L. Lowei*, Wollaston, Trans. Ent. Soc. Lond. p. 174 (1862). — **Taf. 3, Fig. 23.**   Tenerifa.
8. *L. mandibulare*, Wollaston, Ins. Madeir. p. 295 (1854).   Madeira.
9. *L. nigrescens*, Wollaston, Col. Atlant. App. p 44 (1864).   Tenerifa.
10. *L. Bartschti*, Mühl, Wien. Ent. Zeit. Vol. 10, p. 202 (1891).   Wien, Prater.
11. *L. corsicum*, Eichhoff, Ratio Tomic. p. 110 (1879).   Korsika, Italien.
12. *L. genistae*, Aubé, Ann. Soc. Ent. Fr. Vol. 2, p. 388 (1862).   Südfrankreich, Italien.
13. *L. Georgi*, Knotek, Wien. Ent. Zeit. Vol. 14, p. 89 (1895).   Griechenland, Dalmatien, Kaukasus.
14. *L. mori*, Aubé, Ann. Soc. Ent. Fr. p. 387 (1862).   Südfrankreich, Korsika. Ita-
15. *L. Arnoldi*, Șemenow, Rev. Russe d'Ent. Vol. 2, p. 272 (1902).   Kaukasus. [lien, D̦almatien.
16. *L. colchicum*, Semenow, ibidem, Vol. 3, p. 79 (1903).   Kaukasus.

39. Genus DACRYOSTACTUS, Schaufuss

Dacryostactus. Schaufuss, Insektenbörse, p. 79 (1905).

Originaldiagnose : Schaufuss. loc. cit.

« Statura globuliformis. Totus pilosus et supra insuper squamosus. Caput receptum, parum quadrangulariter rostratum. Mandibulæ validæ acutæ. Oculi tenues elongati. Antennarum clava magna, tota cultriformis. apice intus curvata, compressa, pubescens. Funiculus brevis et angustus, tri- an quattuór-articulatus, articulo primo maximo clavato, secundo conico. Scapus sat tenuis, apice clavatus, ibique intus cirro longissimo pilorum testaceoruin ornatus.

» Elytrorum margo basalis elevatus, crenatus; interstitium ex disco depressum. Coxæ anticæ permagnæ globosæ, approximatæ sed non attingentes. Tibiæ anticæ simplices apice in spinam acutam, recte intus versum productæ, dense breviter setosæ; posteriores simplices, rotundato-ampliatæ, compressæ, dente apicali minore. Tarsorum articuli 1-3 gradatim longitudine, at vix latitudine maiores, tertius non lobatus, quartus tres primos longitudine æquans; tarsus anticus tibiam mox longitudine æquans. »

Charaktere. — Körperform kurz eiförmig, fast kugelig, stark beschuppt, nicht behaart.

Kopf in einen kurzen breiten Rüssel verlängert.

Augen schmal, länglich quer gestellt.

Fühler zwischen den Augen und dem Vorderkiefer eingelenkt. Schaft dünn, an der Spitze kolbig verdickt, mit einem Büschel langer Haare seitlich besetzt; Geissel dreigliedrig; erstes Glied gross, keulenförmig, mit einem Haarkranz ringsum besetzt; zweites Glied becherförmig; drittes Glied quer, niedrig, breiter als lang; Keule sehr gross, messerförmig, komprimiert, ohne Nähte, durchweg mit kurzen Borsten besetzt, obere Kante gerade, untere konvex.

Vorderkiefer kräftig, spitz, ungezähnt.

Mittelkiefer mit langen gefiederten Haaren stark besetzt; Innenlade beilförmig, Kaukante mit zehn bis zwölf geraden breiten Stachelzähnen versehen, die unter der Masse auf der Vorderfläche sitzender langer gefiederter Haare fast verschwinden 1).

Kiefertaster : Glied 3 länger als 1 und 2 zusammen, cylindrisch.

Hinterkiefer zu einem langen und schmalen, mit gefiederten langen Haaren besetzten Kinne verschmolzen, in dessen letztem Drittel die kurze, eiförmige, von der Spitze an in steilem Bogen gerundete Zunge sich ansetzt.

Lippentaster lang, erstes Glied am grössten, verkehrt kegelförmig, zweites kurz cylindrisch, letztes lang und dünn, cylindrisch.

Halsschild viel breiter als lang, an der Basis gerandet und ausgebuchtet, seitlich nicht gerandet, in der Mitte der Oberfläche mit Tuberkeln besetzt, stark beschuppt.

Schildchen unsichtbar.

Flügeldecken mit aufgeworfner und gekerbter Basis, nach hinten abfallend, kugelig gewölbt, erster Zwischenraum stark verbreitert, die ganze Oberfläche reichlich mit dicken Schuppen besetzt.

Vorder- und Hinterhüften kugelig, nahe beinanderstehend.

Mittelhüften weit voneinander abstehend.

Schienen : die vorderen ungezähnt, an der Spitze nach innen in einen Zahn verlängert; die hinteren ebenso, aber zusammengedrückt und in einen schwächeren Zahn auslaufend.

Fussglieder : Glied 3 schwach herzförmig verbreitert.

Bauch horizontal.

Geographische Verbreitung der Art. — Es ist nur eine Art aus Südafrika beschrieben; dieselbe findet sich aber auch in Benguella, Portugiesisch Westafrika.

1. *D. Kolbei,* Schaufuss, Insektenbörse, p. 79 (1905). — **Taf. 3, Fig. 24;** Südostafrika.
Taf. 11, Fig. 85, 86, 87.

40. Genus STYRACOPTERUS, Blandford

Styracopterus. Blandford. Ann. Mag. Nat. Hist. Vol. 17, p. 323 (1896).

Originaldiagnose : Blandford, loc. cit.

« Caput globosum receptum; oculi ovales emarginati, antennarum funiculus brevissimus, triarticulatus, clava magna compressa, latitudine longior, oblique subovalis, margine inferiore minus, superiore fortius curvato, suturis tribus notata. Prothorax transversus, fere semiglobosus. Elytrorum margo basalis elevatus, crenatus. Coxæ anticæ subcontiguæ. Pedes fere ut in *Liparthro* constructi, tarsorum articulis primo et secundo perbrevibus. »

Charaktere. — Die Gattung ist mir unbekannt geblieben.

Geographische Verbreitung der Art. — Die einzige Art kommt in Südafrika vor.

1. *S. murex,* Blandford, Ann. Mag Nat. Hist. Vol. 17, p. 324 (1896). Südafrika.

41. Genus HYLOSCYLLUS, Schaufuss

Hyloscyllus. Schaufuss. Tijdschr. v. Ent. Vol. 40. p. 218 (1897).

Originaldiagnose : Schaufuss, loc. cit.

« Da mir nur einzelne Stücke vorliegen, die Gattung übrigens unverkennbar ist, muss vorläufig

---

1) Cf. **Taf. 11, Fig. 86.**

auf eine genaue und eingehende Beschreibung Verzicht geleistet werden; nur folgende Charakteristica seien angeführt :

Charaktere. — Körperform cylindrisch, Farbe schwarz, Skulptur kräftig, Behaarung gering, Länge 3 bis 4.5 mm.

Kopf mit Rüssel versehen.

Stirn mehr weniger gewölbt.

Augen flach, rund, etwas in Querdurchmesser verlängert.

Fühler in tiefer Grube unter der Seitenkante des Rüssels vor den Augen eingelenkt, Geissel siebengliedrig, Keule spitz eiförmig, mit zwei hell behaarten Nähten.

Vorderkiefer schwarz, kräftig gezähnt. Mittel- und Hinterkiefer sind nicht untersucht worden.

Halsschild seitlich gerandet, vorn eingeschnürt, gleichmässig punktiert.

Schildchen nicht sichtbar.

Flügeldecken : Basis aufgeworfen und gekerbt, mit tiefen Punktstreifen; Absturz gewölbt, derb skulptiert und rostrot behaart.

Vorderbrust mit Fortsatz zwischen den Vorderhüften, die auseinander stehen.

Schienen : Aussenkante glatt, der Aussenspitze mit Endhaken.

Fussglied 3 herzförmig verbreitert; Sohlen bebürstet.

Bauch horizontal.

Geographische Verbreitung der Arten. — Es sind drei Arten aus Madagaskar beschrieben :

1. *H. exsculptus*, Schaufuss, Tijdschr. v. Ent. Vol. 40, p. 218 (1897).   Madagaskar.
2. *H. loricatus*, Schaufuss, ibidem, p. 218 (1897).   Madagaskar.
3. *H. radens*, Schaufuss, ibidem, p. 219 (1897).   Madagaskar.

4. TRIBUS CRYPTURGINÆ

UEBERSICHT DER GATTUNGEN

42. GENUS APHANARTHRUM, WOLLASTON

Aphanarthrum. Wollaston. Ins. Madeir. p. 292 (1854).

ORIGINALDIAGNOSE : Wollaston, loc. cit.

« Corpus parvum, cylindricum, læte coloratum. Prothorace amplo convexo, antice producto, sed haud scabroso : elytris apice rotundatis integris : alis amplis. Antennæ capitatæ; scapo longissimo clavato, basi flexuoso; funiculo triarticulato, articulo primo robusto apice truncato basi subflexuoso, secundo et tertio minutissimis brevissimis (hoc vix observando nec non in capitulum oblique inserto); capitulo solido ovato pilosissimo quadriannulato. Labrum obsoletum. Mandibulæ corneæ validæ subtriangulares obtusæ, infra apicem dento obtuso instructæ, ad basin integræ. Maxillæ lobo singulo lato setoso instructæ (interno obsoleto). Palpi conici maxillares minutissimi crassi, articulis primo, secundo et tertio brevissimis transversis, ultimo paulo longiore, graciliore, conico; labiales longiores, articulis subæqualibus primo et secundo crassis, ultimo gracili, ovato, basi truncato. Ligula membranacea elongata, apice truncata. Pedes breves validi : tibiis compressis apicem versus dilatatis, extus fortiter dentatis (dentibus in anticis tribus vel quatuor, in posterioribus septem vel octo), ad apicem internum spina parva recta subacuta armatis : tarsis articulis tribus baseos longiusculis, crassiusculis, subæqualibus (primo vix graciliore), quarto minutissimo, quinto longissimo unguiculis simplicibus munito. »

Charaktere. — Körperform cylindrisch, Länge 1 bis 2 mm., von bunter Grundfärbung; die einzigen Borkenkäfer, bei denen die bunter Färbung nicht durch Schuppen hervorgebracht ist; Skulptur schwach, ebenso die Behaarung.

Kopf in einen kurzen Rüssel verlängert.

Augen länglich, vorne ausgebuchtet.

Fühler mit langem gekeultem Schaft, zweigliedriger Geissel, deren erstes Glied grösser, von Zwiebelform, das zweite sehr klein ist. Keule eichelförmig mit zwei geraden Nähten.

Vorderkiefer schwach.

Mittelkiefer mit kurzer beilförmiger zugespitzter Innenlade, an deren Kaukante kurze dolchförmige Stacheln sitzen.

Kiefertaster dreigliedrig, die beiden ersten Glieder quer breiter, das letzte konisch.

Hinterkiefer zu einem ovalen breiten, an den Seiten stark gerundeten Kinne verschmolzen; die Zunge ist an der Basis des Kinnes angeheftet, daselbst von der Breite des letzteren, nach der Spitze rasch verschmälert und stumpf, also etwa von der Form eines gleichschenkligen Dreiecks.

Lippentaster länger als die Kiefertaster, aber ebenso gebaut.

Halsschild nach vorne verlängert, konvex, am Vorderrande bei einigen Arten mit kleinen Knötchen besetzt, sonst nur gleichmässig punktiert.

Schildchen kaum sichtbar.

Flügeldecken an der Spitze gerundet, nicht abschüssig.

Vorderbrust mit kurzem Fortsatz zwischen den Vorderhüften.

Hüften getrennt.

Beine kurz, stark; Schienen breitgedrückt, an der Aussenkante bedornt, die vorderen an der Aussenspitze gerundet, die hinteren daselbst gerade.

Fussglieder 1, 2, 3 gleichförmig.

Bauch wagerecht.

Geographische Verbreitung der Arten. — Die sämtlich von Wollaston beschriebenen vierzehn Arten und vier Varietäten kommen nur im makronesischen Reich vor und leben daselbst in den baumartigen *Euphorbien*. Ueber ihre Lebensweise ist leider nichts näheres bekannt. Ob die Arten vielleicht Ueberbleibsel aus der Tertiärzeit oder gar einer noch früheren Zeit darstellen, als der Inselschwarm die Bergspitzen eines nunmehr untergegangenen Festlandes bildete, wissen wir nicht; es scheint aber höchst wahrscheinlich zu sein. Eigenartig ist die Verbreitung der Arten auf den einzelnen Inseln : wir finden acht Arten, die nur auf je eine Insel vorkommen, während einige andere Arten auf zwei, drei und vier Inseln gefunden werden.

1. *A. affine*, Wollaston, Aphan. Can. Isl. Ann. Mag. Nat. Hist. (3), Vol. 5,   Lanzarote, Gomera, Fuerte-
   p. 4 (1860).   ventura, Canaria.

2. *A. armatum,* Wollaston, Trans. Ent. Soc. Lond. p. 33 (1862).   Lanzarote.
3. *A. bicinctum,* Wollaston, Aphan. Can. Isl. Ann. Mag. Nat. Hist (3).   Lanzarote, Fuerteventura,
    Vol. 5, p. 3 (1862).   Tenerifa.
    var. obsitum, Wollaston, Col. Atlant. App. p. 43 (1865).   Tenerifa.
    var. vestitum, Wollaston, ibidem, p. 43 (1865).   Tenerifa.
4. *A. bicolor,* Wollaston, Aphan. Can. Isl. Ann. Mag. Nat. Hist. (3).   Madeira, Ferro, Gomera,
    Vol. 5, p. 4 (1860). — **Taf. 3, Fig. 25, 25a, 25b.**   Palma.
5. *A. canariense,* Wollaston, ibidem, p. 3 (1860).   Madeira, Ferro, Gomera,
6. *A. canescens,* Wollaston, Col. Atlant. App. p. 41 (1865).   Gomera. [Palma. Tenerifa.
    var. simplex, Wollaston, ibidem, p. 41 (1865).   Gomera.
7. *A. euphorbiae,* Wollaston, Ins. Mader. p. 293 (1854).   Madeira.
8. *A. glabrum,* Wollaston, Aphan. Can. Isl. p. 5 (1860).   Ferro.
9. *A. hesperidum,* Wollaston, Col. Hesper. p. 117 (1867).   Cap Verde Inseln.
10. *A. jubae,* Wollaston, Aphan. Can. Isl. Ann. Mag. Nat. Hist. (3),   Gomera, Lanzarote.
    Vol. 5, p. 2 (1860).
11. *A. luridum,* Wollaston, ibidem, p. 2 (1860).   Tenerifa, Gomera.
12. *A. piscatorium,* Wollaston, ibidem, p. 5 (1860).   Gomera. Lanzarote. Fuer-
        teventura, Canaria.
13. *A. pygmaeum,* Wollaston, Col. Atlant. App. Ann. Mag. Nat. Hist. (3),   Gomera.
    Vol. 5, p. 42 (1865).
    var. laticolle, Wollaston, ibidem, p. 42 (1865).   Palma.
14. *A. tuberculatum,* Wollaston, ibidem, p. 40 (1865).   Tenerifa.

43. GENUS CRYPTURGUS, ERICHSON

Crypturgus. Erichson, Arch. f. Naturg. Vol. 1, p. 60 (1836).

ORIGINALDIAGNOSE : Erichson, loc. cit.

« Antennæ funiculo biarticulato, capitulo solido. Labium parallelum. Maxillæ mala angusta, setis compressis ciliata. Palpi maxillares, articulis duobus primis minutissimis occultis, tertio crasso, quarto angusto, obtuse subulato. Labium oblongum parallelepipedum : apice setulis ciliatum. Palpos labiales haud observavi. Antennæ scapo elongato, clavato, funiculi articulo primo magno, crasso, secundo transverso : capitulo solido, subovato. Corpus minutum. cylindricum. Tibiæ compressæ, extus denticulatæ. »

Charaktere. — Körperform cylindrisch; Länge 1 bis 1,5 mm.; Farbe hellbraun bis schwarz; Behaarung spärlich; Skulptur schwach.

Kopf merklich nach vorn geneigt. mit schwacher rüsselartiger Verlängerung.

Fühler an den Seiten des Kopfes zwischen Vorderkieferbasis und Augen eingelenkt, Geissel zweigliedrig. Keule schief eiförmig, ohne Nähte, glänzend, länger als die Geissel, mässig behaart.

Augen länglich, vorne ausgerandet.

Vorderkiefer ziemlich kräftig, einzähnig.

Mittelkiefer mit kurzer, an der Kaukante mit etwa zwölf, ziemlich gleichmässig verteilten pergamentartigen Stachelborsten gewimperter Innenlade.

Kiefertaster : die Glieder nehmen an Länge und Breite gleichmässig ab.

Hinterkiefer bilden ein gleichschenklig dreieckiges Kinn, das an der Tastereinlenkung am breitesten, nach der Basis in gleichmässig konvexem, schwachem Bogen verschmälert ist; Zunge dreieckig, bis zur Basis des zweiten Tastergliedes vorragend, vorne etwas abgerundet und etwa ein Drittel so breit als die Lippe.

Lippentaster : die Glieder nehmen an Länge und Breite gleichmässig ab, das letzte ist stumpf zugespitzt.

Halsschild länglich, einfach punktiert, scheint die sekundären Geschlechtsmerkmale zu geben, indem es bei den ♂ länger und paralleler ist als bei den ♀.

Schildchen sehr klein, punktförmig.

Flügeldecken an der Basis einfach abgeschnitten, nach der Spitze gewölbt abfallend; die zwei Seitenstreifen sind nach hinten stärker vertieft, während die übrigen auf dem Absturz feiner werden.

Vorderbrust nicht bis zu den Hüften ausgeschnitten, mit kurzem spitzem Fortsatz.

Vorderhüften berühren sich beinahe.

Mittel- und Hinterhüften stehen voneinander ab.

Schienen nach vorne verbreitert, an der Aussenkante gedornt, die Aussenecke gerundet.

Fussglieder : die drei ersten sind einfach rund und einander gleich.

Bauch gerade.

Geographische Verbreitung der Arten. — Dreizehn Arten sind bekannt, davon neun aus dem alten Nordreich, zwei aus dem neuen, zwei aus dem makronesischen Reich. Eine Art (*pusillus* Gyllenhal) kommt sowohl im alten, wie im neuen Nordreich vor.

1. *C. cedri*, Eichhoff, Berl. Ent. Zeitschr. Vol. 11, p. 403 (1867).	Algier.	
2. *C. cinereus*, Herbst. Käfer Europas, Vol. 5, p. 116 (1793).	Europa.	
var. terminatus, Sahlberg, Ins. Fennica, Vol. 2, p. 140 (1839).	Finnland.	
3. *C. cribrellus*, Reitter, Best.-Tab. Borkenkäfer, p. 64 (1894).	Dalmatien, Frankreich,	
4. *C. Gaunersdorferi*, Reitter, Deutsche Ent. Zeitschr. Vol. 29, p. 390 (1885).	Euböa.	[Korsika.
5. *C. hispidulus*, Thomson, Opusc. Ent. Vol. 3, p. 338 (1870).	Schweden.	
6. *C. hystrix*, Abeille. L'Echange, p. 94 (1894).	Algier.	[Hercegowina.
7. *C. numidicus*, Ferrari. Borkenkäf. p. 6 (1867).	Frankreich, Dalmatien,	
8. *C. pusillus*, Gyllenhal, Ins. Suec. Vol. 3, p. 371 (1813).	Europa, Japan. Nordame-	
9. *C. alutaceus*, Schwarz. Ins. Life, Vol. 5, p. 288 (1893).	Nordamerika.	[rika.
10. *C. atomus*, Le Conte. Trans. Amer. Ent. Soc. Vol. 2, p. 152 (1868). — **Taf. 3, Fig. 26.**	Nordamerika.	
11. *C. concolor*, Wollaston, Col. Atlant. p. 244 (1865).	Ferro.	
12. *C. Wollastoni*, Eichhoff, Ratio Tomic. p. 77 (1879).	Tenerifa.	
13. *C. tuberosus*, Niijima, Journ. Coll. Agric. Tohoku Imp. Univ. Sapporo. Vol. 3 (2), p. 139 (1909).	Japan.	

44. GENUS CISURGUS, REITTER

Cysurgus. Reitter, Cat. Col. Eur. p. 710 (1906) 1).
Cisurgus. Reitter, Best.-Tab. Borkenkäfer, p. 65 (1894).

ORIGINALDIAGNOSE : Reitter loc. cit.

« Mit *Crypturgus* nahe verwandt, aber der Kopf ist mehr vorgestreckt, immer zum Teile sichtbar, der Thorax ist von den Flügeldecken mehr abgerückt, die Flügeldecken haben kaum erkennbare Punktreihen, die ganze Oberseite dicht abstehend wollig behaart, die längere Reihenbehaarung schwer erkennbar. Die Gestalt lang gestreckt parallel, oben etwas abgeflacht. »

Charaktere. — Körperform cylindrisch, dünn; Länge etwa 1 mm.; Farbe gelbbraun, matt oder glänzend; Beine und Fühler heller; Skulptur schwach; Behaarung ebenso.

Kopf mit kurzem Rüssel.

Fühler mit zweigliedriger Geissel und grösserer spitz-eiförmiger solider Keule.

Augen vorn ausgerandet.

Mundwerkzeuge vakant.

Halsschild länger als breit oder quadratisch; Basis nicht gerandet; Oberfläche gleichmässig fein punktiert.

---

1) *Cysurgus* ist ein Druckfehler bei Reitter.

Schildchen nicht sichtbar.

Flügeldecken an der Basis abgeschnitten; am Absturz mässig gewölbt; in undeutlichen Reihen punktiert; Behaarung schwach.

Schienen an der Aussenkante stark gezähnelt.

Fussglieder : die drei ersten einfach und einander gleich.

Bauch gerade.

Geographische Verbreitung der Arten. — Es sind drei Arten bekannt, von denen zwei in den Mittelmeerländern, eine in Transkaspien lebt.

1. *C. filum*, Reitter, Verh. Naturw. Ver. Brünn, Vol. 27, p. 36 (1888).   Transkaspien.
2. *C. maurus*, Eggers, Deutsche Ent. Zeitschr. p. 559 (1910).   Tunis.
3. *C. Ragusae*, Reitter, Verh. Naturw. Ver. Brünn, Vol. 45, p. 241 (1906).   Sizilien, Sardinien, Italien.

45. GENUS DOLURGUS, EICHHOFF

Dolurgus. Eichhoff, Berl. Ent. Zeitschr. p. 151 (1868).

Hylastes. Mannerheim, Bull. Soc. Nat. Moscou, Vol. 2. p 297 (1843).

Aphanarthrum. Le Conte, Trans. Amer. Ent. Soc. Vol. 2, p. 152 (1868).

ORIGINALDIAGNOSE : Eichhoff, Ratio Tomic. p. 83 (1879).

« Caput exsertum, rostello brevi auctum. Maxillæ lobo securiformi, intus setulis ciliato. Palpi articulis magnitudine decrescentibus. Oculi oblongi, antice profunde emarginati. Antennæ funiculo triarticulato, huius articulo primo bulbiformi, secundo multo minore, transverso, tertio parvo ; capitulo corneo, parum compresso, glanduliformi, triarticulato, articulo primo sequentibus multo crassiore, secundo transverso, tertio parvo. Prosternum processu brevi. Mesosternum inter coxas tuberculato-protuberans. Prothorax dorso æqualiter punctatus. Tibiæ compressæ, antrorsum dilatatæ, extus denticulatæ, anteriores apice externo rotundatæ. »

Charaktere. — Körperform lang cylindrisch, Länge 2 mm. Farbe pechbraun, mattglänzend, Bekleidung mit dünnen anliegenden Wollhärchen.

Kopf etwas hervorragend, mit kurzem Rüssel, ziemlich lang und dicht behaart.

Fühler von der Länge des Kopfes, mit dreigliedriger Geissel und eichelförmiger, platter dreigliedriger schwach behaarter Keule.

Augen vorne tief ausgerandet.

Vorderkiefer kräftig.

Mittelkiefer mit beilförmiger Innenlade, deren Kaukante mit Borstenzähnen besetzt ist.

Kiefertaster : Glieder an Grösse abnehmend.

Halsschild kurz eiförmig, kaum länger als breit, mässig gewölbt, ziemlich dicht aber schwach punktiert, mit kurzer, schwacher anliegénder Behaarung.

Schildchen punktförmig.

Flügeldecken cylindrisch, mehr als noch einmal so lang als das Halsschild, an der Basis abgeschnitten, am Absturz einfach abgewölbt, ziemlich tief punktiert-gestreift und mit anliegender dünner Behaarung.

Vorderbrust mit kurzem Fortsatz.

Mittelbrust mit grösserem zwischen den Hüften knötchenförmig hervorragendem Fortsatz.

Hüften voneinander entfernt.

Schienen zusammengedrückt, nach vorn verbreitert; Aussenkante gezähnt; Vorderschienen an der Aussenspitze gerundet, an der Innenspitze mit einem Dorn versehen.

Fussglieder dünn, Glied 1, 2, 3 einander gleich und drehrund.

Bauch gerade.

Geographische Verbreitung der Art. — Es ist nur eine Art aus dem Norden Amerikas bekannt.

1. *D. pumilus*, Mannerheim. Bull. Soc. Nat. Moscou, Vol. 2, p. 152 (1868). Alaska und Oregon.
— Taf. 3, Fig. 27.

46. GENUS TRIOTEMNUS, WOLLASTON

Triotemnus. Wollaston, Cat. Canar. Col. p. 264 (1864).

ORIGINALDIAGNOSE : Wollaston, loc. cit.

« Corpus, antennæ et pedes fere ut in *Aphanarthro*, sed funiculo distincte triarticulato, articulis secundo et tertio parvis (nec minutissimis), inter se æqualibus, capitulo solidissimo compresso (nec 4-annulato); elytris apice subretusis (nec omnino integris); colore obscuro (ut in Tomicidis typicis), nec læte variegato. »

Charaktere. — Körperform länglich, beinahe cylindrisch; Farbe pechschwarz; Behaarung spärlich, grau; Skulptur schwach; Länge 1.5 mm.

Kopf vorgestreckt mit kurzem Rüssel; Stirn beim ♀ tief eingedrückt, glatt, beim ♂ gewölbt und dicht punktiert.

Fühler von der Länge des Kopfes mit viergliedriger Geissel und ovaler, mit sehr schwachen Quernähten versehener Keule.

Augen vorne ausgerandet, oblong.

Halsschild kurz eiförmig, breiter als lang, nach vorn verschmälert, gleichmässig punktiert, mit dünnen grauen aufrechten Haaren spärlich besetzt.

Schildchen klein, schwarz, gerundet.

Flügeldecken cylindrisch; Spitze gewölbt, abschüssig, ziemlich tief punktiert und mit längeren grauen aufrechten Haaren besetzt; Absturz beim ♂ etwas eingedrückt, beim ♀ konvex.

Vorderbrust mit spitzen Fortsatz.

Vorderhüften voneinander entfernt.

Schienen nach vorn breitgedrückt, mit gezähnter Aussenkante; die vorderen an der Aussenspitze abgerundet, die hinteren schräg abgeschnitten.

Bauch gerade.

Geographische Verbreitung der Art. — Es ist nur eine Art von der Kanarischen Insel Gomera bekannt.

1. *T. subretusus*, Wollaston, Cat. Canar. Col. p. 265 (1864).   Gomera.

47. GENUS POLYGRAPHUS, ERICHSON

Polygraphus. Erichson, Arch. f. Naturg. Vol. 1, p. 57 (1836).
Dermestes. Linné, Syst. Nat. (ed., 10), Vol. 2, p. 562 (1758).
Eccoptogaster. Gyllenhal, Fauna Suec. Vol. 3, p. 349 (1811).
Hylesinus. Ratzeburg, Forstinsekten, Vol. 1, p. 182 (1837).
Apate (Lepisomus). Kirby, Faun. Bor. Amer. Vol. 4, p. 183 (1837).
Hylesinus. Mannerheim, Bull. Soc. Nat. Moscou, Vol. 26 (2), p. 237 (1853).
Hylurgus. Schaufuss, Tijdschr. v. Ent. Vol. 34, p. 10 (1890).

ORIGINALDIAGNOSE : Erichson, loc. cit.

« Antennæ funiculo 4-articulato, capitulo solido, subovali acuminato. Tibiæ extus denticulatæ. Maxilla mala lata, submembranacea. Palpi maxillares mala paulo longiores, articulis duobus primis brevissimis, sequentibus cylindricis, sensim angustioribus. Labium planum parallelopipedum, apice vix emarginatum. Palpi labiales articulis·duobus primis magnis, crassis, ultimo minore. Antennæ scapo subrecto, vix clavato, funiculi articulo primo subgloboso, secundo obconico, tertio quartoque transversis. Corpus oblongum convexum. Coxæ anticæ approximatæ. Tibiæ compressæ, extus denticulatæ. Tarsi articulo tertio intergo. Elytra margine antico elevato. »

Charaktere. — Körperform walzenförmig, nach vorn verschmälert, hinten gerundet; Länge 2 bis 3 mm.; Farbe hell- bis dunkelbraun, schwach skulptiert, dicht mit anliegenden Schuppen bedeckt.

Kopf mit schwachem Rüssel.

Stirn mehr weniger behaart und gehöckert, beim ♂ das erstere, beim ♀ das letztere.

Fühler bei Erichson, Ratzeburg und Bach mit viergliedriger, bei Eichhoff und den Neueren mit fünfgliedriger Geissel; für die Europäer stimmt diese letzte Zahl; einige Japaner und die Afrikaner haben aber eine sechsgliedrige Geissel. Diese ist sehr kurz, während die Keule erheblich länger als sie und von schiefer lang eiförmig zugespitzter Form. dabei derb und ungeringelt ist.

Augen durch einen Stirnfortsatz in zwei Teile gespalten.

Vorderschiefer derb, zweizähnig.

Mittelkiefer an der Kaukante mit zwölf bis vierzehn wenig gebogenen Stachelzähnen.

Kiefertaster : erstes Glied nach der Basis verschmälert, die anderen an Dicke und Länge gleichmässig abnehmend.

Hinterkiefer sind zu einem länglich viereckigen, mehr wie doppelt so lang als breiten, Kinne verschmolzen, dessen Seiten parallel sind und sich erst dicht vor der Basis in kurzem Bogen einander zuneigen. Die Zunge ist eiförmig zugespitzt und reicht bis zur Basis des ersten Lippentastergliedes.

Lippentasterglieder an Grösse abnehmend.

Halsschild kürzer als breit, nach vorne verschmälert, glänzend oder durch Punktierung und Beschuppung matt.

Flügeldecken an der Basis erhaben gerandet und gekerbt, von walzenförmiger Gestalt. reifartiger Beschuppung und einfach gewölbtem Absturz.

Vorderbrust mit Fortsatz.

Hüften voneinander entfernt, die vorderen bei einigen Arten einander beinahe berührend.

Schienen breit erweitert, mit gerundeter und gesägter Aussenkante.

Bauch gerade.

Geographische Verbreitung der Arten. — Die Gattung ist subkosmopolitisch; die meisten Arten sind aus dem Himalaya beschrieben, nämlich sieben; vier aus Europa, sechs aus Japan, zwei aus Nordamerika, eine aus Madagaskar. Auch am Kongo und in Kamerun ist die Gattung sehr verbreitet : ich habe drei oder vier verschiedene neue Arten von da in Händen, die noch der Beschreibung harren.

1. *P. amoenus*, Schaufuss, Tijdschr. v. Ent. Vol. 34, p. 10 (1890),   Madagaskar.
2. *P. aterrimus*, Strohmeyer, Ent. Wochenblatt (16), p. 69 (1908).   Himalaya.
3. *P. brevicornis*, Kirby, Fauna Bor. Amer. Vol. 4, p. 194 (1837).   Nordamerika.
4. *P. grandiclava*, Thomson, Bull. Soc. Ent. Fr. p. 62 (1886).   Mitteleuropa..
5. *P. himalayensis*, Stebbing, Ind. For. Mem. Vol. 1, p. 10 (1908).   Ostindien (Himalaya).
6. *P. longifolia*, Stebbing, Dep. Not. Ins. For. Vol. 2, p. 255 (1903).   Ostindien (Himalaya).
7. *P. maior*, Stebbing, ibidem, p. 234 (1903).   Ostindien (Himalaya).
8. *P. minimus*, Stebbing, ibidem, p. 252 (1903).   Ostindien (Himalaya).
9. *P. minor*, Stebbing, ibidem, p. 239 (1903).   Ostindien (Himalaya).
10. *P. miser*, Blandford, Trans. Ent. Soc. Lond. p. 76 (1894).   Japan.
11. *P. oblongus*, Blandford, ibidem, p. 75 (1894).   Japan.
12. *P. poligraphus*, Linné, Syst. Nat. (ed. 10). Vol. 2, p. 562 (1758). —   Europa.
    Taf. 3, Fig. 28, 28a.
13. *P. proximus*, Blandford, Trans. Ent. Soc. Lond.· p. 75 (1894). —   Japan.
    Taf. 3, Fig. 28b.
14. *P. punctifrons*, Thomson, Bull. Soc. Ent. Fr. p. 11 (1886).   Schweden.

15. *P. rufipennis*, Kirby, Fauna Bor. Amer. Vol. 4, p. 193 (1837).   Nordamerika.
16. *P. subopacus*, Thomson, Opusc. Ent. Vol. 4, p. 393 (1871).   Mitteleuropa.
    var. minor, Lindemann, Bull. Soc. Nat. Mo.cou, Vol. 49 (1), p. 242 (1875).   Russland.
17. *P. Treuchi*, Stebbing, Ind. Forestr. Mem. Vol. 1, p. 10 (1908).   Ostindien (Himalaya).
18. *P. gracilis*, Niijima, Journ. Coll. Agric. Tohoku Imp. Univ. Sapporo,   Japan.
    Vol. 3 (2), p. 136 (1909).
19. *P. jezoensis*, Niijima, ibidem, p. 135 (1909)   Japan.
20. *P. Ssiori*, Niijima, ibidem, p. 132 (1909).   Japan.

48. GENUS SPONGOTARSUS, HAGEDORN

Spongotarsus. Hagedorn, Deutsche Ent. Zeitschr. p. 372 (1908).

ORIGINALDIAGNOSE : Hagedorn, loc. cit.

« Caput rostello brevi auctum, subexsertum, labium oblongum, versus basin parum angustatum, ligula angusta prope medium inserta. Maxillæ mala lata, basin versus dilatata rotundata, apicem versus angustata, spinulis compressis ciliata, extus pilis longioribus ornata. Palpi maxillares triarticulati, articulo primo et secundo maioribus, tertio minore, palpi labiales articulo primo maximo tumido, sequentibus minoribus, pilis longis ciliatis. Oculi bipartiti, partibus late distantibus, anteriores rotundi, inferiores ovales emarginati. Antennæ funiculo 6-articulato, clava magna solida acuminata, quam funiculo longiore. Prothorax longitudine latior, æqualiter punctatus, pronotum a prosterno sutura elevata seiunctum, prosternum processu brevi, Coxæ antiores et posticæ approximatæ, mediæ late distantes. Tibiæ apicem versus dilatatæ, apice oblique truncata et hamato, extus denticulatæ. Tarsi spongiosi, articulo tertio cylindrico, articulis 1, 2, 3 æqualibus. Elytra basi crenulata. Corpus oblongo-ovatum. »

Charaktere. — Körperform langgestreckt, eiförmig abgerundet, 7 mm. lang, 4 mm. breit, pechschwarz, mit schwacher Skulptur und ebensolcher Behaarung.

Kopf etwas vorgestreckt mit kurzem, breitem Rüssel.

Augen durch einen breiten Fortsatz der Wangen in zwei Teile geteilt, sodass die oberen runden flachen Teile vorne zu beiden Seiten der Stirne stehen, die unteren dreieckig ovalen unterhalb der Vorderkiefer nach der Kehle zu sich erstrecken.

Fühler zwischen der unteren Augenhälfte und dem Ansatz der Vorderkiefer in einer tiefen Grube eingelenkt, mit langem Schaft, kürzerer sechsgliedriger Geissel und grosser solider zugespitzter eiförmiger Keule, die wohl so lang ist als Schaft und Geissel zusammengenommen. Sie ist flach und mit kurzen Haaren dicht besetzt, ohne Nähte.

Vorderkiefer stark, zweizähnig, schwarz.

Mittelkiefer mit einer breiten, an der Basis stark gerundeten, an der Spitze verschmälerten Innenlade, an deren Kaukante sechzehn leicht gebogene breite spitze Dornen stehen. Die Aussenseite des Mittelkiefers ist mit langen Haaren dicht besetzt.

Kiefertaster verhältnismässig klein, aus drei cylindrischen Gliedern bestehend, deren kleinstes das Endglied ist.

Hinterkiefer zu einem länglichen, schmalen, an der Spitze verbreiterten Kinne verschmolzen, an dessen Mitte die ebenfalls schmale, die Spitze des Kinnes nicht überragende, vorne stark behaarte Zunge angesetzt ist.

Lippentaster : Glied 1 am grössten, geschwollen, die beiden folgenden schmäler, cylindrisch, die beiden ersten mit längeren Haaren besetzt.

Halsschild länger als breit, seitlich stark gegen die Vorderbrust abgesetzt, an der Basis nicht gerandet. Oberfläche gleichmässig punktiert und mit kurzen hellen Haaren bedeckt.

Schildchen nicht sichtbar.

Flügeldecken walzenförmig, an der Basis schwach aufgeworfen und gekerbt, hinten gewölbt abfallend; Skulptur und Behaarung wenig stark.

Vorderbrust mit kurzem Fortsatz.

Vorder- und Hinterhüften genähert, die mittleren weit voneinander abstehend.

Schienen verbreitert. Aussenkante gezähnt, die vorderen an der Spitze abgeschnitten und an der Innenecke mit einem Haken versehen.

Fussglieder 1, 2, 3 rund, nicht verbreitert; Sohlen mit schwammartiger Bürste.

Bauch gerade.

Geographische Verbreitung der Art. — Es ist nur eine Art aus Sumatra bekannt.

1. *S. quadrioculatus*, Hagedorn, Deutsche Ent. Zeitschr. p. 372 (1908). — Sumatra. **Taf. 3, Fig. 29.**

49. GENUS PHRIXOSOMA, BLANDFORD

Phrixosoma. Blandford, Biol. Centr. Amer. Col. Vol. 4 (6), p. 148 (1897).

ORIGINALDIAGNOSE : Blandford, loc. cit.

« Caput vix rostratum. Oculi bipartiti. Atennæ lateraliter insertæ, funiculo 6-articulato, articulis 2-6 latitudine crescentibus, clava haud magna, ovali, compressa, pubescente, suturis tribus leviter curvatis instructa. Tibiae versus apicem dilatatæ, margine superiore in lobum serratum explanato; Tarsi breves, articulo tertio angusto, simplici. »

Charaktere. — Körperform länglich, walzenförmig; Länge 2.4 mm.; Farbe pechschwarz, kurz behaart und ziemlich rauh skulptiert.

Kopf mit kurzem Rüssel.

Augen in zwei ziemlich weit voneinander entfernte, kleine Teile gespalten, von denen der obere halbkreisförmig, der untere grössere halb-elliptisch ist; die einander zugekehrten Seiten sind gerade.

Fühler seitlich an der Spitze von tiefen Gruben, welche an der Kehle einander beinahe berühren, eingelenkt, mit einer kurzen sechsgliedrigen Geissel, deren Glieder nach der Keule zu an Breite zunehnen. Die Keule ist ziemlich klein, oval, abgeflacht, behaart, mit drei schwach sichtbaren gekrümmten Nähten.

Mundteile vakant.

Halsschild halb elliptisch, seitlich ungerandet.

Schildchen klein. gerundet, nicht hereingedrückt.

Flügeldecken sind an der Basis aufgeworfen und gekerbt, an der Spitze schräg abgerundet; von walzenförmiger Form mit derber Skulptur und kurzer Behaarung.

Vorderbrust kurz ausgeschnitten, ohne Forstatz.

Vorderhüften einander berührend.

Schienen nach der Spitze breiter werdend, indem der obere Rand in einen gerundeten gesägten Lappen sich ausdehnt.

Fussglieder : die drei ersten sind kurz, einander ziemlich gleich, nicht verbreitert.

Bauch gerade.

Geographische Verbreitung der Art. — Es ist nur eine Art aus Panama bekannt.

1. *P. rude*, Blandford, Biol. Centr. Amer. Col. Vol. 4 (6), p. 148 (1897).   Panama.

5. TRIBUS CRYPHALINÆ

UEBERSICHT DER GATTUNGEN

50. GENUS COSMODERES, EICHHOFF

Cosmoderes. Eichhoff, Ratio Tomic. p. 495 (1879).

ORIGINALDIAGNOSE : Eichhoff, loc. cit.

« Caput globosum in thoracem receptum. Oculi antice emarginati. Antennæ funiculo biarticulato, clava compressa, subsolida, illo multo longiore. Tibiæ compressæ, externe serratæ, apice rotundatæ, tarsis simplicibus. Prothorax haud transversus, antice tuberculate scabratus, postice granulato-punctatus. Scutellum distinctum. »

Charaktere. — Körperform fast cylindrisch, Farbe hellbraun, Skulptur wenig hervorragend, Bekleidung mit hellen Borsten; Länge etwas über 1 mm.

Kopf in das Halsschild zurückgezogen, ohne Rüssel, kugelig.

Augen vorn ausgerandet.

Fühler mit sehr kurzer zweigliedriger Geissel, flacher, viel grösserer, solider, behaarter Keule ohne deutliche Nähte.

Mundteile vacant.

Halsschild etwas länger als breit, an der Basis gerandet, oben vorn mit Knötchen, hinten mit rauhen Punkten besetzt.

Schildchen halbkreisförmig, matt.

Flügeldecken fast cylindrisch, an der Basis einfach und einzeln gerundet; Absturz schräg abgerundet, ohne Auszeichnung; Skulptur derb; Behaarung in je einer Borstenreihe auf den rippenförmigen Zwischenräumen bestehend.

Schienen breit, mit gesägter Aussenkante und gerundeter Spitze.

Fussglieder rund; 1, 2 und 3 einander gleich.

Bauch gerade.

Geographische Verbreitung der Arten. — Es sind zwei Arten bekannt : eine aus Ostindien, die andere aus Japan.

1. *C. consobrinus*, Blandford, Trans. Ent. Soc. Lond. p. 96 (1894).   Japan.
2. *C. monilicollis*, Eichhoff, Ratio Tomic. p. 495 (1879).   Ostindien.

51. Genus TRIARMOCERUS, Eichhoff

Triarmocerus. Eichhoff, Ratio Tomic. p. 119 (1879).

ORIGINALDIAGNOSE : Eichhoff, loc. cit.

« Caput globosum, insertum. Oculi oblongi, antice subemarginati. Antennæ funiculo 3-articulo, articulo 1º bulbiformi, crassiusculo, 2º multo minore, 3º magno, quam 1º maiore, capitulo annulato. Prosternum processu nullo. Prothorax dorso antice plaga tuberculorum scabratus, posterius punctatus. Tibiæ sublineares, apice oblique truncatæ. Tarsi articulis 1, 2, 3 æqualibus. Corpus ovale, subglabrum. Scutellum conspicuum. »

Charaktere. — Körperform länglich eiförmig, 2 bis 2,5 mm. lang, glänzend gelbbraun, wenig behaart, Skulptur schwarz.

Kopf kugelig, ins Halsschild eingezogen.

Augen vorn ausgerandet.

Fühler mit dreigliedriger Geissel und kreisförmiger, flacher, behaarter Keule mit schwachen Quernähten.

Mundteile vacant.

Halsschild quer, halbkreisförmig oder halbelliptisch, am Vorderrand mit vorragenden Knötchen, auf der Scheibe vorn mit einem starken Höckerfleck, hinten rauh punktiert.

Schildchen quer, glatt.

Flügeldecken ziemlich cylindrisch, an der Basis abgestutzt, hinten einfach abgewölbt, mit mässig derber Skulptur und schwacher, spärlicher Behaarung.

Vorderbrust ohne Fortsatz.

Schienen linienförmig, flach, gegen die Spitze verbreitert, diese schräg abgestutzt.

Aussenkante gezähnt.

Fussglieder 1, 2, 3 gleichrund, 3 nicht verbreitert.

Bauch gerade.

Geographische Verbreitung der Arten. — Eichhoff hat zwei Arten beschrieben aus dem madegassischen und indo-malayischen Reich.

1. *T. birmanus*, Eichhoff, Ratio Tomic. p. 486 (1879).   Birma.
2. *T. cryphaloides*, Eichhoff, ibidem, p. 114 (1879).   Madagaskar.

52. Genus ADIÆRETUS, Hagedorn

Adiæretus. Hagedorn, Deutsche Ent. Zeitschr. p. 745 (1909).

ORIGINALDIAGNOSE : Hagedorn, loc. cit.

« Caput globosum, insertum. Labium cordatum, latitudine vix longius, versus basin angustatum, lateribus rotundatis, apice obtuse rotundatum ; ligula parva lanceolata, labio prope basin inserta. Maxillæ lobo brevi securiformi, apice rotundato, intus spinis rigidis ciliato. Palpi omnes articulis magnitudine gradatim decrescentibus, primo et secundo labialibus tumidis. Antennæ funiculo quadriarticulato, articulo 1° globoso cyathiformi, 2° et 3° transversis, 4° longiore quadrato, clava ovali, quadriarticulata, suturis tribus et setis pennatis ornata. Scutellum minutum, trigonum. Prothorax globosus, dorso anterius plaga tuberculorum spiniformium, margine apicali tuberculis duobus confertis ornatus. Coxæ anteriores prosterni processu brevi seiunctæ, posteriores discretæ. Tibiæ compressæ, extus rotundatæ, spinuloso dentatæ. Tarsorum articuli 1, 2, 3 æquales. »

Charaktere. — Körperform länglich, Farbe schwarz, glänzend, wenig behaart, Skulptur mässig schwach, Länge 3 mm.

Kopf kugelig, im Halsschild zurückgezogen.

Augen flach, oval, vorn ausgerandet.

Fühler mit viergliedriger Geissel, deren letztes Glied fast so gross als das erste und fast so lang als breit ist. Die Keule ist gross, oval, mit zwei oder drei gebogenen Nähten und drei oder vier gekrümmten Reihen gefiederter Borsten besetzt.

Vorderkiefer derb, ungezähnt.

Mittelkiefer mit kurzer beilförmiger Innenlade, an deren Kaukante zwanzig bis vierundzwanzig unten breitere und weiter auseinanderstehende, nach vorn schmäler und gebogener werdende, sowie dichter gedrängte Stachelzähne stehen.

Kiefertaster gekniet. die drei walzenförmigen Glieder an Länge beinahe gleich.

Mittelkiefer zu einem herzförmigen, beinahe so breiten als langem Kinne verschmolzen, das nach der Basis etwas verengert, nach der Spitze abgerundet ist; die Zunge ist an der Basis des Kinnes angesetzt und nach der Spitze, die bis zum Grund des zweiten Tastergliedes reicht, breit lanzenförmig.

Lippentaster : Glied 1 und 2 beinahe gleichgross, breiter als lang, geschwollen; Glied 3 klein, dünn, cylindrisch.

Halsschild kugelförmig, auf der Scheibe mit einem Buckel, der eine Anzahl weitauseinanderstehender starker gekrümmter Dornen trägt. Vorderrand trägt zwei nebeneinanderstehende Hörnchen. Es ist nicht gerandet und auf den hintern und seitlichen Teilen schwach punktiert.

Schildchen klein, dreieckig.

Vorderbrust bis zu den Hüften ausgeschnitten, mit kurzem, schmalem Fortsatz.

Vorderhüften dicht beieinander, aber sich nicht berührend, die andern getrennt.

Schienen platt, aussen gerandet und gezähnt.

Fussglieder 1, 2, 3 gleichrund.

Bauch gerade.

Geographische Verbreitung der Art. — Nur eine Art ist aus Südafrika beschrieben.

1. *A. spinosus*, Hagedorn, Deutsche Ent. Zeitschr. p. 745 (1909). — **Taf. 3, Fig. 30.** Südafrika.

53. Genus CRYPTARTHRUM, Blandford

Cryptarthrum. Blandford, Trans. Ent. Soc. Lond. p. 200 (1896).

ORIGINALDIAGNOSE : Blandford, loc. cit.

« *Cryphalo* affine, discedens prothoracis basi et angulis posticis marginatis, dorso haud evidenter asperato; tarsorum articulo 1° minuto, 2° maiore, compresso, 3° parvo.

» Head concealed, not rostrae. Eyes oval, emarginate. Antennæ with very short four-jointed funiculus, the three distal joints transverse, widened apically, club ovate, compressed, the sutures curved on the inner, straight on the outer face, and ciliate. Prothorax short, much narrowed in front and obtusely subacuminate at apex, the hind angles and base finely margined, surface without evident asperities. Elytra not overlapping the prothorax at base. Anterior coxæ contiguous, the prosternal process short. Anterior tibiæ widened from base to apex, and obliquely truncate, the upper margin sinuate, obsoletely toothed; middle and posterior tibiæ with the upper margin rounded, serrate. Tarsi short, the first joint very small, the second rather large, compressed and trigonate, the third small, the apical joint not so long as the preceeding.

» The single species more nearly resembles a *Cryphalus* than the species of any other genus. »

Charaktere. — Mir ist die Gattung unbekannt geblieben.

Geographische Verbreitung der Art. — Eine Art aus dem indo-malayischen Reich.

1. *C. Walkeri*, Blandford, Trans. Ent. Soc. Lond. p. 200 (1896). Damma Inseln.

54. Genus CRYPHALOMORPHUS, Schaufuss

Cryphalomorphus. Schaufuss, Tijdschr. v. Ent. Vol. 34 p. 13 (1891).

ORIGINALDIAGNOSE : Schaufuss, loc. cit.

« Die rundliche und derbe Keule ist es, welche mich veranlasst, das Thier, das sonst, bis auf seinen Thorax, der nicht quer ist, von *Cryphalus* nicht abweicht, generisch zu trennen. »

Charaktere. — Körperform elliptisch, Länge 1.5 mm., Farbe schwarz, Behaarung schwach. Kopf kugelig.

Augen einfach elliptisch.

Fühler mit viergliedriger Geissel und runder, derber Keule ohne Nähte.

Vorderkiefer kräftig.

Mittelkiefer mit kurzer gerundeter, konisch zugespitzter Innenlade, die an der Kaukante mit steifen, am Grunde verbreiterten Stachelborsten besetzt ist.

Kiefertaster : Glied 1 und 2 quer, das erste länger und breiter als das zweite, das dritte länger und schmäler als das erste.

Hinterkiefer zu einem lang-oblongen, nach der Basis verengten Kinne verschmolzen. Zunge mit Borsten besetzt, reicht bis zum zweiten Tasterglied.

Lippentaster : Glied 1 nach aussen angeschwollen, innen gerade; doppelt so lang und breit als das zweite; drittes Glied cylindrisch, halb so breit als das zweite, doch ebenso lang.

Halsschild breiter als lang, Vorderrand gerundet und bewimpert, vorn mit Höckerchen besetzt, hinten rauh punktiert. an den Seiten gerandet.

Schildchen halbeiförmig.

Flügeldecken eiförmig, an der Basis einfach, konvex nach hinten abfallend, tief gestreift-punktiert und gereiht behaart, Nahtstreifen vertieft.

Vorderbrust mit kurzem, spitzem Fortsatz.

Vorderhüften kugelig, ziemlich zusammenstehend, Mittelhüften länglich, voneinander entfernt, Hinterhüften flach, näher als die Mittelhüften zusammenstehend.

Schienen zusammengedrückt. nach Aussen stark verbreitert, Aussenkante gezähnt.

Fussglieder 1, 2, 3 gleichrund. 3 nicht verbreitert.

Bauch gerade.

Geographische Verbreitung der Art. — Eine Art aus Madagaskar.

1. *C. communis*, Schaufuss, Tijdschr. v. Ent. Vol. 34, p. 12 (1891). Madagaskar.

55. Genus CRYPHALUS, Erichson

Cryphalus. Erichson, Arch. f. Naturg. Vol. 1, p. 61 (1836).
Homœocryphalus. Lindemann, Bull. Soc. Nat. Moscou, Vol. 5o, p. 168 (1876).
Subgenera : **Hypothenemus.** Westwood, Trans. Ent. Soc. Lond. Vol. 1, p. 34 (1834).
    Cryphaloides. Formánek, Ent. Blätter, p. 91 (1908).
    Ernoporus. Thomson, Scand. Col. Vol. 7, p. 360 (1865).
    Trypophlœus. Fairmaire, Faune Ent. Fr. p. (1869).
    (Glyptoderus). Eichhoff, Ratio Tomic. p. 137 (1879).
    Stephanoderes. Eichhoff, Berl. Ent. Zeitsehr. Vol. 15, p. 132 (1871).
    (Tænioglyptes). Bedel, Faune Col. Seine, Vol. 6, p. 398 (1888).

ORIGINALDIAGNOSE : Erichson, loc. cit.

« Antennæ funiculo 4-articulato, capitulo 4-annulato. Labium oblongum, basin versus vix angustatum.

» Maxillæ mala submembranacea, setis rigidis ciliata. Palpi maxillares mala breviores, articulis duobus primis occultis, tertio maximo cylindrico, quarto retracto minuto. Labium oblongum, basin versus sensim et levissime angustatum. Palpi labiales articulo primo crassiusculo, secundo hoc minore, tertio secundo paulo longiore et tenuiore. Antennæ scapo elongato, parum clavato, funiculo articulo primo crassiusculo subgloboso, reliquis tribus minutis inter se æqualibus : capitulo ovali compresso. Corpus parvum subcylindricum. Thorax antice valde elevatus, exasperatus. Tarsi articulis tribus primis subæqualibus. »

UEBERSICHT DER UNTERGATTUNGEŃ 1)

1'. *Fühlergeissel dreigliedrig.*
  2'. *Halsschild seitlich nicht gerandet, Keule oval.* . . . . Subg. HYPOTHENEMUS.
  2. *Halsschild seitlich gerandet, Keule kreisrund* . . . . Subg. CRYPHALOIDES.
1. *Geissel viergliedrig.*
  2'. *Keule mit geraden oder wenig gekrümmten Nähten, Vorderrand des Hals-*
    schildes ohne Höcker, Körper kurz walzenförmig . . . . Subg. CRYPHALUS, s. str.
                                              [(*Taenioglyptes*).
  2. *Keule mit stark bogenförmigen Nähten, Vorderrand des Halsschildes mit*
    Höckern, Körper gestreckt walzenförmig . . . . Subg. ERNOPORUS.
1. *Geissel fünfgliedrig, Vorderrand des Halsschildes mit Höckern.*
  2''. *Keule lang eiförmig zugespitzt, Schildchen deutlich, Flügeldecken mit feinen*
    Punktstreifen, Kinn breit, nach vorne verschmälert . . . . . . Subg. TRYPOPHLOCUS.
  2. *Keule rundlich, Schildchen versteckt, Flügeldecken mit starken Punktstreifen,*
    Kinn gegen die Basis verschmälert, Körper gestreckt walzenförmig. . . Subg. STEPHANODERES.

Charaktere. — Körperform walzenförmig bis kurz-eiförmig; Länge 0.5 bis 3 mm.; Farbe von hellbraun bis schwarz, wird durch mehr weniger schuppen- oder borstenartige Behaarung beeinflusst; Skulptur des Halsschildes meist derb, sonst schwach.

Kopf kugelig, ins Halsschild zurückgezogen.

---

1) ANMERKUNG BEI DER CORRECTUR. — Nüsslin begründet in seiner neuesten Arbeit : « Zur Anatomie und Biologie des Borkenkäfergattung *Cryphalus* », in der *Naturw. Zeitschrift für Forst- und Landwirthschaft*, Vol. 8, p. 288-298 (1910) die schon von Lindemann in der « Monographie des Borkenkäfer Russlands » 1877 ausgesprochene Ansicht, dass die Untergattungen *Ernoporus, Trypophloeus, Hypothenemus* und *Stephanoderes* auf Grund ihrer anatomischen Unterschiede den Rang selbständiger Gattungen einnehmen müssen. Ich bedaure sehr, dass ich diese Arbeit, deren Resultat ich vollkommen beipflichte, zu spät kennen gelernt habe, um eine Umarbeitung des Genus *Cryphalus* vornehmen zu können.

Augen ganzrandig oder vorn ausgerandet, quer oval.

Fühler mit drei- bis fünfgliedriger Geissel, runder ovaler stumpfer oder zugespitzter geringelter Keule.

Vorderkiefer kräftig.

Mittelkiefer mit kurzer, breiter, beilförmiger, nach vorne zugespitzter, an der Kaukante mit zehn bis zwölf geraden oder gebogenen Stachelzähnen besetzter Innenlade.

Kiefertaster kegelförmig, mitunter etwas gekniet, Glied 1 und 2 kurz, breiter als lang, Glied 3 am längsten.

Hinterkiefer zu einem schmalen länglichen, gegen die Basis meistens verschmälerten oder breiteren ovalen, nach der Spitze verschmälerten Kinne verschmolzen; Zunge gleichschenklig dreieckig, schmaler als die Lippe, bis zum zweiten Tasterglied vorragend.

Lippentaster kegelförmig, Glieder an Grösse gleichmässig abnehmend.

Halsschild quer. meist breiter als lang, vorn gekörnt, meist mit ziemlich dreieckigem Höckerfleck, am Vorderrande entweder mit einer feinen Körnchenreihe oder mit wenigen (zwei bis sechs) dornförmig vorragenden Zähnchen in der Mitte versehen. An den Seiten nicht gerandet, an der Basis meistens gerandet.

Schildchen punktförmig.

Flügeldecken an der Basis einfach abgestutzt, mit Schuppen- oder Borstenreihen oder beiden besetzt, am Absturz niemals abgeflacht.

Vorderbrust mit kurzem spitzem Fortsatz.

Vorderhüften zusammenstehend.

Mittel- und Hinterhüften voneinander entfernt.

Schienen flach zusammengedrückt, nach vorne verbreitert, aussen abgerundet und gezähnelt.

Fussglieder : die drei ersten einander gleich, keines verbreitert.

Bauch gerade.

Geographische Verbreitung der Arten. — Die Gattung, von der hundert und zwei Arten beschrieben sind, ist durchaus kosmopolitisch.

1. *C. abietis.* Ratzeburg, Forstinsekten, Vol. 1, p. 163 (1837) (Subg. *Cry-* — Europa.
phalus s. str.)

2. *C. albipilis,* Reitter, Wien. Ent. Zeit. Vol. 6, p. 195 (1887) (Subg. *Ste-* — Syrien.
phanoderes)

3. *C. alni.* Lindemann, Bull. Soc. Nat. Moscou, Vol 49 (1), p. 136 (1875) — Russland.
(Subg. *Trypophloeus*).

4. *C. alutaceus,* Schaufuss, Berl. Ent. Zeitschr. Vol. 42, p. 102 (1897) — Deutsch-Ostafrika.
Subg. *Stephanoderes*).

5. *C. areccae,* Hornung, Stett. Ent. Zeit. Vol. 3, p. 115 (1842) (Subg. — Ostindien, Guinea, Neuca-
Stephanoderes). ledonien.

6. *C. arundinis,* Eichhoff, Ratio Tomic. p. 157 (1879) (Subg. *Stephanoderes*). — Oberitalien.

7. *C. asperatus,* Gyllenhal, Ins. Suec. Vol. 3, p. 368 (1813) (Subg. *Trypo-* — Mitteleuropa.
phloeus).

8. *C. aspericollis,* Wollaston, Ann. Mag. Nat. Hist. Vol. 5, p. 365 (1860) — Madeira, Tenerifa, Cap
(Subg. *Stephanoderes*). Verde Inseln.

9. *C. Boswelliae,* Stebbing, Dep. Not. Ins. For. Vol. 2, p. 261 (1903) — Ostindien.
(Subg. *Cryphalus* s. str.).

10. *C. cassiae,* Eichhoff, Ratio Tomic. p. 152 (1879) (Subg. *Stephanoderes*). — Asien.

11. *C. caucasicus,* Lindemann, Bull. Soc. Nat. Moscou, p. 373 1876) (Subg. — Kaukasus.
Ernoporus).

12. *C. ciliatipes,* Blandford, Ann. Soc. Ent. Belg. Vol. 15, p. 242 (1896) — Neucaledonien.
(Subg. *Cryphalus* s. str.).

13. *C. coffeae*, Hagedorn, Ent. Blätter, Vol. 6, p. 1 (1910) (Subg. *Stepha-*   Uganda, Angola, Java.
    noderes). — **Taf. 3, Fig. 31d.**
14. *C. communis*, Schaufuss, Tijdschr. v. Ent. Vol. 34 p. 11 (1891) (Subg.   Madagaskar.
    Stephanoderes).
15. *C. concolor*, Hagedorn, Deutsche Ent. Zeitschr. p. 744 (1909) (Subg.   Kamerun.
    Hypothenemus). — **Taf. 4, Fig. 32.**
16. *C. coriaceus*, Eichhoff, Ratio Tomic. p. 494 (1879) (Subg. *Stephanoderes*).   Siam.
17. *C. costatus*, Eichhoff, ibidem, p. 154 (1879) (Subg. *Stephanoderes*).   Venezuela.
18. *C. cryptomeriae*, Niijima, Verh. Zool. Bot. Ges. Wien, Vol. 58, p. 91   Japan.
    (1908) (Subg. *Cryphalus* s. str.).
19. *C. deodara*, Stebbing, Dep. Not. Ins. For. Vol. 2, p. 274 (1903) (Subg.   Ostindien.
    Cryphalus s. str.).
20. *C. depressus*, Eichhoff, Ratio Tomic. p. 155 (1879) (Subg. *Stephanoderes*).   Antillen.
21. *C. dilutus*, Eichhoff, ibidem, p. 490 (1879) (Subg. *Cryphalus* s. str.).   Birma.
22. *C. discretus*, Eichhoff, ibidem, p. 490 (1879) (Subg. *Cryphalus* s. str.).   Birma.
23. *C. dissimilis*, Zimmermann, Trans. Amer. Ent. Soc. Vol. 2, p. 144   Nordamerika.
    (1868) (Subg. *Stephanoderes*).
24. *C. Donisthorpei*, Formánek, Ent. Blätter, p. 91 (1908) (Subg. *Cryphaloides*).   ?
25. *C. Ehlersi*, Eichhoff, Ratio Tomic. p. 493 (1879) (Subg. *Stephanoderes*).   Südeuropa.
26. *C. elephas*, Eichhoff, ibidem, p. 142 (1879) (Subg. *Stephanoderes*).   Mauritius.
27. *C. erectus*, Le Conte, Proc. Amer. Philos. Soc. Vol. 15, p. 356 (1876)   Nordamerika.
    (Subg. *Stephanoderes*).
28. *C. eruditus*, Westwood, Trans. Ent. Soc. Lond. Vol. 2, p. 34 (1836)   Der ganze Tropengürtel.
    (Subg. *Hypothenemus*).
29. *C. exiguus*, Blandford, Trans. Ent. Soc. Lond. p 82 (1894) (Subg.   Japan.
    Cryphalus s. str.).
30. *C. expers*, Blandford, ibidem, p. 85 (1894) (Subg. *Hypothenemus*).   Japan.
31. *C. fagi*, Fabricius, Syst. Ent. Suppl. p. 157 (1778) (Subg. *Ernoporus*). —   Mitteleuropa.
    Taf. 4, Fig. 33, 33a, 33b.
32. *C. farinosus*, Blandford, Ann. Soc. Ent. Belg. Vol. 40, p. 242 (1886)   Neucaledonien.
    (Subg. *Hypothenemus*).
33. *C. fuliginosus*, Blandford, Ann. Mag. Nat. Hist. Vol. 15, p. 319 (1895)   Ceylon.
    (Subg. *Cryphalus* s. str.).
34. *C. fulvus*, Niijima, Verh. Zool.-bot. Ges. Wien, Vol. 58, p. 92 (1908).   Japan.
    (Subg. *Cryphalus* s. str.).
35. *C. fungicola*, Eggers, Ent. Blätter, Vol. 4. p. 216 (1908) (Subg. *Stepha-*   Java.
    noderes)
36. *C. fuscicollis*, Eichhoff, Ratio Tomic. p. 148 (1879) (Subg. *Stephanoderes*).   Columbia.
37. *C. Germari*, Eichhoff, ibidem, p. 159 (1879) (Subg. *Stephanoderes*).   Mexiko.
38. *C. granulatus*, Ratzeburg, Forstinsekten, Vol. 1. 164 (1837) (Subg.   Mitteleuropa.
    Trypophloeus).
        var. Trédli, Hagedorn, Münch. Col. Zeitschr. Vol. 2, p. 232 (1904).   Ostpreussen.
39. *C. griseus*, Blackburn, Trans. Dublin Soc. Vol. 3, p. 194 (1885) (Subg.   Sandwich Inseln.
    Hypothenemus).
40. *C. Grothii*, Hagedorn, Münch. Col. Zeitschr. Vol. 2, p. 232 (1904)   Deutschland.
    (Subg. *Trypophloeus*). — **Taf. 3, Fig. 31a, 31b; Taf. 12, Fig. 8.**
41. *C. Hampei*, Ferrari. Borkenkäfer, p. 11 (1867) (Subg *Stephanoderes*).   Frankreich, Siebenbürgen.
42. *C. hispidulus*, Le Conte. Trans. Amer. Ent. Soc. Vol. 2, p. 156 (1858)   Nordamerika.
    (Subg. *Stephanoderes*).
43. *C. horridus*, Eichhoff, Ratio Tomic. p. 488 (1879) (Subg. *Cryphalus* s. str.).   Ostindien.
44. *C. horridus*, Graham, Journ. Econ. Biol. Vol. 3, p. 113 (1908) (Subg.   Westafrika.
    Cryphalus s. str.?).
45. *C. jalappae*, Letzner, Abh. Schles. Jahrb. p. 99 (1844) (Subg. *Ernoporus*).   Mexiko.
46. *C. javanus*, Eggers, Ent. Blätter. Vol. 5, p. 215 (1909) (Subg. *Stepha-*   Java.
    noderes). — **Taf. 3, Fig. 31.**

47. *C. indicus*, Eichhoff, Ratio Tomic. p. 489 (1879) (Subg. *Cryphalus* s. str.). Birma.
48. *C. indicus*, Stebbing, Dep. Nat. Ins. For. Vol. 3, p. 403 (1906) (Subg. Himalaya.
   Cryphalus s. str).
49. *C. inops*, Eichhoff, Berl. Ent. Zeitschr. Vol. 15, p. 131 (1871) (Subg. Guadeloupe.
   Cryphalus s. str.).
50. *C. insularis*, Perkins, Fauna Hawaii. Vol. 2, p. 181 (1900-1903) (Subg. Sandwich Inseln.
   Hypothenemus).
51. *C. intermedius*, Ferrari, Borkenkäfer, p. 79 (1867) (Subg. *Cryphalus* s. str.). Mitteleuropa.
52. *C. Künnemanni*, Reitter, Wien. Ent. Zeitschr. Vol. 21, p. 140 (1907) ?
   (1897) (Subg. *Stephanoderes*).
53. *C. laevigatus*, Blandford, Biol. Centr. Amer. Col. Vol. 4 (6), p. 229 Centralamerika.
   (Subg. *Stephanoderes*).
54. *C. longifolia*, Stebbing, Dep. Not. Ins. For. Vol. 2, p. 267 (1906) Himalaya.
   (Subg. *Cryphalus* s. str.).
55. *C. maior*, Stebbing, ibidem, p. 270 (1906) (Subg. *Cryphalus* s. str.). Himalaya.
56. *C. maculicollis*, Sharp, Trans. Ent. Soc. Lond. p. 101 (1879) (Subg. Sandwich Inseln.
   Hypothenemus).
57. *C. miles*, Le Conte, Proc. Amer. Philos. Soc. Vol. 17, p. 433 (1878) Nordamerika.
   (Subg. *Cryphalus*, s. str.).
58. *C. morinda*, Stebbing, Dep. Not. Ins. For. Vol. 2, p. 265 (1906) (Subg. Ostindien.
   Cryphalus s. str.).
59. *C. moschatae*, Schaufuss, Insektenbörse, p. 8 (1905) (Subg. *Stephanoderes*). Guadeloupe.
60. *C. mucronatus*, Le Conte, Bull. U. S. Geol. Survey, p. 518 (1879) Colorado.
   (Subg. *Cryphalus* s. str.).
61. *C. mucronifer*, Wollaston, Col. Hesper. p. 116 (1867) (Subg. *Cry-* Cap Verde Inseln.
   phalus s. str.)
62. *C. myrmedon*, Eichhoff, Ratio Tomic. p. 160 (1879) (Subg. *Stephanoderes*). Columbia.
63. *C. nanus*, Hagedorn, Deutsche Ent. Zeitschr. p. 744 (1909) (Subg. Argentinien.
   Hypothenemus).
64. *C. numidicus*, Eichhoff, Ratio Tomic. p. 487 (1879) (Subg. *Cry-* Südeuropa.
   phalus s. str.).
65. *C. obscurus*, Ferrari, Borkenkäfer, p. 17 (1867) (Subg. *Cryphalus*, s. str.). Kuba.
66. *C. opacus*, Eichhoff, Berl. Ent. Zeitschr. Vol. 15, p. 132 (1871) (Subg. Südamerika.
   Stephanoderes).
67. *C. paganus*, Eichhoff, Ratio Tomic. p. 129 (1879) (Subg. *Cryphalus* s. str.). Fürsteninsel, Afrika.
68. *C. pallidus*, Eichhoff, Berl. Ent. Zeitschr. Vol. 15, p. 131 (1871) (Subg. Madagascar.
   Cryphalus s. str.).
69. *C. peritus*, Blandford, Trans. Ent. Soc. Lond. p. 84 (1894) (Subg. Japan.
   Stephanoderes).
70. *C. piceae*, Ratzeburg, Forstinsekten, Vol. 1, p. 163 (1837) (Subg. *Cry-* Mitteleuropa, Nordamerika.
   phalus s. str.).
71. *C. pilosellus*, Erichson, Arch. f. Naturg. Vol. 8 (1), p. 212 (1842) (Subg. Van Diemensland.
   Cryphalus s. str.).
72. *C. plumeriae*, Nördlinger, Nachträge zu Ratzeb. Forstinsekt. p. 744 Venezuela.
   (1856) (Subg. *Stephanoderes*).
73. *C. pulverulentus*, Eichhoff, Berl. Ent. Zeitschr. Vol. 15, p. 133 (1871) Mexiko.
   (Subg. *Stephanoderes*).
74. *C. rigidus*, Le Conte. Proc. Amer. Philos. Soc. Vol. 15, p. 362 (1876) Canada.
   (Subg. *Cryphalus* s. str.)
75. *C. robustus*, Eichhoff, Berl. Ent. Zeitschr. Vol. 15, p. 131 (1871) (Subg. Nordamerika.
   Cryphalus, s. str.).
76. *C. rotundicollis*, Eichhoff, Ratio Tomic. p. 145 (1876) (Subg. *Stephanoderes*). Nordamerika.
77. *C. ruficeps*, Perkins, Fauna Hawaii, Vol. 2, p 181 (1900-1903) (Subg. Sandwich Inseln.
   Hypothenemus).
78. *C. Rybinskii*, Reitter, Best.-Tab. Borkenkäfer, p. 72 (1894) (Subg. *Trypo-* Mähren, Galizien.
   phloeus).

79. *C. salluarius*, Weise, Cat. Col. Eur. Caucas. p. 336 (1891) (Subg. *Cry-*   Deutschland, Kaukasus.
    phalus s. str.).
80. *C. scabricollis*, Eichhoff, Ratio Tomic. p. 491 (1879) (Subg. *Cry-*   Ostindien.
    phalus s. str.).
81. *C. Schreineri*, Eichhoff, Eur. Borkenkäfer, p. 185 (1881) (Subg. *Ernoporus*).   Mitteleuropa.
82. *C. seriatus*, Eichhoff, Berl. Ent. Zeitschr. Vol. 15, p. 133 (1871) (Subg.   Nordamerika.
    Stephanoderes).
83. *C. setosus*, Eichhoff, ibidem. Vol. 11, p. 391 (1867) (Subg. *Stephanoderes*).   Guadeloupe.
84. *C. sidneyanus*, Nördlinger, Nachträge zu Ratzeb. Forstins. p. 73 (1856)   Australien.
    (Subg. *Cryphalus* s. str.). — **Taf. 3, Fig. 31e.**
85. *C. Simonis*, Reitter, Wien. Ent. Zeit. Vol. 6, p. 194 (1887) (Subg. *Hypo-*   Syrien.
    thenemus).
86. *C. striatus*, Le Conte, Trans. Amer. Ent. Soc. Vol. 2, p. 156 (1868)   Nordamerika.
    (Subg. *Hypothenemus*).
87. *C. striatulus*, Mannerheim, Bull. Soc. Nat. Moscou, p. 325 (1853) (Subg.   Nordamerika.
    Cryphalus s. str.).
88. *C. submuricatus*, Eichhoff, Ratio Tomic. p. 492 (1879) (Subg. *Cry-*   Ostindien.
    phalus s. str.)
89. *C. sylvicola*, Perkins, Fauna Hawaii. Vol. 2, p. 181 (1900) (Subg. *Hypo-*   Sandwich Inseln.
    thenemus).
90. *C. terminalis*, Mannerheim, Bull. Soc. Nat. Moscou, Vol. 2, p. 298   Nordamerika.
    (1843) (Subg. *Cryphalus* s. str.).
91. *C. tectonae*, Stebbing. Dep. Not. Ind. For. Vol. 2, p. 263 (1903) (Subg.   Ostindien.
    Cryphalus s. str.).
92. *C. tiliae*, Panzer, Fauna Germ. Vol. 8, p. 14 (1793) (Subg. *Cry-*   Europa.
    phalus s. str.).
93. *C. tristis*, Eichhoff, Ann. Soc. Ent. Belg. Vol. 19, p. 200 (1875) (Subg.   Japan.
    Stephanoderes).
94. *C. vafer*, Blandford, ibidem, Vol. 40, p. 242 (1896) (Subg. *Hypothenemus*).   Neucaledonien.
95. *C. validus*, Blandford, Biol. Centr. Amer. Col. Vol. 4 (6), p. 228   Mexiko.
    (1904) (Subg. *Hypothenemus*).
96. *C. vestitus*, Blandford, Ann. Mag. Nat. Hist. Vol. 15, p. 318 (1895)   Ceylon.
    (Subg. *Cryphalus* s. str.).
97. *C. vulgaris*, Schaufuss. Tijdschr. v. Ent. Vol. 40, p. 209 (1897) (Subg.   Seychellen.
    Stephanoderes).
98. *C. Wapleri*, Eichhoff, Berl. Ent. Zeitschr. Vol. 15, p. 131 (1871) (Subg.   Australien.
    Cryphalus s. str.).
99. *C. Winkleri*, Reitter, Wien. Ent. Zeit. Vol. 26, p. 192 (1907) (Subg.   Kamerun.
    Stephanoderes).
100. *C. laricis*, Niijima, Journ. Coll. Agric. Tohoku Imp. Univ. Sapporo,   Japan.
    Vol. 3 (2), p. 142 (1909) (Subg. *Cryphalus* s. str.).
101. *C. malus*, Niijima, ibidem, p. 142 (1909) (Subg. *Cryphalus* s. str.).   Japan.
102. *C. Rhusii*, Niijima, ibidem, p. 142 (1909) (Subg. *Cryphalus* s. str.).   Japan.

6. TRIBUS IPINÆ

UEBERSICHT DER GATTUNGEN

1. *Fühlergeissel viergliedrig.*
    2. *Fühlerkeule solide; Vorderhüften getrennt* . . . . . 56. Genus EIDOPHELUS, Eichhoff.
    2'. *Fühlerkeule mit sieben Nähten.*
        3. *Halsschild vorn gekörnt, hinten punktiert, Basis*
            gerandet . . . . 57. Genus LEPICERUS, Eichhoff.

56. GENUS EIDOPHELUS, EICHHOFF

Eidophelus. Eichhoff, Ann. Soc. Ent. Belg. Vol. 18, p. 200 (1875).

ORIGINALDIAGNOSE : Eichhoff, Ratio Tomic. p. 203 (1879).

« Caput subglobosum, insertum. Maxillæ mala lata, antrorsum sensim angustata, obtuse acuminata, setis rigidis ciliata. Antennæ funiculo 4-articulato, articulo huius 1° magno, bulbiformi, 2° obconico, parvo, 3° et 4° transversis, latitudine crescentibus; capitulo corneo, solido, subcompresso, orbiculari, suturis obsoletissimis, utraque pagina æquali. Tibiæ sublineares, extus spinulosæ. Tarsi articulis 1, 2, 3 æqualibus. Prosternum processu brevi. Prothorax haud transversus, basi leviter marginatus. »

Charaktere. -- Körperform walzenförmig, Farbe braun bis schwarz, glänzend, Behaarung schwach, Skulptur kräftig, Länge 1 bis 1.5 mm.

Kopf kugelig, ins Halsschild zurückgezogen.

Augen länglich, quergestellt, vorn ausgebuchtet.

Fühler mit viergliediger Geissel, runder, solider, mit kaum sichtbaren Nähten versehener Keule; kaum so lang als der Kopf.

Vorderkiefer mässig derb.

Mittelkiefer mit breiter, nach vorn allmählich verschmälerter Innenlade, deren Kaukante mit starren Borstenzähnen besetzt ist.

Halsschild halbelliptisch, nach vorn nicht eingeschnürt, nicht gerandet, vorn mit Knötchen, die bei einer Art in koncentrischen Linien stehen, besetzt, hinten mehr weniger punktiert.

Schildchen dreieckig oder gerundet, glatt, glänzend.

Flügeldecken cylindrisch, an der Basis abgestutzt, hinten einfach abgewölbt oder schräg abgestutzt, Nahtwinkel bei einer Art etwas vorgezogen; Oberfläche schwach skulptiert, Absturz mit kleinen Knötchen besetzt.

Vorderbrust mit kurzem Fortsatz.

Schienen linear, Aussenkante gedornt.

Fussglieder 1, 2, 3 einander ziemlich gleich, 3 einfach.

Bauch gerade.

Geographische Verbreitung der Arten. — Es sind zwei Arten aus Japan beschrieben.

1. *E. imitans*, Eichhoff, Ann. Soc. Ent. Belg. Vol. 18, p. 200 (1875).   Japan.
2. *E. minutus*, Blandford, Trans. Ent. Soc. Lond. p. 88 (1894).   Japan.

57. Genus LEPICERUS, Eichhoff

Lepicerus. Eichhoff, Ratio Tomic. p. 501 (1879).

ORIGINALDIAGNOSE : Eichhoff, loc. cit.

« Caput globosum, insertum, oculis oblongis integris. Antennæ funiculo perbrevi 4-articulato, articulis 2-4 transversis; clava magna imbricata. Prothorax haud transversus, basi marginatus. Prosternum processu nullo. Tibiæ apice compressæ, extus rotundatæ, serratæ; tarsis receptis simplicibus. »

Charaktere. — Körperform walzenförmig, Länge 1.5 mm.; Farbe hellbraun bis schwarz mit gelbroten Flügeldecken. Skulptur kräftig, Behaarung spärlich.

Kopf kugelig, ins Halsschild versenkt.

Stirn konvex, bei den ♂ gekielt, bei den ♀ behaart.

Augen quer oval, nicht ausgerandet.

Fühler kurz, mit viergliedriger Geissel und grosser runder, flacher Keule, die zwei wenig deutliche konvexe Nähte trägt.

Vorderkiefer derb, mit einem Zahn.

Mittelkiefer breit gerundet auf beiden Seiten, Ladenspitze die Taster überragend, Kaukante mit derben breiten Zähnen.

Kiefertaster : Glied 1 so lang als breit, geschwollen; Glied 2 flach, Glied 3 so lang als 1, aber schmäler, cylindrisch.

Hinterkiefer zu einem lang-viereckigen, an der Spitze und den Seiten geradlinien Kinne verschmolzen; Zunge klein und schmal, an der Basis des Kinnes eingelenkt.

Lippentaster : Glied 1 gross, geschwollen, 2 kleiner, 3 klein kegelförmig.

Halsschild wenig länger als breit, seitlich und vorn abgerundet, Basis fein gerandet; auf dem gewölbten Rücken vorn mit Körnern besetzt oder grob punktiert, hinten grob punktiert.

Schildchen klein, dreieckig.

Flügeldecken walzenförmig. Absturz konvex gerundet, Skulptur ziemlich derb.

Vorderbrust ohne Fortsatz.

Vorderhüften zusammenstehend,-Mittel- und Hinterhüften getrennt.

Schienen aussen gerundet und gesägt.

Fussglieder einfach.

Bauch gerade.

Geographische Verbreitung der Arten. — Es sind zwei Arten aus dem indo-malayischen Reich beschrieben.

1. *L. aspericollis*, Eichhoff, Ratio Tomic. p. 5o1 (1879). — **Taf. 4, Fig. 34.**   Birma und Himalaya.
2. *L. nitidus*, Hagedorn, Deutsche Ent. Zeitschr. p. 1 (1910).   Sumatra.

58. GENUS DENDROTERUS, BLANDFORD

Dendroterus. Blandford, Biol. Centr. Amer. Col. Vol. 4 (6), p. 233 (1904).

ORIGINALDIAGNOSE : Blandford, loc. cit.

« Funiculus antennarum perbrevis, 4-articulatus, articulis 2-4 transversis; clava sat magna, breviter ovalis, compressa, 3-articulata, suturis transversis piliferis; tibiæ angustæ, supra dentibus 2 armatæ, ad apicem oblique truncatæ; tarsi breves, articulis 1-3 æqualibus. »

Charaktere. — Körperform walzenförmig.

Kopf herabgebeugt, ohne Rüssel. Stirn mehr (♀) oder weniger (♂) behaart.

Augen ausgerandet oval.

Fühler kurz, mit viergliedriger Geissel und kurz-eiförmiger, abgeplatteter, glänzender, mit zwei geraden beborsteten Nähten besetzter Keule.

Halsschild länger als breit, ohne Basalrand.

Flügeldecken walzenförmig, länger als das Halsschild. Absturz mehr weniger gerundet. Skulptur und Behaarung mässig.

Vorderbrust nicht bis zu den Vorderhüften reichend.

Vorderhüften einander berührend.

Hinterbrust linear.

Schienen schmal, nach der Spitze etwas breiter, Aussenrand mit zwei kleinen Zähnen; Spitze abgestützt, am Innenwinkel kurz gedornt.

Fussglieder kurz, einfach.

Bauch gerade.

Geographische Verbreitung der Arten. — Blandford hat zwei Arten aus Mexiko beschrieben.

1. *D. mexicanus*, Blandford, Biol. Centr. Amer. Col. Vol. 4 (6), p. 233 (1904).   Mexiko.
2. *D. Salléi*, Blandford, ibidem, p. 233 (1904).   Mexiko.

59. GENUS MESOSCOLYTUS, BROUN

Mesoscolytus. Broun, Ann. Mag. Nat. Hist. Vol. 15, p. 125 (1909).

Apate. Broun, cf. Hutton, Index Faun. Novæ Zealand. p. 219 (1904).

ORIGINALDIAGNOSE : Broun, loc. cit.

« Body narrow, cylindrical. Head deeply immersed in the excavate pronotum. Antennæ implanted close to the eyes, basal joint curvate, elongate, twice the length of all the others combined; second joint stout, triangular; remaining joints gradually expanded, extremely short, and so closely articulated as to be almost indistinguishable. Club large, flattened, and compact, broadly oval, not visibly articulated above. Eyes depressed, distinctly facetted, strongly transverse, widely distant. Thorax large, without lateral margins. Scutellum small. Legs slender, femora laterally compressed; tibiæ slender at base, expanded beyond, minutely denticulate externally, the two front pairs obliquely truncate at the extremity, the posterior obliquely rounded. Tarsi filiform and slender, not as long as the tibiæ, the basal three joints elongate and nearly equal, third not lobate, and interposed between it and the elongate terminal joint, there is a minute but distinct fourth joint.

» Front coxæ large, prominent, almost contiguous, the intermediate and posterior just perceptibly separated. Abdomen rather long than the metasternum, its segments with straight sutures, that between the basal two very fine, the others deep. The segments are horizontal and on the same plane, the first is distinctly longer than the second, the third and fourth are nearly equal to one another, but shorter than the proceeding one.

» In *Scolytus* the general form may be termed stumpy, the anterior tibiæ terminate in prominent curvate hooks externally, the elytra are quite truncate at the apex, and the abdomen is retracted and suddenly bent upwards, so that the metasternum is abruptly prominent.

» In the genus here described the tibiæ are unarmed at the outer extremity, the ventral segments are horizontal and are contiguous with the epipleuræ throughout. *Tomicus* more nearly resembles this genus in contour, but the eyes are emarginate and the posterior portions of the elytra are either truncate or excavate and spinose.

» Long. 4 5 mm., Latitud. 1.5 mm. »

Charaktere. — Die Gattung ist mir unbekannt geblieben.

Geographische Verbreitung der Art. — Es ist eine Art aus Neuseeland beschrieben.

1. *M. inurbanus*, Broun, Ann. Mag. Nat. Hist. Vol. 14, p. 125 (1909).   Neuseeland.

60. Genus THAMNURGUS, Eichhoff

Thamnurgus. Eichhoff, Berl. Ent. Zeitschr. Vol. 8, p. 40 (1864).
Bostrichus. Bach, Stett. Ent. Zeit. Vol. 9, p. 199 (1849).

ORIGINALDIAGNOSE : Eichhoff, loc. cit.

» Tarsorum articulis tribus primis subæqualibus, simplicibus. Antennarum funiculo quinquearticulato, clava parva, orbiculata, subannulata. Ligula parte fulcrali multo angustior, haec cordata, basin versus attenuata. Palpi labiales articulo secondo màiore, primo et tertio minoribus. Maxillarum mala intus spinulis rigidis ciliata. »

Charaktere. — Körperform walzenförmig, Länge 1.5 bis 3.5 mm ; Farbe braun bis schwarz, Beine hellgelb bis braungelb; Skulptur nur in Punktierung bestehend; Behaarung ziemlich lang, greis.

Kopf kugelig, im Halsschild versteckt, die Stirn häufig eingedrückt oder gekielt.

Augen länglich, vorne ausgerandet, querstehend.

Fühler lang gestreckt, mit fadenförmiger fünfgliedriger Geissel, deren Glieder länger als breit sind, und auffallend kleiner, ovaler, mit wenig deutlichen Nähten versehener Keule.

Vorderkiefer schwach.

Mittelkiefer mit beilförmiger, an der Kaukante mit etwa zwölf gleichmässig verteilten, lang zugespitzten, geraden Stachelborsten gewimperter Innenlade.

Kiefertasterglieder an Grösse abnehmend.

Hinterkiefer sind zu einem länglich herzförmigèn, nach der Basis stark verschmälerten, gerad-seitigen Kinne verschmolzen; Zunge klein, oval, etwa ein Viertel so breit als das Kinn unterhalb der Tasterbasis, daselbst auch eingelenkt.

Lippentaster : Glied 2 am längsten, doch schmäler als 1, das dritte sehr klein.

Halsschild länger als breit, nirgend gerandet, nach der Spitze verschmälert, auf der Scheibe meist einfach punktiert.

Schildchen kaum sichtbar.

Flügeldecken walzenförmig mit undeutlich gereihten Punkten und flachem, nicht ausge-zeichnetem Absturz; mit ziemlich langer, greiser Behaarung.

Vorderbrust nicht bis zu den Vorderhüften ausgeschnitten, nach hinten mit deutlichem, spitzem, aufgebogenem Fortsatz.

Vorderhüften nahe beinanderstehend, doch nicht einander berührend.

Mittel- und Hinterhüften getrennt.

Schienen gerade, gegen die Spitze verbreitert und daselbst schräg abgeschnitten, Aussenkante bedornt.

Fussglieder einánder gleich, rund.

Bauch gerade.

Geographische Verbreitung der Arten. — Es sind fünfzehn Arten beschrieben, welche in Mitteleuropa, besonders in den Mittelmeerländern, in krautartigen Pflanzen wie *Labiaten, Delphinium, Aconitum* und *Euphorbia* leben.

1. *T. armeniacus*, Reitter, Deutsche Ent. Zeitschr. p. 244 (1897).	Transkaukasien.
2. *T. Brylinskii*, Reitter, ibidem, p. 40 (1887).	Transkaukasien.
3. *T. caucasicus*, Reitter, Wien. Ent. Zeit. Vol. 5, p. 195 (1887).	Kaukasus.
4. *T. characiae*, Rosenhauer, in Eichhoff, Ratio Tomic. p. 513 (1879).	Südeuropa.
5. *T. delphinii*, Rosenhauer, Tiere Andalusiens, p. 302 (1856). — **Taf. 4, Fig. 35.**	Algier, Andalusien.
6. *T. euphorbiae*, Küster, Käfer Europas, Vol. 2, p. 39 (1845).	Südeuropa.
7. *T. Holtzi*, Strohmeyer, Wien. Ent. Zeit. Vol. 26, p. 6 (1907).	Griechenland.
8. *T. Kaltenbachi*, Bach, Stett. Ent. Zeit. Vol. 9, p. 199 (1849).	Mitteleuropa.
9. *T. nitidicollis*, Reitter, Wien. Ent. Zeit. Vol. 6, p. 197 (1887).	Marocco.
10. *T. Normandi*, Eggers, Ent. Blätter. Vol. 6, p. 37 (1910).	Algerien.
11. *T. Petzi*, Reitter, Wien. Ent. Zeit. Vol. 20, p. 183 (1901).	Oesterreich.
12. *T. robustus*, Eggers, Il Natural. Sicil. Vol. 20, n°s 6-8 (1908).	Sicilien.
13. *T. scrutator*, Pandellé, Revue Ent. Caen, Vol. 2, p. 136 (1883).	Frankreich.
14. *T. semirufus*, Reitter, Wien. Ent. Zeit. Vol. 25, p. 36 (1906).	Kleinasien.
15. *T. varipes*, Eichhoff, Stett. Ent. Zeit. p. 370 (1878).	Mitteleuropa.

61. GENUS COCCOTRYPES, EICHHOFF

Coccotrypes. Eichhoff, Ratio Tomic. p. 308 (1879).
Bostrichus. Fabricius, Syst. Eleuth. Vol. 2, p. 387 (1801).
Dryocœtes. Eichhoff, Berl. Ent. Zeitschr. p. 38 (1864).
Anisandrus. Ferrari, Borkenkäfer, p. 24 (1867).

ORIGINALDIAGNOSE : Eichhoff, Ratio Tomic. p. 308 (1879).

« Caput globosum receptum. Mentum cordatum, lateribus rotundatis, apice leviter rotundatum, ligula angusta, ovalis, acte medium menti inserta. Submentum subquadratum, antrorsum angustatum, antice profunde emarginatum. Palpi labiales articulo primo magno, subtumido, secundo multo minore, transverso, tertio parvo. Maxillæ malá antrorsum angustata, obtuse rotundata, intus setis rigidis, falcatis, apice densissimis fasciculatis, ciliata. Oculi simplices. Antennæ funiculo 5-articulato, articulo primo globoso, apice truncato, magno, secundo multo minore, obconico, cæteris transversis, latitudine crescentibus; capitulo tunicato, in parte externo basi corneo, apice oblique truncato, spongioso. Prosternum processu nullo. Prothorax latitudine haud longior,' dorso toto subæqualiter scabratus, basi obsolete marginatus. Tibiæ subrectæ, versus apicem dilatatæ, apice oblique truncato. Corpus subovale, thorace æqualiter scabrato. »

Charaktere. — Körperform lang eiförmig, 1 bis 2 mm. Länge; Farbe braun, ziemlich reichlich behaart; die ♂ sind kleiner, mit kugelig-eiförmig flachgewölbten Flügeldecken.

Kopf kugelig im Halsschild versteckt.

Stirn mit mehr oder minder langen Haaren besetzt.

Augen oblong. vorn wenig eingebuchtet.

Fühler mit fünfgliedriger Geissel und rundlicher, hinten verhüllter Keule, die eine schwammige Konsistenz hat, mit wenig deutlichen Nähten und abgeschrägter Spitze.

Vorderkiefer sehr kräftig, gezähnt.

Mittelkiefer mit gerundeter, nach vorn verschmälerter Innenlade, an deren Kaukante gebogene spitze Stachelzähne. die nach oben dichter zusammenstehen, sich befinden.

Kiefertaster : Glied 1 breit und niedrig, Glied 2 kurz cylindrisch, Glied 3 so lang wie die anderen zusammengenommen, schmäler, cylindrisch, ohne Längsstreifen.

Hinterkiefer bilden ein herzförmiges, an den Seiten gerundetes, an der Spitze gestutztes Kinn, an dessen Vorderrand die kleine ovale Zunge entspringt.

Halsschild so lang als breit, auf der Scheibe ziemlich gleichmässig rauh punktiert, ungerandet.

Schildchen klein. rundlich.

Flügeldecken beim ♀ fast von der Mitte an nach hinten abgewölbt, beim ♂ flacher, kugelig eiförmig; schwach punktiert und ziemlich reichlich behaart,

Vorderbrust ohne Fortsatz.

Vorderhüften einander berührend.

Mittel- und Hinterhüften abstehend.

Schienen gerade, nach der Spitze verbreitert, diese schräg abgestutzt; Aussenkante gezähnt.

Fussglieder 1, 2, 3 gleich rund.

Bauch gerade.

Geographische Verbreitung der Arten. — Die Gattung ist subkosmopolitisch : nur aus Australien ist keine Art bekannt geworden. Die Arten leben alle, soviel bekannt, in harten Fruchtsamen, sind aber wohl nicht Pilzzüchter.

1. *C. advena,* Blandford, Trans. Ent. Soc. Lond. p. 100 (1894).   Japan.
2. *C. cardamomi,* Schaufuss, Insektenbörse, p. 8 (1905).   Ceylon.
3. *C. dactyliperda,* Fabricius, Syst. Eleuth. Vol. 2, p. 387 (1801).   Europa, Afrika, Amerika.
   . *var. obscurus,* Rey, L'Echange, p. 30 (1892).
4. *C. Eggersii,* Hagedorn, Allg. Zeitschr. f. Ent. Vol. 9, p. 449 (1904). —   Südamerika.
   Taf. 13, Fig. 9.
5. *C. graniceps,* Eichhoff, Ratio Tomic. p. 314 (1879).   Japan.
6. *C. Hagedorni,* Eggers, Ent. Blätter, Vol. 4, p. 217 (1908). — **Taf. 4,**   Java.
   Fig. 36.
7. *C. integer,* Eichhoff, Ratio Tomic. p. 311 (1879).   Siam.
8. *C. perditor,* Blandford, Trans. Ent. Soc. Lond. p. 99 (1894).   Japan.
9. *C. pygmaeus,* Eichhoff, Ratio Tomic. p. 310 (1879).   Manila, Madagaskar, Kame-
    'run, St.-Domingo, Guya-
10. *C. robustus,* Eichhoff. ibidem, p. 313 (1879).   Cuba.   [na.
11. *C. tropicus,* Eichhoff, ibidem, p. 312 (1879).   Peru.

62. Genus DRYOCŒTES, Eichhoff

Dryocœtes. Eichhoff, Berl. Ent. Zeitschr. Vol. 8, p. 38 (1864).
Bostrichus. Herbst, Käfer Europas, Vol. 5, p. 121 (1793).
Hylesinus. Fabricius, Syst. Ent. Vol. 1 (2), p. 367 (1792).
Xylocleptes. Ferrari, Borkenkäfer, p. 41 (1867).
Tomicus. Perris, Bull. Soc. Ent. Fr. p. 78 (1855).
Taphrorychus. Eichhoff, Ratio Tomic. p. 209 (1879).
Lymantor. Lovendal, Ent. Medd. Vol. 2, p. 69 (1889).
Xyleborus. Le Conte, Trans. Amer. Ent. Soc. Vol. 2, p. 161 (1868).

ORIGINALDIAGNOSE : Eichhoff, Berl. Ent. Zeitschr. Vol. 8, p. 38 (1864).

« Tarsorum articulis tribus primis subæqualibus, simplicibus. Antennarum funiculo 5-articulato, clava subglobosa subannulata. Ligula subovalis, parte late subcordata fulcrali multo angustior. Palporum articulo primo maiore. Maxillarum mala spinulis rigidis ciliata. »

Charaktere. — Körperform walzenförmig, Länge 2 bis 5 mm., Farbe braun bis schwarz, Behaarung reichlich, Skulptur derb.

Kopf kugelig, ins Halsschild zurückgezogen; Stirn convex mit erhabener Längslinie oder mit glänzendem Flecke oder mit mehr weniger Haaren versehen.

Augen quergestellt, länglich, vorn mehr weniger tief ausgebuchtet

Fühler mit fünfgliedriger Geissel, deren erstes Glied zwiebelförmig mit gerade abgestutzter Spitze, länger als breit und so lang als 2 und 3 zusammen, deren zweites Glied verkehrt kegelförmig, viel kleiner als erstes, die folgenden kürzer als breit, nach der Keule zu an Breite zunehmend sind. Keule kugelig-eiförmig, an der Basis und Hinterfläche verhüllt, vorne an der Spitze schräg abgestutzt, undeutlich geringelt.

Vorderkiefer gross, lang dreieckig, mit zwei Zähnen.

Mittelkiefer mit Innenlade, die nach innen S-förmig geschwungen und nach der Spitze allmählich verschmälert ist, an der Kaukante circa zwölf starke, stumpfe Stachelzähne trägt, welche nach der Spitze zu dichter stehen.

Kiefertaster kegelförmig, an Länge und Breite abnehmend.

Hinterkiefer zu einem breiten, herzförmig dreieckigen nach der Basis verschmälerten, nach vorn abgestumpft gerundeten Kinne mit bauchigen Seitenrändern verschmolzen, an dessen Spitze die kleine ovale Zunge angesetzt ist.

Lippentaster : Glied 1 länger als die beiden andern zusammen, Glied 3 sehr klein, kegelförmig.

Halsschild auf dem ganzen Rücken gleichmässig rauh punktiert, ohne erhöhten Basal- und Seitenrand, eiförmig, seitlich und vorn bauchig gerundet, mässig gewölbt, aber nicht gebuckelt.

Schildchen rundlich, klein.

Flügeldecken meist breiter als die Basis des Halsschildes, walzenförmig, an der Spitze einfach abgewölbt; mässig derb skulptiert, Nahtstreif meist eingedrückt, besonders am Absturz.

Vorderbrust mit deutlichem Fortsatz zwischen den Vorderhüften.

Mittelbrust zwischen den wenig abstehenden Mittelhüften breit, mit hervorragendem Höcker.

Hinterhüften zusammenstehend.

Schienen breitgedrückt mit nach der Spitze gerundeter Aussenkante, diese selbst gesägt oder gezähnt.

Bauch gerade.

Geographische Verbreitung der Arten. — Die Gattung ist subkosmopolitisch : nur aus Australien ist keine Art gemeldet. Es sind sechsunddreissig Arten beschrieben.

1. *D. aceris*, Lindemann, Bull. Soc. Nat. Moscou, Vol. 44 (1), p. 140 (1875).	Mitteleuropa.
2. *D. affaber*, Mannerheim, ibidem, Vol. 25 (2), p. 339 (1852).	Nordamerika.
3. *D. affinis*, Blandford, Trans. Ent. Soc. Lond. p. 93 (1894).	Japan.
4. *D. africanus*, Schreiner, Deutsche Ent. Zeitschr. Vol. 26, p. 246 (1882).	Westafrika.
5. *D. alni*, Georg, Stett. Ent. Zeit. Vol. 16, p. 59 (1856).	Mitteleuropa.
6. *D. apatoides*, Eichhoff, Ann. Soc. Ent. Belg. Vol. 18, p. 201 (1875).	Japan.
7. *D. autographus*, Ratzeburg, Forstinsekten, Vol. 1, p. 160 (1837). — Taf. 4, Fig. 37.	Europa, Japan, Nordamerika.
8. *D. baikalicus*, Reitter, Deutsche Ent. Zeitschr. p. 286 (1899).	Sibirien.
9. *D. bengalensis*, Stebbing, Ind. For. Mem. Vol, 1, p. 12 (1908).	Ostindien.
10. *D. carbonarius*, Ferrari, Borkenkäfer, p. 41 (1867).	Cuba.
11. *D. coryli*, Perris, Bull. Soc. Ent. Fr. p. 78 (1855).	Mitteleuropa.
12. *D. dinoderoides*, Blandford, Trans. Ent. Soc. Lond. p, 97 (1894).	Japan.
13. *D. Eichhoffi*, Ferrari, Borkenkäfer. p. 29 (1867).	Griechenland.
14. *D. Eichhoffi*, Hopkins, Yearbook, U. S. Dep. Agric. p. 320 (1903).	Nordamerika.
15. *D. flavicornis*, Blandford, Ann. Mag. Nat. Hist. Vol. 15. p. 320 (1895).	Ceylon.
16. *D. graniceps*, Eichhoff, Deutsche Ent. Zeitschr. Vol. 21, p. 120 (1877).	Japan.
17. *D. granicollis*, Le Conte, Trans. Amer. Ent. Soc. Vol. 2, p. 162 (1868).	Nordamerika.
18. *D. Hewetti*, Stebbing, Ind. For. Mem. Vol. 1, p. 11 (1908).	Ostindien.
19. *D. himalayensis*, Strohmeyer. Ent. Wochenbl. p. 161 (1908).	Himalaya.
20. *D. Leprieuri*, Perris, Trans. Amer. Soc. Ent. (4), Vol. 6, p. 194 (1866).	Algier.
21. *D. limbàtus*, Blandford, Biol. Centr. Amer. Col. Vol. 4 (6), p. 190 (1904).	Centralamerika.
22. *D. luteus*, Blandford, Trans. Ent. Soc. Lond. p. 94 (1894).	Japan.
23. *D. macilentus*, Blandford, Biol. Centr. Amer. Col. Vol. 4 (6), p. 190 (1904).	Centralamerika.
24. *D. maurus*, Blandford, ibidem, p. 191 (1904).	Centralamerika.
25. *D. melaenus*, Eichhoff, Berl. Ent. Zeitschr. Vol. 8, p, 136 (1871).	Südamerika.
26. *D. minor*, Eggers, Il Natural. Sicil. Vol. 20, Nos 6-8 (1908).	Sicilien.
27. *D. moestus*, Blandford. Trans. Ent. Soc. Lond. p. 96 (1894).	Japan.
28. *D. nubilus*, Blandford, ibidem, p. 95 (1894).	Japan.
29. *D. pilosus*, Blandford, ibidem. p. 92 (1894).	Japan.
30. *D. pumilio*, Eichhoff, Ratio Tomic. p. 295 (1879).	Südamerika.
31. *D. quadrisulcatus*, Strohmeyer, Ent. Wochenblatt, p. 72 (1908).	Himalaya.
32. *D. ramicola*, Reitter, Best.-Tab. Borkenkäfer, p. 94 (1894).	Kleinasien.
33. *D. taprobanus*, Blandford, Trans. Ent. Soc. Lond. p. 203 (1896).	Ceylon.
34. *D. tonsus*, Hagedorn, Bull. Mus. Hist. Nat. Paris, p. 412 (1905).	Südamerika.
35. *D. villosus*, Fabricius, Syst. Ent. Vol. 1 (2), p. 367 (1792).	Europa, Madeira.
36. *D. pini*, Niijima, Journ. Coll. Agric. Tohoku Imp. Univ. Sapporo, Vol 3 (2). p. 152 (1909).	Japan.

63. GENUS STYPHLOSOMA, BLANDFORD

Styphlosoma. Blandford, Biol. Centr. Amer. Col. Vol. 4 (6), p. 232 (1904).

ORIGINALDIAGNOSE : Blandford, loc. cit.

« Funiculus antennarum 5-articulatus ; clava acuminato-ovalis, compressa, 3-articulata, articulo 2º magno, suturis 1ª et 2ª valde curvatis ; prothorax postice subparallelus, dense granulatus ; prosternum processu angusta ; tibiæ lineares, anticæ oblique truncatæ ; tarsi breves, articulis 1-3 subæqualibus. Corpus breviter cylindricum. Elytris dense punctato-rugosis. »

Charaktere. — Körperform walzenförmig, Länge 1.5 mm., Skulptur derb, Bekleidung aus zarten Schuppen und Haaren bestehend.

Kopf zurückgezogen.

Fühler : Schaft kurz; Geissel fünfgliedrig, nach der Spitze wenig verbreitert; Keule eiförmig zugespitzt, flach, dreigliedrig mit kurzhaarigen Nähten : das erste Glied nimmt das Basaldritteil ein, ist durch eine gekrümmte Naht vom zweiten getrennt, welches ziemlich breit ist und vom dritten umfasst wird.

Halsschild kurz, cylindrisch, an der Spitze gerundet und ziemlich abschüssig, ohne erhabenen Seiten- und Basalrand.

Vorderbrust kurz, mit schmalem Fortsatz zwischen den Vorderhüften.

Flügeldecken cylindrisch.

Schienen schmal, schwach gezähnt, das vordere Paar schräg abgestutzt.

Fussglieder kurz.

Mir ist die Gattung unbekannt geblieben. Die von Blandford beschriebene Art soll einem *Hypothenemus* ähnen, aber durch die Fühlerkeule, das cylindrische Halsschild und die Skulptur sich unterscheiden.

Geographische Verbreitung der Art. — Nur eine Art aus Panama.

1. *S. granulatum*, Blandford, Biol. Centr. Amer. Col. Vol. 4 (6), p. 232 (1904). Panama.

64. Genus OZOPEMON, Hagedorn

Ozopemon. Hagedorn, Deutsche Ent. Zeitschr. p. 1 (1910).

ORIGINALDIAGNOSE : Hagedorn, loc. cit.

« Caput globosum receptum. Labium oblongum latitudine longius, versus basin angustatum, apice truncatum, ligula parva oblonga, apicem versus angustata, labio prope apicem inserta. Palpi labiales articulo primo maximo tumidissimo, sequentibus coniunctis maiore, intus villoso-barbato, secundo transverso minimo, tertio conico. Maxillæ mala versus apicem angustata, margine interiore basi rotundato, anterius leniter sinuato, spinulis compressis intus ciliato. Palporum maxillarium articulus primus maior, secundus minor, tertius conicus longior, intus seta unica rigida ornatus. Antennarum funiculus quinque articulatus, articulo 1º crasso bulbiformi, 2º multo longiore obconico, ceteris transversis, latitudine fortiter crescentibus, capitulo ovato tunicato, in parte exteriore oblique truncato, suturis 1-2 obsoletis ornato. Prothorax transversus, gibbus, antice fortius, postice lenius rugoso-punctatus, basi immarginatus. Prosternum processu obsoleto inter coxas anteriores productum, coxæ mediæ et posteriores subcontiguæ. Tibiæ versus apicem dilatatæ, apice compressæ, extus rotundatæ, serratæ; tarsi recepti articulis 1, 2, 3 subæqualibus. Corpus cylindricum, stria suturali in elytris non impressa. »

Charaktere. — Körperform länglich walzenförmig, Länge 4 bis 6 mm., Farbe braun, Skulptur grob, Bekleidung mit mehr minder langen Haaren.

Kopf kugelig, ins Halsschild zurückgezogen.

Augen länglich oval, vorn kaum oder wenig ausgerandet.

Fühler mit fünfgliedriger Geissel und eiförmiger hinten verhüllter, vorn schräg abgestutzter Keule mit eine oder zwei schwachen Nähten.

Vorderkiefer derb, zweizähnig.

Mittelkiefer mit an der Basis gerundeter, an der Spitze verschmälerter Innenlade, an deren Kaukante breite, mehr weniger gebogene Stachelzähne sitzen.

Kiefertaster : Glied 1 und 2 beinahe gleichgross, walzenförmig, letztes Glied erheblich länger und schmäler, an der Innenseite mit einer starren Borste bewehrt.

Hinterkiefer zu einere gleichschenklig-dreieckigen, an der Spitze gerade abgestutztem Kinne verschmolzen, in dessen Mitte die schmale lanzenförmige, bis zum zweiten Tastergliede reichende behaarte Zunge entspringt.

Lippentaster : Glied 1 gross, geschwollen (wie bei *Xyleborus*), innen mit einem Haarflausch besetzt; Glied 2 quer breiter, Glied 3 schmal, kegelförmig.

Halsschild beinahe so lang als breit, mit einem Buckel, gleichmässig rauh punktiert oder gekörnt, an der Basis und den Seiten nicht gerandet

Schildchen klein, dreieckig, glatt, konkav.

Flügeldecken walzenförmig, rauh skulptiert und behaart; Absturz konvex oder flach eingedrückt, Zwischenräume daselbst flach oder granuliert, Nahtstreif mehr weniger vertieft.

Vorderbrust mit schwachem Fortsatz.

Vorderhüften einander beinahe berührend, Mittelhüften getrennt, Hinterhüften beinahe einander berührend.

Schienen nach der Spitze verbreitert, Aussenkante gerundet und gesägt.

Fussglieder 1, 2, 3 ziemlich einander gleich und nicht verbreitert.

Bauch gerade.

Geographische Verbreitung der Arten. — Sieben Arten mit zwei Varietäten aus Sumatra und Borneo.

1. *O. fuscicollis*, Hagedorn, Deutsche Ent. Zeitschr. p. 3 (1910).—**Taf. 9, Fig. 29, 30, 31.** Sumatra.
2. *O. gravidus*, Blandford, Trans. Ent. Soc, Lond. p. 206 (1896). Borneo.
3. *O. obanus*, Hagedorn, Deutsche Ent. Zeitschr. p. 3 (1910).—**Taf. 9, Fig. 26, 27, 28.** Sumatra.
4. *O. regius*, Hagedorn, ibidem, p. 382 (1908). Sumatra.
5. *O. rugatus*, Blandford, Trans. Ent. Soc. Lond. p. 204 (1896). Borneo.
6. *O. sumatranus*, Blandford, ibidem, p. 205 (1896). Sumatra.
7. *O. Thehlae*, Hagedorn, Deutsche Ent. Zeitschr. p. 2 (1910). — **Taf. 4, Fig. 38.** Sumatra.
       var. singalangicus, Hagedorn, ibidem, p. 3 (1910). — **Taf. 9, Fig. 20, 21, 22.** Sumatra.
       var. sirambeanus, Hagedorn, ibidem, p. 3 (1910). — **Taf. 9, Fig. 23, 24, 25.** Sumatra.

65. GENUS PREMNOBIUS, EICHHOFF

Premnobius. Eichhoff, Ratio Tomic. p. 404 (1879).

ORIGINALDIAGNOSE : Eichhoff, loc. cit.

« Mentum oblongum versus basin æqualiter sensim angustatum; ligula angusta, prope basin mento inserta. Palpi labiales articulis magnitudine gradatim decrescentibus. Maxillæ mala intus sinuata, pilis falcatis apice densioribus ciliato. Antennæ funiculo 5-articulato, articulo ejus 1° crassiusculo, segmentibus multo minoribus, crassitie crescentibus, capitulo subsolido, imbricato. Prosternum processu acuto inter coxas longe productum. Episterna metathoracis angusta, sinuata, incurvata. Tibiæ compressæ, versus apicem dilatatæ, extus carinulis transversis porcatæ. »

Charaktere. — Körperform schmal cylindrisch, 3 mm. lang, Farbe braun, am Flügeldecken-absturz schwarz, Skulptur schwach, Behaarung spärlich, daher glänzend.

Kopf kugelig, tief im Halsschild versteckt; Stirn konvex, behaart.

Augen länglich, beinahe nierenförmig wegen der tiefen Ausbuchtung am Vorderrande.

Fühler mit fünfgliedriger Geissel und runder, mit einer schwachen Naht versehener, sonst solider Keule.

Vorderkiefer stark, schwarz, mit einem Zahn.

Mittelkiefer mit breiter, am Innenrand ausgebuchteter, an der Spitze stumpf gerundeter Innen-lade, an deren Kaukante zahlreiche, nach der Spitze dichterstehende breite Stachelzähne von gerader und gebogener Gestalt sitzen.

Kiefertaster : Glied 1 und 2 querbreiter, 3 kegelförmig, mit Längstreifung, wie bei *Xyleborus*.

Hinterkiefer bilden ein längliches, an der Basis verschmälertes Kinn, in dessen Mitte die schmale lanzettförmige Zunge, die starke Borstenhaare trägt, angesetzt ist.

Lippentaster : Glieder sind walzenförmig (Glied 1 nicht geschwollen), ziemlich von gleicher Länge, an Dicke abnehmend.

Halsschild länger als breit, cylindrisch, an den Seiten gegen die Vorderbrust abgesetzt, an der Basis fein gerandet, vorn leicht gekörnt, hinten beinahe glatt.

Schildchen nicht sichtbar.

Flügeldecken lang walzenförmig, nach hinten etwas verschmälert, wenig und unregelmässig punktiert, mit spärlichen Haarreihen besetzt, der Absturz ist herzförmig, tief ausgehöhlt, die Naht in ihm erhaben, der Rand des Absturzes mehr weniger gezähnt oder bedornt. Hinterer Flügeldeckenteil schwarzbraun.

Vorderbrust mit langem spitzem Fortsatz zwischen den Vorderhüften.

Hüften voneinander entfernt.

Schienen hellfarbig, flach, nach der Spitze erweitert : Aussenfläche mit queren Leisten besetzt.

Fussglieder 1, 2, 3 einander gleich.

Bauch gerade.

Geographische Verbreitung der Art. — Nur eine Art mit drei Varietäten, welche merk-würdiger Weise sowohl in Afrika als auch in Südamerika vorkommt, sowie auch in Zanzibarcopal und Akkracopal von mir gefunden ist. Die Varietäten habe ich nur aus Afrika gesehen.

1. *P. cavipennis*, Eichhoff, Ratio Tomic. p. 404 (1879). — **Taf. 4,** Cayenne, Columbien, Kap **Fig. 39, 39a.** der guten Hoffnung, Zan-
   var. nodulosus, Hagedorn, Deutsche Ent. Zeitschr. p. 376 (1908). Congo. [zibarcopal.
   var. spinosus, Hagedorn, ibidem, p. 376 (1908). Congo, Akkracopal.
   var. corthyloides, Hagedorn, ibidem, p. 1 (1910). — **Taf. 9, Fig. 36,** Kamerun.
       37, 38.

66. Genus PITYOPHTHORUS, Eichhoff

Pityophthorus. Eichhoff, Berl. Ent. Zeitschr. Vol. 8, p. 39 (1864).
Bostrichus. Ratzeburg. Forstinsekten. p. 162 (1837).
Cryphalus. Le Conte, Trans. Amer. Ent. Soc. Vol. 2, p. 154 (1868).
Dermestes. Linné, Syst. Nat. (ed. 10), p. 355 (1758).
Crypturgus. Zimmermann, Trans. Amer. Ent. Soc. Vol. 2, p. 142 (1868).
Tomicus. Perris, Ann. Soc. Ent. Fr. (3), Vol. 4, p. 191 (1856).

ORIGINALDIAGNOSE : Eichhoff, loc. cit.

« Tarsorum articulis tribus primis subæqualibus, simplicibus. Antennarum funiculo quinque-articulato, clava ovata, inciso-annulata. Ligula subacuminata parte fulcrali angustior, haec basin versus sensim angustata, elongata. Palpi labiales articulo primo maiore. Maxillarum mala brevis, spinulis rigidis ciliata. »

Charaktere. — Korperform walzenförmig, schmal; Länge 1.3 bis 2.8 mm.; Skulptur schwach, teils glatt, teils mit feiner anliegender Behaarung versehen. Flügeldeckenabsturz meist mehr weniger ausgehöhlt.

Kopf kugelig, ins Halsschild zurückgezogen.

Stirn zeigt häufig sekundäre Geschlechtsmerkmale, beim ♀ hat sie eine starke Haarbürste, beim ♂ ist sie glatt : bei den Arten der *minutissimus*-Gruppe sind die Verhältnisse umgekehrt.

Augen vorne ausgebuchtet.

Fühler mit fünfgliedriger Geissel und beiderseits durch drei gerade Quernähte in vier Glieder abgeteilter Keule. Doch kommen bei der Keule Abweichungen vor. Es ist eine Art (*xylotrupes* Eichhoff), welche nur eine basale Naht zeigt, während bei *incompositus, carinifrons, politus, Deyrollei* und *incommodus* die Nähte nach oben bogenförmig gekrümmt sind.

Vorderkiefer kräftig, mit einem Zahn.

Mittelkiefer mit beilförmiger zugespitzter, an der Kaukante mit Zähnen besetzter Innenlade.

Kiefertaster : Glied 1 quer, Glied 2 quadratisch, Glied 3 schmäler, kegelförmig.

Die Hinterkiefer sind zu einem langgestreckten, vorn stark abgerundeten, nach der Basis verschmälerten Kinne verschmolzen; die Zunge von der Mitte des Kinnes entspringend, schmal, nach vorn verschmälert, stumpf auslaufend.

Lippentaster : Glied 1 am grössten, Glied 2 cylindrisch, kleiner als 1, Glied 3 länger als 2.

Halsschild eiförmig länglich, mit fein gerandeter Basis, vorn stärker, hinten schwächer skulptiert.

Schildchen sichtbar.

Flügeldecken cylindrisch mit schwacher Skulptur, am Absturz meist mit einer Furche versehen, am Nahtwinkel entweder gemeinsam gerundet oder zugespitzt.

Vorderbrust mit scharf vorspringendem Fortsatz zwischen den Hüften.

Hüften einander genähert, aber nicht einander berührend.

Schienen gerade, linealisch, Aussenkante schwach bedornt.

Fussglieder 1; 2, 3 einander gleich, rund.

Bauch gerade.

Geographische Verbreitung der Arten. — Die Gattung umfasst vierundsechzig Arten und ist kosmopolitisch : nur aus Australien sind keine Arten bekannt geworden. Die Hauptmasse verteilt sich auf das alte und neue Nordreich, sowie auf das Südreich.

1. *P. alienus,* Eichhoff, Berl. Ent. Zeitschr. Vol. 15, p. 135 (1871).   Südamerika.
2. *P. amoenus,* Blandford, Biol. Centr. Amer. Col. Vol. 4 (6), p. 237 (1904).   Centralamerika.
   — Taf. 4, Fig. 40b.
3. *P. annectens,* Le Conte, Proc. Amer. Philos. Soc. Vol. 17, p. 622 (1878).   Nordamerika.
4. *P. Buyssoni,* Reitter, Wien. Ent. Zeit. Vol. 20, p. 101 (1901).   Mitteleuropa.
5. *P. cariniceps,* Le Conte, Proc. Amer. Philos. Soc. Vol. 15, p. 353 (1876).   Nordamerika.
6. *P. carinifrons,* Blandford, Biol. Centr. Amer. Col. Vol. 4 (6), p. 244 (1904).   Centralamerika.
7. *P. cacuminatus,* Blandford, ibidem, p. 238 (1904).   Centralamerika.
8. *P. chalcoensis,* Hopkins, Proc. Ent. Soc. Wash. Vol. 7, p. 73 (1905).   Centralamerika.
9. *P. cincinnatus,* Blandford, Biol. Centr. Amer. Col. Vol. 4 (6), p. 242 (1904).   Centralamerika.
10. *P. comatus,* Zimmermann, Trans. Amer. Ent. Soc. Vol. 2, p. 143 (1868).   Nordamerika.
11. *P. concentralis,* Eichhoff, Ratio Tomic. p. 188 (1879).   Centralamerika.
12. *P. confinis,* Le Conte, Proc. Amer. Philos. Soc. Vol. 15, p. 354 (1876).   Nordamerika.
13. *P. confinis,* Blandford, Biol. Centr. Amer. Col. Vol. 4 (6), p. 241 (1904).   Centralamerika.
14. *P. confusus,* Blandford, ibidem, p. 237 (1904).   Centralamerika.
15. *P. coniperda,* Schwarz, Proc. Ent. Soc. Wash. Vol. 3, p. 144 (1895).   Nordamerika.
16. *P. consimilis,* Le Conte, Proc. Amer. Philos. Soc. Vol. 17, p. 622 (1878).   Nordamerika.
17. *P. corticalis,* Eichhoff, Berl. Ent. Zeitschr. Vol. 15, p. 135 (1871).   Südamerika.
18. *P. deletus,* Le Conte, Bull. U. S. Geolog. Surv. Vol. 5, p. 519 (1879).   Nordamerika.
19. *P. deprecator,* Schaufuss, Tijdschr. v. Ent. Vol. 34, p. 15 (1891).   Madagaskar.
20. *P. Deyrollei,* Blandford, Biol. Centr. Amer. Col. Vol. 4 (6), p. 245 (1904).   Centralamerika.
21. *P. digestus,* Le Conte, Trans. Amer. Ent. Soc. Vol. 5, p. 71 (1874).   Nordamerika.
22. *P. diglyphus,* Blandford, Biol. Centr. Amer. Col. Vol. 4 (6), p. 240 (1904).   Centralamerika.

101

23. *P. exsculptus*, Ratzeburg, Forstinsekten, Vol. 1, p. 162 (1837).   Mitteleuropa.
24. *P. flavus*, Stephens, Ill. Brit. Ent. Vol. 3, p. 356 (1830).   England.
25. *P. glabratus*, Eichhoff, Ratio Tomic. p. 179 (1879).—**Taf. 13, Fig. 10.**   Mitteleuropa.
26. *P. guatemalensis*, Blandford, Biol. Centr. Amer. Col. Vol. 4 (6), p. 239   Centralamerika.
(1904).
27. *P. Henscheli*, Seitner, Wien. Ent. Zeit. Vol. 6, p. 44 (1887).   Südeuropa.
28. *P. Herrerai*. Hopkins, Proc. Ent. Soc. Wash. Vol. 7, p. 74 (1905).   Centralamerika.
29. *P. incommodus*, Blandford, Biol. Centr. Amer. Col. Vol. 4 (6), p. 245   Centralamerika.
(1904).
30. *P. incompositus*, Blandford. ibidem, p. 243 (1904).   Centralamerika.
31. *P. jucundus*, Blandford, Trans Ent. Soc. Lond. p. 87 (1894).   Japan.
32. *P. Knoteki*, Reitter, Deutsche Ent. Zeitschr. p. 356 (1898).   Südeuropa.
33. *P. languidus*, Eichhoff, Ratio Tomic. p. 186 (1879).   Südamerika.
34. *P. lautus*, Eichhoff, Berl. Ent. Zeitschr. Vol. 15, p. 135 (1871).   Nordamerika.
35. *P. Lichtensteini*, Ratzeburg, Forstinsekten, Vol. 1. p. 162 (1837).   Nordeuropa.
36. *P. macrographus*, Eichhoff, Europ. Borkenk. p. 200 (1881).   Mitteleuropa.
37. *P. micrographus*, Linné, Syst. Nat. (ed. 10), p. 355 (1758).   Mitteleuropa.
38. *P. minutissimus*, Zimmermann, Trans. Amer. Ent. Soc. Vol. 2, p. 143   Nordamerika.
(1868). — **Taf. 4, Fig. 40, 40a.**
39. *P. nigricans*. Blandford, Biol. Centr. Amer. Col. Vol. 4(6), p. 236(1904).   Centralamerika.
40. *P. nitidulus*, Mannerheim, Bull. Soc. Nat. Moscou, Vol. 16 (2), p. 298   Nordamerika.
(1843).
41. *P. obliquus*, Le Conte, Proc. Amer. Philos. Soc. Vol. 17, p. 432 (1878).   Nordamerika.
42. *P. obsoletus*, Blandford, Biol. Centr. Amer. Col. Vol. 4 (6), p. 242(1904).   Centralamerika.
43. *P. obtusipennis*, Blandford, ibidem, p. 240 (1904).   Centralamerika.
44. *P. obtusus*, Schaufuss, Tijdschr. v. Ent. Vol. 34, p. 17 (1891).   Madagaskar.
45. *P. opaculus*, Le Conte, Proc. Amer. Philos. Soc. Vol. 17, p. 623 (1878).   Nordamerika.
46. *P. peregrinus*, Eichhoff, Ratio Tomic. p. 193 (1879).   Südamerika.
47. *P. pilosus*, Le Conte, Trans. Amer. Ent. Soc. Vol. 2, p. 154 (1868).   Nordamerika.
48. *P. politus*, Blandford. Biol. Centr. Amer. Col. Vol. 4 (6), p. 244 (1904).   Centralamerika.
49. *P. poricollis*. Blandford, ibidem, p. 298 (1904).   Centralamerika.
50. *P. pruinosus*, Eichhoff, Ratio Tomic. p. 198 (1879).   Nordamerika.
51. *P. puberulus*, Le Conte, Trans. Amer. Ent Soc. Vol. 2, p. 157 (1868).   Nordamerika.
52. *P. pubipennis*, Le Conte, Pacific. R. R. Expl. Surv. Ins. p. 59 (1857).   Nordamerika.
53. *P. pulchellus*, Eichhoff, Berl. Ent. Zeitschr. Vol. 12, p. 275 (1868).   Nordamerika.
54. *P. pulicarius*, Zimmermann, Trans. Amer. Ent. Soc. Vol. 2, p. 144(1868).   Nordamerika.
55. *P. pullus*, Zimmermann, ibidem, p. 143 (1868).   Nordamerika.
56. *P. puncticollis*, Le Conte, Trans. Amer. Ent. Soc. Vol. 5, p. 71 (1874).   Nordamerika.
57. *P. pusio*, Le Conte, Proc. Amer. Philos. Soc. Vol. 17, p. 623 (1878).   Nordamerika.
58. *P. pubescens*. Marsham, Ent. Brit. p. 58 (1802).   Mitteleuropa.
59. *P. seriatus*, Le Conte, Proc. Amer. Philos. Soc. Vol. 17, p. 433 (1878).   Centralamerika.
60. *P. similis*, Eichhoff, Berl. Ent. Zeitschr. Vol. 12, p. 275 (1868).   Südamerika.
61. *P. timidus*, Blandford, Biol. Centr. Amer. Col. Vol. 4 (6), p. 241 (1904).   Centralamerika.
62. *P. tomentosus*, Eichhoff, Ratio Tomic. p. 201 (1879).   Nordamerika.
63. *P. tuberculatus*, Eichhoff, ibidem, p. 498 (1879).   Nordamerika.
64. *P. xylotrupes*, Eichhoff, Berl. Ent. Zeitschr. Vol. 15, p. 135 (1871).   Südamerika.

67. Genus IPS, De Geer

Ips. De Geer, Mém. Hist. Ins. Vol. 5, p. 190-192 (1775).
Bostrichus. Fabricius, Syst. Ent. p. 59 (1777).
Tomicus. Latreille, Gen. Crust. Ins. Vol. 2, p. 276 (1807).

Cumatotomĭcus, Cyrtotomicus, Orthotomicus. Ferrari, Borkenkäfer, p. 44 (1867).

Subgenus **Pityogenes.** Bedel, Faune Col. Seine, Vol. 6, p. 397 (1888).

ORIGINALDIAGNOSE : De Geer, loc. cit.

« M. de Linné a placé dans le genre des Dermestes de certains insectes qui, examinés avec attention, n'en ont point les caractères, mais demandent de constituer un genre nouveau ; ils ont de la ressemblance tant avec les Scarabés qu'avec les vrais Dermestes, de sorte qu'ils semblent faire un genre mitoyen entre ces deux insectes. Tels sont le *Dermestes typographus* Linné, *Faune*, ed. 2, n° 418 ; le *Dermestes piniperda*, ibidem, n° 421 ; le *Dermestes stercoreus*, ibidem, n° 432, et d'autres. Je donnerai à ce nouveau genre l'ancien nom d'*Ips*, affecté à des insectes qu'on a cru percer la corne et la vigne, et l'on peut se servir du même nom d'*Ips* en français ou bien de celui de Perce-bois, parce que réellement quelques espèces percent le bois des vieux troncs d'arbres, et d'autres l'intérieur des jeunes tiges du pin.

» Ces insectes ont les caractères génériques suivants : La tête est ronde, presque en forme de boule, et ressemble en quelque manière à celle des fausses chenilles, et elle est un peu baissée ou pendante en bas. Les antennes sont brisées ou coudées, terminées par un bouton qui paraît solide, n'ayant que quelques incisions transversales. Le corselet est fort long, cylindrique et élevé en bosse en dessus, et le ventre est de même cylindrique. La poitrine a beaucoup d'étendue, de sorte que les deux pattes postérieures ont leurs attaches assez proches du derrière. Les jambes proprement dites sont dentelées aux côtés, et enfin tous les tarses sont divisés en quatre articles sans pelottes.

» Ils ressemblent donc aux Scarabés par la longueur de la poitrine et par la situation des pattes postérieures, comme aussi par les dentelures des jambes, et ils semblent convenir à de certains Dermestes par la forme du bouton des antennes et par l'habitude générale du corps ; mais la division des tarses en quatre articles démontre qu'ils n'appartiennent ni à l'un ni à l'autre genre.

» La tête est d'une figure singulière et telle qu'on n'en voit sur aucun autre insecte à étuis écailleux ; elle serait parfaitement sphérique si les dents, quand elles sont formées, ne formaient en devant une pointe conique ; en dessous elle est divisée en deux portions par une suture longitudinale, et en devant elle a de ce côté-là une cavité, dans laquelle sont placés les dents et barbillons qui sont fort courts. Les deux yeux sont petits, de forme allongé, ayant une échancrure en devant, de sorte qu'ils sont un peu en demi-lune.

» Les antennes sont divisées en plusieurs articles ; celui qui est le plus proche de la tête est long et un peu courbé, faisant un coude avec le reste, de sorte que l'antenne est comme brisée ou coudée ; ensuite viennent quatre ou cinq articles courts, les uns plus gros que les autres ; enfin l'antenne est terminée par un bouton ovale avec des incisions transversales, et qui dans les uns est aplati, mais dans les autres convexe ou en boule allongée.

» Le corselet, qui est en quelque forme cylindrique, est grand, élevé en bosse en dessus, et c'est à lui que sont attaché les deux pattes antérieures, comme à l'ordinaire. La poitrine ou la partie à laquelle sont unies les pattes intermédiaires et postérieures, s'étend fort loin vers le derrière, de sorte que les pattes postérieures sont placées assez proches du bout du ventre, qui lui même est fort court. Les étuis écailleux donnent au corps une forme cylindrique, et les ailes ont le double de la longueur du corps, ce qui est très remarquable.

» Les cuisses sont grosses, surtout au milieu. Les jambes sont aplaties, plus larges au bout qu'à leur origine, et garnies du côté extérieur de plusieurs dentelures comme celles des Scarabés. Les quatre articles des tarses sont à peu prés cylindriques, et c'est par le nombre des articles qu'ils diffèrent de ceux des Scarabés, qui en ont constamment cinq. Enfin les tarses sont terminées par deux ongles courbées en forme de crochets. »

UEBERSICHT DER UNTERGATTUNGEN

1'. *Vorderschienen verbreitert, Füsse einlegbar, Halsschildbasis ungerandet. Vorderbrust mit scharfem Fortsatz zwischen den Vorderhüften, Flügeldeckenabsturz punktiert* . . . Subg. Ips, s. str.

1. *Vorderschienen schmal, Füsse nicht einlegbar, Halsschildbasis nur in der Mitte ungerandet, Vorderbrust ohne Fortsatz, Flügeldeckenabsturz nicht punktiert* . . . . Subg. Pityogenes.

Charaktere. — Körperform walzenförmig, Länge 2.5 bis 8 mm.; Färbung braun bis schwarz; Skulptur kräftig; Behaarung meist stark; Flügeldeckenabsturz meist eingedrückt und gezähnt.

Kopf kugelig, mehr weniger unter das Halsschild eingezogen.

Stirn grob skulptiert.

Augen quer oval, vorn ausgerandet.

Fühler mit fünfgliedriger, nach vorn verbreiterter Geissel; die Keule durch den derben Basalring von hinten verhüllt, auf der Vorderseite mit schwammigen Endringen, welche durch mehr weniger gerade oder gebogene Nähte begrenzt werden.

', Vorderkiefer kräftig, gezähnt.

Mittelkiefer mit nach unten erweiterter Innenlade, an deren S-förmig geschwungener Kaukante vierzehn bis sechzehn gerade Stachelzähne abwechselnd mit langen Haaren stehen.

Kiefertaster kegelförmig. Glied 1 so lang als 2 und 3 zusammengenommen, Glied 3 am kürzesten, abgestutzt.

Hinterkiefer zu einem sehr gestreckten, gleich hinter der Mitte verengten und dann vor der Basis wieder deutlich, fast kugelig erweiterten schmalen Kinne verschmolzen. Die Zunge ist so breit als das Kinn; sie reicht mit ihrer vorn abgerundeten Spitze bis etwa zur Mitte des zweiten Tastergliedes.

Lippentaster verhältnissmässig kurz; Glied 2 am grössesten; die beiden ersten Glieder sind verkehrt kegelförmig, das dritte viel kürzer und schmäler als die andern.

Halsschild vorn schuppenartig gehöckert. hinten punktiert.

Schildchen dreieckig, deutlich sichtbar.

Flügeldecken walzenförmig, mit furchenartig vertieften Nahtstreifen und meist eingedrücktem, gezähntem, hinten abgesetzt gerandetem Absturz, der bei den ♂ meist stärker, bei den ♀ schwächer gezähnt ist.

Vorderbrust meist mit einem nach hinten zwischen die Vorderhüften einspringenden Fortsatz. Hüften voneinander mehr weniger entfernt.

Schienen gerade, nach vorn wenig verbreitert, aussen gezähnt, schief abgestutzt, innen mit Endhäkchen.

Fussglieder meist zurücklegbar; Glied 3 einfach; die drei ersten Glieder einander gleich. Bauch gerade.

Geographische Verbreitung der Arten. — Eine kosmopolitische Gattung, deren fünfundsiebzig Arten überall vorkommen, wo Nadelhölzer wachsen, und unter denen sich die gefährlichsten Baumschädlinge befinden.

1. *I. acuminatus,* Gyllenhal, Ins. Suec. Vol. 4. p. 620 (1827) (Subg. *Ips* s. str.).   Europa, Sibirien.

2. *I. adusticollis,* Motschulsky, Bull. Soc. Nat. Moscou, Vol. 36 (2), p. 514 (1863) (Subg. *Ips* s. str.).   Ceylon.

3. *I. amitinus,* Eichhoff, Berl. Ent. Zeitschr. Vol. 15, p. 138 (1871) (Subg. *Ips* s. str.).   Europa.

4. *I. angulatus,* Eichhoff, Ann. Soc. Ent Belg. Vol. 19, p. 200 (1875) (Subg. *Ips* s. str.).   Japan.

5. *I. asper,* Broun, Man. New Zeal. Col. p. 742 (1881) (Subg. *Ips* s. str.).   Neu-Seeland.

6. *I. austriacus*, Wachtl, Mitteil. Nieder-Oestreich. Forst-Vereins, Vol. 31,   Mitteleuropa.
   p. 320 (1887) (Subg. *Pityogenes*).
7. *I. avulsus*, Eichhoff, Berl. Ent. Zeitschr. Vol. 11, p. 402 (1867) (Subg.   Nordamerika.
   Ips s. str.).
8. *I. balsameus*, Le Conte, Proc. Amer. Philos. Soc. Vol. 17, p. 625 (1878)   Nordamerika.
   (Subg. *Pityogenes*).
9. *I. bidentatus*, Herbst, Füssli Archiv. Ent. Vol. 4, p. 24 (1783) (Subg.   Europa.
   Pityogenes). — **Taf. 13, Fig 15.**
10. *I. bistridentatus*, Eichhoff, Ratio Tomic. p. 282 (1879)(Subg. *Pityogenes*).   Mitteleuropa.
   var. coniunctus, Reitter, Wien. Ent. Zeit. Vol. 6, p. 196 (1887).   Südeuropa.
11. *I. Bonanseai*, Hopkins, Proc. Ent. Soc. Wash. Vol. 7, p. 76 (1905)   Mexiko.
   (Subg. *Ips* s. str.).
12. *I. caelatus*, Eichhoff, Berl. Ent. Zeitschr. Vol. 11, p. 402(1867)(Subg.   Nordamerika.
   Ips s. str.).
13. *I. calligraphus*, Germar. Ins. Spec. Nov. p. 461(1824)(Subg. *Ips* s. str.).   Nordamerika.
14. *I. carinulatus*, Le Conte, Trans. Amer. Ent. Soc. Vol. 5, p. 70 (1874)   Nordamerika.
   (Subg. *Pityogenes*).
15. *I. cembrae*, Heer, Observ. Ent. p. 28 (1836) (Subg. *Ips* s. str.).   Europa, Sibirien, Japan.
16. *I. chalcographus*, Linné, Fauna Suec. p. 143 (1761) (Subg. *Pityogenes*).   Europa.
17. *I. cinchonae*, Veen, Bull. Kol. Mus. Haarlem, p. 18 (1897) (Subg.   Java.
   Ips s. str.).
18. *I. concinnus*, Mannerheim, Bull. Soc. Nat. Moscou, Vol. 25 (2). p. 358   Nordamerika.
   (1852) (Subg. *Ips* s. str.).
19. *I. confusus*, Le Conte, Proc. Amer. Philos. Soc. Vol. 15, p. 362 (1876)   Nordamerika.
   (Subg. *Ips* s. str.).
20. *I. coniferae*, Stebbing, Dep. Nat. Ins. For. p. 242(1903)(Subg. *Pityogenes*).   Ostindien.
21. *I. cribricollis*, Eichhoff, Berl. Ent. Zeitschr. Vol. 12, p. 272 (1868)   Mexiko.
   (Subg. *Ips* s. str.).
22. *I. cristatus*, Fabricius. Syst. Eleuth. Vol. 2, p. 389(1801)(Subg. *Ips* s. str.?).   Südamerika.
23. *I. curvidens*, Germar, Ins. Spec. Nov. p. 462 (1824) (Subg. *Ips* s. str.).   Europa, Afrika, Südame-
   — **Taf. 13, Fig. 14.**   rika.
   var. heterodon, Wachtl, Krummzähnige Borkenk. p. 15 (1895).   Mitteleuropa.
   var. spinidens, Reitter, Best.-Tab. Borkenkäfer, p. 84 (1894).   Kaukasus.
   var. Vorontzowi, Jacobson, Hor. Soc. Ent. Ross. Vol. 19, p. 521 (1895).   Mitteleuropa.
24. *I. decretus*, Eichhoff, Berl. Ent. Zeitschr. Vol. 11, p. 462 (1867) (Subg.   Nordamerika.
   Ips s. str.).
25. *I. duplicatus*, Sahlberg, Dissert. Ent. Ins. Fennic. Vol. 2, p. 144 (1836)   Nordeuropa.
   (Subg. *Ips* s. str.).
26. *I. emarginatus*, Le Conte, Proc. Amer. Philos. Soc. Vol. 15, p. 364   Nordamerika.
   (1876) (Subg. *Ips* s. str.).
27. *I. erosus*, Wollaston. Cat. Col. Mader. p. 95 (1857) (Subg. *Ips* s. str.).   Südeuropa, Nordafrika.
   var. robustus, Knotek, Oestreich. Vierteljahrsschr. Forstwesen, Heft 3 und 4.   Hercegowina.
   p. 15 (1899).
28. *I. exiguus*, Walker. Ann. Mag. Nat. Hist. Vol. 3, p. 260 (1859) (Subg.   Ceylon.
   Ips s. str.?).
29. *I. flavipes*, Fabricius, Syst. Eleuth. Vol. 2, p. 308(1801)(Subg. *Ips* s. str.?).   Südamerika.
30. *I. fossifrons*, Le Conte, Proc. Amer. Philos. Soc. Vol. 15, p. 353 (1876)   Nordamerika.
   (Subg. *Pityogenes*).
31. *I. grandicollis*, Eichhoff, Berl. Ent. Zeitschr. Vol. 11, p. 402 (1867)   Nordamerika.
   (Subg. *Ips* s str.).
32. *I. Hauseri*, Reitter, Best.-Tab. Borkenkäfer, p. 81(1894)(Subg. *Ips* s. str.).   Centralasien.
33. *I. hudsonicus*, Le Conte, Proc. Amer. Philos. Soc. Vol. 15, p. 362   Nordamerika.
   (1876) (Subg. *Ips* s. str.).
34. *I. integer*, Eichhoff, Berl. Ent. Zeitschr. Vol. 13, p. 273 (1869) (Subg.   Nordamerika.
   Ips s. str.).

35. *I. interpunctus*, Eichhoff, Stett. Ent. Zeit. Vol. 39, p. 390 (1878) Nordamerika.
(Subg. *Ips* s. str.).

36. *I. interruptus*, Mannerheim; Bull. Soc. Nat. Moscou, Vol. 25 (2), p. 357 Nordamerika.
1852 (Subg. *Ips* s. str.).

37. *I. interstitialis*, Eichhoff, Berl. Ent. Zeitschr. Vol. 12, p. 273 (1868) Centralamerika.
(Subg. *Ips* s. str.).

38. *I. irkutensis*, Eggers, Ent. Blätter, Vol. 6, p. 38 (1910)(Subg. *Pityogenes*). Sibirien.

39. *I. japonicus*, Niijima, Journ. Coll. Agric. Tohoku Imp. Univers. Japan.
Sapporo Japan, Vol. 3 (2), p. 147 (1909).

40. *I. laricis*, Fabricius, Ent. Syst. Vol. 1 (2), p. 365 (1792) (Subg. *Ips* s. str.). Europa.

41. *I. latidens*, Le Conte, Trans. Amer. Ent. Soc. p. 72 (1874) (Subg. Nordamerika.
Ips s. str.).

42. *I. longicollis*, Gyllenhal, Ins. Suec. Vol. 4, p. 621(1877)(Subg. *Ips* s. str.). Europa.

43. *I. Lipperti*, Henschel. Oesterreich. Forstzeit. p. 242 (1885) (Subg. Südeuropa.
Pityogenes).

44. *I. longifolia*, Stebbing, Dep. Not. Ins. aff. Forestry, p. 282 (1903) Himalaya.
(Subg. *Ips* s. str.).

45. *I. Mannsfeldi*, Wachtl, Verh. Zool.-bot. Ges. Wien, Vol. 29, p. 51 Südeuropa.
(1879) (Subg. *Ips* s. str.).

46. *I. mexicanus*, Hopkins, Proc. Ent. Soc. Wash. Vol. 7, p. 75 (1905). Centralamerika.
(Subg. *Ips* s. str.).

47. *I. moderatus*, Walker, Ann. Mag. Nat. Hist. Vol. 3, p. 260 (1859) (Subg. Ceylon.
Ips s. str.?).

48. *I. mutilatus*, Walker, ibidem, p. 286 (1859) (Subg. *Ips* s. str.). Ceylon.

49. *I. nobilis*, Wollaston, Ann. Mag. Nat. Hist. Vol. 9, p. 441 (1862) (Subg. Canarische Inseln.
Ips s. str.).

50. *I. Oregonis*, Eichhoff, Berl. Ent. Zeitschr. Vol. 12, p. 274 (1868) (Subg. Nordamerika.
Ips s. str.)

51. *I. pennidens*, Reitter, Deutsche Ent. Zeitschr. p. 374 (1889) (Subg. Griechenland.
Pityogenes).

52. *I. perexiguus*, Blandford, Trans. Ent. Soc. Lond. p. 201 (1896) (Subg. Damena-Inseln.
Ips s. str.).

53..*I. perturbatus*, Eichhoff, Berl. Ent. Zeitschr. Vol. 12, p. 274 (1868) Nordamerika.
(Subg. *Ips* s. str.).

54. *I. pilidens*, Reitter, Best.-Tab. Borkenk. p. 79 (1894) (Subg. *Pityogenes*). Südeuropa.
— **Taf. 4, Fig. 41**.

55. *I. pini*, Say, Journ. Acad. Natur. Sc. Philad. Vol. 5, p. 257(1826)(Subg. Nordamerika.
Ips s. str.). — **Taf. 5, Fig. 42, 43a, 44, 44a.**

56. *I. plagiatus*, Le Conte, Trans. Amer. Ent. Soc. Vol. 2, p. 261 (1868) Nordamerika.
(Subg. *Pityogenes*).

57. *I. plastographus*, Le Conte, ibidem, p. 163 (1868) (Subg. *Ips* s. str.). Nordamerika.

58. *I. proximus*, Eichhoff, Berl. Ent. Zeitschr. Vol. 11, p. 403 (1867) (Subg. Europa.
Ips s. str.).

59. *I. quadridens*, Hartig, Conversations Lexikon, p. 109 (1834) (Subg. Europa.
Pityogenes). — **Taf. 14, Fig. 16.**
var. *calcaratus*, Dejean, Cat. p. 332 (1837). Europa.

60. *I. quadrispinus*, Motschulsky, Bull. Soc. Nat. Moscou, Vol. 36 (2), Birma.
p. 514 (1863) (Subg. *Ips* s. str.?).

61. *I. rectus*, Le Conte, Proc. Amer. Philos. Soc. Vol. 15, p. 365 (1876) Nordamerika.
(Subg. *Ips* s. str.).

62. *I. scitus*, Blandford, Ind. Mus. Notes, Vol. 3, p. 63(1893)(Subg. *Pityogenes*). Ostindien.

63. *I. serratus*, Fabricius, Syst. Eleuth. Vol. 2, p. 388(1801)(Subg. *Ips* s. str.?). Südamerika.

64. *I. sexdentatus*, Boerner, Oekon. Nachr. Ges. Schles. Vol. 4, p. 78 (1767) Europa, Asien.
(Subg. *Ips* s. str.). — **Taf. 4, Fig. 42, 42a.**

65. *I. shoreae,* Stebbing, Calcutta Forestr. Bull. N° 2, p. 39 (1907) (Subg.	Assam.
	Ips s. str.).
66. *I. sparsus,* Le Conte, Trans. Amer. Ent. Soc. Vol. 2, p. 160 (1868)	Nordamerika.
	(Subg. *Pityogenes*).
67. *I. spinifer,* Eichhoff, Ratio Tomic. p. 499 (1879) (Subg. *Ips* s. str.).	Nordamerika.
68. *I. Stebbingi,* Strohmeyer, Ent. Wochenbl. p. 69 (1908) (Subg. *Ips*	Himalaya.
	s. str.).
69. *I. subelongatus,* Motschulsky, Schrencks Reise, Vol. 2, p. 155 (1805)	Asien.
	(Subg. *Ips* s. str.).
70. *I. suturalis,* Gyllenhal, Ins. Suec. Vol. 4, p. 622 (1827) (Subg. *Ips* s. str.).	Europa.
	— **Taf. 13, Fig. 13.**
71. *I. testaceus,* Walker, Ann. Mag. Nat. Hist. Vol. 3, p. 260 (1859) (Subg.	Ceylon.
	Ips s. str.?).
72. *I. tridens,* Mannerheim, Bull. Soc. Nat. Moscou, Vol. 25, p. 357 (1852)	Nordamerika.
	(Subg. *Ips* s. str).
73. *I. typographus,* Linné, Syst. Nat. (ed. 10), p 355 (1758) (Subg. *Ips* s. str.).	Europa.
	— **Taf. 11, Fig. 91, 92, 93; Taf. 13, Fig. 11, 12.**
74. *I. varians,* Fabricius, Syst. Eleuth. Vol. 2, p. 386 (1801) (Subg. *Ips*	Südamerika.
	s. str.?).
75. *I. vertens,* Walker, Ann. Mag. Nat. Hist. Vol. 3, p. 260 (1859) (Subg.	Ceylon.
	Ips s. str.?).

68. Genus XYLOCLEPTES, Ferrari

Xylocleptes. Ferrari, Borkenkäfer. p. 37 (1867).
Bostrichus. Duftschmid, Fauna Austr. Vol. 3, p. 92 (1825).
Scolytus. Olivier, Ent. Vol. 4, p. 10 (1778).

ORIGINALDIAGNOSE : Ferrari, loc. cit.

« Tarsorum articulis tribus primis subæqualibus simplicibus, secundo paullo breviore. Antennarum funiculo 5-articulato, clava subconcentrice fere imbricato-annulata, parum compressa, suborbiculata. Ligula parte fulcrali angustior, haec elongata, basin versus attenuata. Palpi labiales articulo primo et secundo subæqualibus, tertio valde angustato, parum inclinato, secundo haud breviore. maxillarum mala intus pilis setiformibus, paucis. fere rectis, rigidis, subciliata. »

Charaktere. — Körperform gestreckt, walzenförmig, Länge 2 bis 3.5 mm., mässig skulptiert, mit ziemlich langer Behaarung.

Kopf herabgebeugt, ohne Rüssel.

Augen länglich, vorn ausgerandet.

Fühler mit fünfgliedriger Geissel und kreisrunder Keule, die hinten verhüllt ist und vorne drei concentrische Nähte zeigt, welche das Basalglied kreisförmig einschliessen.

Vorderkiefer derb, zwei- oder dreizähnig.

Mittelkiefer mit breiter oben und unten gerundeter Innenlade, an deren Kaukante zwölf bis fünfzehn gerade, breite, dolchförmige Zähne sitzen.

Kiefertaster kurz, walzenförmig, letztes Glied am schmalsten.

Hinterkiefer zu einem nach der Basis verschmälerten, geradseitigen Kinne verschmolzen, an dessen Spitze die kleine, ovale Zunge angesetzt ist.

Lippentaster : Glied 1 und 2 gleichgross, Glied 3 viel schmäler.

Halsschild vor der Mitte am breitesten, nach vorn und hinten fast gleichmässig gerundet, mit abgerundeten Hinterecken, auf der Scheibe vorn höckerig, hinten einfach punktiert.

Schildchen sehr klein, punktförmig.

Flügeldecken walzenförmig, mit geraden Seiten, schwach vertieftem Nahtstreifen, dichten Punktreihen und einem beim ♂ mit Haken versehenen, beim ♀ kreisrunden Absturz.

Vorderbrust mit kurzem Fortsatz.

Hüften getrennt.

Schienen an der Aussenkante gerundet und gezähnt, an der Spitze die innere Ecke mit einem Enddorn.

Fussglieder rund, drittes nicht verbreitert.

Bauch gerade.

Geographische Verbreitung der Arten. — Es sind zwölf Arten beschrieben : sie finden sich in Europa, Kleinasien, Afrika, Nord- und Südamerika.

1. *X. ambitiosus*, Schaufuss, Berl. Ent. Zeitschr. Vol. 42. p. 109 (1897).   Gabun.
2. *X. bicuspis*, Reitter, Wien. Ent. Zeit. Vol. 6, p. 196 (1887).   Syrien.
3. *X. bispinus*, Duftschmid, Fauna Austr. Vol. 3, p. 92 (1825). — **Taf. 5,**   Europa, Nordamerika.
   Fig. 45.
4. *X. bituberculatus*, Hagedorn, Deutsche Ent. Zeitschr. p. 1 (1910). —   Kamerun.
   Taf. 9, Fig. 32, 33, 34, 35.
5. *X. biuncus*, Reitter, Best.-Tab. Borkenkäfer. p. 87 (1894).   Südeuropa.
6. *X. chiriquensis*, Blandford, Biol. Centr. Amer. Col. Vol. 4 (6), p. 189   Panama.
   (1898).
7. *X. congonus*, Hagedorn, Deutsche Ent. Zeitschr. p. 375 (1908).   Kongo.
8. *X. cucurbitae*, Le Conte, Bull. U. S. Geol. Surv. Vol. 5, p. 519 (1879).   Nordamerika.
9. *X. decipiens*, Le Conte, Proc. Amer. Philos. Soc. Vol. 17, p. 624 (1878).   Nordamerika.
10. *X. exul*, Reitter, Wien. Ent. Zeit. Vol. 10, p. 199 (1891).   Transkaspien.
11. *X. granulatus*, Ferrari, Börkenkäfer, p. 40 (1867).   Venezuela.
12. *X. uncinatus*, Eichhoff, Beri. Ent. Zeitschr. Vol. 15, p. 134 (1871).   Columbien.

69. GENUS ACANTHOTOMICUS, BLANDFORD

Acanthotomicus. Blandford, Trans. Ent. Soc. Lond. p. 89 (1894).

ORIGINALDIAGNOSE : Blandford, loc. cit.·

» Antennarum funiculus 5-articulatus, articulis 2-5 latitudine crescentibus, clava ovalis, compressa, suturis fere obsoletis fortiter curvatis, articulo primo ovali, ceteris lunatis. Prosternum processu nullo. Episterna metathoracica linearia. Tibiæ anticæ ad apicem dilatatæ, spinosæ. Corpus cylindricum, elytris ad apicem retusis, ambitu retusionis fortiter multi-spinato, stria suturali vix impressa.·

» Closely allied to *Tomicus*, but differing in the much stronger elytral armature, which in *Tomicus* exhibits an uniformly progressive diminution, as the species grow smaller, down to the genus or subgenus *Pityogenes* Bedel. The antennal club is oval, its sutures are quite superficial and only marked by a pubescent border, the first joint is longitudinally oval and embraced at the sides by the succeeding joint, as in *Xylocleptes* Ferrari, with which the elytral structure has no affinity. The mouth parts do not differ from these of *Tomicus*, the maxilla is simply sinuate internally, and not produced into a rounded angle, but this angle is wanting in *Pityogenes* and is not a generic character. »

Charaktere. — Die Gattung ist mir unbekannt.

Geographische Verbreitung der Arten. — Es sind drei Arten beschrieben, eine aus Japan, eine aus Ostindien und eine von Sumatra.

1. *A. spinosus*, Blandford, Trans. Ent. Soc. Lond. p. 90 (1894).   Japan.
2. *A. sumatranus*, Strohmeyer, Ent. Wochenblatt, Vol. 16, p. 69 (1908).   Palembang.
3. *A. truncatus*, Stebbing, Calcutta For. Bull. Vol. 2, p. 40 (1907).   Assam.

70. Genus TAPHRORYCHUS, Eichhoff

Taphrorychus. Eichhoff, Ratio Tomic. p. 204 (1879).
Bostrychus. Herbst, Käfer Europas, Vol. 5, p. 116 (1793).
Tomicus. Thomson, Scand. Col. Vol. 7, p. 366 (1857).
Dryocœtes. Ferrari, Börkenkäfer, p. 28 (1867).
Ips. Marsham, Ent. Brit. p. 53 (1802).

ORIGINALDIAGNOSE : Eichhoff, loc. cit.

« Caput globosum, receptum. Mentum oblongo-quadratum, lateribus post medium sinuatum et versus basin iterum dilatatum ; ligula parva, mento prope apicem inserta, obtusa. Submentum occultatum, vix conspicuum. Maxillæ lobo subsecuriformi antrorsum angustato, intus spinulis compressis ciliato. Palpi labiales articulis 1 et 2 longitudine subæqualibus, tertio parvo. Antennæ funiculo 5-articulato, articulo eius primo crasso, sequentibus multo minoribus, latitudine sensim crescentibus, capitulo orbiculari triannulato. Pronotum haud transversum immarginatum. Prosternum processu distincto. Tibiæ sublineares reetæ, apice oblique truncatæ, extus spinuloso-dentatæ. »

Charaktere. — Körperform cylindrisch; Länge 2 bis 2.5 mm.; Farbe schwarzbraun, mässig glänzend; Skulptur wenig kräftig; Behaarung lang, weissgrau.

Kopf kugelig, ins Halsschild zurückgezogen.

Stirn beim ♂ gewölbt, dünn behaart, beim ♀ abgeflacht mit dichter gelber Haarbürste.

Augen oblong, flach, vorn ausgerandet.

Fühler mit fünfgliedriger Geissel, die kürzer als die Keule ist; diese kreisrund, flach, auf beiden Seiten mit zwei oder drei bogenförmigen Nähten.

Vorderkiefer kräftig, gezähnt.

Mittelkiefer mit beilförmiger, nach vorn verschmälerter Innenlade, deren Kaukante mit breitgedrückten geraden Dornzähnen besetzt ist.

Kiefertaster : Glied 1 und 2 gleichlang, Glied 3 am kleinsten.

Hinterkiefer bilden ein beinahe quadratisches, an den Seiten ausgebuchtetes Kinn, an dessen Spitze die kleine stumpfe Zunge sitzt.

Lippentaster : Glied 1 und 2 gleichlang, Glied 3 am kleinsten.

Halsschild so lang als breit, cylindrisch, mit ungerandeter Basis, vorn stärker gerunzelt, hinten punktiert.

Schildchen klein, rundlich, glatt, gewölbt.

Flügeldecken walzenförmig, punktiert-gestreift, Absturz beim ♂ kreisrund, abgeflacht, mit etwas erhöhter Naht, beim ♀ flach gewölbt.

Vorderbrust bis zu den Hüften ausgeschnitten, nach hinten mit scharfspitzigem Fortsatz.

Vorderhüften etwas getrennt, Mittel- und Hinterhüften weiter voneinander entfernt.

Schienen schmal, nach vorn verbreitert, Innenspitze hakenförmig, Aussenkante spärlich gezähnt.

Fussglieder 1, 2, 3 gleichlang und rund.

Bauch gerade.

Geographische Verbreitung der Arten. — Es sind fünf Arten beschrieben, die nur in dem alten Nordreich vorkommen.

1. *T. bicolor*, Herbst, Käfer Europas, Vol. 5, p. 116 (1793).   Europa.
2. *T. Bulmerincqui*, Kolenati, Melet. Ent. Vol. 3, p. 39 (1846).   Kaukasus.

3. *T. hirtellus*, Eichhoff, Ratio Tomic. p. 208 (1879).   Anatolien.
4. *T. siculus*, Eggers, Il Natural. Sicil. Vol. 20, n° 6-8 (1908).   Sizilien.
5. *T. villifrons*, Dufour, Exkurs. Ossan, p. 91 (1843).   Mittelmeerländer.

71. Genus CACTOPINUS, Schwarz

Cactopinus. Schwarz, Psyche, Vol. 8, Suppl. 1, p. 11 (1899).

ORIGINALDIAGNOSE : Schwarz, loc. cit.

« Subfamily *Tomicinae.* Body moderately slender, head subglobose, retracted into the thorax; antennæ short, shape slightly shorter than the funicle, widening apically, convex at outer edge and here furnished with a few long setæ; funicle five-jointed; the first large, obconical, joints 2-4 small, increasing in width. joint 5 closely applied to the club and twice as wide as long; club oval, comparatively small, about as long as the funicle, sparsely pubescent on both sides and with two distinct straight or nearly straight sutures. Clypeus in the ♂ armed with a long process consisting of two cylindrical rods, which are laterally connate except near the tip, where a contraction and separation of the rods takes place.

» Prothorax as long as wide or slightly longer than wide, rounded at the sides, which are not margined; disk in both sexes with longitudinal tuberculated and distinctly elevated median area, which projects beyond the base of the thorax as a triangular lobe.

» Elytra with the basal margin not elevated, conjointly rounded at tip, surface punctate-striate, sutural stria distinctly impressed, declivity steep, with the sutural space sulcate.

» Prosternum very short in front of coxæ, which are nearly contiguous. Abdomen horizontal, segments 1 and 2 of equal length, each about as long as segments 3 and 4 combined. Legs rather short haired; front tibiæ narrow, very little dilated apically, outer edge not arcuate neither denticulate nor serrate, slightly sinuate near apex, outer apical angle moderately produced laterally, terminal mucro straight and moderately slender, middle and hind tibiæ slightly more slender than the anterior tibiæ; tarsi short, joints 1-3 of equal length, joint 3 not dilated, joint 4 distinct, claw-joint long and slender. Length 1.7 to 2.2 mm. »

Charaktere. — Die Gattung ist mir unbekannt geblieben.

Geographische Verbreitung der Art. — Es ist nur eine Art aus Nordamerika beschrieben worden, welche daselbst in Riesenkaktus (*Cereus giganteus*) lebt.
1. *C. Hubbardi*, Schwarz, Psyche. Vol. 8, Suppl. 1, p. 11 (1899).   Arizona.

72. Genus TIAROPHORUS, Schreiner

Tiarophorus. Schreiner. Deutsche Ent. Zeitschr. Vol. 26. p. 246 (1882).

ORIGINALDIAGNOSE : Schreiner, loc. cit.

« Caput in thoracem retractum. Frons in feminis convexa. in maribus excavate et processu marginali elevato circumdata. Oculi simplices reniformes. antice supra antennas insertas emarginati. Antennarum funiculi 6-articulati, articulus primus crassiusculus, bulbiformis. ceteri 5 minores æquales transversi, capitulum compressum, orbiculatum solidum, absque suturis. Thorax latitudine longior, dorso æqualiter profunde punctatus. Elytra punctato-striata, declivitate postica integra. Tibiæ compressæ, extus dentibus serratæ, apice intus spina elongatæ. Tarsorum articulus tertius simplex, secundo duplo fere longior, quartus minimus, ultimus longissimus. Inter *Dryocoetes* et *Hylocurus* inserendus. »

Charaktere. — Die Gattung ist mir unbekannt geblieben.

Geographische Verbreitung der Art. — Es ist nur eine Art aus Afrika beschrieben.

1. *T. elongatus*, Schreiner, Deutsche Ent. Zeitschr. Vol. 26, p. 247 (1882).   Guineaküste.

7. TRIBUS HYLOCURINÆ

UEBERSICHT DER GATTUNGEN

73. GENUS ARAPTUS, EICHHOFF

Araptus. Eichhoff, Berl. Ent. Zeitschr. p. 136 (1871).

ORIGINALDIAGNOSE : Eichhoff, loc. cit.

« Tarsi articulis tribus primis simplicibus, tibiæ lineares, apice truncatæ.

» Caput globosum, oculis simplicibus oblongis. Antennæ funiculo 5-articulato, capitulo maximo ovali solido. Mentum triangulare, ligula- lanceolata, acuminata, apice summa subtilissime emarginata. Maxillae mala intus setis rigidis ciliata. »

Charaktere. — Körperform gestreckt länglich; 3 mm. lang; Farbe braun; Skulptur kräftig; Behaarung spärlich.

Kopf kugelig, in das Halsschild zurückgezogen.

Stirn konkav, stark behaart.

Augen vorn ausgerandet, länglich, querstehend.

Fühler mit fünfgliedriger Geissel und flacher solider nahtloser Keule.

Vorderkiefer kräftig.

Mittelkiefer mit gegen die Spitze verschmälerter Innenlade, deren Kaukante mit geraden starken Borstenzähnen besetzt ist.

Kiefertaster : Glied 1 und 2 querbreiter, Glied 3 kegelförmig, länger als die anderen.

Hinterkiefer zu einem an der Spitze gerundeten, nach der Basis stark verschmälerten Kinne verschmolzen, an dessen Basis die schmale, lanzenförmig zugespitzte, an der Spitze mit langen Haaren besetzte Zunge angefügt ist.

Lippentaster lang, die Glieder an Länge gleich, an Breite nach der Spitze zu abnehmend.

Halsschild kegelförmig, nach vorne verschmälert, an den Seiten und an der Basis gerandet, vorn schwach gehöckert, hinten schwach punktiert.

Schildchen klein, glatt.

Flügeldecken länger als das Halsschild, ziemlich walzenförmig; Absturz mehr weniger steil, mit Zähnen oder Knötchen besetzt, mässig behaart, Naht im Absturz erhaben.

Vorderbrust mit Fortsatz zwischen den Vorderhüften.

Mittelhüften weit voneinander getrennt.

Hinterhüften genähert.

Vorderschienen linear, an der Spitze gestreckt, Aussenkante gezähnt.

Fussglieder 1, 2, 3 einander gleich, rund, mit behaarten Sohlen.

Bauch gerade.

Geographische Verbreitung der Arten. — Es sind nur zwei Arten bekannt, von denen merkwürdiger Weise die eine in Südamerika, die andere in Kamerun gefunden ist.

1. *A. camerunus*, Hagedorn, Deutsche Ent. Zeitschr. p. 743 (1909). — Kamerun.

   Taf. 9, Fig. 42, 43.

2. *A. rufopalliatus*, Eichhoff, Berl. Ent. Zeitschr. Vol. 15, p. 136 (1871). · Neu-Granada.

74. Genus PŒCILIPS, Schaufuss

Pœcilips. Schaufuss, Berl. Ent. Zeitschr. p. 110 (1897).

ORIGINALDIAGNOSE : Schaufuss, loc. cit. giebt die Diagnose von Genus und Species zusammengemischt. Es müssen daher die Gattungsmerkmale herausgesucht werden. In der folgenden Anführung sind also die artlichen Merkmale fortgelassen.

» Oblongus. Antennarum scapus curvatus, clavatus; funiculus 5-articulatus, capitulo brevior. Capitulum rotundato-ovatum, lineis duabus transversis tripartitum. Oculi reniformes, antice excisi. Mentum productum quadratum. Frons transverso-convexa. Thorax latitudine longior, antice marginatus, pronotum a prosterno sutura elevata seiunctum; basis tenuiter marginata; discus glaber, sat dense punctatus, apice scabratus, spatio mediano lævi. Scutellum bene distinctum. Elytra thorace vix latiora, cylindrica, valde convexa, posterius angustata, glabra, punctato-striata. Coxæ anticæ valde globosæ sese tangentes. Tibiæ anticæ extus fere rectæ, intus curvato-ampliatæ, apice oblique truncatæ, extus dentibus tribus vel quatuor magnis armatæ. »

Charaktere. — Körperform länglich, cylindrisch, Farbe hellbraun bis pechschwarz, glänzend, spärlich behaart; Skulptur grob bis mässig stark, Länge 1.6 bis 2.5 mm.

Kopf ins Halsschild zurückgezogen; Stirn konvex oder konkav.

Augen nierenförmig ausgerandet.

Fühler mit fünfgliedriger Geissel und gerundet-eiförmiger Keule mit zwei Nähten.

Vorderkiefer kräftig, ungezähnt.

Mittelkiefer latet.

Hinterkiefer zu einem quadratischen, vorgezogenen Kinne verschmolzen.

Halsschild länger als breit : die grösste Breite liegt im hinteren Drittel, wohin sich das Schild von der Basis an gerade ausbreitet, von da ab zieht es sich in scharfem Bogen nach vorn ein ; der Apex ist für sich allein flach gerundet; seitlich und an der Basis gerandet. Scheibe vorn rauh gehöckert, hinten ziemlich dicht punktiert.

Schildchen klein, aber deutlich dreieckig.

Flügeldecken cylindrisch, nach hinten verschmälert; Schultern etwas erhöht; punktiert gestreift, Zwischenräume prob punktiert mit regelmässigen Borstenreihen.

Vorderbrust mit scharfem, kurzem Fortsatz.

Vorderhüften einander berührend; Mittel- und Hinterhüften voneinander entfernt.

Schienen aussen fast gerade, innen bogenförmig verbreitert, an der Spitze abgestutzt. Aussenkante gezähnt.

Bauch gerade.

Geographische Verbreitung der Arten. — Es sind zwei Arten aus West- und Ostafrika beschrieben worden.

1. *P. ciliatus*, Hagedorn, Deutsche Ent. Zeitschr. p. 743 (1909). — **Taf. 5,**   Deutsch-Ostafrika. **Fig. 46.**

2. *P. sannio*, Schaufuss, Berl. Ent. Zeitschr. Vol. 42, p. 110 (1897).   Gabun; Sierra Leone.

75. GENUS CTENOPHORUS, CHAPUIS

Ctenophorus. Chapuis, Mém. Soc. Sciences Liége, p. 105 (1869); Synops. Scolyt. p. 257 (1873).

Scolytodes. Ferrari, Borkenkäfer, p. 77 (1867).

Bostrichus. Dejean, Cat. (cd. 3), p. 331 (1833-36).

ORIGINALDIAGNOSE : Chapuis, loc. cit.

« Antennarum funiculus 6-articulatus, articulis 4° et 6° maioribus, 3° et 5° minoribus, clava breviter ovalis, solida. Tarsi tenues, cylindrici, articulo 3° integro. »

Charaktere. — Körperform länglich, Länge 2 mm., Farbe braun, glänzend ; Skulptur und Behaarung schwach.

Kopf mit Andeutung eines Rüssels, ins Halsschild zurückgezogen, Stirn behaart oder glatt.

Augen queroval, ganzrandig, flach.

Fühler in einer tiefen Grube vor den Augen eingelenkt, mit sechsgliedriger Geissel, deren Glieder abwechselnd grösser und kleiner sein sollen. Dies trifft aber nicht bei allen Exemplaren zu — vielleicht kommt das nur einem Geschlecht zu.

Vorderkiefer schwach entwickelt.

Mittelkiefer mit gerundeter, stumpfzugespitzter Innenlade, an deren Kaukante circa sechszehn dolchartige spitze Stachelzähne sitzen.

Kiefertaster mit drei cylindrischen, ziemlich gleich langen, aber an Breite abnehmenden Gliedern.

Hinterkiefer zu einem an der Basis verschmälerten, an der Spitze verbreiterten, an den Seiten sanft geschwungenen und leicht eingebogenen Kinne verschmolzen, an dessen Basis die lanzettförmige, mit ihrer scharfen Spitze bis zur Mitte des zweiten Tastergliedes reichende, ebenso wie die Innenfläche des Kinnes mit starren Dornen spärlich besetzte Zunge angesetzt ist.

Lippentaster mit drei ziemlich gleich grossen, verkehrt kegelförmigen Gliedern.

Halsschild wenig länger als breit, nach vorn verengt, seitlich gerandet, stark gewölbt. glatt.

Schildchen klein, dreieckig.

Flügeldecken an der Basis nicht erhaben und nicht gekerbt, nach hinten allmählich abfallend, sehr schwach skulptiert, glatt, glänzend.

Vorderbrust mit kurzem Fortsatz zwischen den Vorderhüften.

Hüften voneinander abstehend, Mittelhüften weiter als Hinterhüften.

Beine lang, Vorderschienen an der Spitze mit zwei stärkeren Zähnchen, Mittel- und Hinterschienen mit schwachen Zähnen an der Aussenkante. Sämmtliche Schienen lang, schmal, wenig nach der Spitze verbreitert.

Fussglieder 1, 2, 3 einander gleich und rund.

Bauch wagerecht.

Geographische Verbreitung der Art. — Es ist nur eine Art aus dem Südreich bekannt.
1. *C. laevigatus*, Ferrari. Borkenkäfer, p. 77 (1867).   Columbia.

76. Genus HEXACOLUS, Eichhoff

Hexacolus. Eichhoff, Berl. Ent. Zeitschr. Vol. 11, p. 399 (1867).

ORIGINALDIAGNOSE : Eichhoff, loc. cit.

« Maxillæ mala extus spinulis compressis obtusis ciliata. Palpi maxillares articulo 1º brevi, transverso, 2º multo longiore, 3º angustiore. Antennæ funiculo 6-articulato, articulo 1º crasso, globoso, 2º parvo obconico, sequentibus latitudine fortiter crescentibus ; capitulo subannulato. Pronotum a prosterno sutura elevata sejunctum. Coxæ anteriores late distantes. » '

Charaktere. — Körperform lang eiförmig, Länge circa 2 mm., Farbe braun, glänzend, Skulptur und Behaarung schwach.

Kopf mit Andeutung eines Rüssels, nicht sehr tief ins Halsschild zurückgezogen.

Stirn behaart oder glatt : ob sekundäres Geschlechtsmerkmal?

Fühler mit sechsgliederiger Geissel, deren erstes Glied dick und kugelförmig, das zweite klein, verkehrt kegelförmig, die folgenden an Breite zunehmend sind. Keule etwas flachgedrückt, oval, mit zwei wenig deutlichen Nähten.

Augen queroval, nicht ausgerandet.

Vorderkiefer schwach.

Mittelkiefer mit breiter, beilförmiger, an der Kaukante mit sechzehn ziemlich geraden, breiten Zähnen besetzt.

Kiefertaster : Glied 1 kurz und querbreiter, 2 viel länger, 3 schmäler.

Hinterkiefer oblong, nach der Basis verschmälert, an der Spitze abgestutzt, Zunge an der Basis der Lippe angesetzt, schmal und lang zugespitzt.

Lippentaster : Glied 1 und 2 querbreiter, 3 schmäler.

Halsschild halbelliptisch, an den Seiten und der Basis erhaben gerandet, an Länge und Breite beinahe gleich.

Schildchen gerandet.

Flügeldecken um die Hälfte länger als das Halsschild, an der Basis gerandet, Spitze konvex gerandet, schwach skulptiert.

Vorderbrust mit Fortsatz zwischen den weit auseinanderstehenden Vorderhüften.

Mittel- und Hinterhüften voneinander getrennt.

Schienen schmal. gegen die abgestutzte Spitze verbreitert, Aussenkante gezähnt.

Fussglieder 1. 2, 3 einander gleich, einfach.

Bauch gerade.

Geographische Verbreitung der Arten. — Die Gattung beschränkt sich auf Centrai- und Südamerika, woselbst sieben Arten vorkommen.

1. *E. bañosus,* Hagedorn, Deutsche Ent. Zeitschr. p. 743 (1909).   Ecuador.
2. *E. Bruchi,* Hagedorn, ibidem, p. 743 (1909). — Taf. **5, Fig. 47, 47a;**   Argentinien.   **Taf. 9, Fig. 39, 40, 41.**
3. *E. glaber,* Eichhoff, Berl. Ent. Zeitschr. p. 400 (1867).   Cuba.
4. *E. melanocephalus,* Blandford, Biol. Centr. Amer. Col. Vol. 4 (6), p. 181   Guatemala.   (1897).
5. *E. piceus,* Blandford, ibidem. p. 183 (1897).   Panama.
6. *E. setosus,* Blandford. ibidem, p. 181 (1897).   Guatemala.
7. *E. unipunctatus,* Blandford, ibidem. p. 182 (1897).   Guatemala.

77. Genus ORTHASPISTES, Hagedorn

Orthaspistes. Hagedorn, Deutsche Ent. Zeitschr. p. 733 (1909).

Hypaspistes. Hagedorn, ibidem, p. 374 (1908).

ORIGINALDIAGNOSE : Hagedorn, loc. cit.

« Caput globosum receptum maris scuto erecto ornatum, feminæ immune. maxillæ mala rotundata, intus spinulis compressis, extus setis longioribus ornata, palpi maxillares articulo 1° maiore, 2° minore, 3° conico longiore. Antennæ funiculus 6-articulatus, articulo 1° crassiusculo balbiformi, 2° multo minore, ceteris transversis latitudine crescentibus, capitulo ovato, suturis duabus incurvatis. Prothorax æqualiter punctatus, pronotum a prosterno sutura elevata sejunctum, prosternum processu brevi. Coxæ anteriores distantes. Tibiæ versus apicem dilatatæ, extus rotundatæ, serratæ. Tarsi recepti articulis 1, 2, 3 subæqualibus. Corpus cylindricum, stria suturali in elytris impressa. »

Charaktere. — Körperform cylindrisch. Länge 3 mm., Farbe braun, glänzend, Behaarung hell, Skulptur derb.

Kopf mässig ins Halsschild zurückgezogen. beim ♀ mit behaarter Stirn, beim ♂ trägt die Stirn einen 1.5 mm. langen, 1 mm. breiten, nach vorn gebogenen Schild und vor demselben zwei einander zugeneigte Dornen von ungleicher Länge.

Augen queroval, vorne ausgerandet.

Fühler in der Ausrandung der Augen hinter der Basis des Kopfschildes eingelenkt. mit sechsgliedriger Geissel und spitz-eiförmiger flacher Keule, die zwei nach der Spitze konvexe Nähte zeigt.

Vorderkiefer kräftig, gezähnt.

Mittelkiefer mit stark gerandeter Innenlade, deren Spitze die Taster überragt und deren Kaukante mit elf leichtgebogenen breiten Stachelzähnen besetzt ist, während die äussere Seite, die squama palpigera, lange Haarborsten trägt.

Kiefertaster sehr tief inseriert, die Glieder 1 und 2 sind cylindrisch, 3 am schmalsten.

Hinterkiefer sind bei der Präparation verloren gegangen.

Halsschild elliptisch, seitlich gerandet, gleichmässig körnig punktiert.

Flügeldecken cylindrisch, Nahtstreifen vertieft, ziemlich grob skulptiert, Absturz beim ♂ stumpf-gewölbt, beim ♀ abgestutzt, mit erhöhter Naht und gerandetem Umfang.

Vorderbrust mit kurzem Fortsatz zwischen den Vorderhüften.

Vorderhüften voneinander abstehend.

Schienen nach der Spitze erweitert, aussen gerundet und bedornt.

Fussglieder 1, 2, 3 einfach, beinahe einander gleich.

Bauch gerade.

Geographische Verbreitung der Art. — Es ist nur eine Art dieser so merkwürdig aus-gezeichneten Gattung aus Kamerun bekannt.

1. *O. camerunus*, Hagedorn. Deutsche Ent. Zeitschr. p. 374 (1908)   Kamerun.

78. GENUS PYCNARTHRUM, EICHHOFF

Pycnarthrum. Eichhoff, Ratio Tomic. p. 104 (1879).
Nemobius. Chapuis, Synops. Scolyt. p. 250 (1873).
Hypoborus. Ferrari, Borkenkäfer p. 19 (1867).

ORIGINALDIAGNOSE : Eichhoff, loc. cit.

« Caput exsertum, rostello brevi auctum. Maxillæ lobo versus apicem angustato, apice intus setulis ciliato. Antennæ funiculo 6-articulato, articulo 1° ejus crassiusculo, bulbiformi, 2° turbinato, ceteris transversis, brevibus, arcte coactis, latitudine sensim crescentibus ; capitulo oblongo-ovato, acuminato 3 articulato. Oculi elongati integri, grosse granulati. Coxæ anteriores late discretæ. Proster-num processu iongo et lato inter coxæ productum. Episterna metathoracis latiuscula. Tibiæ compressæ antrorsum valde dilatatæ, extus parcius dentatæ, anteriores apice extus rotundatæ, posticæ oblique truncatæ. »

Charaktere. — Länglich eiförmig, Länge 2 mm., Farbe heller oder dunkler braun, Skulptur und Bekleidung mit Schuppen mässig kräftig entwickelt.

Kopf mit schwachem Rüssel, nicht vom Halsschild bedeckt.

Augen gross, stossen unten fast zusammen, sind nicht ausgerandet.

Fühler mit sechsgliedriger Geissel und eiförmig zugespitzter Keule mit zwei Nähten. Das unterste Keulenglied ist an der äusseren Seite verhüllt.

Vorderkiefer kräftig.

Mittelkiefer mit schmaler, nach der Spitze verengter Innenlade, deren Kaukante mit Borsten-zähnen besetzt ist.

Kiefertaster : Glied 1 und 2 querbreiter, das dritte so lang als breit, cylindrisch.

Hinterkiefer zu einem oblongen, nach der Basis verschmälerten und eingebuchteten Kinne verschmolzen, in dessen Mitte die schmale und zugespitzte Zunge angeheftet ist.

Lippentaster : Glieder etwas abgeflacht, so lang als breit.

Halsschild seitlich gerandet, oben gewölbt, schmäler als die Flügeldecken, ohne rauhe Skulptur.

Schildchen klein, gerundet.

Flügeldecken breiter als das Halsschild, einfach abgewölbt, stark skulptiert und mit Schuppen und Borsten besetzt.

Vorderbrust mit langem und breitem Fortsatz zwischen den Vorderhüften.

Hüften voneinander abstehend.

Beine : Vorderschenkel lang und stark verbreitert und verdickt, die andern schmal.

Schienen stark nach vorn verbreitert, mit gezähnter Aussenkante, die vorderen nach Aussen abgerundet, die andern einfach abgestutzt.

Fussglieder 1, 2, 3 einfach, rund, dünn.

Bauch horizontal.

Geographische Verbreitung der Arten. — Es sind fünf Arten aus Centralamerika beschrieben :

1. *P. gracile*, Eichhoff, Ratio Tomic. p. 104 (1879). Cuba.
2. *P. Lambottei*, Chapuis, Synops. Scolyt. p. 250 (1873). Mexiko, Guatemala.
3. *P. pallidum*, Chapuis, ibidem, p. 249 (1872). Guadeloupe.
4. *P. setulosum*, Waterhouse, Proc. Linn. Soc. Lond. Vol. 20, p. 553 (1894). Fernando-Norouña.
5. *P. transversum*, Blandford. Biol. Centr. Amer. Col. Vol. 4 (6). p. 177 Guatemala.
   (1897).

79. Genus MICRACIS, Le Conte

Micracis. Le Conte, Trans. Amer. Ent. Soc. Vol. 2, p. 164 (1868).

ORIGINALDIAGNOSE : Le Conte, loc. cit.

« The body in this genus is elongate, cylindrical, with the posterior declivity of the elytra convex, and the suture prolonged into an acute point. The club of the antennæ is oval, compressed, finely pubescent, with an elongated basal smooth spot (the representative of the basal joint as in *Scolytus*), extending for more than half its length ; the other sutures form loops parallel with this smooth space ; the funiculus is closely connected, gradually becoming shorter and broader, forming a conical mass. The scape of the antennæ is broadly dilated and fringed towards the extremity with very long hairs, almost as in some of the genera allied to *Platypus*. »

Charaktere. — Körperform länglich, cylindrisch, Länge 2.5 mm., Farbe braun, Skulptur und Bekleidung schwach ; Flügeldecken in eine Spitze ausgezogen.

Kopf kugelig, ins Halsschild zurückgezogen.

Augen länglich, vorn wenig ausgebuchtet.

Fühler mit dreieckigem zusammengedrücktem Schaft, der an der Spitze ein Büschel langer Haare trägt, kurzer sechsgliedriger Geissel, deren erstes Glied nicht breiter als die folgenden, queren, an Grösse ziemlich gleichen ist; Keule behaart, oval, geschuppt, mit gegen die Spitze winklig geknickten Nähten (**Taf. 5, Fig. 47c**).

Vorderkiefer wenig kräftig, aber spitz.

Hinterkiefer oblong, Zunge nach vorn verschmälert, an der Basis des Kinnes angesetzt.

Lippentaster : Glied 1 länger als die beiden andern.

Halsschild länger als breit, seitlich gerandet.

Schildchen rund.

Flügeldecken mit gerader Basis, schwach reihenförmig punktiert, konvex gerandet, abschüssig, in eine gemeinsame Spitze ausgezogen.

Vorderhüften einander berührend.

Beine kurz ; Schenkel breit zusammengedrückt, Schienen verbreitert, an der Spitze schräg abgestutzt, ganzrandig, in einen Haken ausgezogen.

Fussglieder 1, 2, 3 gleich rund.

Bauch horizontal.

Geographische Verbreitung der Arten. — Es sind sieben Arten aus dem neuen Nordreich und eine aus dem Südreich bekannt.

1. *M. aculeatus*, Le Conte, Trans. Amer. Ent. Soc. Vol. 2, p. 165 (1868).   Nordamerika.
2. *M. acutipennis*, Eichhoff, Ratio Tomic. p. 302 (1879).   Bahia.
3. *M. asperulus*, Le Conte, Proc. Amer. Philos. Soc. Vol. 17, p. 626 (1878).   Nordamerika.
4. *M. hirtellus*, Le Conte, ibidem, Vol. 15, p. 368 (1876).   Nordamerika.
5. *M. nanula*, Le Conte, ibidem. p. 369 (1876).   Nordamerika.
6. *M. opacicollis*, Le Conte, ibidem, Vol. 17, p. 625 (1878).   Nordamerika.
7. *M. rudis*, Le Conte, ibidem, Vol. 15, p. 369 (1876).   Nordamerika.
8. *M. suturalis*, Le Conte, Trans. Amer. Ent. Soc. Vol. 2, p. 165 (1868).   Nordamerika.

80. Genus PRIONOSCELES, Blandford

Prionosceles. Blandford, Biol. Centr. Amer. Col. Vol. 4 (6), p. 177 (1897).

ORIGINALDIAGNOSE : Blandford, loc. cit.

« Prothorax basi distincte marginatus, quam elytra vix angustior. Coxæ anticæ at mediæ late distantes. Abdominis segmenta 3um et 4um brevia. Pedes longi; tibiæ validæ, versus apicem fortiter dilatatæ, extus serratæ, mediæ et posteriores ad apicem rotundatæ; tarsi recepti. »

Charaktere. — Körperform kurz und robust, Länge 1.7 bis 3.4 mm., Farbe dunkel schwarzbraun ; Skulptur und Bekleidung schwach, daher glänzend.

Kopf etwas verlängert, beinahe rüsselförmig ausgezogen.

Augen nierenförmig, vorn stark ausgerandet.

Fühler nicht sehr lang, mit sechsgliedriger Geissel, deren Glieder an Länge, aber nicht an Breite allmählich zunehmen ; Keule länglich-eiförmig mit zwei gebogenen Nähten.

Vorderkiefer breit und vorstehend.

Mittelkiefer mit schmaler, mit enggestellten flachen Dornzähnen an der Kaukante besetzter Innenlade.

Kiefertaster : Glieder gleichlang, nach der Spitze verschmälert, das dritte zweimal so lang als breit.

Hinterkiefer zu einem etwas längeren als breiten, nach der Spitze verbreiterten Kinne verschmolzen, die schmale eiförmige Zunge sitzt nahe der Basis auf und reicht nicht bis zum obern Rande des Kinnes.

Lippentaster : Glieder 1 und 2 so lang als breit, 3 kürzer, aussen beborstet.

Halsschild an der Basis gerandet, cylindrisch, vorn verengt, daselbst gröber skulptiert als hinten.

Schildchen ziemlich gross, gerundet.

Flügeldecken an der Basis gerandet, walzenförmig, hinten gewölbt abfallend, schwach punktiertgestreift und gekörnt im hintern Abschnitt.

Vorderbrust mit starkem querem Fortsatz.

Hüften voneinander abstehend.

Schienen nach der Spitze verbreitert, Aussenrand mit starken Zähnen besetzt, bei den Vorderschienen stehen die beiden letzten, stärksten Zähne durch einen tiefen Einschnitt voneinander getrennt; an den beiden hinteren Paaren ist die Spitze einfach abgerundet und gesägt.

Fussglieder 1, 2, 3 einfach rund, lang und zart, in Furchen an der innern Schienenfläche einlegbar. Bauch horizontal.

Geographische Verbreitung der Arten. —Zwei centralamerikanische Arten sind beschrieben :

1. *P. atratus*, Blandford, Biol. Centr. Amer. Col. Vol. 4 (6), p. 178 (1897).   Guatemala, Panama.[dorn].
2. *P. maurus*, Blandford, ibidem. p. 178 (1897). — **Taf. 5, Fig. 47 b.**   Guatemala, Ecuador (Hage-

81. Genus EPOMADIUS, Blandford

Epomadius. Blandford, Biol. Centr. Amer. Col. Vol. 4 (6), p. 179 (1897).

Originaldiagnose : Blandford, loc. cit.

« Caput subrostratum; antennarum funiculus sat longus, articulis 3°-6ᵐ transversis, latitudine crescentibus, clava ovata. Prothorax elytris angustior, basi submarginatus, anterius supra subasperatus; carina lateralis utroque obsolescens et plaga magna depressa pube densa vestita antice terminata. Coxæ anticæ et intermediæ late distantes. Tibiæ lineares supra spinulis 2 aut 3 serratæ; Tarsi breves, articulo 1° sequenti breviore, 2° et 3° lateraliter compressis. »

Charaktere. — Körperform länglich, schmal, Länge 2.5 mm., Skulptur schwach; Bekleidung mit kurzen, anliegenden Härchen.

Kopf schwach gerüsselt.

Fühler mit sechsgliedriger Geissel, Keule oval mit zwei schwach gekrümmten Nähten.

Augen queroval, sich nicht bis zur Kehle erstreckend.

Vorderkiefer klein, von dem Vorderrand des Clipeus verdeckt.

Mittel- und Hinterkiefer sind unbekannt.

Halsschild an der Basis nicht gerandet, an den Seiten hinten mit schwacher Andeutung eines Randes, der nach vorn in je einen breiten, seichten, mit kurzen gekräuselten Haaren bedeckten Eindruck übergeht; auf der Scheibe vorn stärker, hinten schwächer und spärlicher granuliert.

Schildchen klein, gerundet.

Flügeldecken breiter als das Halsschild, cylindrisch, mit schwacher Skulptur und mit dünner kurzer anliegender Behaarung; Absturz einfach abgewölbt.

Vorder- und Mittelhüften ziemlich weit auseinanderstehend.

Schienen linear, das vordere Paar mit einfachem Aussenrand und mit ein oder zwei rückwärts gerichteten Dornen an dessen Spitze und einem Dorn neben dem Fussgelenk; Aussenrand der Mittel- und Hinterschienen an der Spitze gerundet, mit drei oder vier Dornen.

Fussglieder 1 ist kurz und rund, 2 und 3 sind seitlich zusammengedrückt.

Bauch horizontal, die Segmente 2, 3, 4 einander beinahe gleich.

Geographische Verbreitung der Art. — Die Gattung ist auf eine Art aus Panama gemacht und mir unbekannt geblieben.

1. *E. culcitatus*, Blandford, Biol. Centr. Amer. Col. Vol. 4 (6), p. 179 (1897). Panama.

82. Genus HYLOCURUS, Eichhoff

Hylocurus. Eichhoff, Berl. Ent. Zeitschr. Vol. 15, p. 133 (1871).

Originaldiagnose : Eichhoff, loc. cit.

« Caput globosum, in thoracem retractum. Antennæ funiculo 6-articulato, capitulo oblongo subgloboso, solido. Maxillarum mala intus setis rigidis ciliata. Mentum subcordatum, palpi labiales articulo 1° longitudine sequentibus duobus consumtis maiore. Tibiæ sublineares, tarsi articulis tribus primis simplicibus. Coxæ approximatæ. »

Charaktere. — Körperform walzenförmig, Länge 1.5 bis 3 mm., Farbe dunkelbraun bis schwarz, Skulptur kräftig, Bekleidung aus spärlichen Haaren bestehend.

Kopf kugelig, vom Halsschild überragt.

Augen länglich, vorne ausgebuchtet.

Fühler mit sechsgliedriger Geissel, queren, nach der Keule breiter werdenden Gliedern und kugeliger solider Keule ohne Nähte.

Vorderkiefer derb.

Mittelkiefer mit nach der Spitze verschmälerter Innenlade, an deren Kaukante breitgedrückte Dornenzähne sitzen.

Hinterkiefer zu einem länglich-herzförmigen, nach der Basis verschmälerten Kinne verschmolzen, an dessen Spitze die kleine Zunge eingefügt ist.

Lippentaster : Glied 1 grösser als die beiden andern zusammen.

Halsschild länglich, ungerandet, cylindrisch, gewölbt, vorderer Rand mitunter rauh gekörnt (bei ♂), hintere Fläche punktiert.

Schildchen ziemlich gross, dreieckig.

Flügeldecken nach hinten verbreitert, steil abfallend, in eine gemeinsame Spitze ausgezogen, stark skulptiert durch tiefe Kerbstreifen; Absturz beim ♂ häufig mit Dornen oder Tuberkeln, die in den Zwischenräumen stehen, umgeben, beim ♀ einfach abfallend.

Vorderhüften einander berührend.

Schienen beinahe linear, aussen ganzrandig. Spitze aussen in einem Haken ausgezogen.

Fussglieder 1, 2, 3 gleichförmig rund.

Bauch horizontal.

Geographische Verbreitung der Arten. — Zehn Arten aus Central- und Südamerika sind bekannt geworden.

1. *H. alienus*, Eichhoff, Ratio Tomic. p. 301 (1879).   Mexiko, Antillen.
2. *H. cancellatus*. Blandford, Biol. Centr. Amer. Col. Vol. 4 (6), p. 221 (1898).   Guatemala.
3. *H. discifer*, Eichhoff, Ratio Tomic. p. 300 (1879).   Venezuela.
4. *H. egenus*, Blandford Biol. Centr. Amer. Col. Vol. 4 (6), p. 222 (1898).   Mexiko.
5. *H. elegans*, Eichhoff, Berl. Ent. Zeitschr. Vol. 15, p. 134 (1871).   Mexiko.
6. *H. errans*. Blandford, Biol. Centr. Amer. Col. Vol. 4 (6), p. 224 (1898).   Mexiko.
7. *H. retusipennis*, Blandford, ibidem, p. 223 (1898).   Mexiko.
8. *H. simplex*, Blandford, ibidem, p. 222 (1898).   Guatemala.
9. *H. spinifex*, Blandford, ibidem, p. 225 (1898).   Mexiko.
10. *H. vagabundus*, Blandford, ibidem, p. 224 (1898).   Mexiko.

83. Genus MICROBORUS, Blandford

Microborus. Blandford, Biol. Centr. Amer. Col. Vol. 4 (6), p. 175 (1897).

ORIGINALDIAGNOSE : Blandford, loc. cit.

« Caput exsertum, parum rostratum. Oculi permagni, supra et infra approximati, grosse granulati. Antennæ breves, clava depressa, subtunicata, apice oblique truncate, suturis concentricis notato. Prothorax subcylindricus, lateraliter sinuatus, inde medio quasi subangustatus. Tarsorum articuli tres primi breves, æquales. »

Charaktere. — Körperform lang und schmal, Länge 1.6 mm., Farbe hellbraungelb mit schwarzem Kopf; mässig starke Skulptur und schwache Behaarung.

Kopf mit schwachem Rüssel.

Augen sehr gross, jedes aus fünf Reihen von groben Linsen zusammengesetzt, oberhalb auf dem Kopfe weiter auseinanderstehend als unterhalb auf der Kehle.

Fühler sehr kurz, Schaft gebogen, Geissel sechsgliedrig, Glieder 2-6 einander gleich, Keule kugelig, etwas abgeflacht, die Nähte auf der innern Seite stärker nach der Spitze gezogen als auf der äusseren Seite, so dass die Keule in Seitenansicht halbverhüllt erscheint und der *Xyleborus*-Keule ähnelt.

Halsschild wenig über der Mitte verengt, die Seiten scheinen daher gebuchtet, die Ränder schwach angedeutet.

Schildchen klein, gerundet, flach.

Flügeldecken an der Basis einfach abgestutzt, walzenförmig, Spitze einfach abgewölbt; schwach skulptiert und behaart.

Vorderbrust ohne Fortsatz.

Vorderhüften voneinander entfernt.

Schienen nicht sehr verbreitert; Aussenkante gesägt; das vordere Paar an der Spitze schräg ausgeschnitten und am untern Winkel mit einem Haken versehen.

Fussglieder 1, 2, 3, kurz gleichförmig und einfach.

Bauch horizontal.

Geographische Verbreitung der Art. — Es ist nur eine Art, die auf ein Exemplar gemacht worden ist, aus Guatemala beschrieben. Sie ist mir unbekannt geblieben.

1. *M. boops*, Blandford, Biol. Centr. Amer. Col. Vol. 4 (6), p. 175 (1897).   Guatemala.

84. GENUS THYSANOES, LE CONTE

Thysanoes. Le Conte, Proc. Amer. Philos. Soc. Vol. 15, p. 369 (1876).

ORIGINALDIAGNOSE : Le Conte, loc. cit.

« This genus ist allied to *Micracis;* the front tibiæ are of the same parallel form, as wide at base as at tip, and not serrate on the outer edge; the antennæ are, however, quite different; the scape is fringed as in *Micracis,* the first joint of the funicle is longer than wide, thicker at the extremity; the remaining five joints are very distinctly separated and become rapidly wider and transverse, by being prolonged at the upperside; they are also fringed with very long hair; the club is elliptical, compressed, rather shining, sparsely hairy, without distinct sensitive surface, without sutures on the inner face, with two indistinct sutures on the outer face, of which the lower one seems straight, and the distal one curved. The eyes are large, transverse, coarsely granulated, and not emarginate; they are separated beneath by a wide gular space. The first and second ventral segments are very large, the others short. Length 1.8 mm. »

Charaktere. — Die Gattung ist mir unbekannt geblieben.

Geographische Verbreitung der Art. — Nur eine Art aus Nordamerika ist beschrieben.

1. *T. fimbricornis*, Le Conte, Proc. Amer. Philos. Soc. Vol. 15, p. 370 (1876).   Nordamerika.

8. TRIBUS ECCOPTOGASTRINÆ

UEBERSICHT DER GATTUNGEN

1. *Aussenkante der Vorderschienen glatt, an der äusseren Ecke ein einspitziger Haken.*

2. *Bauch im Winkel aufwärts, nach dem After zu, gebogen.*

85. Genus ECCOPTOGASTER, Herbst

Eccoptogaster. Herbst, Natursyst. Ins. : Die Käfer, Vol. 5, p. 124, 125 (1793).
Coptogaster. Illiger, Mag. f. Insektenk. Vol. 6, p. 321 (1807).
Ips. Marsham, Ent Brit. Vol. 1, p. 548 (1802).
Scolytes. Geoffroy, Hist. Ins. Eur. Vol. 1, p. 309 (1762).

Originaldiagnose : Herbst, loc. cit.

« Die Käfer, die ich zu dieser neuen Gattung rechne, sind zwar denen der vorigen Gattung ungemein ähnlich, und deshalb auch bis jetzt mit darunter gezählt; da aber obige Kennzeichen hier nicht angetroffen werden, so darf ich sie auch nicht mit darunter bringen. Ich hätte lieber den von Geoffroy und Schäfer angenommenen Gattungsnamen *Scolytus* beibehalten; da aber Fabricius diesen Namen wieder ganz andern Käfern gegeben hat, welches in der Naturgeschichte eine höchst verderbliche Sache ist, so würde ich die Verwirrungen nur noch vervielfältigt haben. Folgende Kennzeichen sondern sie hinreichend von den *Bostrichen* ab :

» 1° Die Gestalt ist zwar auch cylindrisch, aber nach vorne zu etwas zugespitzt.

» 2" Die Fühlhörner haben nur vier Glieder. Die beiden untersten Glieder sind kugelförmig, das dritte etwas länglich und das vierte besteht aus einem grossen eiförmigen Knopf, der etwas platt ist. Dieser Knopf besteht nicht aus drei, sondern aus einem einzigen dichten Gliede.

» 3° Die Füsse sind breit und platt, die Schienbeine ungefähnt; die Fussblätter haben drei Glieder, von welchen das letzte herzförmig und gespalten ist; aus demselben tritt das ziemlich lang gezogene Klauenglied hervor, das am Ende eine doppelte Klaue hat.

» Bei denen beiden mir bekannten Arten ist der Bauch unten stark ausgeschnitten, worauf der Gattungsname anspielen soll, so dass er am Ende wie platt zusammengedrückt aussieht. Indessen so weiss ich nicht, ob ich dies mit unter die Gattungskennzeichen rechnen darf. »

Charaktere. — Körperform cylindrisch, meist nach vorn verschmälert, Länge 1.5 bis 7 mm., Farbe glänzend braun bis schwarz; Skulptur schwach, Behaarung spärlich.

Kopf geneigt, mit kurzem breitem Rüssel; Stirn häufig flach ausgehöhlt und mit langen Haaren bedeckt (bei den ♂) oder schwach gewölbt und kahl (bei den ♀).

Augen lang, quer gestellt, vorn etwas ausgebuchtet.

Fühler unten vor den Augen eingelenkt, nicht geknieet, mit kurzem Schaft und siebengliedriger 1) Geissel und derber. grösser, geschuppter Keule, welche länger als die Geissel ist.

Vorderkiefer sehr kräftig, an der Innenkante fein gekerbt.

Mittelkiefer mit kurzer, an der Kaukante mit zwölf bis vierzehn geraden, lang zugespitzten Stachelzähnen und dazwischenstehenden feinen Haaren besetzter Innenlade.

Kiefertaster : Glied 1 und 2 sind nach der Basis stark verschmälert, 3 cylindrisch.

Hinterkiefer sind zu einem spatelförmigen, gerundeten, nach der Basis stark verschmälerten Kinne verschmolzen, an dessen vorderen Rand die ovale, stumpfe, bis zur Mitte des ersten Tastergliedes reichende Zunge aufsitzt und den Raum zwischen den untersten Tastergliedern ausfüllt. Sie ist mit langen Haaren besetzt.

Lippentaster : Glied 1 so lang als 2 und 3 zusammen, nach der Basis stark verschmälert, Glied 2 verkehrt kegelförmig, 3 cylindrisch, alle lang behaart.

Halsschild gross, nach vorn etwas verengt, oben meist fein punktiert, an den Seiten erhaben gerandet.

Schildchen gross, tief zwischen die Flügeldecken eingesenkt.

Flügeldecken flach, an der Basis nicht erhaben gerandet, an der Spitze nicht abschüssig, sondern fast abgestutzt, flach, niemals eingedrückt oder gezähnt, Naht am Schildchen vertieft.

Vorderbrust tief ausgeschnitten, mit kurzem stumpfen Fortsatz nach hinten.

Vorderhüften und Mittelhüften voneinander entfernt, Hinterhüften noch weiter abstehend.

Schienen an der Aussenkante ganzrandig, ohne Zähne oder Dornen, nur mit einem starken Endhaken an der Spitze.

Fussglieder : das dritte zweilappig, viel breiter als das vorhergehende.

Bauch nach dem After zu aufsteigend oder ausgeschnitten, häufig an dem zweiten, dritten, vierten Bauchring in Gestalt von Höckern oder längeren Fortsätzen sekundäre Geschlechtsmerkmale tragend.

Geographische Verbreitung der Arten. — Die einundsechzig Arten der Gattung verteilen sich auf sämmtliche Erdteile mit Ausnahme von Australien ; sie ist also subkosmopolitisch.

---

1) Die Abbildung **Fig. 94, Taf. 11** stellt eine Monstrosität dar, indem Glied 3 und 4 verschmolzen, die Geissel daher nur sechsgliedrig ist. Monstrositäten scheinen bei den *Ipiden* selten vorzukommen. Dies ist die einzige, welche ich gesehen habe. Nördlinger erwähnt *Stett. Entom. Zeit.* Vol. 9, p. 244 (1848) eine solche am Halsschild bei *Pityophthorus Lichtensteini* Ratzeburg.

1. *E. aceris*, Knotek, Wien. Ent. Zeit. Vol. 11, p. 235 (1892).   Südeuropa.
2. *E. agnatus*, Blandford, Trans. Ent. Soc. Lond. p. 78 (1894).   Japan.
3. *E. amurensis*, Eggers, Wien. Ent. Zeit. p. 144.   Sibirien.
4. *E. amygdali*, Guérin, Bull. Soc. Ent. Fr. Vol. 28, p. 46 (1847).   Südeuropa.
    var. rufipennis, Brancsik, Berl. Ent. Zeitschr. Vol. 18, p. 135 (1874).   Südeuropa, Kaukasus.
5. *E. aratus*, Blandford, Trans. Ent. Soc. Lond. p. 79 (1894).   Japan.
    var. aequipunctatus, Nijsima, Journ. Sapporo Agric. Coll. Vol. 2, p. 71 (1905).   Japan.
6. *E. assimilis*, Boheman, Resa Freg. Eugen. p. 88 (1859).   Argentinien.
7. *E. atratus*, Chapuis. Synops. Scolyt. p. 266 (1873).   Columbien.
8. *E. californicus*, Le Conte, Trans. Amer. Ent. Soc. Vol. 2, p. 166 (1868).   Nordamerika.
9. *E. carinatus*, Chapuis. Synops. Scolyt. p. 263 (1873).   Columbien.
10. *E. carpini*, Ratzburg, Forstinsekten, Vol. 1, p. 187 (1837).   Mitteleuropa.
11. *E. Chikisanii*, Niijima, Journ. Sapporo Agric. Coll. Vol. 2, p. 59 (1905).   Japan.
12. *E. claviger*, Blandford, Trans. Ent. Soc. Lond. p. 80 (1894).   Japan.
13. *E. costellatus*, Chapuis, Synops. Scolyt. p. 266 (1873).   Brasilien.
14. *E. curviventralis*, Niijima, Journ. Sapporo Agric. Coll. Vol. 2, p. 70 (1905).   Japan.
15. *E. dahuricus*, Chapuis, Synops. Scolyt. p. 268 (1873).   Sibirien.
16. *E. deodara*, Stebbing. Dep. Not. Ins. aff. Forestry, Vol. 2, p. 220 (1903).   Himalaya.
17. *E. dimidiatus*, Chapuis, Synops. Scolyt. p. 265 (1873).   Centralamerika.
18. *E. Eichhoffi*, Reitter, Best.-Tab. Borkenkäfer, p. 40 (1894).   Centralasien.
19. *E. ensifer*, Eichhöff, Europ. Börkenkäfer, p. 163 (1881).   Frankreich, Südrussland
20. *E. esuriens*, Blandford, Trans. Ent. Soc. Lond. p. 77 (1894).   Japan.
21. *E. fagi*, Walsh, Pract. Ent. Vol. 2, p. 58 (1867).   Nordamerika.
22. *E. fasciatus*, Reitter. Deutsche Ent. Zeitschr. p 394 (1890).   Transkaukasien.
23. *E. frontalis*, Blandford, Trans. Ent. Soc. Lond. p. 79 (1894).   Japan.
24. *E. javanus*, Chapuis, Synops. Scolyt. p. 264 (1873).   Java.
25. *E. japonicus*, Chapuis, Ann. Soc. Ent. Belg. Vol. 18, p. 199 (1895).   Japan.
26. *E. Jaroschewskii*, Schewyrew, Rev. Russe d'Ent. p. 38 (1904).   Kaukasus.
27. *E. intricatus*, Ratzeburg, Forstinsekten, Vol. 1, p. 186 (1837).   Europa.
28. *E. Kirschii*, Skalitzki, Ent. Monatsbl. p. 110 (1876).   Mitteleuropa.
29. *E. Koenigi*, Schewyrew, Rev. Russe d'Ent. Vol. 2, p. 206 (1902).   Centralasien.
30. *E. Koltzei*, Reitter, Wien. Ent. Zeit. Vol. 13, p. 128 (1894).   Sibirien.
31. *E. laevis*, Chapuis, Synops. Scolyt. p. 262 (1873).   Mitteleuropa.
32. *E. Leonii*, Eggers, Il Natural. Sicil. Vol. 20, n° 9 (1908).   Italien.
33. *E. maior*, Stebbing, Dep. Not. Ins. aff. Forestry, Vol. 2, p. 203 (1903).   Ostindien.
34. *E. mali*, Bechstein, Forstinsekten, Vol. 3, p. 882 (1805).   Mitteleuropa, Sibirien.
    var. pyri, Ratzeburg, Forstinsekten, Vol. 1, p. 164 (1837).   Mitteleuropa.
    var. strigillatus, Reitter, Wien. Ent. Zeit. Vol. 27, p. 23 (1908).   Mitteleuropa.
35. *E. marginatus*, Chapuis, Synops. Scolyt. p. 264 (1873).   Centralamerika.
36. *E. minor*, Stebbing, Dep. Not. Ins. aff. Forestry, Vol. 2, p. 207 (1903).   Ostindien.
37. *E. Morawitzi*, Semenow, Rev. Russe d'Ent. Vol. 2, p. 267 (1902).   Sibirien.
38. *E. mullistriatus*, Marsham, Ent. Brit. p. 54 (1802).   Europa.
    var. triornatus, Eichhoff, Europ. Borkenkäfer, p. 160 (1881).   Mitteleuropa.
39. *E. muticus*, Say, Journ. Acad. Natur. Sc. Philad. Vol. 3, p. 323 (1826).   Nordamerika.
40. *E. numidicus*, Brisout de Barneville, Rev. d'Ent. Caën, Vol. 2, p. 147 (1883).   Algier.
41. *E. peregrinus*, Eggers, Ent. Blätter. Vol. 4, p. 215 (1908).   Unbekannt.
42. *E. piceae*, Swaine, The Canad. Entom. Vol. 42, p. 33 (1910).   Nordamerika.
43. *E. praeceps*, Le Conte, Proc. Amer. Philos. Soc. Vol. 15, p. 371 (1876).   Nordamerika.
44. *E. productus*, Hagedorn, Bull. Mus. Hist. Nat. Paris. Vol. 10, p. 547 (1904).   Südamerika.
45. *E. propinquus*, Blandford, Biol. Centr. Amer. Col. Vol. 4 (6), p. 121 (1897).   Centralamerika.
46. *E. proximus*, Chapuis, Synops. Scolyt. p. 265 (1873).   Südamerika.
47. *E. pygmaeus*, Fabricius, Mant. Ins, Vol. 1. p. 37 (1787).   Mitteleuropa.

48. *E. quadrispinosus*, Say, Journ. Acad. Natur. Sc. Philad. Vol. 3, p. 323 (1826).   Nordamerika.
49. *E. Ratzeburgi*, Janson, The Ent. Annual, p. 87 (1856). — **Taf. 14, Fig. 17.**   Europa.
5o. *E. rugulosus*, Ratzeburg, Forstinsekten, Vol. 1, p. 187 (1837). — **Taf. 14,**   Europa, Nordamerika.
       Fig. 18.
       var. Fauveli, Reitter, Best.-Tab. Borkenkäfer, p. 43 (1894).   Kleinasien.
51. *E. Schewyrewi*, Semenow, Rev. Russe Ent. Vol. 2, p. 265 (1902).   Centralasien.
       var. sinensis, Eggers, Ent. Blätter, Vol. 6, p. 35 (1910).   China.
52. *E. scolytus*, Fabricius, Syst. Ent. p. 59 (1775). — **Taf. 5, Fig. 49 ; Taf. 11,**   Europa, Nordamerika.
       Fig. 94, 95, 96.
53. *E. siculus*, Eggers, Il Natural. Sicil. Vol. 20, n° 9 (1908).   Sicilien.
54. *E. subscaber*, Le Conte, Proc. Amer. Philos. Soc. Vol. 15, p. 37 (1876).   Nordamerika.
55. *E. sulcatus*, Le Conte, Trans. Amer. Ent. Soc. Vol. 2, p. 167 (1868).   Nordamerika.
56 *E. thoracicus*, Chapuis, Synops. Scol. p. 263 (1873). — **Taf. 5, Fig. 48.**   Südamerika.
57. *E. trispinosus*, Strohmeyer, Ent. Wochenbl. Vol. 16, n° 16 (1908).   Japan.
58. *E. ulmi*, Redtenbacher, Fauna Austr. Vol. 1, p. 361 (1849). ·   Mitteleuropa.
59. *E. unispinosus*, Le Conte, Proc. Amer. Philos. Soc. Vol. 15, p. 371 (1876).   Nordamerika.
60. *E. ventrosus*, Schewyrew, Mélanges Biol. Bull. Acad. Sc. St-Pétersbourg.   Sibirien.
       Vol. 13, p. 98 (1890).
61. *E. ventralis*, Le Conte, Trans. Amer. Ent. Soc. Vol. 2, p. 167 (1868).   Nordamerika.

86. Genus SCOLYTOPSIS, Blandford

Scolytopsis, Blandford. Biol. Centr. Amer. Col. Vol. 4 (6), p. 123 (1896).

ORIGINALDIAGNOSE : Blandford, loc. cit.

« Differt a *Scolyto* elytris leviter convexis, circa marginem apicalem non impressis, ad latera supra metasternum fortiter emarginatis; abdominis segmentis tribus ultimis sursum reflexis. »

Charaktere. — Körperform länglich, Länge 2.5 mm.; Farbe schwarz mit helleren Extremitäten; Skulptur mässig derb, Behaarung schwach, hell.

Kopf in einen kurzen Rüssel verlängert, Stirn beim ♂ lang gelb behaart.

Augen queroval, reichen unten fast bis zur Kehlnaht.

Fühler mit siebengliedriger Geissel, komprimierter und einnähtiger Keule.

Vorderkiefer gross, glänzend schwarz, spitz, ungezähnt.

Mittelkiefer mit kurzer, nach oben verschmälerter Innenlade, an deren Kaukante zwölf bis vierzehn langzugespitzte Stachelzähne stehen.

Kiefertaster : Grundglied breit, cylindrisch, ganz in den Tasterträger versenkt, zweites und drittes Glied lang cylindrisch, an Breite abnehmend.

Hinterkiefer zu einem in der Mitte verschmälerten, nach der Spitze viel stärker als nach der Basis verbreiterten Kinne verschmolzen.

Lippentaster : Glied 1 so lang als 2 und 3 zusammen, nach der Basis stark verschmälert, Glied 2 fast quadratisch, Glied 3 cylindrisch.

Zunge beginnt in der verschmälerten Mitte des Kinnes und reicht als stumpf gerundetes· Läppchen bis zur Basis des ersten Tasterglieder. Sie ist stark beborstet.

Halsschild an der Basis und den Seiten erhaben gerandet.

Schildchen klein, dreieckig.

Flügeldecken von der Basis bis zur Spitze gewölbt; die laterale Kante ist gegenüber dem Metasternum tief ausgeschnitten; die Ränder des Ausschnitts bilden zusammen mit dem Seitenrand des Halsschildes ein stumpfwinkeliges Dreieck, dessen Spitze hinter dem Schulterwinkel liegt, und dessen hinterer Winkel vor dem hinteren Ende des Metathorax gerundet ist.

Vorderbrust mit kurzem, lang behaarten Fortsatz zwischen den Vorderhüften.

Vorderhüften genähert, aber nicht einander berührend, stark behaart, Mittelhüften weiter, Hinterhüften weniger weit voneinander abstehend.

Beine kräftig, Vorderschienen stark gekrümmt mit glattem Aussenrand und Endhaken.

Bauch ist bis zum dritten Segment horizontal, dann verkürzen sich die Ringe und steigen steil nach der Spitze auf.

Fussglieder : Glied 1 so lang als 2-4 zusammen; Glied 3 ausgerandet.

Geographische Verbreitung der Art. — Nur eine Art aus dem Südreich ist beschrieben worden.

1. *S. puncticollis*, Blandford, Biol. Centr. Amer. Col. Vol. 4 (6), p. 123   Guatemala, Brasilien, Argentinien.
(1896). — **Taf. 5, Fig. 49a, 49b.**

87. Genus CAMPTOCERUS, Latreille

Camptocerus, Latreille, Règne Anim. (ed. 2), Vol. 5, p. 91 (1829).
Hylesinus, Fabricius, Syst. Eleuth. Vol. 2, p. 392 (1801).

ORIGINALDIAGNOSE : Latreille, loc. cit.

« Les *Camptocères* (*Camptocerus* Dejean, *Hylesinus* Fabricius), dont les mâles ont les antennes fortement coudées, garnies extérieurement de long poils ou filets; elles sont insérées à une distance notable des yeux, qui sont elliptiques et obliques (*Hylesinus aeneipennis* Fabricius). »

Charaktere. — Körperform eiförmig bis cylindrisch, Länge 3 bis 8 mm., Farbe braun bis schwarz, bei einer Art — als Unicum unter den Ipiden — mit grünglänzenden Flügeldecken, Skulptur meist schwach, Bekleidung meist in Schuppen bestehend, manchmal fehlend.

Kopf mit breitem Rüssel ; Stirn beim ♂ ausgehöhlt und mit langen gelben Haarbüscheln besetzt, beim ♀ gewölbt und unbehaart.

Augen nierenförmig, vorn tief ausgebuchtet.

Fühler zwischen Augen und Vorderkiefern an der Vorderseite des Rüssels in tiefer Grube eingelenkt, mit siebengliedriger Geissel, deren Glieder beim ♀ einfach, beim ♂ mit langen, bis zur Keulenspitze reichenden, starren Haarborsten innen besetzt sind ; Keule verkehrt eiförmig, solide, länger als die Geissel, mit unbestimmten gebogenen Nähten.

Vorderkiefer kräftig, breit zweizähnig.

Mittelkiefer mit langer, gerundeter Innenlade, an deren Kaukante circa vierzehn bis zwanzig breite, gerade, dolchartige Zähne sitzen; Aussenkante mit langem Fortsatz und langen starken Borsten.

Kiefertaster zwischen den beiden erwähnten Fortsätzen tief eingesenkt, so dass kaum das kleine Endglied hervorragt; Glied 1 cylindrisch, so lang als 2 und 3 zusammen, Glied 2 kleiner, cylindrisch, 3 am kleinsten.

Hinterkiefer bilden ein gleichseitig-dreieckiges, an den Ecken abgerundetes, nach der Basis verschmälertes Kinn, an dessen Grund die linealische, oben gerundete und dort mit Haaren besetzte Zunge entspringt, die bis zur Mitte des ersten Tasterglieder reicht.

Lippentaster: Glied 1 am längsten, verkehrt kegelförmig, 2 und 3 im stumpfen Winkel dazu abgesetzt, 2 cylindrisch, 3 klein, schmal walzenförmig.

Halsschild gross, breiter als lang, nach vorn plötzlich verengt, seitlich und am Grunde gerandet, schwach skulptiert.

Schildchen gross, halbkreisförmig, konkav.

Flügeldecken cylindrisch oder nach hinten verengt, schwach gestreift und [punktiert, glänzend glatt metallisch grün oder mit Schuppen besetzt, besonders in dem flach abgewölbten Absturz. An der Spitze einzeln abgerundet und fein gerandet.

Vorderbrust breit, mit dreieckigem Fortsatz zwischen den Vorderhüften.

Hüften wenig voneinander entfernt.

Vorderschienen flachgedrückt, wenig verbreitert, mit glatter Aussenkante, an der Aussenecke mit grossem spitzen Haken.

Mittel- und Hinterschienen mit kleinerem Haken, nach der Spitze verbreitert. Aussenkante glatt. Bauch aufsteigend, häufig behaart.

Geographische Verbreitung der Arten. — Eine Gattung des Südreiches, in dem acht Arten vorkommen, während Centralamerika eine Art birgt.

1. *C. aeneipennis*. Fabricius, Syst. Eleuth. Vol. 2, p. 392 (1801). — Taf. 5,   Südamerika.
     Fig. 50; Taf. II, Fig. 97, 98.
2. *C. auricomus*, Blandford, Biol. Centr. Amer. Col. Vol. 4 (6), p. 125 (1895).   Nicaragua.
3. *C. costatus*, Chapuis, Synops. Scolyt. p. 259 (1873).   Brasilien.
4. *C. fasciatus*, Fabricius, Syst. Eleuth. Vol. 2, p. 393 (1801).   Südamerika.
5. *C. gibbus*. Fabricius, ibidem. p. 393 (1801).   Südamerika.
6. *C. niger*, Fabricius, ibidem. p. 393 (1801).   Südamerika.
7. *C. squamiger*, Chapuis, Synops. Scolyt. p. 259 (1873).   Cayenne.
8. *C. striatulus*. Hagedorn, Bull. Mus. Hist. Nat. Paris, Vol. 10, p. 547 (1904).   Guyana.
9. *C. suturalis*, Fabricius, Syst. Eleuth. Vol. 2, p. 393 (1801).   Südamerika.

88. Genus CERATOLEPIS, Chapuis

Ceratolepis. Chapuis, Synops. Scolyt. p. 260 (1873).

Originaldiagnose : Chapuis, loc. cit.

« Antennarum funiculus 7-articulatus, articulis 2-7 in fœmina simplicibus, clava solida. Oculi transverse reniformes. Tibiæ extus integerrimæ. Tarsorum articulo 1. duobus sequentibus æqualis, 3 bilobus. »

Charaktere. — Körperform eiförmig bis länglich-eiförmig, Länge 2 bis 2.6 mm., Farbe schwarz, Skulptur mässig derb, Bekleidung in anliegender Pubescenz oder aufgerichteten Borstenreihen auf den Flügeldecken bestehend.

Kopf mit schwachem Rüssel, beim ♂ die Stirn wenig ausgehöhlt.

Augen nierenförmig, querstehend.

Fühler mit siebengiedriger Geissel, deren Glieder beim ♂ mit Haarborsten besetzt sind, die leicht länger als die Keule sind. Keule gross, beilförmig abgerundet mit einer undeutlichen Naht.

Vorderkiefer kräftig, ungezähnt.

Mundteile unbekannt.

Halsschild an der Basis gerandet oder ungerandet, seitlich ungerandet, bogenförmig gekrümmt; im Ganzen von elliptischer Form, beinahe so lang als breit; Oberfläche stark punktiert.

Schildchen punktförmig.

Flügeldecken länger als das Halsschild, an der Basis einzeln gerundet, aber nicht gerandet; Oberfläche ziemlich tief gestreift, Zwischenräume mit Borsten oder anliegender Behaarung bekleidet und rauh skulptiert.

Schienen an der Aussenkante glatt, mit Endhaken an der Aussenspitze.

Fussglieder : erstes Glied lang, drittes Glied zweilappig oder wenigstens ausgerandet.

Bauch gleichmässig von der Basis zum After gerundet.

Geographische Verbreitung der Arten. — Drei Arten aus Central- und Südamerika sind beschrieben worden.

1. *C. errans,* Blandford, Biol. Centr. Amer. Col. Vol. 4 (6), p. 127 (1895).   Mexiko.
2. *C. jucunda,* Chapuis, Synops. Scolyt. p. 260 (1873).   Brasilien.
3. *C. maculicornis,* Blandford, Biol. Centr. Amer. Col. Vol. 4 (6), p. 125 (1895).   Panama.

89. Genus LOGANÍUS, Chapuis.

Loganius, Chapuis, Synops. Scolyt. p. 260 (1873).

ORIGINALDIAGNOSE : Chapuis, loc. cit.

« Antennarum maris articuli 2-7 appendiculati, clava suturis concentricis ornata. Oculi transverse reniformes. Tibiæ extus integerrimæ. Tarsorum articuli 1 et 2 æquales, 3 subdilatatus. »

Charaktere. — Körperform oval oder länglich cylindrisch, Farbe dunkelbraun, Länge 1.5 bis 2.5 mm., Skulptur mässig derb, Behaarung mehr weniger lang, sekundäre Geschlechtsmerkmale an Stirn und Fühlern.

Kopf kugelig, in einen kleinen Rüssel verlängert ; Stirn beim ♂ eingedrückt, behaart, beim ♀ konvex.

Augen queroval, vorn ausgerandet.

Fühler mit siebengliedriger Geissel, die Glieder seitlich verbreitert und zu mehr minder langen Fortsätzen ausgezogen, von denen beim ♂ sehr lange, beim ♀ kürzere oder sehr kurze, dicke Haarborsten entspringen, die länger als der ganze Fühler sein können; Keule oval, von einer, zwei oder drei Nähten durchzogen.

Vorderkiefer kräftig.

Mittelkiefer mit stark gerundeter, in einen breiten stumpfen Spitzenfortsatz ausgezogener Innenlade, an deren Kaukante elf breite, kurze, dolchartige Stachelzähne sitzen, während ihre Aussenkante stark gerundet und mit langen Haaren besetzt ist.

Kiefertaster : Glied 1 querbreiter, cylindrisch, 3 kegelförmig, so lang als 1 und 2 zusammen, mit Längsstreifen versehen.

Hinterkiefer zu einen länglich viereckigen, an der Basis gerundeten, daselbst etwas schmäler als an der bogenförmig konvex abgewölbten Spitze gestalteten Kinne verschmolzen, von dessen Mitte die etwas schmälere, abgestumpft zungenförmige, bis zur Mitte des ersten Tastergliedes reichende Zunge entspringt.

Lippentaster : Glied 1 am grössesten, verkehrt kegelförmig, 2 querbreiter, schräg abgestumpft, 3 viel schmäler, länger als 2, cylindrisch. Glied 3 ist im rechten Winkel gegen 1 und 2 abgebogen.

Halsschild meist länger als breit, cylindrisch, an den Seiten und der Basis gerandet oder ungerandet ; Oberseite schwach gewölbt, einfach punktiert.

Schildchen klein, dreieckig oder gerundet.

Flügeldecken walzenförmig, hinten gewölbt abfallend, glatt oder schwach behaart, Zwischenräume flach oder gekielt.

Vorderbrust tief ausgeschnitten, zwischen den weit abstehenden Vorderhüften mit einem Fortsatz.

Mittel- und Hinterhüften weit voneinander entfernt.

Schienen gerade, Aussenkante ungezähnt, aber Spitze mit Endhaken.

Fussglieder 1 und 2 gleich, rund, 3 etwas verbreitert.

Bauch im gewölbten (konvexen) Bogen gerundet ansteigend.

Geographische Verbreitung der Arten. — Es sind acht Arten beschrieben, welche sich auf das neue Nordreich und das Südreich verteilen.

1. *L. atratus*, Blandford, Biol. Centr. Amer. Col. Vol. 4 (6), p. 129 (1896).   Panama.
2. *L. exiguus*, Blandford, ibidem. p. 130 (1896).   Panama.
3. *L. ficus*, Schwarz, Proc. Ent. Soc. Wash. Vol. 3, p. 44 (1895).   Florida.
4. *L. flavicornis*, Chapuis, Synops. Scolyt. p. 260 (1873).   Cumana.
5. *L. longicollis*, Blandford, Biol. Centr. Amer. Col. Vol. 4 (6), p. 128 (1896).   Mexiko.
6. *L. minusculus*, Blandford, ibidem, p. 130 (1896).   Panama.
7. *L. panamensis*, Blandford, ibidem, p. 129 (1896).   Panama.
8. *L. scaliger*, Hagedorn, Deutsche Ent. Zeitschr. p. 5 (1910). — **Taf. 5,** Argentinien.
    Fig. 51.

90. Genus CNEMONYX Eichhoff

Cnemonyx. Eichhoff, Berl. Ent. Zeitschr. Vol. 12, p. 150 (1868).

Originaldiagnose : Eichhoff, loc. cit.

« Antennarum funiculus 7-articulatus, articulis intus longe ciliatis, capitulo solido, compresso, subovato. Tibiæ compressæ extus integræ, apice acuminatæ. Abdomen normale. Tarsorum articulo 3° marginato. »

Charaktere. — Körperform länglich, cylindrisch, Länge 1.5 mm., Farbe braunschwarz, Skulptur und Behaarung schwach.

Kopf mit schwachem Rüssel, Stirn lang behaart.

Fühler mit siebengliedriger Geissel, deren Glieder einseitig verbreitert und mit mässig langen Haaren besetzt sind, Keule kurz eiförmig, abgestumpft, ohne Nähte.

Halsschild etwas länger als breit. seitlich kaum gerandet, schwach runzelig punktiert mit spärlichen gelben Haaren.

Flügeldecken an der Basis aufgeworfen und gekerbt und einzeln gerundet. Scheibe schwach, Absturz stärker granuliert, mit Borstenreihen besetzt, nach der Spitze etwas verengert.

Schienen aussen nicht gezähnt.

Fussglieder fadenförmig verlängert, 1 und 2 rund, 3 sehr klein, *nicht* verbreitert.

Bauch schwach ansteigend.

Geographische Verbreitung der Art. — Nur eine Art aus Chile ist beschrieben.

1. *C. galeritus*, Eichhoff, Berl. Ent Zeitschr. p. 150 (1868).   Chile.

91. Genus BOTHROSTERNUS, Eichhoff

Bothrosternus. Eichhoff, Berl. Ent. Zeitschr. Vol. 12, p. 150 (1868).

Originaldiagnose : Eichhoff, loc. cit.

« Caput exsertum, rostro brevi auctum. Antennæ scapo longe ciliato, funiculo 7-articulato, capitulato 4-annulato, elongato, obtuso. Prosterni lateribus utrinque ad recipiendas pedes excavatis. Tibiæ (anticæ) apice dentibus 2 armatæ, dente anteriore duplice recurvato. Tarsi articulo tertio cordato. •

Charaktere. — Körperform lang eiförmig, Länge 2.5 bis 4 mm., Farbe braun bis schwarz, Skulptur derb, Bekleidung keine oder nur Behaarung an dem Flügeldeckenabsturz.

Kopf mit kurzem Rüssel; Stirne mehr weniger punktiert beim ♀; beim ♂ glatt oder gekielt.

Augen schmal. vorn ausgerandet.

Fühler in tiefer Fühlergrube vor den Augen eingelenkt, Schaft mit starkem Haarbüschel besetzt, Geissel siebengliedrig, Keule lang zugespitzt, mit zwei geraden Nähten.

Vorderkiefer derb.

Mittelkiefer mit stark gerundeter Innenlade, die in einen kurzen stumpfen oberen Fortsatz ausgezogen und an der Innenkante mit zwölf bis vierzehn breiten, gebogenen Zähnen besetzt ist.

Kiefertaster : Glied 1 breiter als lang, 2 quadratisch, 3 kegelförmig, schmäler, mit dunklen Längslinien gestreift.

Hinterkiefer zu einem so langen als breiten oder breiteren als langen, am Grunde schildförmig oder halbkreisförmig gerundeten Kinne verschmolzen, an dessen Basis die dreieckige in eine lange mit Haaren besetzte Spitze ausgezogene Zunge beginnt, die bis zum Grunde des ersten, bisweilen sogar des zweiten Tasterglieder reicht.

Lippentaster : Glied 1 sehr gross. aussen stark gerundet, innen gradlinig; 2 klein, so lang als breit oder breiter als lang; 3 kegelförmig, schmal.

Halsschild punktiert, mit einem kielartigen Seitenrand, der am Grunde beginnt und sich bis zur Mitte erstreckt.

Schildchen deutlich, gerundet.

Flügeldecken nach hinten verengt, meist stark skulptiert, mindestens nach der Spitze und daselbst auch behaart, und im dritten Zwischenraum.

Vorderbrust mit breitem Fortsatz zwischen den Vorderhüften.

Hüften voneinander entfernt.

Schienen : Vorderschienen nach der Spitze verbreitert, diese in einen Lappen, der zwei schwache, rückwärts gekrümmte Dornen trägt, ausgezogen; Aussenkante schwach gezähnt; bei den Mittel- und Hinterschienen ist diese Bildung sehr schwach ausgeprägt.

Fussglied 3 herzförmig.

Bauch etwas ansteigend.

Geographische Verbreitung der Arten. — Es sind sieben Arten aus dem neuen Nordreich und dem Südreich beschrieben.

1. *B. bicaudatus*, Blandford. Biol. Centr. Amer. Col. Vol. 4 (6), p. 133 (1895).   Panama.
2. *B. cancellatus*, Chapuis. Synops. Scolyt. p. 233 (1873).   Brasilien.
3. *B. costatus*, Chapuis. ibidem, p. 233 (1873).   Brasilien.
4. *B. Hubbardi*, Schwarz, Ent. Amer. Vol. 2, p. 54 (1886).   Florida.
5. *B. Lacordairei*, Chapuis, Synops. Scolyt. p. 233 (1873).   Brasilien.
6. *B. sculpturatus*, Blandford, Biol. Centr. Amer. Col. Vol. 4 (6) p. 132 (1896).   Panama.
7. *B. truncatus*, Eichhoff, Berl. Ent. Zeitschr. Vol. 12, p. 150 (1868).   Venezuela.

92. Genus EUPAGIOCERUS, Blandford

Eupagiocerus. Blandford, Biol. Centr. Amer. Col. Vol. 4 (6), p. 133 (1896).

ORIGINALDIAGNOSE : Blandford, loc. cit.

« Oculi sat magni emarginati; rostrum latum. Clava antennarum suturis curvatis instructa. Prothorax lateraliter acute marginatus. supra dense strigosus. Elytra ad basin subtransversa, interstitiis haud carinatis. Tibiæ anticæ fortius spinosæ; tarsi validi, articulo 3o emarginato. »

Mir ist die Gattung unbekannt geblieben. Sie ist aufgestellt für eine einzelne Art, welche *Bothrosternus* mit *Pagiocerus* verbindet, ohne jedoch ganz in eines dieser Genera zu fallen.

Charaktere. — Der Rüssel ist viel breiter als bei *Pagiocerus*, die Augen sind ziemlich breit und ausgerandet. Die Fühlergeissel ist gegen die Spitze verbreitert und siebengliedrig; die Nähte der Keule sind gebogen, diese geschuppt, aber sie ist länglich wie bei *Bothrosternus* und nicht so solide und oval wie bei *Pagiocerus*. Das Halsschild hat einen scharfen Seitenrand und ist skulptiert wie bei *Cnesinus*. Der Basalrand der Flügeldecken ist schwach erhöht und quer, nirgends die Halsschildbasis überragend, nicht gekerbt; die Zwischenräume sind nicht gerippt und der dritte ist hinten nicht erhöht wie bei *Bothrosternus*. Die Dornen der Vorderschienen sind breit; der Spitzenfortsatz der mittleren und hinteren Paare sind schmal und gespalten, der obere Rand der ersteren hat zwei kleine Dornen, der des letzteren ist unbedornt.

Geographische Verbreitung der Art. — Eine Art aus Guatemala ist beschrieben.

1. *E. dentipes*, Blandford, Biol. Centr. Amer. Col. Vol. 4 (6), p. 133 (1896).   Guatemala.

93. Genus CNESINUS, Le Conte

Cnesinus. Le Conte, Trans. Amer. Ent. Soc. Vol. 2, p. 171 (1868).
Nemophilus. Chapuis, Synops. Scolyt. p. 235 (1873).

ORIGINALDIAGNOSE : Le Conte, loc. cit.

« Elongate cylindrical, head convex, beak very short, eyes oblique, transverse, broadly emarginated, finely granulated; antennæ with the scape as long as the funiculus, much curved, slender at base, moderately thickened towards the tip; first joint of the funiculus thick, as broad as long, remaining joints forming an elongate mass, gradually becoming wider externally, showing under a high magnifying power the appearance of six closely connected joints; club elongate oval, somewhat shining except at tip, feebly pubescent, transversely annulate, the sutures furnished with fringes of long hairs; prothorax longitudinally aciculate; elytra deeply striate, convex at tip, basal edge acute and serrate; front tibiæ dilated, armed externally near the tip, which is prolonged, with large, acute teeth; middle and hind tibiæ dilated, feebly serrate; tarsi with the joints 1-3 moderately dilated, third emarginate, fourth slender, as long as the two preceding united; first joint of front tarsi shorter than the second, of the middle and hind tarsi equal to it.

» The anterior coxæ are large and prominent, widely separated; the mesosternum is pertuberant.

» A peculiar genus, differing in appearance from the others of the tribe by the more cylindrical form, the prothorax being parallel on the sides, except near the apex, where they are rounded. The sculpture of the prothorax is also unusual, being composed of dense longitudinal aciculations. »

Charaktere. — Körperform länglich cylindrisch, Länge 1.7 bis 3 mm., Farbe braun, Skulptur kräftig, Behaarung, die in der Hauptsache auf den hintern Teilen der Flügeldecken ausgeprägt ist und aus aufrechten Borsten und anliegenden kurzen Haaren besteht, ist gering.

Kopf in einen kurzen Rüssel ausgezogen, der beim ♀ flach und wenig behaart ist, beim ♂ mit einem Eindruck, der mit kurzen feinen Haaren besetzt ist. Stirn beim ♂ häufig glänzend oder (und) gekielt, beim ♀ matt, ohne Glanz.

Augen quer oval, gross, mehr weniger auf der Stirn einander genähert.

Fühler an den Seiten des Rüssels in einer Grube eingelenkt; Schaft stark gekeult und mit einem langen Haarbüschel besetzt, mit siebengliedriger Geissel; Keule spitz-eiförmig, mit zwei oder drei quer verlaufenden, geraden Nähten.

Vorderkiefer schwach gezähnt.

Mittelkiefer mit einer schmalen an der Spitze gerundeten, an der Kaukante mit flachen Stachelzähnen besetzten Innenlade.

Kiefertaster mit an Grösse abnehmenden Gliedern, die beiden ersten kurz und breit, das letzte viel länger als breit.

Hinterkiefer sind zu einem schildförmigen, so lang als breiten, an der Spitze abgestutzten Kinne verschmolzen, an dessen Grund die Zunge entspringt, die nach der Spitze zu verschmälert und mit Haaren besetzt ist.

Lippentaster : erstes Glied. breit, kegelförmig, zweites kurz und quer, drittes schmal, länger als breit.

Halsschild breiter als lang oder so lang als breit, nach vorn verschmälert, Vorderrand stark gerundet; Seiten nicht erhaben gerandet, Grund mit erhabenen Rand. Skulptur mässig, strich- oder punktförmig; manchmal schwache Behaarung.

Schildchen deutlich, dreieckig oder gerundet.

Flügeldecken walzenförmig, am Grunde einzeln gerundet, manchmal aufgeworfen und gekerbt. Skulptur grob, meist tiefe Punktstreifen mit erhabenen Zwischenräumen, die am einfach gewölbten Absturz mit zwei Arten von Haaren, längeren aufrechten und kurzen, anliegenden besetzt sind.

Vorderbrust mit Fortsatz zwischen den auseinanderstehenden Vorderhüften.

Hüften stehen alle weit auseinander.

Schienen nach der Spitze verbreitert, an der Aussenkante glatt; an den Vorderschienen ist der obere Winkel in einen zweispitzigen flachen Zahn verlängert, vor dem an der Aussenkante noch ein kleinerer zu sitzen pflegt. An den Mittel- und Hinterschienen ist diese Zahnbildung eben angedeutet.

Fussglieder 1, 2 und 3 gleich rund; 3 nicht verbreitert.

Bauch horizontal.

Geographische Verbreitung der Arten. — Es sind dreizehn Arten bekannt, eine davon in Nordamerika, die andern in Central- und Südamerika.

1. *C. costulatus*, Blandford, Biol. Centr. Amer. Col. Vol. 4 (6), p. 137 (1895).	Venezuela.
2. *C. elegans*, Blandford, ibidem, p. 140 (1895).	Venezuela, Mexiko.
3. *C. gibbus*, Chapuis, Synops. Scolyt. p. 236 (1873).	Cumana.
4. *C. gracilis*, Blandford, Biol. Centr. Amer. Col. Vol. 4 (6), p. 141 (1895).	Panama.
5. *C. Lecontei*, Blandford, ibidem, p. 138 (1895).	Panama, Guatemala.
6. *C. ocularis*, Blandford, ibidem, p. 140 (1895).	Venezuela.
7. *C. paleatus*, Blandford, ibidem, p 138 (1895).	Guatemala.
8. *C. porcatus*, Blandford, ibidem, p. 137 (1895).	Guatemala.
9. *C. pullus*, Blandford, ibidem, p. 141 (1895).	Guatemala.
10. *C. punctatus*, Blandford, ibidem, p. 136 (1895).	Panama.
11. *C. setulosus*, Blandford, ibidem, p. 139 (1895).	Panama.
12. *C. strigicollis*, Le Conte, Trans. Amer. Ent. Soc. Vol. 2. p. 171 (1868).	Nordamerika.
13. *C. teres*, Blandford, Biol. Centr. Amer. Col. Vol. 4 (6), p. 141 (1895).	Venezuela.

94. Genus PAGIOCERUS, Eichhoff

Pagiocerus. Eichhoff, Berl. Ent. Zeitschr. Vol. 12, p. 148 (1868).

ORIGINALDIAGNOSE : Eichhoff, loc. cit.

« Tarsorum articulus tertius cordatus. Tibiæ anticæ rectae extus denticulatæ. Antennarum funiculis 7-articulatus, capitulo ovali solido. Elytra apice declivia. Abdomen normale. »

Charaktere. — Körperform eiförmig länglich, Länge etwas über 2 mm., Farbe dunkelbraun, Skulptur kräftig, Behaarung gering.

Kopf mit deutlichem Rüssel, dieser ist mit Vertiefungen (beim ♀) oder Dornfortsätzen (beim ♂) versehen, bildet ein wichtiges sekundäres Geschlechtsmerkmal.

Augen quer-oval, nicht ausgerandet.

Fühler sitzen in einer tiefen Grube, an der Seite des Rüssels, unterhalb der Augen. Geissel mit sieben queren, an Breite zunehmenden Gliedern; Keule länglich-eiförmig, behaart, mit zwei gebogenen Näbten.

Vorderkiefer kräftig, gezähnt.

Mittelkiefer mit einer schmalen, an der Spitze gerundeten Innenlade, deren Kaukante mit flachen Dornzähnen besetzt ist.

Kiefertaster : Glied 1 und 2 kurz und quer-breiter, 3 viel länger als breit.

Hinterkiefer zu einem so langen wie breiten, an der Spitze abgestutzten, schildförmigen Kinne verschmolzen, an dessen Grund die Zunge angesetzt ist, die nach der Spitze verschmälert und behaart ist und etwas die Kinnspitze überragt.

Lippentaster : Glied 1 breit, konisch, 2 quer-breiter, kurz, 3 schmal und länger als breit.

Halsschild fast quadratisch, nach vorn verengt, an den Seiten nicht gerandet, aber für die Aufnahme der Beine eingedrückt. Scheibe gewölbt, mit einem feinen Netzwerk von streifigen Punkten skulptiert.

Schildchen deutlich, dreieckig.

Flügeldecken gewölbt abfallend, stark gekerbt-gestreift.

Vorderbrust mit breitem Fortsatz zwischen den Vorderhüften.

Hüften weit voneinander getrennt.

Vorderschienen nach der Spitze verbreitert, daselbst am Aussenwinkel mit einem zweispitzigen Fortsatz, vor welchem an der Aussenkante noch ein kleiner Zahn steht, während die Aussenkante im übrigen glatt ist.

Mittel- und Hinterschienen gerade, Aussenkante sehr schwach gezähnt.

Bauch horizontal.

Geographische Verbreitung der Arten. — Nur zwei Arten, deren eine im Südreich lebt, die andere aber von da nach Centralamerika sich verbreitert hat, sind bekannt.

1. *P. cribricollis*, Eichhoff, Berl. Ent. Zeitschr. Vol. 12, p. 148 (1868).   Brasilien.
2. *P. rimosus*, Eichhoff, ibidem, p. 148 (1868). — **Taf. 5, Fig. 52.**   Chile, Cuba, Mexiko, Panama, Guatemala.

95. Genus SCOLYTOGENES, Eichhoff

Scolytogenes. Eichhoff, Ratio Tomic. p. 497 (1879).

ORIGINALDIAGNOSE : Eichhoff, loc. cit.

« Caput globosum, oculis simplicibus, antice medio emarginatis. Antennarum funiculus 4-articulatus; articulo 1° globoso, incrassato, 2° multo minore, obconico, 3° et 4° transversis, latitudine crescentibus, clava imbricata, solida. Prothorax subglobosus, antice tubertulato-scabratus, postice granulatus. Elytra thorace vix longiora, subquadrata, depressa, apice vix declivia. Coxæ anticæ contiguæ, posteriores minus late distantes. Tibiæ latæ, ad recipiendos tarsos sulcatæ, extus subserratæ, ciliatæ, tarsorum articulis simplicibus. Prosternum processu brevi, acuto. Episterna metathoracis triangularia, postice dilatata. Venter a basi versus anum convexe ascendens.

» Habitu totali, præcipue structura abdominis, elytrorum, antennarum clavæ propinquitatem notabilem *Scolyti* significans, sed capite globoso, prothorace antice tuberculate scabrato, tibiis extus serratis, tarsis simplicibus instructus ideoque notas generales Tomicinorum exhibens. »

Charaktere. — Die Gattung, von welcher nur eine Art in einem Exemplar in der Dohrn'schen Sammlung existiert (oder existierte?), blieb mir unbekannt.

Geographische Verbreitung der Art. — Die einzige Art ist aus Birma beschrieben.

1. *S. Darwinii*, Eichhoff, Ratio Tomic. p. 407 (1879). Birma.

96. GENUS PACHYCOTES, SHARP

Pachycotes. Sharp, Ent. M.·Mag. Vol. 14, p. 10 (1877-78).

ORIGINALDIAGNOSE : Sharp, loc. cit.

« Fusco-ferrugineus, opacus, crassiusculus, subcylindricus, elytris minus elongatis, crenato-striatis, interstitiis rugosis, parte apicali setis parcis erectis fulvis instructa. Long. 4.5 mm., latit. 2 mm.

» Antennæ moderately long, basal joint elongate, second very short, 4-7 very short and very closely packed, 8-11 forming a rather but little flattened acuminate club. ·Head very short, large, rather coarsely and closely punctured. Thorax about as long as broad, a good deal narrowed towards the front, coarsely punctured, with a very·narrow space along the middle forming an obsolete carina. Elytra rather short, coarsely sculptured, the apical part bearing distinct erect tawny hairs. Riccarton, New Zealand, a single individual found by Mr. Wakefield.

» After an examination of this specimen, which belongs to the *Scolytidae*, its exact affinities appear to me so doubtful that I have given it a new generic name. The club of the antennæ is rather large and but little flattened, covered with hairs, but these do not extend over the whole perface, so that the four joints can be discriminated. Eyes moderately coarsely granulated, very distant on the vertex, transverse, separated from the antennæ by a rather deep constriction. Anterior coxæ distinctly separated, middle coxæ broadly separated. Ventral segments rather short, the basal one peculiarly prominent, as long as the three following short ones together, these being about equal interse and separated by very deep sutures. Tibiæ not stout, moderately broad at the apex, with their outer edge and apex denticulate, their front face rough, their posterior one pubescent (not smooth or excavate); tarsi slender, lobes at the third joint but little developed. The insect has the form and appearance of *Hylurgus liquiperda*, but is rather shorter and thicker, but the granulation of the eyes is distinctly coarser, and the peculiar prominence of the basal abdominal segment suggests an early stage of *Scolytus*. Differentation, to which genus however its relationship is otherwise quite remote; I think for the present it may be placed near *Hylurgus liquiperda*. »

Charaktere. — Die nur in einem Exemplare existierende Gattung ist mir nicht bekannt.

Geographische Verbreitung der Art. — Diese ist aus Neuseeland beschrieben.

1. *P. ventralis*, Sharp, Ent. M. Mag. Vol. 14, p. 10 (1877-1878). Neuseeland.

97. GENUS ERINEOPHILUS, HOPKINS

Erineophilus. Hopkins, Proc. Ent. Soc. Wash. Vol. 5, p. 34 (1902).

ORIGINALDIAGNOSE : Hopkins, loc. cit.

« Head medium in size; not rostrate, front narrow and fringed in the ♀ ; broader, convex and nearly smooth in the ♂; anterior margin (epistoma) strongly produced over base in mandibles; eyes oblong, narrow, closely joined to antennal scrobe and extending more than half their length above it. Maxilla short, broad; cardo more than one-half as long as remaining portion and less than one-half as broad at base; stipes short, continuous with subgalea, but with distinct suture between it and the palpiger, which is large, stout, and as long as the three-jointed palpi, its outer angle bearing numerous longs hairs, the tips of which extend beyond the tip of the palpus; galea narrow, as long as the palpi; and armed on the inner edge with closely set compressed teeth with rounded tips; palpi stout, distinctly three-jointed, the joints nearly equal in length; joint 1 nearly twice as broad as 2, which is also nearly twice as broad as 3, which is truncate at tip; 1 and 2 with a few hairs in the outer portion toward the anterior margins. Mentum short, rather broad, anterior portion broader than base; ligula short, connate, not extending to tip, sparsely clothed with short hairs; palpi difficult to define. appear to be two-jointed and differ in the sexes as indicated in the figures. That of the ♂ appears to have the second joint globular and the tip concave, and the inner edge armed with a small chitinous piece, while in the ♀ it is narrower toward the tip, obliquely excavated and the surface chitinous. Antennæ : funiculus six-jointed (appears to be five-jointed in some examples), joint 1 large, globular, nearly as long as the others united, 2-5 about equal length, 5-6 compressed, closely joined. irregular and difficult to determine, except in balsam under high magnification; club oblong, compressed, broadly rounded from middle to tip, narrowing toward base, divided on its outer face by two sutures, the first nearly straight, the second strongly curved, inner surface shining, not annulated. In balsam the first suture shows a prominent chitinous piece, as in figure; the remaining surface, especially near the suture, marked with numerous punctures and clothed with long hairs, which rise from minute granules. Scape simple, clavate. scarcely as broad as the first joint of funiculus.

    » Front tarsi slender, shorter than tibiæ, joints increasing in length from base, 1 short and constricted in middle, 2 broader at tip, 3 simple, oval cylindrical, 4 short and narrow but distinct, 5 rather stout at tip and as long as 2 and 3 together.

    » Front tibiæ stout, broad at base, slightly broader at tip, upper or outer edge armed with three or four stout, broad, triangular teeth, connected with transverse elevations on the outer face, and increasing in size toward the outer angle, which is strongly produced into a broad outward and upward curved mucron; inner edge nearly straight, pubescent, angle with cylindrical upward curved tooth. Middle and hind tibiæ narrow at base, dilated towards tip, and evenly serrate on outer edge; outer angle not produced but broadly rounded to inner angle. Front coxæ widely separated, large. almost contiguous with anterior margin of prosternum; middle and hind coxæ small.

    » Prothorax : sternum broad, subquadrate; episternum with posterior portion excavated for reception of femur; notum slightly shorter than broad, sides parallel and margined to middle. Anterior portion broadly rounded, declivous, concealing the head from above, roughened with transverse rugosities; posterior surface smooth, shining, punctured, basal angle acute.

    » Mesothorax : episternum large, opaque; epimerum very small, narrow, obscure.

    » Metathorax : episternum narrow, elevated, base strongly oblique, ventral angle acute; sternum large, with short median groove. toward the posterior margin, in ♀.

    » Abdomen : ventral segments 1 and 2 equal width, both together as long as the others united, 3, 4, 5 equal length, sutures nearly straight, posterior margin of 5 concave, not strongly reflexed as is usual. Pygidium prominent and extending beyond tip of elytra in both sexes, but much more pubescent in the ♂, strongly punctured in the ♀; propygidium smooth, chitinous and the posterior margin more shining in the ♂, not chitinous in the ♀.

    » Elytra : sides parallel or faintly rounded for more than half their length, slightly wider in middle than prothorax; not elevated or roughened at base, but faintly margined; surface nearly smooth, shining, striæ and interspaces punctured in rows, declivity plain. »

Geographische Verbreitung der Art. — Es ist nur eine, mir unbekannt gebliebene Art aus Nordamerika beschrieben worden.

1. *E. Schwarzi*, Hopkins. Proc. Ent. Soc. Wash. Vol. 5, p. 36 (1902). Florida.

98. GENUS SCOLYTOMIMUS, BLANDFORD

Scolytomimus. Blandford, Ann. Mag. Nat. Hist. Vol. 15, p. 319 (1895).

ORIGINALDIAGNOSE : Blandford, loc. cit.

« Caput rotundatum, obtectum; oculi ovales, emarginati. Antennarum scapus longus, funiculus perbrevis, 6-articulatus, articulis 3o-6m transversis, latitudine haud crescentibus, clava permagna, ovalis, compressa, solida, sutura unica obliqua in margine externo incipiente et medium attinente notata; mentum oblongum. lateribus incurvatis, ligula ovali medio inserta. palpis labialibus longis.

» Prothorax transversus, semiorbiculatus. Scutellum magnum. Elytra depressa, posterius vix declivia. Abdomen versus apicem ascendens.

» Coxæ anticæ approximatæ; tibiæ compressæ, extus rotundatæ, anticæ extus serratæ; tarsi recepti breves, articulis tribus primis æqualibus.

» Intermediate between *Xyloctonus* and *Scolytogenes*. »

Geographische Verbreitung der Art. — Nur eine mir unbekannte Art aus Ceylon ist beschrieben.

1. *S. dilutus*, Blandford, Ann. Mag. Nat. Hist. Vol. 15, p. 319 (1895). Ceylon.

99. GENUS XYLOCTONUS, EICHHOFF

Xyloctonus. Eichhoff, Berl. Ent. Zeitschr. Vol. 15, p. 134 (1871).

ORIGINALDIAGNOSE : Eichhoff, loc. cit.

« Caput subgloborum, oculis bipartitis. Antennæ funiculo 6-articulato, capitulo imbricato circulari (suturis concentricis vix conspicuis). Tibiæ compressæ latæ, extus rotundatæ, serratæ, tarsi articulis 3 primis simplicibus. Abdomen a basi versus apicem ascendens. Maxillarum mala intus setis rigidis subhirtella. Mentum oblongo-quadratum, palpi labiales articulo primo sequentibus duobus consumtis duplo maiore. »

Charaktere. — Körperform oval, pechbraun oder heller, Länge 2.5 mm., ohne Glanz und ohne Bekleidung.

Kopf kugelig, ins Halsschild zurückgezogen, Stirn gewölbt.

Augen in zwei Teile von dreiecksform geteilt.

Fühler mit sechsgliedriger Geissel und kreisförmiger, flacher, mit kaum sichtbaren koncentrisch gebogenen Nähten.

Vorderkiefer kräftig.

Mittelkiefer an der Kaukante mit breitgedrückten geraden Zähnen besetzt.

Hinterkiefer bilden ein länglich viereckiges, an der Spitze geradlinig abgestutztes Kinn mit grosser, am Grunde befestigster Zunge, die daselbst so breit wie das Kinn ist und sich nach vorn in eine abgerundete Spitze verschmälert, so dass die ganze Zunge gleichschenklig dreieckig ist.

Lippentaster : Glied 1 länger als die beiden andern zusammen, Glied 3 kegelförmig.

Halsschild halbkreisförmig, stark gewölbt, von dunklerer oder hellerer Färbung als der übrige

Körper, am Vorderrand mit zwei spitzen Knötchen, auf der vorderen Oberfläche mit einem Höckerfleck, hinten runzelig punktiert, seitlich und am Grunde gerandet.

Schildchen versenkt, kaum sichtbar.

Flügeldecken flach, stark gekerbt-gestreift, Zwischenräume erhaben, glatt; Nahtstreifen vertieft; Hinterteil flach, kaum abfallend.

Vorderbrust ohne Forstatz.

Hüften : vordere und hintere genähert, mittlere entfernt.

Schienen sehr breit, flachgedrückt, aussen verbreitert-gerundet, gesägt, mit Furchen für die Füsse.

Fussglieder gleichförmig rund, 3 nicht verbreitert.

Bauch ansteigend.

Geographische Verbreitung der Art. — Es ist eine Art beschrieben, welche in Südafrika vorkommt.

1. *X. scolytoides*, Eichhoff, Berl. Ent. Zeitschr. Vol. 15, p. 134 (1871). — Afrika (Natal).
Taf. 10, Fig. 44.

100. GENUS CTONOXYLON, HAGEDORN

Ctonoxylon. Hagedorn, Deutsche Ent. Zeitschr. p. 4 (1910).

ORIGINALDIAGNOSE : Hagedorn, loc. cit.

« Caput globosum exsertum. Labium oblongum antrorsum dilatatum, apice rotundato, ligula angusta marginibus crenulata, labio in medio inserta, apice subacuta. Palpi labiales angustatæ articulo primo sequentibus consumptis longiore, secundo parvo, tertio conico. Maxillæ mala spinulis compressis intus ciliata. Palporum maxillarium articulus tertius longitudinaliter striolatus. Oculi bipartiti, pars superior rotunda, inferior oblonga. Antennæ funiculo 7-articulato, articulo 1° crassiusculo bulbiformi, 2° obconico minore, sequentibus transversis latitudine crescentibus, capitulo‾ obovali imbricato, suturis fere concentricis et plaga obscuriore mediana. Tibiæ latæ, compressæ, extus ampliatæ, rotundatæ, serratæ, pro receptione tarsorum canaliculatæ. Femora omnia et antennæ in foveas retrahenda sunt, sicut est in *Byrrho* et in *Histere*. Venter a basi versus anum ascendens.

» *Xyloctono* generi similis et affinis, sed systemate membrorum exbariorum et antennis 7-articulatis bene distinctus. »

Charaktere. — Körperform längs-oval, nach hinten zugespitzt, Länge 2 bis 4.5 mm., Farbe hellgelb bis braun, Skulptur derb. Behaarung in hellen Borsten bestehend.

Kopf kugelig, im Halsschild nur wenig zurückgezogen.

Augen zweiteilig, der obere Teil rund, der untere quer-oval.

Fühler mit siebengliedriger Geissel und gerundeter, beilförmiger Keule, welche flachgedrückt und behaart ist. Auf der Vorderfläche befindet sich ein dunkler Fleck, von dem aus ein Netzwerk von miteinander verbundenen radiären Nähten, deren Schnittpunkte in zwei koncentrischen Linien liegen, ausgeht.

Vorderkiefer kräftig, dreizähnig.

Mittelkiefer mit breiter, stumpfgerundeter Innenlade, an deren Kaukante vierzehn bis sechszehn dolchförmige, gerade, spitze, breitgedrückte Stachelzähne sitzen, und deren Tasterträger mit starken, gefiederten Haarborsten reichlich besetzt ist.

Kiefertaster mit drei walzenförmigen, an Breite abnehmenden Gliedern, deren letztes am Grunde längsgestreift ist.

Hinterkiefer zu einem oblongen, am Grunde schmäleren, an der gerandeten Spitze breiteren Kinne mit geraden Seiten verschmolzen, in dessen Mitte die zungenförmige, an den Rändern gekerbte Zunge angesetzt ist, deren Spitze bis beinahe zum ersten Drittel des ersten Tastergliedes reicht.

Lippentaster : Glied 1 sehr gross, viel länger als 2 und 3 zusammengenommen.

Halsschild kugelig, oben kissenförmig gewölbt, mit einem Höckerfleck vorn in der Mitte der Oberfläche; am Vorderrande stehen zwei vorragende Hörnchen. Basis gerandet.

Schildchen deutlich, dreieckig, konkav.

Flügeldecken vorn gerandet und gekerbt, aber nicht aufgeworfen, mit derber tiefstreifiger Skulptur und Beborstung auf den Zwischenräumen; nach hinten verschmälert, in je eine Spitze auslaufend. Oberfläche schwach abgewölbt.

Vorderbrust ohne Fortsatz.

Hüften : Vorderhüften einander berührend, Mittel- und Hinterhüften weit voneinander entfernt.

Schienen breitgedrückt mit gerundeter und gesägter Aussenkante, mit Furche für die Füsse.

Fussglieder 1, 2, 3 einfach rund und einander ziemlich gleich.

Bauch ansteigend.

Sämmtliche Extremitäten können in Gruben dem Körper angelegt werden, sodass sie nicht über die Ebene desselben vorragen.

Geographische Verbreitung der Arten. — Die vier Arten mit zwei Varietäten stammen aus Kamerun.

1. *C. auratum*, Hagedorn, Deutsche Ent. Zeitschr. p. 4 (1910).   Kamerun.
2. *C. camerunum*, Hagedorn, ibidem, p. 4 (1910).   Kamerun.
       var. flavescens, Hagedorn, ibidem, p. 4 (1910) — **Taf. 5, Fig. 53, 53a.**   Kamerun.
       var. hirsutum, Hagedorn, ibidem. p. 4 (1910). — **Taf. 10, Fig. 45, 46.**   Kamerun.
3. *C. crenatum*, Hagedorn, ibidem, p. 5 (1910).   Kamerun.
4. *C. fuscum*, Hagedorn, ibidem, p. 5 (1910). — **Taf. 10, Fig. 47, 48.**   Kamerun.

III. SUBFAM. SÆTIDENTATÆ

9. TRIBUS CORTHYLINÆ

UEBERSICHT DER GATTUNGEN

1. *Flügeldecken an der Spitze ausgebreitet, Geissel dreigliedrig.*
   2. *Fühlerkeule lang-eiförmig* . . . . 101. Genus AMPHRICANUS, Erichson.
   2'. *Fühlerkeule dreieckig.* . . . . 102. Genus STEGANOCRANUS, Eichhoff.
1'. *Flügeldecken an der Spitze nicht ausgebreitet, an der Nahtspitze ausgerandet oder gemeinsam abgerundet.*
   2. *Fühlerkeule lang zugespitzt.*
      3'. *Fühlergeissel eingliedrig* . . . . 103. Genus BRACHYSPARTUS, Ferrari.
      3''. *Fühlergeissel zweigliedrig.*
         4'. *Fühlerschaft gedreht oder gewunden* . . . . 104. Genus ANCHONOCERUS, Eichhoff.
         4''. *Fühlerschaft gerade.* . . . . 105. Genus PHTHORIUS, Eichhoff.
      3'''. *Fühlergeissel dreigliedrig* . . . . 106. Genus GLOCHINOCERUS, Blandford.

2'. *Fühlerkeule rund oder eckig.*
   3. *Flügeldeckenspitze gemeinsam abgerundet.*
      4. *Fühlergeissel eingliedrig.*

101. Genus AMPHICRANUS, Erichson

Amphicranus. Erichson, Arch. f. Naturg. Vol. 2 (1), p. 63 (1836).
Piezorhopalus. Guérin, Rev. Zool. p. 107 (1838).

Originaldiagnose : Erichson, loc. cit.

« Antennæ funiculo biarticulato, capitulo subsolido. Labium triangulare. Maxillæ mala coriacea, subtiliter ciliata. Palpi maxillares articulis 2 primis brevissimis. 3º cylindrico, 4º minuto, subulato. Labium triangulare. Palpi labiales articulis 2 primis magnis, 3º elongato-subulato. Antennæ scapo elongato, recto, apice breviter clavato, funiculi articulo 1º crassiusculo, obconico, 2º minuto ; capitulo magno, valde compresso, obsolete annulato : segmento 1º minutissimo, glabro, reliquis subæqualibus, pubescentibus. Corpus subcylindricum. Tibiæ angustæ, extus parum denticulatæ. Tarsi articulo 1º reliquis paullo longiore. »

Charaktere. — Körperform cylindrisch, Länge 3 bis 9 mm. Farbe schwarz und roth, glatt, glänzend, Bekleidung keine, Skulptur schwach, nur der Flügeldeckenabsturz ist ausgezeichnet.

Kopf fast vollkommen in das Halsschild zurückgezogen.

Augen länglich, vorn ausgerandet.

Fühler mit keulenförmigem Schaft, dreigliedriger Geissel und lang-eiförmiger, zusammengedrückter Keule, die behaart und mit zwei gebogenen oder geknickten Nähten versehen ist.

Vorderkiefer klein aber kräftig gebaut.

Mittelkiefer mit breiter lederartiger Innenlade, die an der Spitze zurückgefaltet und mit feinen sichelförmigen Borsten besetzt ist, während die Kaukante breitere, spitze dornartige Borsten trägt.

Kiefertaster dreigliedrig, Glied 1 und 2 quer. 3 kegelförmig, mit dunklen Längslinien gestreift.

Hinterkiefer zu einem breiten, gegen die Basis stark verschmälerten Kinne verschmolzen, das an der Spitze rechts und links abgeschrägt, in der Mitte gerade abgestutzt ist. Zunge am Grunde des Kinnes angesetzt, häutig, lanzenförmig mit spitzem Ende.

Lippentaster : Glied 1 und 2 gross, 3 klein.

Halsschild bei den grossen Formen nach vorn steil abfallend, oft dreibuchtig, bei den kleinen Formen ist es entweder steil oder schräg abfallend oder mit einem gerundeten oder zugespitzten Fortsatz, der den Kopf überragt. Vorn ist es schwach körnig gerauht.

Schildchen gross oder mittelgross, dreieckig.

Flügeldecken walzenförmig, hinten tief ausgehöhlt und entweder flach an der Spitze ausgebreitet, oder in zwei parallele geigenförmige Fortsätze ausgezogen, die durch einen schmalen Zwischenraum getrennt und auf der Innenkante konkav sind.

Vorderbrust : bei den grossen Formen ist der vor den Hüften liegende Teil kurz, bei den kleinen Formen sehr lang ; der hintere Rand ist quer abgeschnitten, so dass die Vorderhüften in einer gemeinsamen Gelenkhöhle zu sitzen scheinen.

Hüften : Vorderhüften einander berührend.

Schienen schmal, Aussenkante gekerbt-gezähnt.

Fussglieder : das erste ist länger als die folgenden.

Bauch gerade, häufig mit spärlicher Behaarung, während der Oberkörper glatt ist.

Geographische Verbreitung der Arten. — Zwanzig Arten sind beschrieben. Sie kommen nur in Süd- und Centralamerika vor.

1. *A. balteatus*, Blandford, Biol. Centr. Amer. Col. Vol. 4 (6), p. 291   Centralamerika. (1905).
2. *A. Belti*, Blandford, ibidem, p. 292 (1905).   Centralamerika.
3. *A. bipunctatus*, Eichhoff, Ratio Tomic. p. 469 (1879).   Südamerika.
4. *A. brevipennis*, Blandford, Biol. Centr. Amer. Col. Vol. 4 (6), p. 293   Centralamerika. (1905).
5. *A. collaris*, Blandford, ibidem, p. 294 (1905).   Centralamerika.
6. *A. elegans*, Eichhoff, Berl. Ent. Zeitschr. Vol. 12, p. 276 (1868).   Centralamerika.
7. *A. fastigatus*, Blandford, Biol. Centr. Amer. Col. Vol. 4 (6), p. 296   Centralamerika. (1905).
8. *A. filiformis*, Blandford, ibidem, p. 295 (1905).   Centralamerika.
9. *A. Fryi*, Blandford, ibidem, p. 291 (1905).   Südamerika.
10. *A. Grouvellei*, Blandford, ibidem, p. 294 (1905).   Südamerika.
11. *A. hybridus*, Blandford, ibidem, p. 298 (1905).   Centralamerika.
12. *A. Lesnei*, Hagedorn, Bull. Mus. Hist. Nat. Paris, Vol. 10, p. 551   Südamerika. (1904).
13. *A. politus*, Eichhoff, Berl. Ent. Zeitschr. Vol. 12, p. 276 (1868).   Südamerika.
14. *A. propugnatus*, Blandford, Biol. Centr. Amer. Col. Vol. 4 (6), p. 297   Centralamerika. (1905).
15. *A. retusus*, Eichhoff, Berl. Ent. Zeitschr. Vol 12, p. 276 (1868).   Südamerika.
16. *A. Schaufussi*, Blandford, Biol. Centr. Amer. Col. Vol. 4 (6). p. 293 (1905).   Südamerika.
17. *A. tenuis*, Blandford, ibidem, p. 295 (1905).   Centralamerika.
18. *A. terebella*, Blandford, ibidem, p. 296 (1905).   Centralamerika.
19. *A. thoracicus*, Erichson, Arch. f. Naturg. Vol. 2 (1), p. 37 (1836).   Südamerika.
20. *A. torneutes*, Blandford, Biol. Centr. Amer. Col. Vol. 4 (6), p. 292 (1905).   Centralamerika.

102. Genus STEGANOCRANUS, Eichhoff

Steganocranus. Eichhoff, Ratio Tomic. p. 460 (1879).

ORIGINALDIAGNOSE : Eichhoff, loc. cit.

« Caput subliberum, thorace acuminato superfastigiatum. Antennæ funiculo 3-articulato, capitulo magno, triangulari. oblique inserto. 3-articulato. Pronotum apica acuminato supra caput in cornu productum. Pedes graciles, femoribus anticis latis, compressis, intus emarginatis, tibiis linearibus, anticis extus biseriatim denticulato-porcatis, apice uncinatis ; tarsis tenuibus, articulo 1º sequente paullo longiore. »

Charaktere. — Die nur auf zwei Exemplare einer Art gegründete Gattung ist mir unbekannt.

Geographische Verbreitung der Art. — Das Vaterland der Art ist ungewiss ; vermutlich Südamerika.

1. *S. Dohrnii*, Eichhoff, Ratio Tomic. p. 461 (1879).

103. Genus BRACHYSPARTUS, Ferrari

Brachyspartus. Ferrari, Baumzuchtschädliche Borkenk. p. 65 (1867).

ORIGINALDIAGNOSE : Ferrari, loc. cit.

« Tarsi filiformes, articulo primo, secundo tertioque singulatim, fere dimidio longiore, his duobus inter se longitudine æqualibus, ultimo reliquis simul sumtis breviore. Antennarum fractarum funiculo brevissimo, uniarticulato, clava compressa, magna, acuminata, intus magis dilatata, biarticulata, sutura recta.

» Ligula brevissima, convexa, glabra, subobtusa, parte fulcrali angustior, haec parum elongata, basin versus valde successive angustata, antice subinflata.

» Palpi labiales valde porrecti, articulo secundo primo subæquali, tertio angusto, brevi, obconico.

» Maxillarum mala intus pilis falcatis densissime fimbriato ciliata. »

Charaktere. — Körperform kurz walzenförmig, Farbe braun, glänzend, Skulptur und Bekleidung schwach. Länge 2.5 mm.

Kopf kugelig, im Halsschild versteckt. Stirn beim ♀ gewölbt, beim ♂ eingedrückt.

Augen vorn ausgerandet.

Fühler mit eingliedriger Geissel, und grosser, solider, flacher, dreieckiger Keule, die mit zwei Quernähten versehen und beim ♂ spitzer, beim ♀ stumpfer ist.

Vorderkiefer derb, ungezähnt.

Mittelkiefer mit breiter, an der Spitze zurückgeschlagener Innenlade, die ganz mit sichelförmigen Borsten an der Kaukante besetzt ist.

Kiefertaster dreigliedrig, erstes Glied am grössesten, letztes kegelförmig, mit dunklen Längslinien dicht gestreift.

Hinterkiefer gegen die Basis verschmälert, oblong, mit kleiner häutiger Zunge, die vor der Mitte des Kinnes eingefügt ist.

Lippentaster : Glied 1 und 2 grösser, einander gleich, Glied 3 klein.

Halsschild kurz-eiförmig oder länger als breit, an der Basis gerandet (bei einer Art nicht!), Vorderfläche gerunzelt oder mit kleinen Höckern besetzt, die in der Mitte des Vorderrandes bisweilen vorstehen.

Schildchen dreieckig, abgerundet an der Hinterecke.

Flügeldecken walzenförmig, am Grunde gradlinig abgeschnitten, Absturz ziemlich steil, Skulptur schwach, ebenso wie die spärliche Behaarung.

Vorderbrust bis zu den Hüften ausgeschnitten.

Beine : Vorderschienen haben eine gekrümmte, fein gesägte Aussenkante; die beiden andern Paare sind flach und gegen die Spitze verbreitert, an der Aussenkante mit ein paar stärkeren Dornen versehen.

Fussglieder : Glied 1 länger, 2 und 3 kürzer, alle rund ; 3 nicht verbreitert.

Bauch wagerecht.

Geographische Verbreitung der Arten. — Es sind drei Arten aus Panama und Venezuela bekannt.

1. *B. barbatus*, Blandford, Biol. Centr. Amer. Col. Vol. 4 (6), p. 265 (1904).   Panama.
2. *B. ebeninus*, Blandford, ibidem, p. 265 (1904).   Panama.
3. *B. Moritzi*, Ferrari, Baumzuchtsch. Borkenk. p. 68 (1867).   Venezuela.

104. Genus ANCHONOCERUS, Eichhoff

Anchonocerus. Eichhoff, Ratio Tomic. p. 431 (1879).

Originaldiagnose : Eichhoff, loc. cit.

« Caput globosum, insertum. Mentum triangulum, versus basin angustatum, apice truncatum. Palpi labiales longi, articulo 1º subquadrato, 2º cylindrico, longissimo, 3º conico, parvo. Maxillæ fulcro subcoriaceo, granulis in ordines creberrimas concinne dispositis ornato; lobo magno, intus setis rigidis et spinulis ciliato, apice rotundato. setis subtilibus creberrimis, conglutinatis omnino cincta. Palpi maxillares articulo ultimo lineis obscuris notato. Antennæ in foveis profundis insertæ, scapo depravatius contorto-flexuoso, funiculo brevissimo, biarticulato; articulo hujus 1º bulbiformi, crassiusculo, 2º brevi obconico, capitulo intime applicato; hoc compresso, longissimo, 3-articulato. Tibiæ anteriores compressæ, extus subtilissime crenulato-serratæ. »

Charaktere. — Körperform lang-walzenförmig, Farbe kastanienbraun, glänzend. Bekleidung keine, Skulptur nur am Flügeldeckenabsturz kräftig, Länge 5 bis 5.5 mm.

Kopf kugelig, ins Halsschild zurückgezogen. Stirn konvex, behaart.

Augen querstehend, lang, vorn tief ausgerandet.

Fühler seitlich vor den Augen in tiefen Gruben eingelenkt; Schaft gedreht, abgeplattet, grau behaart; Geissel sehr kurz, zweigliedrig; Keule gross und lang zugespitzt, solid, innere Fläche eben, äussere gewölbt, mit zwei geraden, schräg verlaufenden, parallelen Nähten versehen.

Vorderkiefer kräftig, schwarz.

Mittelkiefer mit grossem Fulcrum, das mit zahlreichen, enggestellten, parallelen Körnchenreihen besetzt ist und grosser Innenlade, deren Kaukante Borstenhaare und Stachelzähne trägt; an der Spitze ist sie abgerundet und mit zahlreichen dünnen, zopfartig zusammenhaltenden Borsten bekränzt.

Kiefertaster : letztes Glied mit Längsstreifen versehen.

Hinterkiefer zu einem dreieckigen, nach dem Grunde verschmälerten, an der Spitze abgestutzten Kinne verschmolzen.

Lippentaster lang, erstes Glied fast quadratisch, zweites walzenförmig, sehr lang, drittes klein, kegelförmig.

Halsschild länger als breit, vorn stark gerundet; Oberfläche gewölbt, vorn mit Runzeln und Höckerchen besetzt, hinten glatt.

Schildchen klein, hinten gerundet.

Flügeldecken walzenförmig, etwas länger als das Halsschild, am Grunde einfach abgeschnitten, am Absturz schräg abgestutzt und daselbst mit grösseren und kleineren Körnchen besetzt; Spitzenwinkel gemeinschaftlich tief buchtig ausgerandet.

Vorderbrust glatt.

Beine behaart, Schenkel ziemlich breit und abgeflacht; Schienen mässig erweitert und gekrümmt, aussen gerundet und sehr fein gekerbt-gesägt.

Fussglieder : 1 am längsten, 2 und 3 kürzer, gleich gross und rund.

Bauch wagrecht.

Geographische Verbreitung der Art. — Eine Art aus Südamerika ist beschrieben.

1. *A. rufipes*, Eichhoff, Ratio Tomic. p. 431 (1879).   Neu-Granada.

105. Genus PHTHORIUS, Eichhoff

Phthorius. Eichhoff, Ratio Tomic. p. 433 (1879).
Pterocyclon. Eichhoff, Berl. Ent. Zeitschr. p. 278 (1868).

Originaldiagnose : Eichhoff, loc. cit.

« Caput globosum, insertum. Mentum oblongum, triangulum, versus basin fortiter angustatum, apice truncato, ligula membranacea, longissima lanceolata, apice subcoriaceo, piloso, in apice menti inserta. Palpi labiales perlongi, articulo 2° longiore, 3° minuto. Maxillæ mala lata, obtuse acuminata, intus pilis rigidis ciliata, apice replicato toto setis subtilibus creberrimis coactis cincto. Palpi maxillares articulis 1° et 2° brevibus, transversis, 3° prioribus longiore, lineis longitudinalibus obscurioribus insignito. Antennæ funiculo 2-articulato, capitulo solido, 3-articulato elongato, acuminato. Tibiæ anticæ extus granulato-porcatæ. »

Charaktere. — Körperform schmal, walzenförmig, Länge 3 bis 7 mm. Farbe gelbbraun, Behaarung spärlich, Skulptur nur am Flügeldeckenabsturz kräftig.

Kopf kugelig, im Halsschild versteckt; Stirn mit wenigen kurzen Haaren besetzt.

Augen nierenförmig, vorn stark ausgerandet.

Fühler : Schaft lang, keulenförmig, Geissel zweigliedrig, erstes Glied gross, becherförmig, zweites klein, der Keule innig anliegend; diese selbst lang zugespitzt, mit zwei geraden, breiten Nähten, mässig mit kurzen Haaren bedeckt.

Vorderkiefer kräftig, schwarz.

Mittelkiefer mit breiter Innenlade, die an der Kaukante mit zur Spitze hin schmäleren und dichterstehenden Borsten besetzt ist.

Kiefertaster : Glied 1 und 2 kurz und breit, 3 länger, mit dunklen Längsstreifen gezeichnet.

Hinterkiefer bilden ein längliches, am Grunde verschmälertes, an der Spitze gerade abgestutztes Kinn, an dessen vorderen Rand die schmale, lange, zugespitzte Zunge angesetzt ist.

Lippentaster : Glied 1 kurz und breit, zweites viel länger, drittes klein.

Halsschild walzenförmig, oberhalb gewölbt, vorn mit Runzeln besetzt, hinten glatt.

Schildchen klein, gerundet.

Flügeldecken cylindrisch, glatt, schwach skulptiert, am Absturz herzförmig ausgehöhlt, punktiert, Rand mit oder ohne Zähne

Vorderbrust mit kurzem Fortsatz.

Hüften : Vorderhüften zusammen-, Mittel- und Hinterhüften nur wenig auseinanderstehend.

Schienen : die vorderen gekrümmt, auf der Aussenfläche grob gekörnt, Aussenkante gezähnt.

Fussglieder 1 am längsten, 3 einfach.

Bauch gerade.

Geographische Verbreitung der Arten. — Zwei Arten aus Südamerika sind bekannt.

1. *P. edentatus*, Hagedorn, Bull. Mus. Hist. Nat. Paris, Vol. 10, p. 550 (1904).   Venezuela.
— Taf. 6, Fig. 54, 54a.
2. *P. ingens*, Eichhoff, Berl. Ent. Zeitschr. Vol. 12. p. 278 (1868).   Columbia.

106. Genus GLOCHINOCERUS, Blandford

Glochinocerus. Blandford, Biol. Centr. Amer. Col. Vol. 4 (6), p. 266 (1904).

Originaldiagnose : Blandford, loc. cit.

« Antennæ lateraliter insertæ; scapo sat longo, recto; funiculo 3-articulato; clava elongata,

3-articulata, angusta, suturis transversis; articulo ultimo ceteris consumtis fere æquali; in medio constricto. Prothorax antice oblique declivis. Elytra cylindrica, postice retusa, apice suturæ integro. Tibiæ anticæ angustæ, curvatæ, extus granulatæ, margine superiore subserrato. Tarsi graciles.

» *Mas :* fronte integra, antennarum clava breviore; prothoracis apice bituberculato.

» *Femina :* fronte excavata, fasciata; antennarum clava longiore; prothoracis apice integro. »

Charaktere. — Körperform länglich walzenförmig, Länge 3.6 bis 4 mm.; Farbe dunkelbraun, Bekleidung and Skulptur spärlich, letztere nur am Vorderteil des Halsschildes und am Flügeldecken-absturz ausgeprägt.

Kopf kugelig, ins Halsschild zurückgezogen, Stirn beim ♀ tief ausgehöhlt und mit einem Haarkranz besetzt.

Augen vorn tief ausgerandet.

Fühler in der Ausrandung der Augen eingelenkt, mit ziemlich langem Schaft, der beim ♀ etwas verbreitert und nach der Spitze abgeflacht ist; Geissel kurz, dreigliedrig, erstes Glied becherförmig, die andern kegelförmig und allmählich breiter werdend; Keule verlängert, und abgeflacht beim ♀, dreigliedrig mit queren Nähten, das erste Glied dreieckig, das zweite quer, das dritte beinahe so lang als die andern zusammen, stumpfspitzig und in der Mitte eingeschnürt.

Mittelkiefer beim ♂ mit viereckiger Innenlade, an deren innern Spitzenwinkel in einen kurzen mit dichten feinen gekrümmten Borsten besetzten Fortsatz ausgezogen; die Kaukante ziemlich gerade, mit längeren geraden Borsten besetzt.

Kiefertaster an dem äusseren Spitzenwinkel angesetzt, die beiden ersten Glieder kurz, das dritte länger als breit.

Hinterkiefer beim ♂ zu einem langen, schmalen Kinne verschmolzen, das am Grunde einge-schnürt ist, nach der Spitze zu allmählich verbreitert, gerundet und behaart. Zunge in der Mitte des Kinnes angesetzt, nach vorn verbreitert; die Spitze des Kinnes überragend.

Lippentaster am Grunde einander berührend, gross, das erste Glied kelchförmig, quer, das zweite beinahe zweimal so lang als breit, aussen behaart, das dritte schlank, aber nicht quer.

Halsschild schräg nach der Spitze abfallend, diese beim ♂ mit zwei Knötchen besetzt, die Seiten eingedrückt, aber nicht gerandet.

Schildchen ziemlich gross, dreieckig gerundet.

Flügeldecken cylindrisch, hinten abgestutzt, an der Nahtspitze nicht ausgerandet oder aus-gebuchtet.

Vorderbrust kurz, eng die Hüften umschliessend und in der Mitte etwas vorgezogen.

Beine : Vorderschenkel breit, nach der Spitze lappenförmig verbreitert; Vorderschienen lang, schlank, gebogen, mit schwach gesägter Aussenkante und rauher Aussenfläche.

Mittel- und Hinterschienen spatelförmig verbreitert, Aussenrand kaum gesägt.

Fussglieder lang und zart, Glied 1 länger als jedes der beiden folgenden ; 3 einfach.

Bauch gerade.

Das Genus ist den Gattungen *Anchonocerus* und *Phthorius* ähnlich, besonders in Bezug auf die Fühlerkeule ; es unterscheidet sich von beiden durch die dreigliedrige Fühlergeissel und den nicht ausgerandeten Flügeldeckenabsturz.

Geographische Verbreitung der Arten. — Zwei Arten aus Centralamerika sind beschrieben.

1. *G. gemellus*, Blandford, Biol. Centr. Amer. Col. Vol. 4 (6). p. 267 Guatemala. (1904).

2. *G. retusipennis*, Blandford, ibidem, p. 266 (1904).   Guatemala.

107. Genus CORTHYLUS, Erichson

Corthylus. Erichson, Arch. f. Naturg. Vol. 2, p. 64 (1836); Lacordaire, Gen. Col. Vol. 7, p. 86 (1866).
Pseudocorthylus. Ferrari, Baumzuchtsch. Borkenk. p. 71 (1867).
Morizus. Ferrari, ibidem, p. 69 (1867).
Crypturgus. Zimmermann, Trans. Amer. Ent. Soc. Vol. 2, p. 142 (1868).
Cryphalus. Le Conte, ibidem, p. 154 (1868).

ORIGINALDIAGNOSE : Erichson, loc. cit.

« Antennæ funiculo uni-articulato, capitulo 4-annulato. Labium triangulare. Palpi maxillares articuli 2 primis crassis, brevissimis, vix distinguendis, 3° longiore cylindrico, 4° obsoleto. Labium elongatum triangulare. Palpi labiales articulis 2 primis crassis, 2° longiore, 3° minuto, obtuso. — Antennæ scapo subclavato : articulo 2° obconico, crassiusculo, capitulo compresso, suborbiculari, 4-articulato. — Corpus cylindricum. Tibiæ compressæ, extus serratæ. Tarsi articulo 1° reliquis longiore. »

Charaktere. — Körperform cylindrisch, Farbe braun, meistens glänzend, Skulptur und Bekleidung schwach, Länge von 2 bis 4 mm.; sekundäre Geschlechtsmerkmale an Fühlern und Stirn.

Kopf kugelig, ins Halsschild eingezogen; Stirn konkav und behaart bei den ♀, konvex und haarlos bei den ♂.

Augen sehr gross, quer-oval, vorn tief ausgerandet.

Fühler mit eingliedriger Geissel; Keule klein, oval oder länglich bei den ♂, sehr gross, asymmetrisch, dreieckig, beilförmig oder nierenförmig, mit langen Haarbüscheln am Aussenrande besetzt bei den ♀.

Vorderkiefer stark gebaut.

Mittelkiefer mit breiter gerundeter Innenlade, die an der abgerundeten Spitze auf beiden Kanten mit feinen Borsten dicht gesäumt, an der Kaukante mit langen sichelförmig gekrümmten Borsten besetzt ist.

Kiefertaster auf der Spitze des Fulcrum angesetzt, Glied 1 und 2 kurz und quer, 3 länger, oben abgerundet und mit dunklen Längslinien gestreift.

Hinterkiefer sind zu einem schmalen, im der Mitte noch mehr verengten, am Grunde und an der Spitze gleichmässig verbreiterten Kinne verschmolzen, das an der Spitze nach rechts und links abgeschrägt ist. Zunge ist nicht sichtbar.

Lippentaster : Glied 1 und 2 gleich, walzenförmig, 3 sehr klein.

Halsschild meist oval, an der Basis gerandet.

Schildchen dreieckig.

Flügeldecken walzenförmig, an der Spitze einzeln gerundet, daher das Pygidium sichtbar, Absturz steil und eben, oder gewölbt.

Vorderbrust bis zu den Vorderhüften ausgeschnitten.

Hüften ziemlich dicht beieinanderstehend, aber sich nicht berührend.

Beine zart; Schienen schlank, kaum verbreitert nach der Spitze, an der äusseren Kante mit zwei oder drei Zähnen besetzt, Vorderschienen am Innenwinkel in einen Haken endigend.

Fussglieder kurz, 3 einfach.

Bauch gerade.

Geographische Verbreitung der Arten. — Die Gattung ist auf das Südreich und das neue Nordreich beschränkt. Von den vierundzwanzig bekannten Arten kommen zweiundzwanzig in Süd- und Centralamerika, drei in Nordamerika vor.

1. *C. abbreviatus*, Eichhoff, Berl. Ent. Zeitschr. Vol. 12, p. 279 (1868). — Columbia.
 Taf. 6, Fig. 56f, 56g.
2. *C. castaneus*, Ferrari, Borkenkäfer, p. 60 (1867). Venezuela.
3. *C. collaris*, Blandford, Biol. Centr. Amer. Col. Vol. 4 (6), p. 261 (1904). Guatemala.
4. *C. columbianus*, Hopkins, W. Virginia Agric. Exper. Stat. Bull. Vol. 36, Virginia.
 p. 313 (1894).
5. *C. comatus*, Blandford, Biol. Centr. Amer. Col. Vol. 4 (6), p. 258 (1904). Guatemala.
6. *C. compressicornis*, Fabricius, Syst. Eleuth. Vol. 2, p. 388 (1801). — Central- und Südamerika.
 Taf. 6, Fig. 56, 56a, 56b, 56c, 56d.
7. *C. dimidiatus*, Ferrari, Borkenkäfer, p. 57 (1867). Venezuela.
8. *C. discoideus*, Blandford, Biol. Centr. Amer. Col. Vol. 4 (6), p. 262 (1904). Venezuela.
9. *C. excisus*, Ferrari, Borkenkäfer, p. 71 (1867). Venezuela.
10. *C. flagellifer*, Blandford, Biol. Centr. Amer. Col. Vol. 4 (6), p. 255 (1904). Central- und Südamerika.
 — Taf. 6, Fig. 55.
11. *C. fuscus*, Blandford, ibidem, p. 262 (1904). Brasilien.
12. *C. Letzneri*, Ferrari, Borkenkäfer, p. 59 (1867). Venezuela.
13. *C. luridus*, Blandford, Biol. Centr. Amer. Col. Vol. 4 (6), p. 256 (1904). Panama.
14. *C. macrocerus*, Eichhoff, Berl. Ent. Zeitschr. Vol. 12, p. 279 (1868). Columbia.
15. *C. panamensis*, Blandford, Biol. Centr. Amer. Col. Vol. 4 (6), p. 259 (1904). Panama.
16. *C. papulans*, Eichhoff, Berl. Ent. Zeitschr. Vol. 12, p. 280 (1868). Brasilien.
17. *C. parvulus*, Blandford, Biol. Centr. Amer. Col. Vol. 4 (6), p. 261 (1904). Guatemala.
18. *C. ptyocerus*, Blandford, ibidem, p. 257 (1904). Panama.
19. *C. punctatissimus*, Zimmermann, Trans. Amer. Ent. Soc. Vol. 2, p. 144 Nordamerika.
 (1868).
20. *C. Redtenbacheri*, Ferrari, Borkenkäfer, p. 70 (1867). Venezuela.
21. *C. rubricollis*, Blandford, Biol. Centr. Amer. Col. Vol. 4 (6), p. 260 (1904). Guatemala.
22. *C. spinifer*, Schwarz, Proc. Ent. Soc. Wash. Vol. 2, p. 114 (1891). Florida.
23. *C. transversus*, Eichhoff, Berl. Ent. Zeitschr. Vol. 12, p. 279 (1868). Neu-Grenada.
24. *C. tulcanus*, Hagedorn, Deutsche Ent. Zeitschr. p. 6 (1910). — Taf. 6, Ecuador.
 Fig. 56e.

108. Genus METACORTHYLUS, Blandford

Metacorthylus. Blandford, Biol. Centr. Amer. Col. Vol. 4 (6), p. 263 (1904).

Originaldiagnose : Blandford, loc. cit.

« Antennarum funiculus 1-articulatus; clava haud permagna, late obovata, 3-articulata, in pagina interna parum concava, pilis longis haud fasciculatis exstructa. Tibiæ sublineares, anticæ curvatæ, extus scabrosæ, margine serrato; tarsi longi, postremi tibiis longiores, articulo primo quam sequenti dimidio longiore. Corpus cylindricum, elytris ad apicem retusis, integris. »

Charaktere. — Körperform ähnt einem cylindrischen *Corthylus*.

Kopf nicht ausgehöhlt, aber auf der Stirn abgeflacht und mit einer ovalen, erhabenen Platte versehen.

Fühler : Schaft dünn, nach der Spitze etwas verdickt, aber nicht verbreitert oder zusammen-gedrückt; die Geissel hat ein knotenartiges Glied. Keule ist mässig gross, abgeflacht, einem gleichseitigen Dreieck mit gerundeten Seiten ähnlich, mit zwei Nähten, die auf der innern Seite gerade, auf der äusseren gekrümmt sind; ihre Spitze ist mit einem dünnen Schopf langer direkt nach vorwärts ragender Haare versehen.

Halsschild walzenförmig, nirgends gerandet, vorn rauh gekörnt, hinten glatt.

Schildchen klein, dreieckig.

Flügeldecken sind walzenförmig, Oberfläche glatt, Absturz ziemlich steil, längs-oval, nicht gerandet; Nahtwinkel nicht klaffend.

Vorderschienen sind lang. dünn und gekrümmt, auf dem Aussenrand gesägt, auf der Aussenfläche gerauht, wie bei *Pterocyclon*. Mittel- und Hinterschienen sind linear und an der Aussenkante nur spärlich gesägt.

Fussglieder lang und dünn, das hintere Paar länger als die Schienen; das erste Glied ist ein Halbmal so lang als jedes der folgenden; drittes Glied einfach, rund.

Bauch gerade.

Geographische Verbreitung der Art. — Die Gattung ist auf ein Exemplar einer aus Panama stammenden Art aufgestellt worden und mir unbekannt geblieben. Sie steht in der Mitte zwischen *Corthylus* und *Brachyspartus*.

1. *M. nigripennis*. Blandford, Biol. Centr. Amer. Col. Vol. 4(6), p. 263 (1904).   Panama.

109. Genus GNATHOTRICHUS, Eichhoff

Gnathotrichus. Eichhoff, Berl. Ent. Zeitschr. Vol. 12, p. 275 (1868).
Pityophthorus. Gemminger & Harold, Cat. Col. Vol. 9, p. 2688 (1872).
Cryphalus. Eichhoff, Ratio Tomic. p. 202 (1879); Le Conte, Trans. Amer. Ent. Soc. Vol. 2. p. 153 (1868).
Crypturgus. Zimmermann, Trans. Amer. Ent. Soc. Vol. 2, p. 142 (1868).
Pityophthorus. Le Conte, Proc. Amer. Philos. Soc. Vol. 15, p. 350 (1876).
Bostrichus. Blanchard in Gay, Hist. fis. Chile, Vol. 5, p. 429 (1851).

ORIGINALDIAGNOSE : Eichhoff, loc. cit.

« Tarsorum articulis tribus primis simplicibus. Antennarum funiculus 5-articulatus, capitulo distincte triannulato. Ligula parte fulcrali angustior. Palpi labiales articulis 1º et 2º subæqualibus, simplicibus, 3º minimo. Maxillarum mala apice rotundata. setis falcatis densissime ciliato, palporum articulo 1º maiore obconico, 2º minore subquadrato, 3º cylindrico elongato. »

Charaktere. — Körperform gestreckt walzenförmig, Länge 2 bis 4 mm., Farbe braun, glänzend, ohne längere Behaarung und mit schwacher Skulptur.

Kopf kugelig, ins Halsschild zurückgezogen; Stirn beim ♂ kahl, beim ♀ behaart.

Augen länglich, querstehend, vorne ausgebuchtet.

Fühler mit fünfgliedriger Geissel und rundem, flachem Knopf mit zwei gebogenen Nähten und langer Behaarung.

Vorderkiefer kräftig entwickelt, ungezähnt.

Mittelkiefer mit breiter gerundeter Innenlade, an der Kaukante mit schmalen, langen, an der breit abgerundeten Ladenspitze dichterstehenden Borsten besetzt.

Kiefertasterglieder an Grösse abnehmend, letztes Glied mit dunklen Längsstreifen.

Hinterkiefer zu einem länglichen, gegen den Grund verschmälerten, an der Spitze breit abgerundeten Kinne verschmolzen; die lineare, lange Zunge ist unter der Mitte des Kinnes angesetzt; deren ausgerandete, verbreiterte Spitze ist an den Ecken mit längeren Haaren besetzt.

Lippentaster sehr verlängert, Glied 1 und 2 gleichlang, 3 klein.

Halsschild cylindrisch, ungerandet, sehr zart punktiert.

Schildchen ziemlich gross, dreieckig.

Flügeldecken cylindrisch, fein punktiert, nie gestreift; Absturz beim ♂ schrägabfallend, ausgehöhlt, beim ♀ konvex, mit Körnchen etc. besetzt.

Vorderbrust ohne Fortsatz..
Hüften auseinanderstehend.
Schienen linear, Aussenkante gezähnt, an der Spitze abgestutzt.
Füssglieder gleichförmig, rund; 3 einfach.
Bauch gerade.

Geographische Verbreitung der Arten. — Elf Arten sind beschrieben. Sie leben im Südreich und im neuen Nordreich.

1. *G. asperulus*, Le Conte, Trans. Amer. Ent. Soc. Vol. 2, p. 155 (1868).   Nordamerika.
2. *G. bituberculatus*, Blandford, Biol. Centr. Amer. Col. Vol. 4 (6), p. 248   Centralamerika.
    (1904).
3. *G. consentaneus*, Blandford, ibidem, p. 247 (1904).   Centralamerika.
4. *G. consobrinus*, Eichhoff. Ratio Tomic. p. 409 (1879).   Chile.
5. *G. longipennis*, Eichhoff, ibidem, p. 408 (1879). — **Taf. 6, Fig. 57.**   Chile.
6. *G materiarius*, Pitch, Trans. New York Agric. Soc. Vol. 3, p. 246(1855).   Nordamerika.
7. *G. nanus*, Eichhoff, ibidem, p. 410 (1855).   Chile.
8. *G. nitidifrons*, Hopkins, Proc. Ent. Soc. Wash. Vol. 7, p. 72 (1905).   Centralamerika.
9. *G. occidentalis*, Hopkins, Bull. U. S. Dep. Agric. Vol. 32, p. 14 (1902).   Nordamerika.
10. *G. retusus*, Le Conte, Trans. Amer. Ent. Soc. Vol. 2, p. 155 (1868).   Nordamerika.
11. *G. sulcatus*, Le Conte, ibidem, p. 155 (1868).   Nordamerika.

110. Genus PTEROCYCLON, Eichhoff

Pterocyclon. Eichhoff, Berl. Ent. Zeitschr. Vol. 12, p. 277 (1868).
Corthylus. Erichson, Arch. f. Naturg. Vol. 2 (1), p. 64 (1836).
Monarthrum. Kirsch, Berl. Ent. Zeitschr. Vol. 10, p. 213 (1866).
Microcorthylus. Ferrari, Borkenkäfer, p. 58 (1867).
Corthylomimus. Ferrari, ibidem, p. 48 (1867).
Cosmocorynus. Ferrari, ibidem. p. 62 (1867).
Trypocranus. Eichhoff, Ratio Tomic. p. 435 (1879).
Cryphalus. Le Conte, Trans. Amer. Ent. Soc. Vol. 2, p. 154 (1868).
Crypturgus. Zimmerman, ibidem, p. 143 (1868).
Bostrichus. Say, Journ. Acad. Natur. Sc. Philad. Vol. 5, p. 253 (1828).

ORIGINALDIAGNOSE : Eichhoff, loc. cit.

« Tarsorum articulis tribus primis simplicibus. Antennarum funiculo 2-articulato, capitulo 3-annulato. Labium (pars fulcralis) triangulare (ligula haud observata). Palpi labiales articulis duobus primis subæqualibus, tertio minuto. Maxillarum mala intus pilis rigidis rarius, apice setis falcatis densissime ciliata. »

Charaktere. — Körperform walzenförmig, Länge 1.5 bis 6 mm., Farbe hell- bis dunkelbraun, auch hellgelb mit dunklen Binden, mit geringer Behaarung und bis auf den Flügeldeckenabsturz schwacher Skulptur.

Kopf kugelig, im Halsschild mehr weniger versteckt; Stirn ist bei einigen ♀ Träger von sekundären Geschlechtsmerkmalen : entweder einfach, ohne Behaarung, oder vertieft mit Franzen *(fimbriaticorne, lobatum, Ferrarii).*

Augen oblong, vorn ausgerandet.

Fühler mit zweigliedriger Geissel und ovaler Keule, welche bei den ♂ ohne lange Haare, bei den ♀ mit langen Wimpern oder büschelförmigen langen Haaren besetzt ist.

Vorderkiefer kräftig.

Mittelkiefer mit breiter, an der Spitze gerundeter, daselbst mit feinen dichten Borsten besetzter Innenlade, an deren Kaukante feine, starre Borsten stehen.

Kiefertaster an der Spitze des Fulcrums angefügt; letztes Glied mit dunkler Längsstreifung.

Hinterkiefer zu einem länglichen, am Grunde verengten, an der Spitze gerundeten Kinne verschmolzen, an dessen Vorderrand die schmale, sehr lange, lanzenförmige Zunge entspringt.

Lippentaster : Glied 2 am längsten, 3 am kürzesten.

Halsschild nach vorn schräg abfallend und daselbst schwach gekörnt; seitlich gerandet.

Schildchen dreieckig.

Flügeldecken walzenförmig, an der Spitze einzeln gerundet, an der Naht mehr weniger ausgerandet; Absturz entweder konvex und nur längs der Naht eingedrückt oder mehr weniger ausgehöhlt mit sehr verschiedenartiger Armatur; die Spitzenwinkel endigen in einen schmalen aufgebogenen Rand und sind niemals abgeflacht oder vorgezogen. Oberfläche kahl, schwach skulptiert.

Vorderbrust mit dem Vorderrand bis zu den Vorderhüften ausgeschnitten und umgeben, nach hinten ohne Fortsatz.

Vorder- und Mittelhüften dicht zusammenstehend, Hinterhüften voneinander entfernt.

Schienen am oberen Rand gesägt; die äussere (obere) Fläche mit Querreihen von mehr weniger in einanderfliessenden Körnern besetzt.

Fussglieder dünn; erstes länger, zweites und drittes kürzer; drittes einfach.

Bauch gerade.

Geographische Verbreitung der Arten. — Wieder eine Gattung, die auf Amerika beschränkt ist. Von den dreiundvierzig beschriebenen Arten leben fünf im alten Nordreich, die übrigen in Central- und Südamerika.

1. *P. bicolor*, Ferrari, Borkenkäfer, p. 54 (1867).	Südamerika.
2. *P. bidens*, Blandford, Biol. Centr. Amer. Col. Vol. 4 (6), p. 277 (1904).	Centralamerika.
3. *P. bispinum*, Blandford, ibidem, p. 281 (1904).	Centralamerika.
4. *P. brunneum*, Eichhoff, Berl. Ent. Zeitschr. Vol. 12, p. 278 (1868).	Südamerika.
5. *P. Chapuisii* Kirsch, ibidem, Vol. 10, p. 213 (1866).	Südamerika.
6. *P. cincinnatum*, Eichhoff, Ratio Tomic. p. 435 (1879).	Südamerika.
7. *P. consimile*, Blandford, Biol. Centr. Amer. Col. Vol. 4 (6), p. 275 (1904).	Centralamerika.
8. *P. cordatum*, Blandford, ibidem, p. 279 (1904).	Centralamerika.
9. *P. dentigerum*, Le Conte. Proc. Amer. Philos. Soc. Vol. 15, p. 349 (1876).	Nordamerika.
10. *P. difficile*, Blandford, Biol. Centr. Amer. Col. Vol. 4 (6), p. 276 (1904).	Centralamerika.
11. *P. dimidiatum*, Hagedorn, Bull. Mus. Hist. Nat. Paris, Vol. 10, p. 550 (1904).	Südamerika.
12. *P. egenum*, Blandford, Biol. Centr. Amer. Col. Vol. 4 (6), p. 280 (1904).	Centralamerika.
13. *P. elegans*, Eichhoff, Berl. Ent. Zeitschr. Vol. 12, p. 277 (1868).	Südamerika.
14. *P. exile*, Eichhoff, Ratio Tomic. p. 451 (1879).	Südamerika.
15. *P. fasciatum*, Say, Journ. Acad. Natur. Sc. Philad. Vol. 5, p. 255 (1825).	Nordamerika.
16. *P. Ferrarii*, Blandford, Biol. Centr. Amer. Col. Vol. 4 (6), p. 284 (1904).	Centralamerika.
17. *P. fimbriaticorne*, Blandford, ibidem, p. 278 (1904).	Centralamerika.
18. *P. glabratum*, Ferrari, Borkenkäfer p 54 (1867).	Südamerika.
19. *P. glabrifrons*, Blandford, Biol. Centr. Amer. Col. Vol. 4 (6), p. 278 (1904).	Centralamerika.
20. *P. gracile*, Eichhoff, Ratio Tomic. p. 444 (1874).	Nordamerika.
21. *P. Hoegei*, Blandford, Biol. Centr. Amer. Col. Vol. 4 (6), p 274 (1904).	Centralamerika.
22. *P. laevigatum*, Eichhoff, Berl. Ent. Zeitschr. Vol. 12, p. 274 (1868).	Südamerika.
23. *P. laterale*, Eichhoff, ibidem, p. 278 (1868).	Centralamerika.
24. *P. lobatum*, Ferrari, Borkenkäfer, p. 57 (1867).	Südamerika.
25. *P. luctuosum*, Blandford, Biol. Centr. Amer. Col. Vol. 4 (6), p. 276 (1904).	Centralamerika.
26. *P. mali*, Fitch, New York Report Nox. Ins. Vol. 2, N° 5 (1855). — Taf. 6, Fig. 58, 58a.	Nordamerika.

27. *P. melanura*, Blandford, Biol. Centr. Amer. Col. Vol. 4 (6), p. 272 (1904). Centralamerika.
28. *P. parvulum*, Ferrari, Borkenkäfer, p. 53 (1867). Südamerika..
29. *P. penicillatum*, Eichhoff, Ratio Tomic. p. 457 (1879). Südamerika.
30. *P. plagiatum*, Eichhoff, ibidem, p. 455, (1879). Südamerika.
31. *P. praeruptum*, Blandford, Biol. Centr. Amer. Col. Vol. 4 (6), p. 273 (1904). Centralamerika.
32. *P. pumilio*, Eichhoff, Ratio Tomic. p. 445 (1879). Südamerika.
33. *P. punctifrons*, Blandford, Biol. Centr. Amer. Col. Vol. 4 (6), p. 278 (1904). Centralamerika.
34. *P. quadridens*, Eichhoff, Berl. Ent. Zeitschr Vol. 12, p. 277 (1868). Südamerika.
35. *P. scrobiceps*. Eichhoff, Ratio Tomic. p. 458 (1879). Südamerika.
36. *P. scutellare*. Le Conte, Ent. Report p. 59 (1857). Nordamerika.
37. *P. sulcatum*. Blandford, Biol. Centr. Amer. Col. Vol. 4 (6), p. 284 (1904). Centralamerika.
38. *P. terminatum*, Blandford, ibidem, p. 280 (1904). Centralamerika.
39. *P. tomicoides*, Blandford, ibidem, p. 273 (1904). Centralamerika.
40. *P. umbrinum*, Blandford, Biol. Centr. Amer. Col. Vol. 4 (6), p. 275 (1904). Centralamerika.
41. *P. validum*, Ferrari, Borkenkäfer, p. 53 (1867). Südamerika.
42. *P. vittatum*, Blandford, Biol. Centr. Amer. Col. Vol. 4 (6). p. 282 (1904). Centralamerika.
43. *P. volvulum*, Eichhoff, Berl. Ent. Zeitschr. Vol. 12, p. 279 (1868). Südamerika.

III. Genus TRICOLUS, Blandford

Tricolus. Blandford, Biol. Centr. Amer. Col. Vol. 4 (6), p. 286 (1904).

· Originaldiagnose : Blandford, loc. cit.

« Funiculus antennarum triarticulatus; clava haud magna, ovalis vel orbiculata. Prothorax a basi usque ad apicem subconvexus, anterius declivis. Elytra postice oblique excavata, ad apicem emarginata. »

Charaktere. — Diese Gattung, die mir nicht bekannt geworden ist, unterscheidet sich nach Blandford von *Pterocyclon* nur durch wenige Merkmale. Die Fühlergeissel ist drei- (nicht zwei-) gliedrig, die Fühlerkeule oval oder kreisförmig. Der Körper ist weniger lang und cylindrisch, das Halsschild subkonvex von der Basis bis zur Spitze und mehr weniger abschüssig nach der Stirne hin. Die Flügeldecken und Beine zeigen keine materielle Differenzen von denen bei *Pterocyclon*.

Geographische Verbreitung der Arten. — Zwei Arten, jede auf ein Exemplar hin, hat Blandford beschrieben. Sie stammen aus Centralamerika.

1. *T. nodifer*, Blandford, Biol. Centr. Amer. Col. Vol. 4 (6). p. 287 (1904). Guatemala.
2. *T. ovicollis*, Blandford, ibidem. p. 287 (1904). Guatemala.

10. TRIBUS XYLEBORINÆ

UEBERSICHT DER GATTUNGEN

1'. *Augen einfach, oblong, vorn ausgerandet. Fühlergeissel fünfgliedrig, länger*
 als die Keule, Keule abgestutzt. Vorderbrust mit Fortsatz zwischen den
 Hüften . . . . 112. Genus Xyleborus, Eichhoff.
1'. *Augen geteilt, Fühlergeissel viergliedrig, kürzer als die Keule, diese*
 solid, Vorderbrust ohne Fortsatz. . . . . 113. Genus Xyloterus, Erichson.

112. Genus XYLEBORUS, Eichhoff

Xyleborus. Eichhoff, Berl. Ent. Zeitschr. Vol. 8, p. 37 (1864).
Apate. Fabricius, Syst. Ent. Vol. 1, p. 363 (1792).
Bostrichus. Herbst, Käfer, Vol. 5, p. 113 (1793).
Tomicus. Thomson, Scand. Col. p. 369 (1865).
Scolytus. Peck, Massach. Agric. Journ. Vol. 4, p. 205 (1817).
Xyloborus. Bedel, Panne Col. Seine, Vol. 6, p. 402 (1888).
Anæretus. Dugès, Ann. Soc. Ent. Belg. Vol. 31, p. 140.

Subgenera :

Anisandrus. Ferrari, Borkenkäfer, p. 24 (1867) (pars).
Eurydactylus. Hagedorn, Deutsche Ent. Zeitschr. p. 733 (1909), nom. nov. für **Platydactylus,**
Eichhoff, Notes Leyd. Mus. Vol. 8, p. 25 (1886).
Phlœotrogus. Motschulsky, Bull. Soc. Nat. Moscou, Vol. 1, p. 512 (1863).
Progenius. Blandford, Ann. Soc. Ent. Fr. Vol. 65, p. 20 (1896).

UEBERSICHT DER UNTERGATTUNGEN

1'. *Kopf leicht schnauzenförmig, Halsschild quadratisch, gebuckelt* . . . . . . Subg. Phlœotrogus.
1. *Kopf kugelig.*
    2'. ♂ *von hugeliger Form* . . . . Subg. Anisandrus.
    2. ♂ *nicht kugelig, aber in verschiedenen Formen vom* ♀ *abweichend.*
        3'. *Schienen linealisch, Kinn schmal und lang* . . . . Subg. Progenius.
        3. *Schienen breitgedrückt.*
            4'. *Alle Fussglieder rund und einfach* . . . . Subg. Xyleborus s. str.
            4. *Nur die vorderen Fussglieder rund, die hinteren dreieckig* . . . Subg. Eurydactylus.

Originaldiagnose : loc. cit.

« Tarsorum articulis tribus primis subæqualibus, simplicibus. Antennarum funiculo 5-articulato, clava subglobosa, subannulata. Ligula parte fulcrali multo angustior. Palpi labiales articulo primo maximo, inflato, villoso-barbato. Maxillarum mala intus pilis falcatis dense ciliata, articulo ultimo palporum antecedentibus longiore. »

Charaktere. — Bei der grossen Verschiedenheit der Geschlechter müssen ♀ und ♂ gesondert behandelt werden.

Weibchen. — Körperform kurz oder lang walzenförmig, Länge 1 bis 8 mm., Farbe hellbraun bis schwarz, Behaarung schwach bis stark, daher glatt und glänzend bis matt und rauh, Skulptur fein und schwach bis grob und rauh, besonders der Flügeldeckenabsturz manchmal sehr stark bedornt oder bezahnt.

Korpf meist kugelig, im Halsschild versteckt.

Stirn mehr minder gekörnt und behaart.

Augen queroval, vorn ausgerandet.

Fühler mit fünfgliederiger Geissel und ovaler, an der abgestutzten Spitze schwammiger Keule mit wenig deutlichen Nähten, hinten verhüllt.

Vorderkiefer kräftig, häufig schwach gezähnt.

Mittelkiefer mit gerundeter, gegen die Spitze verschmälerter Innenlade, an deren Kaukante sichelförmig gebogene feine Kauborsten sitzen, die gegen die Spitze dichter beisammen stehen.

Kiefertaster: Glied 1 grösser, 2 kleiner, 3 länger, kegelförmig, meistens mit dunklen Längsstreifen versehen.

Hinterkiefer bilden ein längliches, schmales, am Grunde verbreitertes, beiderseits ausgebuchtetes, vorn erweitertes, an der Spitze abgestutztes Kinn, an dessen Vorderrand sich die kleine ovale Zunge ansetzt.

Lippentaster : Glied 1 sehr gross, geschwollen, innen mit Flauschhaaren besetzt, Glied 2 klein, querbreiter, Glied 3 kegelförmig.

Halsschild elliptisch, quadratisch bis kugelförmig, vorn mit Höckern besetzt, hinten schwach punktiert oder glatt, häufig in der Mitte gebuckelt.

Schildchen meist deutlich, verschieden geformt.

Flügeldecken walzenförmig, Absturz flach oder steil abfallend, mit allerhand Dornen, Körnern, Haaren u. s. w. besetzt; Nahtstreifen meist nicht vertieft; Bekleidung verschieden.

- Vorderbrust bis zu den Hüften ausgeschnitten, mit kurzem Fortsatz.

Hüften : Vorderhüften getrennt, Mittel- und Hinterhüften weiter voneinander abstehend.

Beine : Schienen entweder gerade oder nach der Spitze verbreitert, zusammengedrückt, mit meist abgerundeter, gesägter Aussenkante.

Fussglieder gegen die Schienen zurücklegbar, die drei ersten Glieder, mit Ausnahme von *Eurydactylus* (Subgenus), gleichförmig rund und einfach.

Bauch gerade.

Männchen. — Körperform entweder im Ganzen kugelig oder flach, nach vorn und hinten abfallend, oder walzenförmig.

Halsschild gewöhnlich nach vorn herabgeneigt und den Kopf verhüllend, oder breit eingedrückt, mit schwachen Rauhigkeiten, aber am vorderen Rande häufig ausgeschnitten oder mit Fortsätzen versehen; Körper verhältnissmässig kleiner und weniger robust als beim ♀; ungeflügelt oder mit verkümmerten Unterflügeln.

Man kann sechs verschiedene männliche Typen unterscheiden :

Form 1 : *Körper kurz und kugelig* . . . . DISPAR. Fabricius.

» 2 : *Körper cylindrisch, ähnlich dem ♀, aber kürzer, konvexer und weniger kräftig.* . . . . XYLOGRAPHUS, Say.

» 3 : *Halsschild vorn eingedrückt und in einen Fortsatz ausgezogen* . . . . DRYOGRAPHUS, Ratzeburg.

» 4 : *Halsschild vorn eingedrückt und in mehrere oder in einen gespaltenen Fortsatz verbreitert* . . . . SPATHIPENNIS, Eichhoff.

» 5 : *Halsschild vorwärts abwärts in eine flache Platte vorgezogen* . . . . CUCULLATUS. Blandford.

» 6 : *Halsschild den Kopf frei lassend, aber die Mitte der Basis ist in eine breite Spitze ausgezogen; Flügeldeckenabsturz bedornt* . . . . PERVERSUS, Hagedorn.

Die ♂ sind viel seltener als die ♀ und von den meisten Arten noch nicht bekannt; das Verhältniss beider Geschlechter ist beispielsweise bei *dispar* Fabricius 1 : 4, bei *xylographus* Say 1 : 25. bei *monographus* Fabricius 1 : 25, bei *dryographus* Ratzeburg 1 : 14, u. s. w.

Geographische Verbreitung der Arten. — Die Gattung ist durchaus kosmopolitisch. Ihre grösseste Verbreitung hat sie in dem Tropengürtel, während nach den Polen zu die Zahl der Arten und der Individuen abnimmt. Es sind zwei hundert sechsundvierzig Arten bekannt, deren einige auch in dem diluvialen resp. alluvialen Kopal gefunden worden sind, aber nur Arten, die heute noch in denselben Gegenden leben. Es ist die Gattung die grösseste unter den Ipiden, sowohl was Artenzahl als

Individuenzahl betrifft. Durch ihre Lebensweise — es sind Pilzzüchter, Ambrosiakäfer — und die Verschiedenheit der Geschlechter, besonders die Flugunfähigkeit der ♂, sind die die daraufhin erforschten Arten besonders bemerkenswert.

1. *X. adelographus*, Eichhoff, Berl. Ent. Zeitschr. Vol. 11, p. 400 (1867).   Brasilien.
2. *X. adumbratus*, Blandford, Trans. Ent. Soc. Lond. p. 115 (1894).   Japan.
3. *X. aemulus*, Wollaston, Ann. Mag. Nat. Hist. Vol. 4, p. 321 (1869).   St. Helena.
4. *X. affinis*, Eichhoff, Berl. Ent. Zeitschr. Vol. 11, p. 401, ♂ ♀ (1867).   Tropengürtel.
5. *X. agamus* Perkins, Fauna Hawaii. Vol. 2, p. 178 (1900).   Sandwich-Inseln.
6. *X. Alluaudi*, Schaufuss, Tijdschr. v. Ent. Vol. 40, p. 210, ♂ ♀ (1897).   Madagaskar.
7. *X. alni*, Niijima, Journ. Coll. Agric. Tohoku Imp. Univ. Sapporo.   Japan.
   Vol. 3 (2), p. 160 (1909).
8. *X. alternans*, Eichhoff, Berl. Ent. Zeitschr. Vol. 11, p. 280 (1868).   Haiti.
9. *X. amanicus*, Hagedorn, Deutsche Ent. Zeitschr. p. 11 (1910). —   Deutsch-Ost-afrika.
   Taf. 10, Fig. 64, 65, 66.
10. *X. amphicranoides*, Hagedorn, ibidem, p. 379 (1908). — **Taf. 7,**   Sumatra.
    Fig. 65, 65a.
11. *X. amplexicauda*, Hagedorn, ibidem, p. 9 (1910).   Sumatra.
12. *X. amplicollis*, Eichhoff, Berl. Ent Zeitschr. Vol. 11, p. 280 (1868).   Portoriko.
13. *X. amputatus*, Blandford, Trans. Ent. Soc. Lond. p. 575 (1894).   Japan.
14. *X. andamanensis*, Blandford. ibidem, p. 222 (1896).   Andamanen.
15. *X. Andrewesi*, Blandford, ibidem, p. 227 (1896).   Ostindien.
16. *X. angustatus*, Eichhoff, Berl. Ent. Zeitschr. Vol. 10, p, 278 (1866).   Volhyaien.
17. *X. apicalis*, Blandford, Trans. Ent. Soc. Lond. p. 105 (1894)   Japan.
18. *X. aquilus*, Blandford, ibidem, p. 109 (1894).   Japan.
19. *X. arcticollis*, Blandford. ibidem, p. 217, ♂ (1896).   Sumatra.
20. *X. armatus*, Schaufuss. Tijdschr. v. Ent. Vol. 34, p. 30 (1891).   Madagaskar.
21. *X. artestriatus*, Eichhoff, Ratio Tomic. p. 507 (1879).   Ostindien.
22. *X. asperatus*, Blandford, Ann. Mag. Nat. Hist. Vol. 15, p. 321 (1895).   Ceylon.
23. *X. atratus*, Eichhoff, Ann. Soc. Ent. Belg. Vol. 18, p. 201 (1875).   Japan.
24. *X. attenuatus*, Blandford, Trans. Ent. Soc. Lond. p. 114 (1894).   Japan.
25. *X. ? attenuatus*, Motschulsky, Bull. Soc. Nat. Moscou, Vol. 36 (2),   Ostindien.
    p. 512 (1863) (Subg. *Phloeotrogus*).
26. *X. aurilegulus*, Schaufuss, Berl. Ent. Zeitschr. Vol. 42, p. 112 (1897).   Brasilien.
27 *X. badius*, Eichhoff, ibidem, Vol. 12, p. 280 (1868).   Cuba, Tahiti, Japan, Mada-
28. *X. barbatus*, Hagedorn, Deutsche Ent. Zeitschr. p. 11 (1910). —   Sumatra.   [gaskar.
    Taf. 10, Fig. 67, 68, 69.
29. *X. bicolor*, Blandford, Trans. Ent. Soc. Lond. p. 113 (1894).   Japan.
30. *X. bidentatus*, Motschulsky, Bull. Soc. Nat. Moscou, Vol. 36(2), p. 514   Ostindien.
    (1863).
31. *X. bispinatus*, Eichhoff, Berl. Ent. Zeitschr. Vol. 12, p. 146 (1868).   Südamerika.
32. *X. brevis*, Eichhoff, Deutsche Ent. Zeitschr. p. 121 (1877).   Japan.
33. *X. bucco*, Schaufuss, Tijdschr. v. Ent. Vol. 40, p. 212 (1897).   Seychellen.
34. *X. caelebs*, Blandford, Biol. Centr. Amer. Col. Vol. 4 (6), p. 198, ♂   Panama.
    (1898).
35. *X. camerunus*, Hagedorn, Deutsche Ent. Zeitschr. p. 9 (1910).   Kamerun.
36. *X. camopinus*, Hagedorn, Bull. Mus. Hist. Nat. Paris, Vol. 10, p. 549   Guyana.
    (1904).
37. *X. camphorae*, Hagedorn, Deutsche Ent. Zeitschr. p. 378 (1908).   Mauritius.
38. *X. canus*, Niijima, Journ. Coll. Agric. Tohoku Imp. Univ. Sapporo,   Japan.
    Vol. 3 (2), p. 161 (1909).
39. *X. capito*, Schaufuss, Tijdschr. v. Ent. Vol. 40, p. 215 (1897).   Philippinen.
40. *X. capucinus*, Eichhoff, Deutsche Ent. Zeitschr. p. 281 (1877).   Centralamerika.
41. *X. catulus*, Blandford, Biol. Centr. Amer. Col. Vol. 4 (6), p. 215 (1898).   Centralamerika.
42. *X. celsoides*, Hagedorn, Deutsche Ent. Zeitschr. p. 379 (1908).   Australien.

43. *X. celsus*, Eichhoff, Berl. Ent. Zeitschr. Vol. 11, p. 400, ♂ ♀ (1867). — Nordamerika.
44. *X. coffeae*, Wurth, Mededeel. Allg. Proefst. Java (2), n°3, ♂ ♀ (1908). — Java, Tonkin.
— Taf. 6, Fig. 59.
45. *X. cognatus*, Blandford, Ann. Soc. Ent. Fr. Vol. 65, p. 19, ♂♀ (1896). — Tonkin.
46. *X. colossus*, Blandford, Trans. Ent Soc. Lond. p. 207 (1896). — Neu-Guinea.
47. *X. commixtus*, Blandford, Biol. Centr. Amer. Col. Vol. 4 (6), p. 208 — Centralamerika.
(1898).
48. *X. compactus*, Eichhoff, Ann. Soc. Ent. Belg. Vol. 18, p. 202 (1875). — Japan.
49. *X. concisus*, Blandford, Trans. Ent. Soc. Lond. p. 107 (1894). — Japan.
50. *X. confusus*, Eichhoff, Berl. Ent. Zeitschr. Vol. 11, p. 401, ♂ ♀ (1867). — Tropengürtel.
51. *X. congonus*, Hagedorn, Deutsche Ent. Zeitschr. p. 379 (1908). — Kongo.
52. *X. conifer*, Hagedorn. Bull. Mus. Hist. Nat. Paris, Vol. 10, p. 549 (1904). — Guyana.
53. *X. Conradti*, Hagedorn, Deutsche Ent. Zeitschr. p. 8 (1910). — Taf. 10, — Kamerun.
Fig. 58, 59.
54. *X. cordatus*, Hagedorn, ibidem, p. 12 (1910). — Taf. 10, Fig. 55, — Sumatra.
56, 57.
55. *X. cornutus*, Schaufuss, Tijdschr. v. Ent. Vol. 34, p. 17 (1891). — Madagaskar.
56. *X. costaricensis*. Blandford, Biol. Centr. Amer. Col. Vol. 4 (6), p. 210 — Centralamerika.
(1898).
57. *X. crassus*, Hagedorn, Deutsche Ent. Zeitschr. p. 8 (1910). — Sumatra.
58. *X. ? crenipennis*, Motschulsky, Etud. Ent. p. 64 (1858). — Ostindien.
59. *X. cristatus*, Hagedorn, Deutsche Ent. Zeitschr. p. 377 (1908). — — Himalaya.
Taf. 6, Fig. 62, 62a.
60. *X. crucifer*, Hagedorn. ibidem, p. 381 (1908). — Kamerun.
61. *X. cryptographus*, Ratzeburg, Forstinsekten, Vol. 1, p. 160, ♂ ♀ (1837). — Mitteleuropa.
62. *X. cucullatus*, Blandford, Trans. Ent. Soc. Lond. p. 121, ♂ (1894). — Japan.
63. *X. cuneatus*, Eichhoff, Ratio Tomic. p. 380 (1879). — Central- und Südamerika.
64. *X. curtulus*, Eichhoff, Berl. Ent. Zeitschr. Vol. 12, p. 281 (1868). — Südamerika.
65. *X. declivis*, Eichhoff, ibidem, p. 280 (1868). — Centralamerika.
66. *X. defensus*, Blandford, Trans. Ent. Soc. Lond. p. 118 (1894). — Japan.
67. *X. dentatus*, Blandford, Ann. Mag. Nat. Hist. Vol. 15, p. 323 (1895). — Ceylon.
68. *X. denticulus*, Motschulsky, Bull. Soc. Nat. Moscou, Vol. 36 (2), — Ostindien.
p. 512 (1863).
69. *X. derelictus*, Hagedorn, Deutsche Ent. Zeitschr. p. 12, ♂ (1910). — Deutsch-Ostafrika.
70. *X. destruens*. Blandford, Trans. Ent. Soc. Lond. p. 221, ♂ ♀ (1896). — Gilolo-Insel.
71. *X. dichrous*, Eichhoff, Berl. Ent. Zeitschr. Vol. 12, p. 145 (1868). — Südamerika.
72. *X. dilatatus*, Eichhoff, Ratio Tomic. p. 393 (1879). — Mauritius.
73. *X. discolor*. Blandford, Trans. Ent. Soc. Lond. p. 429 (1898). — Ceylon.
74. *X. dispar*, Fabricius, Ent. Syst. Vol. 1, p. 363 (1792) (Subg. *Anisandrus*). — Europa, Asien, Nordame-
— Taf. 14, Fig. 21. rika.
75. *X. distinctus*, Motschulsky, Bull. Soc. Nat. Moscou, Vol. 39 (2), p. 403 — Ceylon.
(1866).
76. *X. dolosus*, Blandford, Trans. Ent. Soc. Lond. p. 225 (1896). — Borneo.
77. *X. dryographus*, Ratzeburg, Forstinsekten, Vol. 1, p. 167, ♂ ♀ (1837). — Europa, Nordafrika.
78. *X. dubiosus*, Perkins, Fauna Hawaii. Vol. 2, p. 177 (1900). — Sandwich-Inseln.
79. *X. ebriosus*, Niijima, Journ. Coll. Agric. Tohoku Imp. Univ. Sapporo, — Japan.
Vol. 3 (2). p. 154 (1909).
80. *X. Eichhoffi*, Schreiner, Deutsche Ent. Zeitschr. Vol. 26 (1882). — Guinea.
81. *X. Eichhoffi*, Schaufuss, Tijdschr. v. Ent. Vol. 34, p. 25 (1891). — Madagaskar.
82. *X. emarginatus*, Eichhoff, Ratio Tomic. p. 510 (1879). — Birma.
83. *X. eurygraphus*, Ratzeburg, Forstinsekten, Vol. 1, p. 168, ♂ ♀ (1837). — Südeuropa.
84. *X. exaratus*, Blandford, Biol. Centr. Amer. Vol. 4 (6). p. 206 (1898). — Centralamerika.
85. *X. excavatus*, Hagedorn, Verh. Ver. Naturw. Hamburg, Vol. 13. p. 111 — Madagaskar.
(1907).

86. *X. exesus*, Blandford, Trans. Ent. Soc. Lond. p. 119 (1894).   Japan.
87. *X. exiguus*, Walker, Ann. Mag. Nat. Hist. Vol. 3, p. 260 (1857).   Ceylon.
88. *X. exsectus*, Perkins, Fauna Hawaii. Vol. 2, p. 179 (1900).   Sandwich-Inseln.
89. *X. fallax*, Eichhoff, Ratio Tomic. p. 508 (1879).   Birma.
90. *X. ferox*, Blandford. Biol. Centr. Amer. Col. Vol. 4 (6), p. 201   Centralamerika.
    (1898).
91. *X. ferrugineus*, Fabricius, Syst. Eleuth. Vol. 2, p. 388 (1801).   Cuba.
92. *X. festivus*, Eichhoff, Ann. Soc. Ent. Belg. Vol. 18, p. 202 (1875).   Japan.
93. *X. Fleutiauxi*, Blandford, Ann. Soc. Ent. Fr. Vol. 65, p. 21 (1896)   Indo-China.
    (Subg. *Progenius*).
94. *X. Fischeri*, Hagedorn, Deutsche Ent. Zeitschr. p. 380 (1908).   Sumatra.
95. *X. Försteri*, Hagedorn, ibidem, p. 7 (1910). — **Taf. 10, Fig. 52,**   Sumatra.
    53, 54.
96. *X. fornicatus*, Eichhoff. Berl. Ent. Zeitschr. Vol. 12, p. 151 (1868)   Ceylon.
97. *X. fraterculus*, Schaufuss, Insektenbörse p. 19 (1903).   Madagaskar.
98. *X. fraternus*, Blandford, Trans. Ent. Soc. Lond. p. 112 (1896).   Ceylon.
99. *X. frigidus*, Blackburn. Fauna Haiwaii. p. 178 (1885).   Sandwich-Inseln.
100. *X. fuscatus*, Eichhoff, Berl. Ent. Zeitschr.Vol. 15, p. 400, ♂ ♀ (1871).   Nord- und Südamérika.
101. *X. galeatus*, Blandford, Trans. Ent. Soc. Lond. p. 123, ♂ (1894).   Japan.
102. *X. Geayi*, Hagedorn, Bull. Mus. Hist. Nat. Paris, Vol. 11, p. 412 (1905).   Guyana.
103. *X. geminatus*, Hagedorn, ibidem, Vol. 10, p. 126 (1904).   Himalaya.
104. *X. germanus*, Blandford, Trans. Ent. Soc. Lond. p. 106 (1894).   Japan.
105. *X. gilvipes*, Blandford, Biol. Centr. Amer. Col. Vol. 4 (6), p. 205 (1898).   Centralamerika.
106. *X. glabratus*, Eichhoff, Deutsche Ent. Zeitschr. Vol. 21, p. 127 ♂ ♀   Japan.
    (1877).
107. *X. globus*, Blandford, Trans. Ent. Soc. Lond. p. 208 (1896).   Neu-Guinea.
108. *X. Godmani*, Blandford, Biol. Centr. Amer. Col.Vol. 4 (6), p. 197 (1898).   Centralamerika.
109. *X. gracilipes*, Eichhoff, Notes Leyd. Mus. Vol. 8, p. 25 (1886)   Molukken.
    (Subg. *Eurydactylus*).
110. *X. gracilis*, Eichhoff, Berl. Ent. Zeitschr. Vol. 12, p. 45 (1868).   Südamerika.
111. *X. grandis*, Eichhoff, ibidem, p. 281 (1868).   Südamerika.
112. *X. granifer*, Eichhoff, Ratio Tomic. p. 502 (1879).   Birma.
113. *X. gravidus*, Blandford, Trans. Ent. Soc. Lond. p. 427 (1898).   Ostindien.
114. *X. guanajuatensis*, Dugès, Ann. Soc. Ent. Belg. Vol. 31, p. 140 (1888).   Centralamerika.
115. *X. hawaiiensis*, Perkins, Fauna Hawaii. Vol. 2, p. 175 (1900).   Sandwich-Inseln.
116. *X. hirtus*, Hagedorn, Bull. Mus. Hist. Nat. Paris, Vol. 10, p. 126 (1904).   Himalaya.
117. *X. horridus*, Eichhoff, Berl. Ent. Zeitschr. Vol. 12, p. 282 (1868).   Centralamerika.
118. *X. ignobilis*, Perkins. Fauna Hawaii. Vol. 2, p. 180 (1900).   Sandwich-Inseln.
119. *X. immaturus*, Blackburn, Trans. Dublin. Soc. Vol. 3, p. 178 (1886).   Sandwich-Inseln.
120. *X. imbellis*, Blandford, Biol. Centr. Amer. Col. Vol. 4 (6), p. 211 (1898).   Centralamerika.
121. *X. impressus*, Eichhoff, Berl. Ent. Zeitschr. Vol. 11, p. 400 (1867).   Nordamerika.
122. *X. indicus*, Eichhoff. Ratio Tomic. p. 354 (1879).   Java.
123. *X. inermis*, Eichhoff, Berl. Ent. Zeitschr. Vol. 11, p. 401 (1867).   Nordamerika.
124. *X. infans*, Hagedorn, Deutsche Ent. Zeitschr. p. 7 (1910).   Sumatra.
125. *X. insignis*, Eichhoff, Berl. Ent. Zeitschr. Vol. 12, p. 282 (1868).   Südamerika.
126. *X. interjectus*, Blandford. Trans. Ent. Soc. Lond. p. 576 (1894).   Japan.
127. *X. interpunctatus*, Blandford, Biol. Centr. Amer. Col. Vol. 4 (6),   Centralamerika.
    p. 206 (1898).
128. *X. intersetosus*, Blandford, ibidem, p. 211 (1898).   Centralamerika.
129. *X. interstitialis*, Eichhoff, Ratio Tomic. p. 375 (1879).   Centralamerika.
130. *X. intrusus*, Blandford, Biol. Centr. Amer. Col. Vol. 4 (6), p. 213 (1898).   Centralamerika.
131. *X. ishidai*, Niijima, Journ. Coll. Agric. Tohoku. Imp. Univ. Sapporo   Japan.
    Vol. 3 (2), p. 156 (1909).
132. *X. hauaiensis*, Perkins. Fauna Hawaii. Vol. 2, p. 174 (1900).   Sandwich-Inseln.

133. *X. laciniatus*, Hagedorn. Deutsche Ent. Zeitschr. p. 7 (1910). — Sumatra.
134. *X. laetus*, Niijima, Journ. Coll. Agric. Tohoku Imp. Univ. Sapporo, — Japan.
Vol. 3 (2). p. 159 (1909).
135. *X. laeviusculus*. Blandford, Ann. Soc. Ent. Fr. Vol. 65, p. 21 (1896) — Indo-China.
(Subg. *Progenius*).
136. *X. laticollis*, Blandford, Trans. Ent. Soc. Lond. p. 226 (1896). — Ostindien.
137. *X. lauaiensis*, Perkins, Fauna Hawaii. Vol. 2, p. 176 (1900). — Sandwich-Inseln.
138. *X. Lewisi*, Blandford, Trans. Ent. Soc. Lond. p. 104 (1894). — Japan.
139. *X. littoralis*, Perkins. Fauna Hawaii. Vol. 2, p. 179 (1900). — Sandwich-Inseln.
140. *X. longipennis*, Blanchard, in Gay, Hist. fis. Chile, Vol. 5, p. 429 (1851). — Chile.
141. *X. macer*, Blandford, Biol. Centr. Amer. Col. Vol. 4 (6), p. 218 (1898). — Centralamerïka.
142. *X. madagascariensis*, Schäufuss, Tijdschr. v. Ent. Vol. 34, p. 23 (1891). — Madagaskar.
143. *X. mancus*, Blandford, Trans. Ent. Soc. Lond. p. 428 (1898). — Ceylon.
144. *X. mascarenus*, Hagedorn, Deutsche Ent. Zeitschr. p 379 (1908). — Deutsch-Ostafrika, Mau-
145. *X. mauiensis*, Perkins, Fauna Hawaii. Vol. 2, p. 175 (1900). — Sandwich-Inseln. [ritius.
146. *X. Meuseli*, Reitter, Wien. Ent. Zeit. Vol. 24, p. 249 (1905). — Russland.
147. *X. minutus*, Blandford, Trans. Ent. Soc. Lond. p. 116 (1894). — Japan.
148. *X. monachus*, Blandford, Biol. Centr. Amer. Col. Vol. 4 (6), p. 204, — Centralamerika.
♂ (1898).
149. *X. molokaiensis*, Perkins, Fauna Hawaii. Vol. 2, p. 174 (1900). — Sandwich-Inseln.
150. *X. monographus*, Fabricius, Ent. Syst. Vol. 1 (2), p. 365, ♂♀ (1792). — Europa.
— Taf. 14, Fig. 19.
151. *X. morigerus*, Blandford, Insect Life, Vol. 6, p. 260, ♂♀ (1894). — Neu-Guinea, Mauritius.
152. *X. morulus*, Blandford, Biol. Centr. Amer. Col. Vol. 4 (6), p. 212 (1898). — Centralamerika.
153. *X. muticus*, Blandford, Trans. Ent. Soc. Soc. Lond. p. 112 (1894). — Japan.
154. *X. mutilatus*, Blandford, ibidem, p. 103 (1894). — Japan.
155. *X. nanus*, Blandford, Ann. Soc. Ent. Belg. Vol. 40, p. 242 (1896). — Neu-Caledonien.
156. *X. natalensis*. Schaufuss, Tijdschr. v. Ent. Vol. 34, p. 20 (1891). — Madagaskar.
157. *X. Neptunus*, Schaufuss, ibidem, p. 22, ♂ ♀ (1891). — Madagaskar.
158. *X. oahuensis*, Perkins, Fauna Hawaii. Vol. 2, p. 177 (1900). — Sandwich-Inseln.
159. *X. obesus*, Le Conte, Trans. Amer. Ent. Soc. Vol. 2, p. 159, ♂♀ (1868). — Nordamerika.
var. *minor*, Swaine, The Canad. Entom. Vol. 42. p. 164 (1910).
160. *X. obliquecauda*, Motschulsky, Bull. Soc. Nat. Moscou, Vol. 36 (2), — Ceylon, Japan.
p. 315 (1863) (Subg. *Phloeotrogus*).
161. *X. obliquus*, Sharp. Trans. Dublin. Soc. Vol. 3, p. 196 (1885). — Sandwich-Inseln.
162. *X. orbatus*, Blandford, Trans. Ent. Soc. Lond. p. 123, ♂ (1894). — Japan.
163. *X. papuanus*, Blandford, ibidem, p. 209 (1896). — Neu-Guinea.
164. *X. parvulus*, Eichhoff, Berl. Ent. Zeitschr. Vol. 12, p. 152 (1868). — Ceylon.
var. *submarginatus*, Blandford, Ann. Mag Nat. Hist. (6), Vol. 15, p. 332 (1895). — Ceylon.
165. *X. pelliculosus*, Eichhoff, Ratio Tomic. p. 336 (1879). — Japan.
166. *X. penicillatus*, Hagedorn, Deutsche Ent. Zeitschr. p. 7 (1910). — — Sumatra.
Taf. 6, Fig. 63, 63a; Taf. 10, Fig. 49, 50, 51.
167. *X. perebeae*, Nördlinger, Berl. Ent. Zeitschr. Vol. 12, p. 276 (1868). — Südamerika.
168. *X. perforans,* Wollaston, Cat. Col. Mader. p. 96, ♂ ♀ (1857). — Tropengürtel.
169. *X. perversus*, Hagedorn, Bull. Mus. Hist. Nat. Paris, Vol. 11, p. 412, — Guyana.
♂ (1905).
170. *X. Pfeili*, Ratzeburg, Forstinsekten, Vol. 1, p. 168, ♂ ♀ (1837). — Mittel- und Südeuropa.
171. *X. piceus*, Motschulsky. Bull. Soc. Nat. Moscou, Vol. 36(2), p. 512 (1863). — Ceylon.
172. *X. pini*, Eichhoff, Berl. Ent. Zeitschr. Vol. 11, p. 401 (1867). — Nordamerika.
173. *X. politus*, Hagedorn, Bull. Mus. Hist. Nat. Paris, Vol. 11, p. 12 (1905). — Südamerika.
174. *X. posticus*, Eichhoff, Berl. Ent. Zeitschr. Vol. 12, p. 281 (1868). — Central- und Südamerika.
175. *X. praevius*, Blandford, Trans. Ent. Soc. Lond. p. 110 (1894). — Japan.
176 *X. princeps*, Blandford, Biol. Centr Amer. Col. Vol. 4 (6), p. 208 (1898). — Centralamerika.
177. *X. principalis*, Eichhoff, Ratio Tomic. p. 357 (1879). — Guinea.

178. *X. procer*, Eichhoff, Ratio Tomic. p. 402, ♂ ♀ (1879). — **Taf. 7,** Central- und Südamerika.
Fig. 67.
179. *X productus*, Hagedorn, Bull. Mus. Hist. Nat. Paris, Vol. 11, p. 412 (1905). Südamerika.
180. *X. propinquus*, Eichhoff, Berl. Ent. Zeitschr. Vol. 12, p. 281 (1868). Central- und Südamerika.
181. *X. pruinosus*, Blandford, Trans. Ent. Soc. Lond. p. 214 (1896). Borneo.
182. *X. puberulus*, Blandford, ibidem, p. 215 (1896). Borneo.
183. *X. pubescens*, Zimmermann, Trans. Amer. Ent. Soc. Vol. 2, p. 145, ♂ ♀ Nordamerika.
(1868).
184. *X. punctatissimus*, Eichhoff, Notes Leyd. Mus. Vol. 2, p. 189 (1880). Sumatra.
185. *X. quadratus*, Blandford, Biol. Centr. Amer. Col. Vol. 4 (6), p. 209 (1898). Centralamerika.
186. *X. quadrispinosus*, Eichhoff, Ratio Tomic. p. 396 (1879). Südafrika.
187. *X. retusicollis*, Zimmermann. Trans. Amer. Ent. Soc. Vol. 2, p. 146 (1868). Nordamerika.
188. *X. retusus*, Eichhoff, Berl. Ent. Zeitschr. Vol. 12, p. 151 (1868). — Südamerika.
Taf. 7, Fig. 66.
189. *X. Riehlii*, Eichhoff, Ratio Tomic. p. 346 (1879) (Subg. *Progenius*). — Celebes.
Taf. 10, Fig. 63.
190. *X. ruber*, Eichhoff, Berl. Ent. Zeitschr. Vol. 12, p. 145 (1868). Südamerika.
191. *X. rubricollis*, Eichhoff, Ann. Soc. Ent. Belg. Vol. 18, p. 202 (1875). Japan.
192. *X. rufithorax*, Eichhoff, Berl. Ent. Zeitschr. Vol. 12, p. 281 (1868). Südamerika.
var. *nigricollis*, Hagedorn, Bull. Mus. Hist. Nat. Paris, Vol. 11, p. 412 (1905). Südamerika.
193. *X. rugatus*, Blackburn, Trans. Dublin Soc. Vol. 3, p. 170 (1886). Sandwich-Inseln.
194. *X. rugicollis*, Blandford, Biol. Centr. Amer. Col. Vol. 4 (6), p. 207 (1898). Centralamerika.
195. *X. Salvinii*, Blandford, ibidem, p. 200, ♂ ♀ (1898). Centralamerika.
196. *X. sanguinicollis*, Blandford, ibidem. p. 198 (1898). Centralamerika.
197. *X. scabripennis*, Blandford, Trans. Ent. Soc. Lond. p. 216 (1896). Borneo.
198. *X. Schaufussi*, Blandford. ibidem. p. 117, ♂ ♀ (1894). Japan.
199. *X. scobinatus*, Hagedorn, Deutsche Ent. Zeitschr. p. 8 (1910). Kamerun.
200. *X. semigranosus*, Blandford, Trans. Ent. Soc. Lond. p. 211 (1896). Sumatra.
201. *X. seminitens*, Blandford, Ann. Mag. Nat. Hist. Vol. 15, p. 322 (1895). Ceylon.
202. *X. semiopacus*, Eichhoff, Ratio Tomic. p. 334 (1879). Japan.
203. *X. semirudis*, Blandford, Trans. Ent. Soc. Lond. p. 210 (1896). Borneo.
204. *X. sentosus*, Eichhoff, Berl. Ent. Zeitschr. Vol. 12, p. 146 (1868). Südamerika.
205. *X. septentrionalis*, Niijima, Journ. Coll. Agric. Tohoku Imp. Univ. Japan.
Sapporo, Vol. 3 (2), p. 162 (1909).
206. *X. seriatus*, Blandford, Trans. Ent. Soc. Lond. p. 111 (1894). Japan.
207. *X. sexspinosus*. Motschulsky, Bull. Soc. Nat. Moscou, Vol. 36 (1), Ostindien, Philippinen.
p. 515 (1863) (Subg. *Eurydactylus*). — **Taf. 6, Fig. 60.**
var. *multispinosus*. Hagedorn, Deutsche Ent. Zeitschr. p. 377 (1908). Deutsch-Ostafrika, Kamerun.
208. *X. Sharpi*, Blandford, Biol. Centr. Amer. Col. Vol. 4 (6), p. 199 Centralamerika.
(1898).
209. *X. simillimus*, Perkins, Fauna Hawaii. Vol. 2, p. 176 (1900). Sandwich-Inseln.
210. *X. siporanus*. Hagedorn, Deutsche Ent. Zeitschr. p. 11 (1910). Sumatra.
211. *X. sisyrnophorus*. Hagedorn, ibidem, p. 7 (1910). Morawa.
211. *X. sobrinus*, Eichhoff, Ann. Soc. Ent. Belg. Vol. 18, p. 202 (1875). Japan.
213. *X. solidus*, Eichhoff, Berl. Ent. Zeitschr. Vol. 12, p. 151 (1868). Australien.
214. *X. sordicauda*, Motschulsky, Bull. Soc. Nat. Moscou, Vol. 36 (1), Birma.
p. 514 (1863) (Subg. *Phloeotrogus*).
215. *X. spathipennis*, Eichhoff, Berl. Ent. Zeitschr. Vol. 12, p. 154 (1868) ♂ ♀. Centralamerika.
216. *X. spathulatus*, Blandford, Trans. Ent. Soc. Lond. p. 218 (1896). Borneo.
217. *X. spiculatus*, Schaufuss, Tijdschr. v. Ent. Vol. 34. p. 28 (1891). Madagaskar.
218. *X spinosus*, Schaufuss, ibidem, p. 27 (1891). Madagaskar.
219. *X. spinulosus*, Blandford, Biol. Centr. Amer. Col. Vol. 4 (6), p. 201, Centralamerika.
♂ ♀ (1898).
220. *X. splendidus*, Schaufuss, Berl. Ent. Zeitschr. p. 111 (1897). Südamerika.

221. *X. squamulatus*, Eichhoff, Berl. Ent. Zeitschr. Vol. 12, p. 282 (1868).   Südamerika.
222. *X. subcostatus*, Eichhoff, ibidem, p. 281 (1868) (Subg. *Progenius*).   Siam.
223. *X. subcribrosus*, Blandford, Trans. Ent. Soc. Lond. p. 224 (1896).   Singapore.
224. *X. submarginatus*, Blandford, ibidem. p. 223 (1896).   Ostindien.
225. *X. sumatranus*, Hagedorn, Deutsche Ent. Zeitschr. p. 381 (1908). —   Sumatra.
    Taf. 7, Fig. 64, 64a.
226. *X. tachygraphus*, Zimmermann, Trans. Amer. Ent. Soc. Vol. 2, p. 440   Nordamerika.
    (1868) ♂ ♀ (Subg. *Anisandrus*).
227. *X. tanganus*, Hagedorn, Deutsche Ent. Zeitschr. p. 8 (1910).   Deutsch-Ostafrika.
228. *X testaceus*, Walker. Ann. Mag. Nat. Hist. Vol. 3, p. 260 (1829).   Ceylon.
229. *X. torquatus*, Eichhoff, Berl. Ent. Zeitschr. Vol. 12, p. 146 (1868).   Tropengürtel.
230. *X. Triton*. Schaufuss. Insektenbörse, p. 18 (1905).   Madagaskar.
231. *X. tropicus*, Hagedorn, Deutsche Ent. Zeitschr. p. 12 (1910). —   Kamerun.
    Taf. 10, Fig. 60, 61, 62.
232. *X. truncatus*, Erichson, Arch. f. Naturg. Vol. 8 (1), p. 212 (1842).   Van Diemensland.
233. *X. truncatus*, Sharp, Fauna Hawaii. Vol. 2 (3), Col. 1, p. 175 (1885).   Sandwich-Inseln.
234. *X. tuberculatus*, Motschulsky. Bull. Soc. Nat. Moscou, Vol. 36 (2),   Ceylon.
    p. 511 (1863).
235. *X. tumucensis*, Hagedorn, Bull. Mus. Hist. Nat. Paris, Vol. 11,   Südamerika.
    p. 412 (1905).
236. *X. ursinus*, Hagedorn, Deutsche Ent. Zeitschr. p. 381 (1908).   Sumatra.
237. *X. validus*, Eichhoff, Ann. Soc. Ent. Belg. Vol. 18, p. 202 (1875).   Japan.
238. *X. vicarius*, Eichhoff, ibidem, p. 203, ♂ ♀ (1875).   Japan.
239. *X. vicinus*, Eichhoff, Ratio Tomic. p. 394 (1879).   Südamerika.
240. *X. viduus*, Eichhoff. ibidem, p. 391, ♂ (1879).   Südamerika.
241. *X. villosulus*, Blandford, Biol. Centr. Amer. Col. Vol. 4 (6), p. 204   Centralamerika.
    (1898).
242. *X. vulcanus*. Perkins, Fauna Hawaii. Vol. 2, p. 179 (1900).   Sandwich-Inseln.
243. *X. Wallacei*, Blandford, Trans. Ent. Soc. Lond. p. 220 (1896).   Neu-Guinea.
244. *X. xanthopus*, Eichhoff, Berl. Ent. Zeitschr. Vol. 12, p. 151 (1868).   Südafrika.
245. *X. xylographus*, Say. Journ. Acad. Natur. Soc. Philad. Vol. 5, p. 256,   Canarische Inseln, Nord-
    ♂ ♀ (1826). — **Taf. 14, Fig. 20.**   amerika, Europa, Nord-
246. *X. serratus*, Swaine, The Canad. Entom. Vol. 42, p. 162 (1910).   Canada.   [asien.

113. Genus XYLOTERUS, Erichson.

Xyloterus. Erichson, Arch. f. Naturg. Vol. 2 (1), p. 60 (1836).
Trypodendron. Stephens, Ill. Brit. Ent. Vol. 3, p. 353 (1830) (pars).
Dermestes. Linné, Syst. Nat. (ed. 10), p. 356 (1758).
Apate. Fabricius, Syst. Eleuth. Vol. 2, p. 382 (1787).
Bostrichus. Ratzeburg. Forstinsekten, Vol. 1, p. 164 (1837).

ORIGINALDIAGNOSE : Erichson loc. cit.

« Antennæ funiculo 4-articulato, capitulo solido. Labium parallelum. Maxilla mala brevi, undique setis ciliata. Palpi maxillares articulo 1⁰ abscondito, 2⁰ tertioque brevibus, 4⁰ longiore subcylindrico. Labium oblongum parallelopipedum. Palpi labiales articulis duobus primis crassis, subæqualibus, tertio minuto, obtuse subulato. — Antennæ scapo elongato, subclavato, compresso : funiculo articulo 1⁰ subgloboso, reliquis tribus minutis, arcte coactis : Capitulo solidissimo, compresso, subovato. Corpus oblongum convexum. Frons in maribus profunde excavata. Tibiæ apice compresso, extus rotundato, serratoque. Tarsi articulis tribus primis subæqualibus. »

Charaktere. — Körperform walzenförmig, Länge 3 bis 5 mm., Farbe hellgelb mit dunklen Streifen auf den Flügeldecken oder gleichförmig, sonst schwarz, ausser Beinen und Fühlern, glänzend; Behaarung schwach, Skulptur nur auf dem Halsschild kräftiger.

Kopf kugelig, im Halsschild verborgen ; Stirn beim ♂ tief ausgehöhlt, beim ♀ gewölbt.

Augen in zwei Teile getheilt.

Fühler mit viergliedriger Geissel, sehr grosser, flacher, ungeringelter, derber Keule.

Vorderkiefer kräftig, gezähnt.

Mittelkiefer mit an der Spitze abgestumpfter Innenlade, deren Kaukante mit feinen Borsten besetzt ist, die nach der Spitze zu dichter stehen.

Kiefertaster dreigliedrig ; Glied 1 und 2 kurz und quer, 3 länger, mit dunklen Längsstreifen.

Hinterkiefer zu einem länglichen, am Grunde verschmälerten, an der Spitze abgestutzten Kinne verschmolzen, auf dessen Mitte die schmale, lanzettförmige Zunge eingefügt ist.

Lippentaster : Glied 1 kurz, grösser als 2, geschwollen, 3 am kleinsten, mit abgerundeter Spitze, breiter als lang ; auf der Oberseite beider ersten Glieder bartartige Flauschbehaarung.

Halsschild quer oder kugelförmig, vorn stark skulptiert.

Schildchen deutlich, gerundet.

Flügeldecken walzenförmig, an der Spitze ungezähnt, höchstens schwach gefurcht, Bekleidung schwach.

Vorderbrust bis zu den Hüften ausgeschnitten, ohne Fortsatz nach hinten.

Hüften : Vorderhüften zusammenstehend, Mittel- und Hinterhüften entfernt voneinander.

Schenkel an der Spitze innen lappenförmig erweitert.

Schienen nach vorne breit gedrückt, aussen abgerundet und gesägt, zur Aufnahme der Fussglieder ausgehöhlt.

Fussglieder mit einfach runden Gliedern.

Bauch gerade.

Geographische Verbreitung der Arten. — Es sind elf Arten bekannt, die im alten und neuen Nordreich vorkommen. Eine Art lebt im Makronesischen Reich und eine ist in Nordamerika im Tertiär fossil gefunden worden.

1. *X. domesticus*, Linné. Syst. Nat. (ed. 10), p. 356 (1758).   Altes Nordreich.
2. *X. impressus*, Scudder, Bull U. S. Geol. Surv. Vol. 2, p. 83 (1876)   Wyoming.
   (fossil).
3. *X. lineatus*, Olivier, Ent. Vol. 4, p. 18 (1795).   Altes und neues Nordreich.
4. *X. longicollis*, Wollaston, Cat. Col. Canar. p. 256 (1864).   Makronesisches Reich.
5. *X. politus*, Say, Journ. Acad. Natur. Soc. Philad. Vol. 5, p. 256 (1827). Neues Nordreich.
   — **Taf. 7, Fig. 68.**
6. *X. proximus*, Niijima, Journ. Coll. Agric. Tohoku Imp. Univ. Sapporo,   Altes Nordreich (Japan).
   Vol. 3 (2), p. 195 (1909).
7. *X. pubipennis*, Blandford, Trans. Ent. Soc. Lond. p. 125 (1894).   Altes Nordreich (Japan).
8. *X. retusus*, Le Conte, Trans. Amer. Ent. Soc. Lond. Vol. 2, p. 158   Neues Nordreich.
   (1868).
9. *X. serratus.* Panzer, Ent. Germ. p. 288 (1795).   Altes Nordreich.
10. *X. signatus*, Fabricius, Syst. Eleuth. Vol. 2, p. 383 (1787).   Altes Nordreich.
11. *X. scabricollis*, Le Conte, Trans. Amer. Ent. Soc. Lond. Vol. 2, p. 158 Neues Nordreich.
    (1868).
12. *X. sordidus*, Blandford, Trans. Ent. Soc. Lond. p. 557 (1894).   Altes Nordreich (Japan).
13. *X. unicolor*, Eichhoff, Berl. Ent. Zeitschr. Vol. 15, p. 136 (1871). Neues Nordreich.

IV. SUBFAM. MIXTODENTATÆ

II. TRIBUS SPONGOCERINÆ

114. Genus SCOLYTOPLATYPUS, Schaufuss

Scolytoplatylus. Schaufuss, Tijdschr. v. Ent. Vol. 34, p. 31 (1891).
Subgenera : **Spongocerus.** Blandford, Trans. Ent. Soc. Lond. p. 431 (1893).
Tæniocerus. Blandford, ibidem, p. 437 (1893).

UEBERSICHT DER UNTERGATTUNGEN

1. *Halsschildbasis in der Mitte nicht vorspringend* . . . . Subg. Spongocerus.
1'. *Halsschildbasis in der Mitte deutlich vorspringend.*
   2. *Flügeldecken vor der Spitze nicht gestreift* . . . . Subg. Scolytoplatypus s. str.
   2'. *Flügeldecken vor der Spitze stark gestreift* . . . . Subg. Tæniocerus.

Originaldiagnose : Schaufuss, loc. cit.

« Corpus breviter cylindricum. Caput a thorace receptum, fronte truncato, pro receptione antennarum subtus versus os canaliculatum, os apertum.

» Oculi elongati, angusti, parum convexi, granulati.

» Antennæ antice inter oculos et mandibularum basin insertæ, scapo apice geniculato et subito tumido, funiculo articulo primo magno, semigloboso, tribus sequentibus brevibus, capitulo maximo, ovato, solido, valde compresso, spongioso.

» Prothorax transverse quadratus, lateraliter pro pedum receptione excisus.

» Pygidium elytris obtectum. Pedes validi, elongati, femora tibiæque compressa, femora antica robustiora, subtus pro tibiarum receptione excisa. Tarsi elongati, graciles, tibiis breviores, articulo primo secundo duplo longiore, apice parum clavato, secundo et tertio conicis, tertio secundo longiore et validiore, quarto minimo, cylindrico, quinto 2-4 cunctis longiore, curvato, apice incrassato, unguibus binis curvatis instructis.

» Coxæ anticæ maximæ, subglobosæ, valde distantes, posteriores minores transversæ, subplanæ, mediæ valde distantes, posticæ approximatæ.

» Prosternum antice valde emarginatum, in medio dimidiam longitudinem metasterni æquans, metasternum antice lateraliter pro pedum mediorum receptione impressum, postice pro posticorum profunde excisum. Abdomen quinque segmentis compositum. »

Charaktere. — Körperform kurz cylindrisch, Länge 2 bis 4 mm. Farbe hellgelbbraun bis schwarz, Skulptur meist kräftig, Bekleidung verschieden, starke Behaarung.

Kopf etwas in das Halsschild zurückgezogen, nicht breiter als dieses, leicht rüsselförmig vorgezogen.

Augen länglich, querstehend, gross, nicht ausgerandet.

Fühler zwischen den Vorderkiefern und unterem Augenwinkel eingelenkt, Schaft ziemlich lang,

Geissel sechsgliedrig, Keule gross, platt, ohne Nähte, stark und meistens lang behaart, teils eiförmig, teils langgestreckt.

Vorderkiefer stark gebaut, zweizähnig.

Mittelkiefer mit quadratischer in eine Spitze ausgezogener Innenlade, auch der äussere Spitzenwinkel ist verlängert, so dass die Taster zwischen beiden Spitzen liegen. Die Kaukante ist mit groben, sichelförmig gebogenen und zwischen ihnen stehenden an der Spitze zahlreicheren, gebogenen Haarborsten besetzt.

Kiefertaster kurz, dreigliedrig. mit einem deutlich abgegrenzten Tasterträger, Glieder cylindrisch, erstes und zweites kurz, drittes länger als breit und mit einem Haarkranz an der Basis, der eine Längsstreifung vortäuscht.

Hinterkiefer zu einem in der Mitte verengten, an beiden Enden verbreiterten Kinne verschmolzen, in dessen Mitte die zungenförmige, so breit als das Kinn erscheinende, bis zur Spitze desselben reichende Ligula angesetzt ist.

Lippentaster dreigliedrig : erstes Glied länger als breit, zweites quer, drittes so lang als breit, alle cylindrisch.

Halsschild quadratisch, Seiten gerandet und mit tiefen Gruben zur Aufnahme der Vorderbeine und der Fühler versehen, vorn abgestutzt, beim ♀ mit einer runden Pore in mitten der Oberfläche.

Schildchen dreieckig, gross, mit aufgebogener Spitze.

Flügeldecken breiter als die Halsschildbasis, walzenförmig, mit konvexer, stark abfallender, das Pygidium bedeckender Spitze; auf dem Absturz mehr weniger stark skulptiert und behaart.

Vorderbrust mit grossem quadratischen Fortsatz, auf dem bei den ♂ verschiedene Fortsätze in Hakenform und Grüben sich vorfinden, während er bei den ♀ einfach und flach ist.

Vorderhüften gross, kugelig, weit voneinander getrennt, ebenso die andern Hüften.

Vorderbeine stark, Schenkel zusammengedrückt, Schienen gebogen, nach der Spitze erweitert, daselbst ausgehöhlt und mit starkem Dorn versehen, auf des Aussenfläche reihig gehöckert. Aussenkante gezähnt; bei ♀ und ♂ verschieden gestaltet.

Mittel- und Hinterbeine mit länglich viereckigen Schenkeln. gebogenen Schienen, an der Aussenkante gesägt, zur Aufnahme der Fussglieder canalisiert.

Fussglieder nicht länger als die Schienen, einfach rund, das erste Glied etwas länger als das zweite; das vierte Glied sehr klein, verkehrt kegelförmig.

Hinterbrust noch mit Gruben für die Beine versehen.

Bauch etwas gewölbt.

Sekundäre Geschlechtsmerkmale sind zu finden an der Stirn, den Fühlern, der Vorderbrust, dem Vorderrücken, den Flügeldecken und den Vorderbeinen.

Geographische Verbreitung der Arten. — Diese höchst eigenartige Gattung ist in siebzehn Arten bekannt. Die Untergattung *Scolytoplatypus* s. str. ist auf Afrika und Madagaskar bschränkt, während *Taeniocerus* und *Spongocerus* in Japan, dem Himalaya, Ostindien und dem indo-malayischen Archipel vorkommen, aber Afrika fremd zu sein scheinen.

SUBGENUS SCOLYTOPLATYPUS, S. STR.

1. *S. Eichelbaumi*, Hagedorn, Insektenbörse, p. 64 (1905). — **Taf. 7,** Deutsch-Ostafrika. **Fig. 69, 69a.**
2. *S. fasciatus*, Hagedorn, Stett. Ent. Zeit. Vol. 65, p. 405 (1904). — Südafrika. **Taf. 10, Fig. 70, 73, 75, 76.**
3. *S. Hova*, Schaufuss, Insektenbörse, p. 12 (1905). Madagaskar.
4. *S. permirus*, Schaufuss, Tijdschr. v. Ent. Vol. 34, p. 31 (1891). Madagaskar.

Subgenus TÆNIOCERUS

5. S. *Brahma*, Blandford, Trans. Ent. Soc. Lond. p. 431 (1893).	Ostindien.
6. S. *eutomoides*, Blandford, ibidem; p. 196 (1896).	Celebes.
7. S. *hamatus*, Hagedorn, Insektenbörse, p. 260 (1904).	Java.
8. S. *Mikado*, Blandford, Trans. Ent. Soc. Lond. p. 437 (1893).	Japan.
9. S. *minimus*, Hagedorn, Bull. Mus. Hist. Nat. Paris, Vol. 10, p. 125 (1904).	Himalaya.
10. S. *Raja*, Blandford, Trans. Ent. Soc. Lond. p. 470 (1893). — **Taf. 10, Fig. 72.**	Himalaya.

Subgenus SPONGOCERUS

11. . *Daimio*, Blandford, Trans. Ent. Soc. Lond. p. 433 (1893).	Japan.
12. . *Kunala*, Strohmeyer, Ent. Wochenbl. p. 161 (1908).	Kashmir.
13. . *muticus*, Hagedorn, Bull. Mus. Hist. Nat. Paris, Vol. 10, p. 124 (1904).	Japan.
14. **S.** *pubescens*, Hagedorn, ibidem, p. 123 (1909). — **Taf. 7, Fig. 69 b; Taf. 10, Fig. 71, 74.**	Himalaya.
15. S. *Shogun*, Blandford, Trans. Ent. Soc. Lond. p. 126 (1894).	Japan.
16. S. *Siomio*, Blandford, ibidem, p. 436 (1893).	Japan.
17. S. *Tycon*, Blandford, ibidem, p. 432 (1893).	Japan.

GENUS INCERTÆ SEDIS

115. Genus OLONTHOGASTER, Motschulsky

Olonthogaster. Motschulsky, Bull. Soç. Nat. Moscou, Vol. 39 (2), p. 401 (1866).
Holonthogaster. Gemminger & Harold, Cat. Col. Vol. 9, p. 2676 (1872).

ORIGINALDIAGNOSE : war mir nicht zugänglich.

Geographische Verbreitung der Arten. — Ceylon.

1. O. *nitidicollis*, Motschulsky, Bull. Soc. Nat. Moscou, Vol. 39 (2), p. 401 (1866).	Ceylon.
2. O. *nudifrons*, Motschulsky, ibidem, p. 402 (1866).	Ceylon.

INDEX

ERKLÄRUNG DER TAFELN

TAFEL 1

Fig.   1.   *Dactylipalpus transversus*, Chapuis.

—   1*a*.   —   *similis*, Hagedorn, zweites bis viertes Fussglied.

—   1*b*.   —   —   Fühler.

—   2.   —   *africanus*, Schaufuss, i. l.

—   3.   *Phloeoborus rudis*, Erichson.

—   3*a*.   —   —   —   Kopf.

—   3*c*.   —   *scaber*,   —   Fühler.

Fig. 4. *Phloeotrupes grandis*, Erichson.
— 4*a*. — — — Fühler.
— 5. *Diamerus impar*, Chapuis.
— 6. — *ater*, Hagedorn.
— 7. *Coptonotus cyclopus*, Chapuis. ♂.
— 7*a*. — — — ♂. Kopf.
— 7*b*. — — — ♂, Absturz.
— 8. — — · — ♀.

Tafel 2

Fig. 9. *Phloeotribus setulosus*, Eichhoff.
— 9*a*. — *armatus*, Blandford. Fühler.
— 10. *Aricerus Eichhoffii*, Blandford.
— 11. *Hylastes pinifex*, Pitch.
— 12. — *opacus*, Erichson.
— 13. *Hylesinus fraxini*, Panzer.
— 14. — *sumatranus*, Hagedorn, i. l.
— 15. *Sphaerotrypes barbatus*, Hagedorn.
— 16. *Hylurgus ligniperda*, Fabricius.
— 16*a*. *Myelophilus piniperda*, Linné, Vorderkiefer.
— 16*b*. — — Fühler.
— 17. *Chortastus Schenklingi*, Hagedorn.
— 17*a*. — — — Absturz.
— 18. *Kissophagus fasciatus*, Hagedorn.
— 18*a*. — *hederae*, Schmitt. Fühler.
— 18*b*. — *fasciatus*, Hagedorn. Fühler.
— 19. *Dendroctonus micans*, Kugelann.
— 20. *Carphoborus Bonnairei*, Brisout de Barneville.

Tafel 3

Fig. 21. *Xylechinus nigrosetosus*, Hagedorn.
— 21*a*. — — — Flügeldeckenskulptur.
— 21*b*. — — — Vordertibia.
— 22. *Chramesus icoriae*, Le Conte. ♂.
— 22*b*. — — — ♀.
— 23. *Liparthrum Lowei*, Wollaston.
— 24. *Dacryostactus Kolbei*, Schaufuss.
— 25. *Aphanarthrum bicolor*, Wollaston.
— 25*a*. — — — Fühler.
— 25*b*. — — — Vorderfuss.
— 26. *Crypturgus atomus*, Le Conte.
— 27. *Dolurgus pumilus*, Mannerheim.
— 28. *Polygraphus poligraphus*, Linné.
— 28*a*. — — — Fühler.
— 28*b*. — *proximus*, Blandford, Fühler.

Fig. 28c. *Polygraphus congonus*, Hagedorn, i. l., Fühler.
— 28d. — *camerunus*, — i. l., Fühler.
— 29. *Spongotarsus quadrioculatus*, Hagedorn.
— 30. *Adiaeretus spinosus*, Hagedorn.
— 31. *Stephanoderes javanus*, Eggers.
— 31a. *Cryphalus Grothii*, Hagedorn, Fühler.
— 31b. — — — Vorderbein.
— 31c. *Stephanoderes*, nov. spec. aus Amani, Fühler.
— 31d. — *coffeae*, Hagedorn, Fühler.
— 31e. *Cryphalus sidneyanus*, Nördlinger, Fühler.
— 31f. *Stephanoderes philippinensis*, Hagedorn, i. l., Fühler.
— 31g. — *Emmi*, Hagedorn, i. l. (Madagaskarkopal), Fühler.

TAFEL 4

Fig. 32. *Hypothenemus concolor*, Hagedorn.
— 33. *Ernoporus fagi*, Fabricius.
— 33a. — — — Fühler.
— 33b. — — — Vorderbein.
— 34. *Lepicerus aspericollis*, Eichhoff.
— 35 *Thamnurgus delphinii*, Rosenhauer.
— 36. *Coccotrypes Hagedorni*, Eggers.
— 37. *Dryocoetes autographus*, Ratzeburg.
— 38. *Ozopemon Theklae*, Hagedorn.
— 39. *Premnobius cavipennis*, Eichhoff.
— 39a. — — — Absturz.
— 40. *Pityophthorus minutissimus*, Zimmermann, ♂.
— 40a. — — — ♀.
— 40b. — *amoenus*, Blandford, Fühler.
— 41. *Pityogenes pilidens*, Reitter.
— 42. *Ips sexdentatus*, Boerner.
— 42a. — — — Absturz.

TAFEL 5

Fig. 43. *Ips pini*, Say, ♂.
— 43a. — — — ♂, Absturz.
— 44. — — — ♀.
— 44a. — — — ♀, Absturz.
— 45. *Xylocleptes bispinus*, Duftschmid.
— 46. *Poecilips ciliatus*, Hagedorn.
— 47. *Hexacolus Bruchi*, Hagedorn.
— 47a. — — — Vorderfuss.
-- 47b. *Prionosceles maurus*, Blandford, Fühler.
— 47c. *Micracis*, Le Conte, sp., Fühler.
— 48. *Eccoptogaster thoracicus*, Chapuis.

Fig. 49. *Eccoptogaster scolytus*, Fabricius.
— 49*a*. *Scolytopsis puncticollis*, Blandford, Vorderbein.
— 49*b*. — — — Fühler.
— 50. *Camptocerus aeneipennis*, Fabricius.
— 51. *Loganius scaliger*, Hagedorn.
— 52. *Pagiocerus rimosus*, Eichhoff.
— 53. *Ctonoxylon var. flavescens*, Hagedorn.
— 53*a*. — — — — Unterseite.

TAFEL 6

Fig. 54. *Phthorius edentatus*, Hagedorn.
— 54*a*. — — — Fühler.
— 55. *Corthylus flagellifer*, Blandford.
— 56. — *compressicornis*, Fabricius.
— 56*a*. — — — Absturz.
— 56*b*. — — — Muskulatür des Oberschenkels.
— 56*c*. — — — Muskulatur des Unterschenkels.
— 56*d*. — — — Fühler.
— 56*e*. — *tulcanus*, Hagedorn, Flügel.
— 56*f*. — *abbreviatus*, Eichhoff, Fühler des ♂.
— 56*g*. — — — Fühler des ♀.
— 57. *Gnathotrichus longipennis*, Eichhoff.
— 58. *Pterocyclon mali*, Fitch.
— 58*a*. — *exile*, Eichhoff. Fühler.
— 59. *Xyleborus coffeae*, Wurth.
— 60. — *sexspinosus*, Motschulsky.
— 61. — *Lewekianus*, Hagedorn, i. l.
— 62. — *cristatus*, Hagedorn.
— 62*a*. — — — Absturz.
— 63. — *penicillatus*, Hagedorn.
— 63*a*. — — — Absturz.

TAFEL 7

Fig. 64. *Xyleborus sumatranus*, Hagedorn, i. l.
— 64*a*. — — — Absturz.
— 65. — *amphicranoides*, Hagedorn.
— 65*a*. — — — Seitenansicht.
— 66. — *retusus*, Eichhoff.
— 67. — *procer*, — ♂.
— 68. *Xyloterus politus*, Say.
— 69. *Scolytoplatypus Eichelbaumi*, Hagedorn.
— 69*a*. — — — Seitenansicht.
— 69*b*. — *pubescens*, — Flügel.

Tafel 8

Fig. 1. *Diamerus impar*, Chapuis, Fühler.
—   2.   —   —   —   Hinterkiefer.
—   3.   —   —   —   Mittelkiefer.
—   4.   —   *tuberculatus*, Hagedorn, Hinterkiefer.
—   5.   —   *luteus*,   —   Hinterkiefer.
—   6.   —   —   —   Fühler.
—   7.   —   —   —   Mittelkiefer.
—   8.   —   *caesius*,   —   Hinterkiefer.
—   9.   —   —   —   Mittelkiefer.
— 10.   —   —   —   Fühler.
— 11. *Bothryperus psaltes*,   —   Fühler.
— 12. *Strombophorus cordatus*,   —   Mittelkiefer.
— 13.   —   *camerunus*,   —   Fühler.
— 14. *Xylechinus pilosus*, Knoch.   Mundteile.
— 15. *Chortastus Schenklingi*, Hagedorn, Fühler.
— 16.   —   *camerunus*, Schaufuss, Hinterkiefer.
— 17.   —   —   —   Fühler.
— 18.   —   —   —   Fühler.
— 19.   —   —   —   Mittelkiefer.

Tafel 9

Fig. 20. *Ozopemon Theklae var. sirambeanus*, Hagedorn, Hinterkiefer.
— 21.   —   —   —   —   —   Mittelkiefer.
— 22.   —   —   —   —   —   Fühler.
— 23.   —   —   — *singalangicus*,   —   Mittelkiefer.
— 24.   —   —   —   —   —   Hinterkiefer.
— 25.   —   —   —   —   —   Fühler.
— 26.   —   *obanus*, Hagedorn, Fühler.
— 27.   —   —   —   Mittelkiefer.
— 28.   —   —   —   Hinterkiefer.
— 29.   —   *fuscicollis*,   —   Hinterkiefer.
— 30.   —   —   —   Mittelkiefer.
— 31.   —   —   —   Fühler.
— 32. *Xylocleptes bituberculatus*, Hagedorn, Vorderkiefer.
— 33.   —   —   —   Hinterkiefer.
— 34.   —   —   —   Mittelkiefer.
— 35.   —   —   —   Fühler.
— 36. *Premnobius var. corthyloides*,   —   Mittelkiefer.
— 37.   —   —   —   —   Hinterkiefer.
— 38.   —   —   —   —   Fühler.
— 39. *Hexacolus Bruchi*,   —   Hinterkiefer von vorn.
— 40.   —   —   —   Hinterkiefer Seitensicht.

Fig. 41. *Hexacolus Bruchi*, Hagedorn, Mittelkiefer.
— 42. *Araptus camerunus*, — Fühler.
— 43. — — — Vorderbein.

TAFEL 10

Fig. 44. *Xyloctonus scolytoides*, Eichhoff, Fühler.
— 45. *Ctonoxylon camerunum var. hirsutum*, Hagedorn, Fühler.
— 46. — —· Hagedorn, Fühler.
— 47. — *fuscum*, — Fühler.
— 48.· — — — Mittelkiefer.
— 49. *Xyleborus penicillatus*, — Vorderbein.
— 50. — — — Hinterkiefer.
— 51. — — — Mittelkiefer.
— 52. — *Försteri*, — Mittelkiefer.
— 53. — . — — Hinterkiefer.
— 54. — — — Fühler.
— 55. — *cordatus*, — Fühler.
— 56. — — — Mittelkiefer.
— 57. — — — Hinterkiefer.
-- 58. — *Conradti*, — Fühler.
— 59. — — — Mittelkiefer.
— 60. — *tropicus*, — Hinterkiefer.
— 61. — — — Fühler.
— 62. — — — Mittelkiefer.·
— 63. — *Riehli*, Eichhoff, Hinterkiefer.
— 64. — *dmanicus*, Hagedorn, Mittelkiefer.
— 65. — — — Hinterkiefer.
— 66. — — — Fühler.
— 67. — *barbatus*, — Hinterkiefer.
— 68. — — — Mittelkiefer.
— 69. — — — Fühler.
— 70. *Scolytoplatypus fasciatus*, Hagedorn ♂, Vorderbein.
— 71. — *pubescens*, — ♀, Fussglied IV.
— 72. — *Raja*, Blandford ♀, Mittelkiefer.
— 73. — *fasciatus*, Hagedorn ♂, Kiefertasterendglied.
— 74. — *pubescens*, — ♀, Kiefertasterendglied.
— 75. — *fasciatus*, — ♂, Kinn.
— 76. — — — ♀, Lippentaster.

TAFEL 11

Fig. 77. *Phloeotrupes grandis*, Erichson, Mittelkiefer.
— 78. — — — Hinterkiefer.
— 79. *Coptonotus cyclopus*, Chapuis, Fühler.
— 80. — — — Mittelkiefer.

Fig. 81. *Coptonotus cyclopus*, Chapuis, Hinterkiefer ♀.
— 82. — — — Hinterkiefer ♂.
— 83. *Dendroctonus micans*, Kugelann, Mittelkiefer.
— 84. — — — Hinterkiefer.
— 85. *Dacryostactus Kolbei*, Schaufuss, Fühler.
— 86. — — — Mittelkiefer.
— 87. — — — Hinterkiefer.
— 88. *Chramesus acuteclavatus*, Hagedorn, Fühler.
— 89. — — — Mittelkiefer.
— 90. — — — Hinterkiefer.
— 91. *Ips typographus*, Linné, Fühler.
— 92. — — — Mittelkiefer.
— 93. — — — Hinterkiefer.
— 94. *Eccoptogaster scolytus*, Fabricius, Fühler (Monstrosität).
— 95. — — — Mittelkiefer.
— 96. — — — Hinterkiefer.
— 97. *Camptocerus aeneipennis*, — Mittelkiefer.
— 98. — — — Hinterkiefer.
— 99. *Corthylus pectinicornis*, Hagedorn, i. l. Fühler.
— 100. — — — Hinterkiefer.
— 101. — — — Mittelkiefer.

TAFEL 12

Fig. 1. Mutter- und Larvengänge von *Phloeophthorus rhodadactylus*, Marsham, in *Spartium scoparium*.
— 2. Mutter- und Larvengänge von *Phloeophthorus spinulosus*, Rey, in *Picea excelsa*.
— 3. Eiablage in Einzelnischen und Haufen von *Hylurgops palliatus*, Gyllenhal, in Fichte.
— 4. *Hylesinus fraxini*, Panzer, Frassbild in Eschenholz.
— 5. *Dendroctonus micans*, Kugelann, Käfernachfrass in Fichte.
— 6. — — — Harztrichter in Fichte.
— 7. *Xylechinus pilosus*, Knoch, regelmässiges Gangsystem in Fichte.
— 8. *Trypophloeus Grothii*, Hagedorn, Aussenfläche der Rinde von Aspe mit Fluglöchern und über den Gängen geplatzter Oberhaut.

TAFEL 13

Fig. 9. *Coccotrypes Eggersii*, Hagedorn, Frass in Steinnuss (*Phytelephas macrocarpa*).
— 10. *Pityophthorus glabratus*, Eichhoff, Frassbild in Kiefer.
— 11. *Ips typographus*, Linné, und *Pityogenes chalcographus*, Linné, Eiablage in Fichte.
— 12. — — Linné, Mutter- und Larvengänge in Fichte.
— 13. — *suturalis*, Gyllenhal, Frassbild in Kiefer.
— 14. — *curvidens*, Germar, Frassbild in Tanne.
— 15. *Pityogenes bidentatus*, Herbst, Frassbild in Kiefer.

TAFEL 14

Fig. 16. *Pityogenes quadridens*, Hartig, Frassbild in Kiefer.
— 17. *Eccoptogaster Ratzeburgi*, Janson, Muttergang und Larvengänge auf Birkenstamm.

Fig. 18. *Eccoptogaster rugulosus*, Ratzeburg, Frassbild in Weissdorn.
— 19. *Xyleborus monographus*, Fabricius, Frassbild in Eiche.
— 20. — *xylographus,* Say, Familienwohnung in Eiche.
— 21. — *(Anisandrus) dispar* Fabricius, Familienwohnung in Eiche.

Die Habitusbilder auf Tafel 1-7 sind von Herrn H a n s L e w e k nach der Natur gezeichnet, die Photographieen der Frassstücke auf Tafel 11-14 hat Herr Dr L. R e h nach Præparaten des Verfassers ausgeführt — beiden freundwilligen Mitarbeitern sei auch hier verbindlichster Dank gesagt!

Die mikroskopischen Details sind vom Verfasser nach eigenen Præparaten mittels eines *Leitzschen* Zeichenprismas gezeichnet.

———————

Hamburg, 15. October 1910.

ERRATA ET CORRIGENDA

Pag. 1. — Zeile 10 ist zu setzen statt « Dan » « Dann ».

Pag. 5. — Zeile 18 « zugleich » fällt fort.

Pag. 25. — Zeile 17 « zart gelb » fällt fort.

Pag. 72. — Zeile 14 ist zu setzen statt « bunter » « bunte ».

Pag. 84. — Zeile 7 von unten ist zu setzen statt « TRYPO-PHLOCUS » « TRYPOPHLOEUS ».

Pag. 98. — Zeile 1 ist zu setzen statt « einere » « einem ».

Pag. 133. — Zeile 9 von unten ist zu setzen statt « liguiperda » « ligniperda ».

Ebenso Zeile 12 von unten ist zu setzen statt « liguiperda » « ligniperda ».

Pag. 135. — Zeile 4 von unten ist zu setzen statt « befestigster» « befestigter ».

Pag. 159. — Zeile 4 von oben ist zu setzen statt « Scolyto-platylus » « Scolytoplatypus ».

Pag. 172. — I. Fig. 9-10 incl. stehen auf Tafel 1 und nicht auf Tafel 2.

II Es fehlt Fig. 14 a . . . « Fühler ».

Pag. 173. — I. Zeile 12 ist zu setzen statt « Fühler » « Vorder-bein».

II. Fig. 43-44a incl. stehen auf Tafel 4 und nicht auf Tafel 5.

Pag. 174. — I. Fig. 54-55 incl. stehen auf Tafel 5 und nicht auf Tafel 6.

II. Es fehlt : Fig. 61a . . . « Seitenansicht ».

Auf **Tafel 2** ist noch ein Druckfehler übersehen : es muss da-selbst heissen in der Legende zu Fig. 19.
« Dendroctonus » und nicht Deudroctonus.

Lightning Source UK Ltd.
Milton Keynes UK
UKHW011533090119
334994UK00008B/766/P